MATHEMATICS FOR HEALTH SCIENCES

Online Lessons

▶ Contain highly engaging and interactive videos that use cutting-edge Cloud Learning technologies.

▶ Break down math concepts into logical and intuitive steps that enhance the learning process.

▶ Prepare students for upcoming classes, labs, and quizzes through self-study lessons.

▶ Contain lessons that are self-paced and are excellent for visual learners.

Online Labs

▶ Contain a comprehensive test-bank of real-world problems, which may be used as an assessment tool.

▶ Break down every answer into dynamic, step-by-step solutions.

▶ Provide unlimited amount of practice through algorithmically generated problems.

▶ Contain numerous statistical tools to analyze students' strengths and weaknesses.

MATHEMATICS FOR HEALTH SCIENCES

First Edition

Authors

Irene Lee, *Humber College*

Thambyrajah Kugathasan, *Seneca College*

Sean Saunders, *Sheridan College*

Copyright © 2017 by Vretta Inc.

ISBN: 978-1-927737-09-5

Mathematics for Health Sciences, First Edition

Textbook printed in Canada

Authors: Irene Lee, Thambyrajah Kugathasan, Sean Saunders

Textbook Editor: Lakshmi Kugathasan
Developmental Editor: Arbana Miftari
Copy Editor: Connor Peebles
Art Director: Aleksandar Vozarevic
Assistant Editors: Erika De Vega, Uma Kalkar

Video Tutorials: Jeff Fennell
PowerPoint Presentations: Ali Alavi, Uma Kalkar
Instructional Design: Charles Anifowose, Elisa Romeo, Danny Panche Barrios
Interactive Technology & Data Solutions: Taylor Anderson, Zach Williams, Nabil Fannoush
Marketing: Harsha Varlani, James Howell

Expert Advice: TK Academic Consulting Inc.
Pharmaceutical Drug Labels, Used with permission: Copyright GlaxoSmithKline Group of Companies, Amgen, Teva Pharmaceutical Industries Ltd., AstraZeneca, Novartis International AG
Turning Technologies' Student Response System (Clickers) Integrated into Powerpoint Presentations
Online Resources Management System: Intromath.ca

Disclaimer

Vretta Inc. has taken complete care to trace the ownership of copyright material contained in these resources. However, if you have any information which would enable us to rectify any reference or credit for subsequent editions and/or identify any errors or omissions which require correction, please email us at copyright@vretta.com.

The examples, exercises, and cases in the Mathematics of Business and Finance resources are fictitious, unless otherwise stated. Any resemblance to real life people, businesses, organizations, institutions, facts or circumstances is purely coincidental.

MATHEMATICS FOR HEALTH SCIENCES

Brief Contents

Contents

Chapter 3

Operations with Exponents and Integers 88

Chapter 4
Basic Algebra 134

Chapter 5
Ratios, Proportions, Percents, and Percent Changes 168

Chapter 6
Units of Measurement 214

Chapter 7

Basic Geometry 258

Chapter 8
Graphs and Systems of Linear Equations.................................320

Chapter 9
Exponents and Logarithms 370

Chapter 10
Dosage Calculations and Medication Administration 404

List of Exhibits and Tables

Exhibits

Tables

Preface

Greetings! First of all, thank you for considering this resource. As professors teaching mathematics, we know first-hand many of the challenges that professors and students face when it comes to finding connections between the basic mathematics of arithmetic, algebra, geometry, and functions that are required in most health sciences programs, and the careers that students wish to pursue. As the authors of this book, we have over 60 years of combined teaching experience in mathematics, of which over half of that experience is teaching math for health sciences. Thus, here is a list of frequently-asked questions that we would want answered if we were considering using a resource for a Math for Health Sciences course:

"When am I ever going to use this?"

This is a common question heard by many professors and instructors teaching a post-secondary math course to students who are not majoring in mathematics. The **Mathematics for Health Sciences** resource you have in your hands was created to not only answer this question for students who are pursuing a career in the health sciences, but to hopefully prevent it from being asked in the first place! This book is loaded, from beginning to end, with relevant, practical, and modern examples that students will actually encounter in their future vocations in the health sciences field, whether in nursing, pharmacy, athletic therapy, kinesiology, or in paramedical services.

"What is so different about this resource?"

There are many foundational math textbooks in the market today, though few (if any) have a health sciences focus; similarly, there are also many textbooks focusing on the mathematics of pharmacy and dosage calculations, but they do not typically cover all the basic mathematical concepts required in sufficient depth. What makes this resource unique is that it covers all the concepts found in a foundational math course, but with a motivation and a focus rooted firmly in the health sciences. We have not seen another resource in the market that takes the time to explain the basic concepts as thoroughly as you will find in this resource, while motivating students and reinforcing the concepts with practical, health-related examples and exercises.

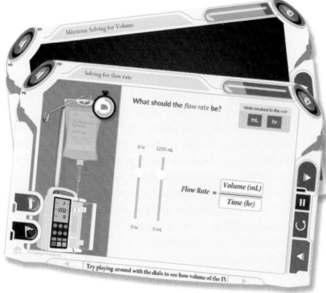

88%   91%   96%   80%   79%

"Why the Vretta Hybrid Learning Platform?"

This resource is only "one side of the equation" when it comes to ensuring student success. To optimize the learning experience, we have leveraged the cutting-edge technologies available to us to provide students with a highly immersive and engaging learning experience. Realizing that every student learns differently, students are given access to innovative online tools, tailored to each individual student's personal strengths and areas that need development. These tools are designed to help them master the concepts using diverse methods of learning, such as interactive online lessons which provide an understanding of the concepts before class, and our online lab system which assesses all the core concepts covered throughout the course, so students will know how well they are doing **before** they write the test! These interactive, voice-enabled, online resources help overcome the negative perceptions associated with mathematics, and help students create those connections between the course material and their professional field.

Whether you are a professor or a student, we trust that you will find this **Mathematics for Health Sciences** resource to be useful and beneficial in the teaching and learning experience in your course. At Vretta, we believe that if you learn math, you will live smarter. We truly believe that this hybrid resource will help students develop an appreciation for the mathematical concepts taught within, and discover the deep, relevant connections that exist between mathematics and the health sciences, which will, ultimately, lead to a more enriching and satisfying experience, both in their professions and in their lives!

Irene Lee, Thambyrajah Kugathasan, and Sean Saunders

Textbook

Language

The language used in this textbook is simple and straight-forward, while maintaining the levels of sophistication required to thoroughly prepare students for the next stage in their academic and professional careers.

Pedagogies and Learning Methods

Numerous pedagogies and learning methods that have been developed and proven over 60 years are incorporated into the textbook. These pedagogies have succeeded in simplifying critical mathematical concepts and significantly improving retention of concepts. The different learning methods to solve problems have also proven to cater to the varied student learning styles.

Exercises

The textbook has 2877 exercises, review exercises, and self-test exercises, as well as 345 solved examples. Problems are designed to test students on real-world, practical applications and are presented in increasing levels of difficulty, with the most difficult problems being indicated by a dot (•). The problems are categorized into pairs of similar questions to provide professors with an opportunity to solve the even-numbered problems in class and assign the odd-numbered problems as homework.

Solution Manual

All problems in the end-of-section exercises, review exercises, self-test exercises, and cases have been solved using detailed step-by-step methods, as demonstrated in the solved examples. The solution manual is available online.

PowerPoint Presentations

The animated PowerPoint presentations are available for professors to use in class. The PowerPoint presentations are designed to work with clickers in class to gauge student understanding of concepts.

Test Bank

A comprehensive test bank, of 2000+ problems in varying levels of difficulty, that covers all concepts in the textbook is provided for professors to use as a database for exercises, quizzes, cases, group projects, or assignments.

Online Lessons

The online lessons are created as a pre-study component for students. They contain pedagogies that are highly interactive and engaging, and which teach concepts in a very logical and intuitive way. These lessons are not PowerPoint presentations but are interactive videos that have been created to enrich and enhance the learning experience. Every frame is locked to ensure that students go through the lessons sequentially as they are designed to build on learning concepts in succession. The system automatically records students' progress and performance. Once students complete a lesson, the frame unlocks itself, allowing students to navigate back and forth through the lesson. Professors, on the other hand, have administrative access which allows them to navigate through the online lessons without any restrictions.

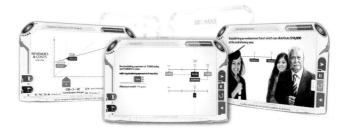

Online Labs

The online lab assessment system contains a rich comprehensive test-bank of real-world problems that are algorithmically generated and that provide students with dynamic feedback on their responses. The labs can also be customized based on course requirements. A few of the customizable features include: previewing and selecting questions, setting the number of questions, setting and modifying start and due dates, opening, closing and re-opening labs, creating new labs and quizzes, and determining the weighting and number of attempts for each question.

Administrative Tools

The following administrative tools will provide professors with the ability to monitor overall class performance and individual student performance on online lessons and labs.

Performance Dashboard for Professors

The lesson performance dashboard provides professors with the average completion percentage per chapter, including a lesson-by-lesson percentage completed visualization for the entire class. The lab performance dashboard provides them with the average percentage mark on each lab for the class. Professors can also download or export individual grades for lessons and labs to a spreadsheet or to the college's course management system.

Performance Dashboard for Students

The lesson performance dashboard provides students with their chapter completion mark, including a lesson-by-lesson percentage completed visualization. The lab performance dashboard provides them with their lab percentage marks.

Lab Management System The lab management system is provided for administrators or subject leaders to create new labs, quizzes and case studies, preview and select questions, set the number of questions, set and modify start and due dates, open, close and re-open labs, and determine the weighting and number of attempts for each question.

MATHEMATICS FOR HEALTH SCIENCES

First Edition

Authors

Irene Lee, *Humber College*

Thambyrajah Kugathasan, *Seneca College*

Sean Saunders, *Sheridan College*

1 WHOLE NUMBERS

LEARNING OBJECTIVES

- Identify place values of whole numbers.
- Read, write, and round whole numbers correctly.
- Solve problems involving arithmetic operations on whole numbers.
- Determine the least common multiple and highest common factor.
- Perform order of operations with whole numbers.

CHAPTER OUTLINE

1.1 Understanding Whole Numbers

1.2 Arithmetic Operations with Whole Numbers

1.3 Factors and Multiples

1.4 Powers, Square Roots, and Order of Operations

Introduction

Arithmetic is the elementary branch of mathematics that we use in everyday life. When we count or perform the simple operations of addition, subtraction, multiplication, and division, we use the principles of arithmetic. We use arithmetic for everyday tasks such as buying, selling, estimating expenses, and checking bank balances. Arithmetic is woven into our general interaction with the real world and, as such, it forms the basis of all science, technology, engineering, and business. In this chapter, you will learn about mathematical operations involving whole numbers, including powers and roots of perfect squares.

Whole numbers are simply the numbers 0, 1, 2, 3, 4.... They include all the counting numbers, also known as the **natural numbers** or positive integers (1, 2, 3, 4...), and zero (0).

All whole numbers are integers. However, whole numbers and integers are not the same because integers include both the counting numbers (positive integers) and their negatives (negative integers).

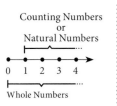

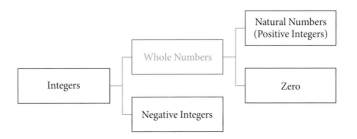

1.1 | Understanding Whole Numbers

Place Value of Whole Numbers

All numbers can be made up using the digits **0, 1, 2, 3, 4, 5, 6, 7, 8, and 9**. Numbers may consist of one or more digits. When a number is written using the above digits, it is said to be in **standard form**.

For example, 7, 85, and 2,349 are examples of numbers in their standard form, where 7 is a single-(one) digit number, 85 is a two-digit number, and 2,349 is a four-digit number.

The **position** of each digit in a whole number determines the **place value** for the digit.

Exhibit 1.1-a illustrates the place value of the ten digits in the whole number: 3,867,254,129. In this whole number, 4 occupies the 'thousands' place value and represents 4 thousand, or 4,000; whereas 7 occupies the 'millions' place value and represents 7 million, or 7,000,000.

The place value of 'ones' is 10^0 (= 1) and each position has a value 10 times the place value to its right, as shown in Table 1.1.

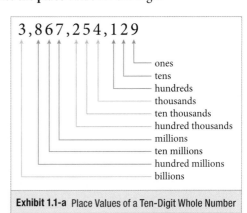

Exhibit 1.1-a Place Values of a Ten-Digit Whole Number

Table 1.1	Place Value Chart of Whole Numbers

10^9	10^8	10^7	10^6	10^5	10^4	10^3	10^2	10^1	10^0
1,000,000,000	100,000,000	10,000,000	1,000,000	100,000	10,000	1,000	100	10	1
Billions	Hundred millions	Ten millions	Millions	Hundred thousands	Ten thousands	Thousands	Hundreds	Tens	Ones

We read and write numbers from the left to the right. A number in standard form is separated into groups of three digits using commas (or alternatively, spaces), thereby making it easier to read. The red, vertical lines denote the positions of the commas that separate the groups of three numbers, starting from the place value for 'ones'.

When written in standard form, the ten-digit number in Exhibit 1.1(a) is written as 3,867,254,129.

3	8	6	7	2	5	4	1	2	9
Billions	Hundred millions	Ten millions	Millions	Hundred thousands	Ten thousands	Thousands	Hundreds	Tens	Ones

Numbers can also be written in **expanded form** using figures, by writing the number as a sum of what each place value represents.

For example, the number 3,867,254,129 in standard form can be written in expanded form, as follows:

$$3,000,000,000 + 800,000,000 + 60,000,000 + 7,000,000 + 200,000 + 50,000 + 4,000 + 100 + 20 + 9$$

Example 1.1-a	Identifying the Place Value of a Digit and the Amount it Represents

What is the place value of the digit 5 in each of the following numbers and what amount does it represent?

(i) $2,543   (ii) $75,342   (iii) $6,521,890   (iv) $915,203,847

Solution

	(i) $2,543	(ii) $75,342	(iii) $6,521,890	(iv) $915,203,847
Place value of the digit 5:	Hundreds	Thousands	Hundred thousands	Millions
Amount it represents:	$500	$5,000	$500,000	$5,000,000

Example 1.1-b	Identifying the Digit of a Number Given its Place Value

In the number 5,320,948 identify the digit that occupies the following place values:

(i)   Hundred thousands   (ii)   Ten thousands   (iii)   Thousands
(iv)   Tens   (v)   Hundreds   (vi)   Millions

Solution

(i)   5,320,948   (ii)   5,320,948   (iii)   5,320,948
    ↑   ↑   ↑
  Hundred thousands   Ten thousands   Thousands

(iv)   5,320,948   (v)   5,320,948   (vi)   5,320,948
    ↑   ↑   ↑
    Tens   Hundreds   Millions

| Example 1.1-c | **Writing Numbers in Expanded Form** |

Write the following numbers in expanded form:

(i)   698   (ii)   8,564   (iii)   49,005

(iv)   521,076   (v)   9,865,323   (vi)   43,583,621

Solution

(i)   698

600 + 90 + 8

(ii)   8,564

8,000 + 500 + 60 + 4

(iii)   49,005

40,000 + 9,000 + 5

(iv)   521,076

500,000 + 20,000 + 1,000 + 70 + 6

(v)   9,865,323

9,000,000 + 800,000 + 60,000 + 5,000 + 300 + 20 + 3

(vi)   43,583,621

40,000,000 + 3,000,000 + 500,000 + 80,000 + 3,000 + 600 + 20 + 1

Reading and Writing Whole Numbers

To make it easier to read and write numbers, any number larger than three digits is separated into smaller groups of three digits, starting from the 'ones' digit of the number. Each group of these three digits has a name.

- The first group of 3 digits on the right is the "**Units**" group.

- The second group from the right is the "**Thousands**" group.

- The third group from the right is the "**Millions**" group.

- The fourth group from the right is the "**Billions**" group.

- The fifth group from the right is the "**Trillions**" group and so on, as shown in the following chart.

Trillions			Billions			Millions			Thousands			Units		
Hundreds	Tens	Ones	Hundreds	Tens	Ones	Hundreds	Tens	Ones	Hundreds	Tens	Ones	Hundreds	Tens	Ones

Follow these steps to write whole numbers in word form:

Step 1:   Start from the group furthest to the left and write the number formed by the digits in that group, followed by the name of the group.

Step 2:   Moving to the next group (to the right), write the numbers formed by this next group, followed by its name. Continue to do this for each of the groups.

Step 3:   For the last group (i.e., the group furthest to the right), write the numbers formed by the group; however, for this group, do **not** write the name of the group (i.e., units).

Note: When all three digits in a group are zero, that group is neither read nor written.

Also, commas and hyphens are used when expressing numbers in word form.

- Commas (,) are used between the groups to separate them.

- Hyphens (-) are used to express the two digit numbers in each group;
  i.e., 21 to 29, 31 to 39, 41 to 49,...91 to 99.

For example, 2,835,197,000,642 expressed in word form using the above rules would be as follows:

Trillions			Billions			Millions			Thousands			Units		
Hundreds	Tens	Ones	Hundreds	Tens	Ones	Hundreds	Tens	Ones	Hundreds	Tens	Ones	Hundreds	Tens	Ones
	2	8	3	5	1	9	7	0	0	0	6	4	2	

Two trillion, | eight hundred thirty-five billion, | one hundred ninety-seven million, | | six hundred forty-two

The word 'and' does not appear in the word form of whole numbers.

When writing the numbers in word form, the names of the groups remain in their singular form, irrespective of the number preceding; i.e., hundred, thousand, million, billion, trillion, etc.

For example,

- Eight **hundred** thirty-five **billion**.
- One **hundred** ninety-seven **million**.

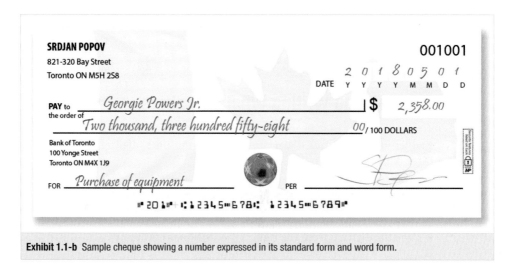

Exhibit 1.1-b Sample cheque showing a number expressed in its standard form and word form.

Example 1.1-d	**Writing Numbers in Word Form Given their Standard Form**

Write the following numbers in word form:

(i)	743	(ii)	5,006	(iii)	15,017
(iv)	800,629	(v)	6,783,251	(vi)	52,630,042

Solution

(i)	743	Seven hundred forty-three
(ii)	5,006	Five thousand, six
(iii)	15,017	Fifteen thousand, seventeen
(iv)	800,629	Eight hundred thousand, six hundred twenty-nine
(v)	6,783,251	Six million, seven hundred eighty-three thousand, two hundred fifty-one
(vi)	52,630,042	Fifty-two million, six hundred thirty thousand, forty-two

Example 1.1-e | **Writing Numbers in Standard Form Given their Word Form**

Write the following numbers in standard form:

(i)   Two hundred five

(ii)   Six thousand, four

(iii)   Thirty-five thousand, eight hundred twenty-five

(iv)   Eight hundred thousand, five

(v)   Two million, three hundred forty-two thousand, six hundred seventeen

(vi)   Half of a million

(vii)   One-quarter of a billion

Solution

(i)	Two hundred five	205
(ii)	Six thousand, four	6,004
(iii)	Thirty-five thousand, eight hundred twenty-five	35,825
(iv)	Eight hundred thousand, five	800,005
(v)	Two million, three hundred forty-two thousand, six hundred seventeen	2,342,617
(vi)	Half of a million	$\dfrac{1,000,000}{2} = 500,000$
(vii)	One-quarter of a billion	$\dfrac{1,000,000,000}{4} = 250,000,000$

Representing Whole Numbers on a Number Line

The number line has **whole numbers** written in order from smallest to largest on a horizontal line. Whole numbers can be represented graphically as a point on the horizontal line, as shown below.

The arrowhead at the end shows that the line continues indifinitely in that direction.

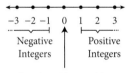

Zero is neither positive nor negative.

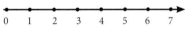

The smallest whole number is zero (0). It is not possible to find the largest whole number because for any given number, there will always be another number greater than that number.

Writing numbers on a number line helps in comparing and identifying numbers that are smaller or larger than other numbers. Numbers that lie to the left of a number (i.e., closer to zero) on the number line are less than (i.e., smaller than) that number, and numbers that lie to the right of a number on the number line are greater than (i.e., bigger than) that number.

For example,

- 6 is greater than 2 (or 2 is less than 6).

  That is, 6 is on the right side of 2 (or 2 is on the left side of 6).

- 5 is less than 7 (or 7 is greater than 5).

  That is, 5 is on the left side of 7 (or 7 is on the right side of 5).

The signs used to show the relative position of two numbers (or quantities) that are not equal are:

The signs '>' and '<' always point towards the smaller number, and are always open towards the larger number.

(i)   ' > ' read as "**greater than**", meaning that the number on the left of the sign has a value greater than that on the right.

   For example, "6 is greater than 2" which is written as 6 > 2.

   This is the same as "2 is less than 6" which is written as 2 < 6.

(ii) '<' read as **less than**, meaning that the number on the left of the sign has a value less than that on the right.

For example, "5 is less than 7" which is written as 5 < 7.

This is the same as "7 is greater than 5" which is written as 7 > 5.

Example 1.1-f | **Plotting Numbers on a Number Line and Using Signs to Show the Relative Positions of the Numbers**

Plot the following numbers on a number line and place the correct sign of inequality, '>' or '<', in the space between the numbers.

| (i) | 7 ⬚ 11 | (ii) | 7 ⬚ 5 | (iii) | 11 ⬚ 5 |
| (iv) | 5 ⬚ 12 | (v) | 3 ⬚ 5 | (vi) | 12 ⬚ 11 |

Solution

| (i) | 7 < 11 | (ii) | 7 > 5 | (iii) | 11 > 5 |
| (iv) | 5 < 12 | (v) | 3 < 5 | (vi) | 12 > 11 |

Example 1.1-g | **Writing a Statement to Represent '>' or '<'**

Write statements using the words "greater than" or "less than" for the following expressions:

(i) 24 > 22   (ii) 36 < 39   (iii) 9 > 0   (iv) 0 < 5

Solution

(i) 24 > 22

24 is greater than 22 *or* 22 is less than 24.

(ii) 36 < 39

36 is less than 39 *or* 39 is greater than 36.

(iii) 9 > 0

9 is greater than 0 *or* 0 is less than 9.

(iv) 0 < 5

0 is less than 5 *or* 5 is greater than 0.

Rounding Whole Numbers

Rounding numbers makes them easier to work with and easier to remember. Rounding changes some of the digits in a number but keeps its value close to the original. In the sciences, rounding is used in population estimations, chemical calculations, and measurement conversions.

For example, the population of Canada in 2016 was approximately 36 million (rounded to the nearest million) or the maximum recommended dosage of acetaminophen per day for adults is approximately 4,000 mg, rounded to the nearest thousand.

Rounding Whole Numbers to the Nearest Ten, Hundred, Thousand, etc.

Rounding whole numbers to the nearest ten, hundred, thousand, etc. refers to changing the value of a whole number to the nearest multiple of 10, 100, 1,000, etc., respectively.

For example,

- Rounding a whole number to the nearest ten is the same as rounding it to a multiple of 10.

- Rounding a whole number to the nearest hundred is the same as rounding it to a multiple of 100.

- Rounding a whole number to the nearest thousand is the same as rounding it to a multiple of 1,000.

For example,

- Rounding 114 m to the nearest ten is 110 m. 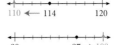 114 is closer to 110 than 120. Therefore, round down to 110.

- Rounding 97 m to the nearest ten is 100 m. 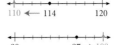 97 is closer to 100 than 90. Therefore, round up to 100.

| Example 1.1-h | Rounding Numbers Using a Number Line (Visual Method) |

Round the following numbers to the indicated place value using a number line:

(i)   624 to the nearest ten (multiple of 10).

(ii)   150 to the nearest hundred (multiple of 100).

(iii)   1,962 to the nearest hundred (multiple of 100).

Solution

We can visualize these numbers on a number line to determine the nearest number:

(i)   624 to the nearest ten (multiple of 10).

624 is closer to 620 than to 630.

Therefore, 624 rounded to the nearest ten is 620.

(ii)   150 to the nearest hundred (multiple of 100).

150 is exactly between 100 and 200. By convention, if a number is exactly in the middle, we round it up.

Therefore, 150 rounded to the nearest hundred is 200.

(iii)   1,962 to the nearest hundred (multiple of 100).

1,962 is closer to 2,000 than to 1,900.

Therefore, 1,962 rounded to the nearest hundred is 2,000.

Instead of using a number line, which can be tedious, we can follow these steps to round whole numbers:

Step 1:   Identify the digit to be rounded (this is the place value for which the rounding is required).

Step 2:   If the digit to the immediate right of the required rounding digit is less than 5 (0, 1, 2, 3, 4), do not change the value of the rounding digit.

If the digit to the immediate right of the required rounding digit is 5 or greater than 5 (5, 6, 7, 8, 9), increase the value of the rounding digit by one (round up by one number).

Step 3:   Change the value of all digits that are to the right of the rounding digit to 0.

| Example 1.1-i | Rounding Numbers Using a Number Line (Visual Method) |

Round the following to the indicated place values:

(i) $568 to the nearest $10.

(ii) $795 to the nearest $10.

(iii)   5,643 g to the nearest 100 g.

(iv)   19,958 g to the nearest 100 g.

Solution

(i) Rounding $568 to the nearest $10.

Identify the rounding digit in the tens place: 5**6**8 (6 is the digit in the tens place).

The digit to the immediate right of the rounding digit is 8, which is greater than 5; therefore, increase the value of the rounding digit by one, from 6 to 7, and change the value of the digits that are to the right of the rounding digit to 0, which will result in 57**0**.

Therefore, $568 rounded to the nearest $10 (or multiple of 10) is $570.

(ii) Rounding $795 to the nearest $10.

Identify the rounding digit in the tens place: 7**9**5 (9 is the digit in the tens place).

The digit to the immediate right of the rounding digit is 5; therefore, increase the value of the rounding digit by one, from 9 to 10. This is done by replacing the rounding digit 9 with 0, and increasing the next digit to its left by one, from 7 to 8. Change the value of the digits that are to the right of the rounding digit to 0, which will result in 80**0**.

Therefore, $795 rounded to the nearest $10 (or multiple of 10) is $800.

(iii) Rounding 5,643 g to the nearest 100 g.

Identify the rounding digit in the hundreds place: 5,**6**43 (6 is the digit in the hundreds place).

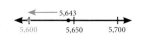

The digit to the immediate right of the rounding digit is 4, which is less than 5; therefore, do not change the value of the rounding digit, but change the value of the digits that are to the right of the rounding digit to 0, which will result in 5,6**00**.

Therefore, 5,643 g rounded to the nearest 100 g (or multiple of 100) is 5,600 g.

(iv) Rounding 19,958 g to the nearest 100 g.

Identify the rounding digit in the hundreds place: 19,**9**58 (9 is the digit in the hundreds place).

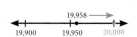

The digit to the immediate right of the rounding digit is 5; therefore, increase the value of the rounding digit by one, from 9 to 10. This is done by replacing the rounding digit 9 with 0 and increasing the next digit to its left by one. In this case, it is 9 as well, so replace that digit 9 with 0 and increase the number to its left by one, from 1 to 2. Change the value of the digits that are to the right of the rounding digit to 0, which will result in 20,0**00**.

Therefore, 19,958 g rounded to the nearest 100 g (or multiple of 100) is 20,000 g.

1.1 | Exercises

Answers to odd-numbered problems are available at the end of the textbook.

For Problems 1 to 4, write (i) the place value of the underlined digit and (ii) the value it represents.

1. a. 7, 6<u>2</u>8　　　b. 4,68<u>7</u>　　　c. <u>9</u>4,083　　　2.　a. 4,7<u>9</u>2　　　b. 5,3<u>5</u>2　　　c. 45,<u>7</u>21

3. a. 204,<u>0</u>95　　　b. 3<u>5</u>,217,123　　　c. 4,<u>3</u>85,207　　　4.　a. 3<u>1</u>9,526　　　b. 7,8<u>2</u>5,500　　　c. 1<u>6</u>,702,555

For Problems 5 to 10, write the numbers in their (i) expanded form and (ii) word form.

5. a. 860　　　　　　b. 7,805　　　　　　6.　a. 407　　　　　　　b. 2,056

7. a. 94,975　　　　　b. 684,137　　　　　8.　a. 29,186　　　　　b. 464,448

9. a. 9,084,351　　　b. 23,006,045　　　10.　a. 2,604,325　　　b. 15,300,604

For Problems 11 to 16, write the numbers in their (i) standard form and (ii) word form.

11. a. 400 + 50 + 6　　　b. 1,000 + 900 + 30 + 2　　　12.　a. 600 + 70 + 9　　　b. 3,000 + 100 + 40 + 7

13. a. 5,000 + 300 + 1　　　b. 7,000 + 80 + 8　　　14.　a. 2,000 + 600 + 5　　　b. 9,000 + 20 + 4

15. a. 60,000 + 700 + 80　　　b. 20,000 + 100 + 4　　　16.　a. 40,000 + 900 + 90　　　b. 10,000 + 50 + 3

For Problems 17 to 24, write the numbers in their (i) standard form and (ii) expanded form.

17. a. One thousand, five

    b. Seven thousand, twenty

18. a. Five hundred seventy

    b. Eight hundred three

19. a. Sixty-five thousand, two hundred forty-four

    b. Eight hundred thirty-three thousand, six hundred forty-one

20. a. Eighty thousand, six hundred thirty

    b. Seventy-five thousand, twenty-five

21. a. Two billion, one thousand

    b. One billion, twenty-five thousand

22. a. Twelve million, four hundred fifty-two thousand, eight hundred thirty-two

    b. Thirty-two million, six hundred eighty-four thousand, two hundred fifty-six

23. a. Half of a billion

    b. One-tenth of a billion

24. a. One-fifth of a million

    b. One-quarter of a million

For Problems 25 and 26, plot the numbers on a number line.

25. a. 18, 9, 6, 11   b. 4, 10, 7, 16   26. a. 14, 19, 15, 7   b. 12, 8, 17, 5

For Problems 27 and 28, place the correct sign of inequality, '<' or '>', in the space between the numbers.

27. a. 12 ☐ 17   b. 8 ☐ 5   c. 17 ☐ 0   d. 0 ☐ 8

28. a. 7 ☐ 15   b. 19 ☐ 14   c. 0 ☐ 5   d. 19 ☐ 0

For Problems 29 and 30, express the relationship between the numbers using the statement (i) "less than" and (ii) "greater than".

29. a. 4 < 7   b. 16 > 7   c. 10 < 16   d. 0 < 4

30. a. 6 < 9   b. 18 > 11   c. 5 < 11   d. 11 > 0

For Problems 31 to 34, arrange the numbers in order from smallest to largest.

31. a. 58; 129; 147; 49; 68   b. 836; 820; 805; 873; 875

32. a. 87; 108; 99; 103; 96   b. 159; 141; 108; 139; 167

33. a. 2,668; 2,630; 2,579; 2,759   b. 68,336; 69,999; 69,067; 68,942

34. a. 2,067; 2,040; 2,638; 2,533   b. 79,487; 79,534; 79,468; 78,812

For Problems 35 and 36, create the (i) smallest and (ii) largest possible numbers using all the given digits.

35. a. 6, 1, 7   b. 9, 4, 8, 5   c. 4, 7, 2, 6, 5

36. a. 9, 2, 5   b. 7, 9, 1, 8   c. 3, 5, 4, 8

For Problems 37 and 38, round the numbers to the (i) nearest ten, (ii) nearest hundred, and (iii) nearest thousand.

37.

	Number	Nearest Ten	Nearest Hundred	Nearest Thousand
a.	1,625			
b.	9,157			
c.	25,972			
d.	139,835			

38.

	Number	Nearest Ten	Nearest Hundred	Nearest Thousand
a.	1,645			
b.	6,354			
c.	53,562			
d.	235,358			

For Problems 39 and 40, round the numbers to the (i) nearest ten thousand, (ii) nearest hundred thousand, and (iii) nearest million.

39.

	Number	Nearest Ten Thousand	Nearest Hundred Thousand	Nearest Million
a.	759,850			
b.	3,254,599			
c.	7,555,450			
d.	2,959,680			

40.

	Number	Nearest Ten Thousand	Nearest Hundred Thousand	Nearest Million
a.	875,555			
b.	1,656,565			
c.	3,368,850			
d.	4,598,310			

1.2 | Arithmetic Operations with Whole Numbers

Addition of Whole Numbers

Addition can be done in any order and the sum will be the same.

A + B = B + A

For example,

9 + 5 = 14, and 5 + 9 = 14

This is known as the **commutative property** of addition.

Addition of whole numbers refers to combining two or more numbers, referred to as the **addends**, to determine the total, also known as the **sum**.

The symbol '+' denotes addition.

For example, 9 + 5 refers to adding 9 and 5.

$$
\begin{array}{r}
9 \\
+ 5 \\
\hline
14
\end{array}
$$

Plus sign → + 5 ← Addends

9 ← Addends

14 ← Total or sum

Follow these steps to add one number to another number:

Step 1: Start by writing the numbers one under the other by aligning the place values (ones, tens, hundreds, etc.) of these numbers and drawing a horizontal line underneath.

Step 2: Starting with the ones place value, add all the numbers in the 'ones' column. If their total is less than 10, write the total under the horizontal line. If the total is 10 or more, write the 'ones' digit of the total under the horizontal line and write the tens digit above the tens column. This is called 'carrying'.

Step 3: Add the numbers in the tens column, followed by the hundreds column, etc., by following the same procedure for each column.

The above steps for adding whole numbers are demonstrated in detail in Example 1.2-a below.

Example 1.2-a   **Adding Whole Numbers**

Perform the following additions:

(i)   3,514 + 245

(ii)   8,578 + 3,982 + 564 + 92

Solution

(i)   3,514 + 245

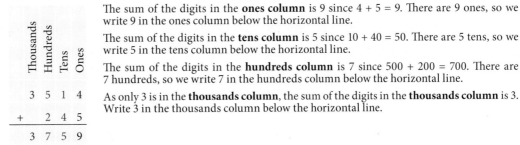

The sum of the digits in the **ones column** is 9 since 4 + 5 = 9. There are 9 ones, so we write 9 in the ones column below the horizontal line.

The sum of the digits in the **tens column** is 5 since 10 + 40 = 50. There are 5 tens, so we write 5 in the tens column below the horizontal line.

The sum of the digits in the **hundreds column** is 7 since 500 + 200 = 700. There are 7 hundreds, so we write 7 in the hundreds column below the horizontal line.

As only 3 is in the **thousands column**, the sum of the digits in the **thousands column** is 3. Write 3 in the thousands column below the horizontal line.

Therefore, adding 3,514 and 245 results in 3,759.

(ii)   8,578 + 3,982 + 564 + 92

The sum of the digits in the **ones column** is 16 since 8 + 2 + 4 + 2 = 16, which is 1 ten and 6 ones. Write 6 in the ones column below the horizontal line and carry the 1 above the tens column.

The sum of the digits in the **tens column** is 31 since 70 + 80 + 60 + 90 + **10** (carried from the ones column) = 310, which is 3 hundreds and 1 ten. Write 1 in the tens column below the horizontal line and carry the 3 above the hundreds column.

The sum of the digits in the **hundreds column** is 22 since 500 + 900 + 500 + **300** (carried from the tens column) = 2,200, which is 2 thousands and 2 hundreds. Write 2 in the hundreds column below the horizontal line and carry the 2 above the thousands column.

The sum of the digits in the **thousands column** is 13 since 8,000 + 3,000 + **2,000** (carried from the hundreds column) = 13,000, which is 1 ten thousand and 3 thousands. Write 3 in the thousands column and 1 in the ten thousands column below the horizontal line for the final answer.

Therefore, adding 8,578, 3,982, 564, and 92 results in 13,216.

Subtraction of Whole Numbers

Subtraction of whole numbers refers to finding the difference between numbers. This is the reverse process of addition.

When numbers are subtracted, the number from which another number is subtracted is called the **minuend** and the number that is being subtracted is called the **subtrahend**. The result or answer is called the **difference**. The symbol '–' denotes subtraction.

For example, 8 – 5 refers to subtracting 5 from 8. This is read as 8 minus 5.

Subtraction must be done in the written order.

A – B ≠ B – A

For example,

8 – 5 = 3, but 5 – 8 = –3

i.e., 5 – 8 gives the negative answer of 8 – 5.

$$
\begin{array}{r}
8 \\
-\ 5 \\
\hline
3
\end{array}
$$

Minus sign ⟶ (– 5) ⟵ Subtrahend; 8 ⟵ Minuend; 3 ⟵ Difference

Follow these steps to subtract a number from another number:

Step 1:   Start by writing the numbers one under the other by aligning the place values (ones, tens, hundreds, etc.) of these numbers and drawing a horizontal line underneath. Ensure that the minuend is the number on top and the subtrahend is the number on the bottom.

Step 2:   Starting from the ones place value, subtract the bottom number from the top number. If the top digit is greater than (or equal to) the bottom digit, write the difference under the horizontal line. If the top digit is smaller than the bottom digit, borrow one from the digit in the top number that is one place value to the left, and add ten to the digit in the current place value of the top number. Then, find the difference and write it under the horizontal line. This is called "borrowing".

Step 3:   Subtract the numbers in the tens column, followed by the hundreds column, etc., and follow the same procedure for each column.

The above steps for subtracting whole numbers are demonstrated in detail in Example 1.2-b below.

| Example 1.2-b | **Subtracting Whole Numbers** |

Perform the following subtractions:

(i)   Subtract 1,314 from 3,628   (ii)   Subtract 789 from 8,357

Solution

(i)   Subtract 1,314 from 3,628

Thousands	Hundreds	Tens	Ones
3	6	2	8
– 1	3	1	4
2	3	1	4

The difference of the digits in the **ones column** is 4 since 8 – 4 = 4. There are 4 ones, so we write 4 in the ones column below the horizontal line.

The difference of the digits in the **tens column** is 1 since 20 – 10 = 10. There is 1 ten, so we write 1 in the tens column below the horizontal line.

The difference of the digits in the **hundreds column** is 3 since 600 – 300 = 300. There are 3 hundreds, so we write 3 in the hundreds column below the horizontal line.

The difference of the digits in the **thousands column** is 2 since 3,000 – 1,000 = 2,000. There are 2 thousands, so we write 2 in the thousands column below the horizontal line.

Therefore, subtracting 1,314 from 3,628 results in 2,314.

(ii)   Subtract 789 from 8,357

Thousands	Hundreds	Tens	Ones
7	12	14	17
8̶	8̶	5̶	7̶
–	7	8	9
7	5	6	8

In the **ones column**, the ones digit on the top (7) is smaller than the ones digit on the bottom (9). Borrow one ten from the tens digit on the top row and add it to the 7 ones to get 17 ones. 17 – 9 = 8, so we write 8 in the ones column below the horizontal line.

In the **tens column**, the tens digit on the top (4, after borrowing 1 for the ones column) is smaller than the tens digit on the bottom (8). Borrow one hundred from the hundreds digit on the top row and add it to the 4 tens to get 14 tens. 14 – 8 = 6, so we write 6 in the tens column below the horizontal line.

In the **hundreds column**, the hundreds digit on the top (2, after borrowing 1 for the tens column) is smaller than the hundreds digit on the bottom (7). Borrow one thousand from the thousands digit on the top row and add it to the 2 hundreds to get 12 hundreds. 12 – 7 = 5, so we write 5 in the hundreds column below the horizontal line.

As only 7 (after borrowing 1 for the hundreds column) is in the **thousands column**, write 7 in the thousands column below the horizontal line.

Therefore, subtracting 789 from 8,357 results in 7,568.

Multiplication of Whole Numbers

Multiplication can be done in any order and the product will be the same.

$A \times B = B \times A$

For example,

$5 \times 4 = 20$, and $4 \times 5 = 20$

This is called the **commutative property** of multiplication.

Multiplication is the process of finding the product of two numbers. Multiplication of whole numbers can be thought of as repeated additions. The symbol '$\times$' denotes multiplication.

For example, 5×4 refers to repeatedly adding 5, four times. This is read as 'five times four', and can also be written as $5 \cdot 4$ or $5(4)$.

5×4 can be represented pictorially as:

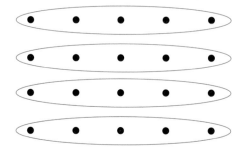

Here, the size of the set is 5 and it is repeated 4 times:
$5 + 5 + 5 + 5 = 20$

This can also be viewed as 4×5:

Here, the size of the set is 4 and it is repeated 5 times:
$4 + 4 + 4 + 4 + 4 = 20$

The numbers that are being multiplied are referred to as **factors** and the result is referred to as the **product**.

$$
\begin{array}{r}
5 \\
\times\ 4 \\
\hline
20
\end{array}
$$

Multiplication sign → ; Factors ; Product

Table 1.2-a

Multiplication Table

Memorization of the multiplication table is necessary for computations.

Multiplication table - 12 × 12												
	1	**2**	**3**	**4**	**5**	**6**	**7**	**8**	**9**	**10**	**11**	**12**
1	1	2	3	4	5	6	7	8	9	10	11	12
2	2	4	6	8	10	12	14	16	18	20	22	24
3	3	6	9	12	15	18	21	24	27	30	33	36
4	4	8	12	16	20	24	28	32	36	40	44	48
5	5	10	15	20	25	30	35	40	45	50	55	60
6	6	12	18	24	30	36	42	48	54	60	66	72
7	7	14	21	28	35	42	49	56	63	70	77	84
8	8	16	24	32	40	48	56	64	72	80	88	96
9	9	18	27	36	45	54	63	72	81	90	99	108
10	10	20	30	40	50	60	70	80	90	100	110	120
11	11	22	33	44	55	66	77	88	99	110	121	132
12	12	24	36	48	60	72	84	96	108	120	132	144

Note: The portions above and below the diagonal are the same, as a result of the commutative property discussed above. For example, 8 × 4 and 4 × 8 are both equal to 32, as highlighted in the table.

In order to multiply whole numbers, first align the factors by place value and draw a horizontal line underneath, as done for addition and subtraction. Next, multiply each digit of the first factor by each digit of the second factor, starting with the ones place value, as demonstrated in Example 1.2-c below:

Example 1.2-c

Multiplying Whole Numbers

Perform the following multiplications:

(i)   Multiply 38 by 6   (ii)   Multiply 76 by 24   (iii)   Multiply 263 by 425

Solution

(i)   Multiply 38 by 6

$$
\begin{array}{r}
\text{Hundreds} \quad \text{Tens} \quad \text{Ones} \\
4 \\
3\ \ 8 \\
\times\ \ 6 \\
\hline
2\ \ 2\ \ 8
\end{array}
$$

Multiplying 8 ones by 6 results in 48 ones. This is 4 tens and 8 ones. Write 8 in the ones column below the horizontal line and 4 above the tens column.

Multiplying 3 tens by 6 results in 18 tens. Add the 4 tens to 18 to obtain 22 tens. Write 2 in the tens column and 2 in the hundreds column below the horizontal line for the final answer.

Therefore, multiplying 38 by 6 results in 228.

(ii)   Multiply 76 by 24

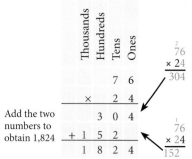

Add the two numbers to obtain 1,824

$\overset{2}{7}6$
$\times\ 24$
$\overline{304}$

Multiply 76 by 4 ones, as shown, to obtain 304.

$\overset{1}{7}6$
$\times\ 24$
$\overline{152}$

Multiply 76 by 2 tens, as shown, to obtain 152. Line up the product starting in the column representing the tens place value (you may wish to write a '0' as a place-holder in the ones column).

Therefore, multiplying 76 by 24 results in 1,824.

(iii)   Multiply 263 by 425

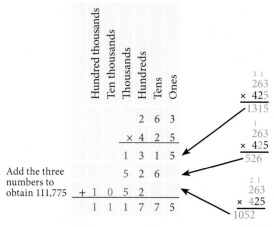

Add the three numbers to obtain 111,775

$\overset{3\ 1}{263}$
$\times\ 425$
$\overline{1315}$

Multiply 263 by 5 ones, as shown, to obtain 1,315.

$\overset{1}{263}$
$\times\ 425$
$\overline{526}$

Multiply 263 by 2 tens, as shown, to obtain 526. Line up the product starting in the column representing the tens place value.

$\overset{2\ 1}{263}$
$\times\ 425$
$\overline{1052}$

Multiply 263 by 4 hundreds, as shown, to obtain 1,052. Line up the product starting in the column representing the hundreds place value.

Therefore, multiplying 263 by 425 results in 111,775.

Division of Whole Numbers

Division must be done in the written order.

$A \div B \neq B \div A$

For example,

$20 \div 5 = 4$, but $5 \div 20 = \frac{1}{4}$

i.e., $5 \div 20$ gives the reciprocal of $20 \div 5$.

Division is the process of determining how many times one number is contained in another. This is the inverse process of multiplication. When a larger number is divided by a smaller number, this division can be thought of as repeated subtractions. The symbol '÷' denotes division.

For example, $20 \div 5$ refers to how many times 5 can be subtracted from 20. This is read as 'twenty divided by five', and can also be written as $5\ \overline{)\,20}$.

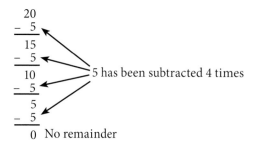

In a set of 20 items, we can create four groups of 5:

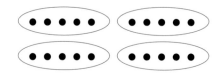

Therefore, $20 \div 5 = 4$.

When dividing one number by another number, the number that is being divided is called the **dividend**, the number by which the dividend is divided is called the **divisor**, and the answer is called the **quotient**. If the dividend cannot be divided evenly by the divisor, the number left over is called the **remainder**.

For example, $25 \div 7$

$$
\begin{array}{r}
3 \quad \longleftarrow \text{Quotient} \\
\text{Divisor} \longrightarrow 7\overline{)25} \quad \longleftarrow \text{Dividend} \\
\underline{21} \\
4 \quad \longleftarrow \text{Remainder}
\end{array}
$$

Note the following special relationship between the four components of a division problem:

$$\text{Dividend} = \text{Divisor} \times \text{Quotient} + \text{Remainder}$$
$$25 = 7 \times 3 + 4$$

The steps for dividing whole numbers are demonstrated in detail in Example 1.2-d below.

| Example 1.2-d | Dividing Whole Numbers |

Perform the following divisions and state the quotient and remainder:

(i)   Divide 76 by 3   (ii)   Divide 637 by 25   (iii)   Divide 6,543 by 12

Solution

(i)   Divide 76 by 3

$$
\begin{array}{r}
25 \\
3\overline{)76} \\
\underline{-6\downarrow} \\
16 \\
\underline{-15} \\
1
\end{array}
$$

7 can be divided by 3. Therefore, determine the number of multiples of 3 there are in 7.

There are two 3's in 7. Write 2 in the quotient area above 7.

Multiply 2 by 3 (= 6) and subtract this from 7. Write the remainder 1.

Bring down the 6 from the dividend and determine the number of multiples of 3 there are in 16.

There are five 3's in 16. Write 5 in the quotient area above 6.

Multiply 5 by 3 (= 15) and subtract this from 16 to get the final remainder of 1.

The quotient is 25 and the remainder is 1. Therefore, $76 = 3 \times 25 + 1$.

(ii)   Divide 637 by 25

$$
\begin{array}{r}
25 \\
25\overline{)637} \\
\underline{-50\downarrow} \\
137 \\
\underline{-125} \\
12
\end{array}
$$

6 cannot be divided by 25. Therefore, determine the number of multiples of 25 there are in 63.

There are two 25's in 63. Write 2 in the quotient area above 3.

Multiply 2 by 25 (= 50) and subtract this from 63. Write the remainder 13.

Bring down the 7 from the dividend and determine the number of multiples of 25 there are in 137.

There are five 25's in 137. Write 5 in the quotient area above 7.

Multiply 5 by 25 (= 125) and subtract this from 137 to get the final remainder of 12.

The quotient is 25 and the remainder is 12. Therefore, $637 = 25 \times 25 + 12$.

(iii)   Divide 6,543 by 12

$$
\begin{array}{r}
545 \\
12\overline{)6543} \\
\underline{-60\downarrow} \\
54 \\
\underline{-48\downarrow} \\
63 \\
\underline{-60} \\
3
\end{array}
$$

6 cannot by divided by 12. Therefore, determine the number of multiples of 12 there are in 65.

There are five 12's in 65. Write 5 in the quotient area above 5. Multiply 5 by 12 (= 60) and subtract this from 65. Write the remainder 5. Bring down the 4 from the dividend and determine the number of multiples of 12 there are in 54.

There are four 12's in 54. Write 4 in the quotient area above 4. Multiply 4 by 12 (= 48) and subtract this from 54. Write the remainder 6. Bring down the 3 from the dividend and determine the number of multiples of 12 there are in 63.

There are five 12's in 63. Write 5 in the quotient area above 3. Multiply 5 by 12 (= 60) and subtract this from 63 to get the final remainder of 3.

The quotient is 545 and the remainder is 3. Therefore, $6,543 = 12 \times 545 + 3$.

Arithmetic Operations with Zero and One

Table 1.2-b **Arithmetic Operations with Zero**

Operation	Description	Examples
Addition	When 0 is added to a number, or when a number is added to 0, there will be no change to that number.	$25 + 0 = 25$ $0 + 25 = 25$
Subtraction	When 0 is subtracted from a number, there will be no change to that number.	$16 - 0 = 16$
	When a number is subtracted from 0, the answer will be the negative value of that number.	$0 - 16 = -16$
Multiplication	When 0 is multiplied by a number, or when a number is multiplied by 0, the answer will be 0.	$0 \times 35 = 0$ $35 \times 0 = 0$
Division	When 0 is divided by a number, the answer will be 0.	$0 \div 25 = 0$
	When a number is divided by 0, the answer is undefined.	$25 \div 0 = \text{Undefined}$

Table 1.2-c **Arithmetic Operations with One**

Operation	Description	Examples
Multiplication	When 1 is multiplied by a number, or when a number is multiplied by 1, there will be no change to that number.	$1 \times 12 = 12$ $12 \times 1 = 12$
Division	When 1 is divided by a number, the answer is the reciprocal of that number.	$1 \div 35 = \dfrac{1}{35}$
	When a number is divided by 1, there will be no change to that number.	$35 \div 1 = \dfrac{35}{1} = 35$

Estimating by Rounding Whole Numbers to the Indicated Place Values

The rounding of whole numbers makes arithmetic operations faster and easier, especially when determining the exact answer is not required.

For example, if you are required to estimate the area of a rectangular plot of land that measures 123 m by 99 m, you would have to multiply 123 by 99, which would result in 12,177 m^2. However, rounding the measurements to the nearest ten can provide a quick estimate or an approximate value. Rounding 123 to the nearest ten is 120, rounding 99 to the nearest ten is 100. Multiplying 120 by 100 will result in an estimated area of 12,000 m^2.

Example 1.2-e **Estimating by Rounding Whole Numbers to the Nearest Ten**

For the following problems (a) estimate the answer by rounding each number to the nearest ten and (b) calculate the exact answer.

(i) $52 + 75$ (ii) $95 - 37$ (iii) 62×65 (iv) $187 \div 11$

Solution   (i)   52 + 75

Estimating by rounding to the nearest ten:

52 rounded to the nearest ten is 50 and 75 rounded to the nearest ten is 80.

Estimated value: 50 + 80 = 130

Exact answer: 52 + 75 = 127

(ii)   95 – 37

Estimating by rounding to the nearest ten:

95 rounded to the nearest ten is 100 and 37 rounded to the nearest ten is 40.

Estimated answer: 100 – 40 = 60

Exact answer: 95 – 37 = 58

(iii)   62 × 65

Estimating by rounding to the nearest ten:

62 rounded to the nearest ten is 60 and 65 rounded to the nearest ten is 70.

Estimated answer: 60 × 70 = 4,200

Exact answer: 62 × 65 = 4,030

(iv)   187 ÷ 11

Estimating by rounding to the nearest ten:

187 rounded to the nearest ten is 190 and 11 rounded to the nearest ten is 10.

Estimated answer: 190 ÷ 10 = 19

Exact answer: 187 ÷ 11 = 17

Example 1.2-f	Estimating by Rounding Whole Numbers to the Nearest Hundred

For the following problems (a) estimate the answer by rounding each number to the nearest hundred and (b) calculate the exact answer.

(i)   4,239 + 1,384   (ii)   3,250 – 1,238   (iii)   1,750 × 309   (iv)   1,971 ÷ 219

Solution   (i)   4,239 + 1,384

Estimating by rounding to the nearest hundred:

4,239 rounded to the nearest hundred is 4,200 and 1,384 rounded to the nearest hundred is 1,400.

Estimated answer: 4,200 + 1,400 = 5,600

Exact answer: 4,239 + 1,384 = 5,623

(ii)   3,250 – 1,238

Estimating by rounding to the nearest hundred:

3,250 rounded to the nearest hundred is 3,300 and 1,238 rounded to the nearest hundred is 1,200.

Estimated answer: 3,300 – 1,200 = 2,100

Exact answer: 3,250 – 1,238 = 2,012

Solution
continued

(iii) $1,750 \times 309$

Estimating by rounding to the nearest hundred:

1,750 rounded to the nearest hundred is 1,800 and 309 rounded to the nearest hundred is 300.

Estimated answer: $1,800 \times 300 = 540,000$

Exact answer: $1,750 \times 309 = 540,750$

(iv) $1,971 \div 219$

Estimating by rounding to the nearest hundred:

1,971 rounded to the nearest hundred is 2,000 and 219 rounded to the nearest hundred is 200.

Estimated answer: $2,000 \div 200 = 10$

Exact answer: $1,971 \div 219 = 9$

Note: There are no set rules for estimating by rounding. The goal of rounding is to estimate the answer as accurately and efficiently as possible.

The examples and exercises in this textbook will indicate the place value to which you should round when estimating. However, in practice you will need to determine this for yourself, based on the context of the situation.

1.2 | Exercises

Answers to odd-numbered problems are available at the end of the textbook.

For the addition Problems 1 to 8, (i) estimate the answer by rounding each number to the nearest ten and (ii) calculate the exact answer.

1.   a. 16 + 79   b. 69 + 47   2.   a. 48 + 29   b. 38 + 95

3.   a. 459 + 27   b. 356 + 65   4.   a. 875 + 48   b. 574 + 79

5.   a. 989 + 215 + 25   b. 798 + 237 + 12   6.   a. 286 + 109 + 15   b. 839 + 645 + 27

7.   a. 896 + 642 + 9   b. 995 + 724 + 8   8.   a. 195 + 459 + 8   b. 996 + 816 + 6

For the addition Problems 9 to 14, (i) estimate the answer by rounding each number to the nearest hundred and (ii) calculate the exact answer.

9.   a. 357 + 245   b. 451 + 645   10.   a. 745 + 668   b. 427 + 225

11.   a. 6,950 + 2,367   b. 3,765 + 1,992   12.   a. 1,883 + 5,466   b. 2,157 + 3,459

13.   a. 1,650 + 1,647 + 875 + 167   b. 3,869 + 1,967 + 550 + 745   14.   a. 2,635 + 372 + 1,524   b. 653 + 2,188 + 891

For the subtraction Problems 15 to 22, (i) estimate the answer by rounding each number to the nearest ten and (ii) calculate the exact answer.

15.   a. 43 − 27   b. 71 − 59   16.   a. 62 − 25   b. 33 − 18

17.   a. 327 − 28   b. 500 − 73   18.   a. 208 − 79   b. 315 − 47

19.   a. 904 − 629   b. 584 − 167   20.   a. 767 − 159   b. 804 − 308

21.   a. 9,185 − 6,728   b. 5,765 − 777   22.   a. 8,302 − 7,244   b. 2,927 − 888

For the subtraction Problems 23 to 28, (i) estimate the answer by rounding each number to the nearest hundred and (ii) calculate the exact answer.

23.   a. 868 − 745   b. 495 − 357   24.   a. 946 − 452   b. 855 − 251

25.   a. 2,955 − 1,350   b. 1,967 − 352   26.   a. 2,950 − 2,275   b. 3,961 − 1,833

27.   a. 7,676 − 3,969   b. 5,789 − 5,626   28.   a. 3,513 − 2,846   b. 3,981 − 1,657

For the multiplication Problems 29 to 34, (i) estimate the answer by rounding each number to the nearest ten and (ii) calculate the exact answer.

29. a. 35×97　　　　　b. 95×71　　　　　30. a. 58×75　　　　　b. 63×59

31. a. 482×95　　　　　b. 755×55　　　　　32. a. 764×53　　　　　b. 799×68

33. a. $2,996 \times 32$　　　　b. $2,995 \times 38$　　　　34. a. $1,995 \times 37$　　　　b. $2,150 \times 59$

For the division Problems 35 to 44, (i) estimate the answer by rounding each number to the nearest ten and (ii) perform the exact division and state the quotient and the remainder.

35. a. $69 \div 7$　　　　　b. $85 \div 9$　　　　　36. a. $78 \div 5$　　　　　b. $36 \div 8$

37. a. $59 \div 12$　　　　b. $95 \div 18$　　　　38. a. $86 \div 27$　　　　b. $78 \div 19$

39. a. $777 \div 16$　　　b. $255 \div 19$　　　40. a. $654 \div 14$　　　b. $396 \div 24$

41. a. $2,097 \div 55$　　b. $1,795 \div 64$　　42. a. $2,578 \div 18$　　b. $1,225 \div 28$

43. a. $3,895 \div 264$　　b. $5,195 \div 255$　　44. a. $3,004 \div 204$　　b. $6,501 \div 498$

45. a. What amount is $79 less than $487?　　　　b. What amount is $97 more than $52?

46. a. What amount is $65 less than $784?　　　　b. What amount is $35 more than $98?

47. a. What amount is $745 increased by $1,274?　　b. What amount is $526 decreased by $346?

48. a. What amount is $515 increased by $847?　　　b. What amount is $745 decreased by $125?

49. If you save $125 every month, how much will you save in one year?

50. If there are 24 latex gloves in a box, how many latex gloves are there in 15 boxes?

51. If 8 people can be seated at a table, how many tables are required to seat 280 people?

52. A piece of gauze 420 centimetres (cm) long is to be cut into pieces that are 35 cm long. How many pieces can be cut?

53. If you work 25 hours per week as a registered nurse, how many weeks will it take you to accumulate 450 hours of experience?

54. If you save $15 a week, how many weeks will it take you to save $675?

55. If you earn $18 per hour, how much will you earn in a week in which you have worked 32 hours?

56. If there are 16 chairs in a row, how many chairs are there in 22 rows?

57. As a nurse, Sam's overtime rate is $37 per hour. Calculate her overtime pay in a week in which she worked 29 hours overtime.

58.   Peter earns $18 per hour as a veterinarian assistant. Calculate his total earnings in a week in which he worked 35 hours.

59. There were 744 students enrolled in a nursing program at a local college. In June, some of the students graduated, and afterwards 576 students remained. How many of the students in the nursing program graduated in June?

60. Mythili went to a drugstore to fill her prescription which costs $47. She gave the cashier a $100 bill. How much change did she receive?

61. Andy has $1,238 and Bozena has $346 less than Andy.
     a. By rounding the values to the nearest ten, estimate the amount of money they have together.
     b. Using the original values, calculate the exact amount of money they have together.

62. A wheelchair costs $245 more than a walker. A walker costs $55.
     a. By rounding the values to the nearest ten, estimate how much it will cost to buy both the wheelchair and walker.
     b. Using the original values, calculate the exact amount of money it will cost to buy both the wheelchair and walker.

63. A large group of patients agreed to be part of a drug trial for a new drug treating sleeping disorders. 275 of the patients experienced side-effects, while 487 of the patients did not. Of the patients participating in the trial, 313 were male.
     a. By rounding the values to the nearest ten, estimate the number of patients that participated in the drug trial.
     b. Using the original values, calculate the exact number of patients that participated in the drug trial.
     c. By rounding the values to the nearest ten, estimate the number of female participants.
     d. Using the original values, calculate the exact number of female participants.

64. In the last three months, 415 boys and 375 girls were seen by doctors in the ER. 450 of those children were six-years-old or under.

    a. By rounding the values to the nearest ten, estimate the number of children seen in the ER.

    b. Using the original values, calculate the exact number of children seen in the ER.

    c. By rounding the values to the nearest ten, estimate the number of children over the age of six.

    d. Using the original values, calculate the exact number of children over the age of six.

65. There were 2,456 patients seen at a clinic over the course of the year. 1,179 of them were men, 325 were children, and the rest were women.
    a. By rounding the values to the nearest hundred, estimate how many more men than women patients were at the clinic.
    b. Using the original values, calculate exactly how many more men than women patients were at the clinic.

66. Out of the 3,678 people admitted as inpatients last month in the hospitals in a certain region, 1,469 were men, 1,234 were women, and the rest were children.
    a. By rounding the values to the nearest hundred, estimate how many more adults than children were admitted as inpatients last month.
    b. Using the original values, calculate exactly how many more adults than children were admitted as inpatients last month.

67. Girija wanted to lose 65 lbs for health reasons. Her goal is to lose this weight in four months. In the first month, she lost 19 pounds. The next month, she lost 27 pounds. In the third month, she lost only 5 pounds. In order to reach her goal, how many pounds does she need to lose in the final month?

68. Aran had some money saved up. On his birthday, Aran's grandparents gave him $125. After spending $98 on school supplies and $75 on clothes, he had $115 remaining. How much did Aran have in his savings before his birthday?

69. There are 22 nurses working in a certain hospital department. 10 of the nurses are wearing blue scrubs and 2 are wearing green scrubs. The rest of the nurses are wearing red scrubs. How many nurses are wearing red scrubs?

70. There are 19 girls in a class of 43 students. 15 of the girls and 11 of the boys are wearing eyeglasses.
    a. How many boys are there in the class?
    b. How many students do not wear eye glasses?

1.3 | Factors and Multiples

1 is a factor of every number and every number is a factor of itself.

Factors of a number are whole numbers that can divide the number evenly (i.e., with no remainder).

For example, to find factors of 12, divide the number 12 by 1, 2, 3, 4, ...; the numbers that divide 12 evenly are its factors.

$$12 \div 1 = 12$$
$$12 \div 2 = 6$$
$$12 \div 3 = 4$$
$$12 \div 4 = 3$$
$$12 \div 6 = 2$$
$$12 \div 12 = 1$$

Therefore, 1, 2, 3, 4, 6, and 12 are factors of 12.

Note: 5, 7, 8, 9, 10, and 11 will not divide 12 evenly. Therefore, they are not factors of 12.

We can also express factors of a number by showing that the product of two factors will result in the number.

$$12 = 1 \times 12 \quad \text{or} \quad 12 \times 1$$
$$12 = 2 \times 6 \quad \text{or} \quad 6 \times 2$$
$$12 = 3 \times 4 \quad \text{or} \quad 4 \times 3$$

Natural numbers are counting numbers, 1, 2, 3, 4...

Multiples of a number are the products of the number and the natural numbers (1, 2, 3, 4,...).

For example, the multiples of 10 are 10, 20, 30, 40, 50, etc.:

$$10 \times 1 = 10 \qquad 10 \times 2 = 20 \qquad 10 \times 3 = 30 \qquad 10 \times 4 = 40 \qquad 10 \times 5 = 50$$

Note: Multiples of a number can always be divided by the number with no remainder.

Prime Numbers and Composite Numbers

A **prime number** is a natural number (counting number) that has only two different factors: 1 and the number itself; i.e., prime numbers can be divided evenly by only 1 and the number itself.

For example, 7 is a prime number because it only has two factors: 1 and 7.

A **composite number** is a natural number that has at least one factor other than 1 and the number itself; i.e., all natural numbers greater than 1 that are not prime numbers are composite numbers.

For example, 8 is a composite number because it has more than 2 factors: 1, 2, 4, and 8.

Note: 0 and 1 are neither prime numbers nor composite numbers because 0 is not a natural number and 1 has no factor other than itself.

Example 1.3-a	**Identifying Prime Numbers**

Identify all the prime numbers up to 20.

Solution

All the prime numbers up to 20 are: 2, 3, 5, 7, 11, 13, 17, and 19.

Example 1.3-b	**Identifying Composite Numbers**

Identify all the composite numbers up to 20.

Solution

All the composite numbers up to 20 are: 4, 6, 8, 9, 10, 12, 14, 15, 16, 18, and 20.

Note: All even numbers greater than 2 are composite numbers, and all two-digit or higher numbers ending in 5 or 0 are composite. Hence, to find prime numbers for two-digit or higher numbers, we only need to consider numbers that end in 1, 3, 7, or 9.

Example 1.3-c	**Finding Factors of Prime Numbers**

Find all the factors of 13.

Solution

1 and 13 are the only factors of 13.

Example 1.3-d	**Finding All Factors of Composite Numbers**

Find all the factors of:

(i)   16   (ii)   20

Solution

(i)   The factors of 16 are: 1, 2, 4, 8, and 16.   (ii)   The factors of 20 are: 1, 2, 4, 5, 10, and 20.

Example 1.3-e	**Finding the Prime Factors of Composite Numbers**

Find all the prime factors of 24.

Solution

All the factors of 24 are: 1, 2, 3, 4, 6, 8, 12, and 24.

Of the above factors, only 2 and 3 are prime numbers.

Therefore, the prime factors of 24 are 2 and 3.

Factors and Prime Factorizations Using Factor Trees

A factor tree helps to find all of the prime factors of a number by continually expressing the number as a product of two smaller numbers, until only prime numbers remain. It also shows the number of times that each prime factor appears. When a number is written as a product of all its prime factors (including repeated prime factors), this is called a **prime factorization**.

The following example shows how to create a factor tree for the number 24:

Step 1: Write 24. Draw two short lines down at diverging angles as shown.

Step 2: 24 is divisible by the first prime number 2; i.e., $24 = 2 \times 12$.

Write these factors at the end of the lines. Now 24 is at the top and 2×12 is the 2nd layer below it, as shown.

Step 3: Now, 12 is divisible by the prime number 2; i.e., $12 = 2 \times 6$.

Write these factors below 12; i.e., the 3rd layer is $2 \times 2 \times 6$, as shown.

Step 4: Next, 6 is divisible by the prime number 2; i.e., $6 = 2 \times 3$.

Write these factors below 6; i.e., the 4th layer is $2 \times 2 \times 2 \times 3$.

Step 5: The factors at the 4th layer are all prime numbers and cannot be factored any more. Therefore, $24 = 2 \times 2 \times 2 \times 3$.

Note: It is not necessary to do every step starting with a prime number. You may start with any two factors that multiply together to get the number.

For example, $24 = 4 \times 6$

Then continue with the factoring until you are left with only prime numbers, as shown. The answer will always be the same.

Least or Lowest Common Multiple (LCM)

LCM is the smallest integer that is a common multiple of two or more numbers.

The **Least Common Multiple (LCM)** of two or more whole numbers is the smallest multiple that is common to those numbers. The LCM can be determined from one of the following methods:

Method 1:

- First, select the largest number and check to see if it is divisible by all the other numbers. If it is, then the largest number is the LCM.

  For example, in finding the LCM of 2, 3, and 12, the largest number 12 is divisible by the other numbers 2 and 3. Therefore, the LCM of 2, 3, and 12 is 12.

- If the numbers have no common factors, then the LCM of the numbers is the product of all the numbers.

  For example, in finding the LCM of 2, 5, and 7, these numbers have no common factors. Therefore, the LCM of 2, 5, and 7 is $2 \times 5 \times 7 = 70$.

- If the largest number is not divisible by the other numbers and the numbers have a common factor, then find a multiple of the largest number that is divisible by all the other numbers.

  For example, in finding the LCM of 3, 5, and 10, the largest number 10 is not divisible by 3, and 5 and 10 have a common factor of 5. Multiples of 10 are 10, 20, 30, 40,... ; 30 is divisible by both 3 and 5. Therefore, the LCM of 3, 5, and 10 is 30.

Method 2:

Step 1: Determine the prime factors of each of the numbers using a factor tree and list the different prime numbers (creating a factor tree is shown above and in the example below).

Step 2: Count the number of times each different prime number appears in each of the factorizations.

Step 3: Determine the largest of these counts for each prime number.

Step 4: List each prime number as many times as you counted it in Step 3. The LCM is the product of all the prime numbers listed.

Example 1.3-f   Finding the Least Common Multiple

Find the LCM of 9 and 15.

Solution

Method 1:   The largest number, 15, is **not** divisible by 9.

Multiples of 15 are: 15, 30, 45...

45 is divisible by 9.

Therefore, the LCM of 9 and 15 is 45.

Method 2:

1	9 $\overset{\wedge}{3 \times 3}$	15 $\overset{\wedge}{3 \times 5}$
2	Number of 3's = 2	Number of 3's = 1 Number of 5's = 1
3	Largest count for the prime number 3 = 2 Largest count for the prime number 5 = 1	
4	LCM = $3 \times 3 \times 5 = 45$	

Example 1.3-g   Finding the Least Common Multiple

Find the LCM of 3, 5, and 8.

Solution

Method 1:   The largest number, 8, is **not** divisible by 3 and 5.

Since 3, 5, and 8 have no common factors, the LCM is the product of all the numbers: $3 \times 5 \times 8 = 120$.

Therefore, the LCM of 3, 5, and 8 is 120.

Method 2:

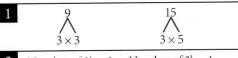

1	3	5	8 $\overset{\wedge}{2 \times 4}$ $\overset{/\wedge}{2 \times 2 \times 2}$
	3 is a prime number.	5 is a prime number.	
2	Number of 3's = 1	Number of 5's = 1	Number of 2's = 3
3	Largest count for the prime number 2 = 3 Largest count for the prime number 3 = 1 Largest count for the prime number 5 = 1		
4	LCM = $2 \times 2 \times 2 \times 3 \times 5 = 120$		

Example 1.3-h **Finding the Least Common Multiple**

Find the LCM of 3, 6, and 18.

Solution

Method 1: The largest number, 18, is divisible by both 6 and 3.

Therefore, the LCM of 3, 6, and 18 is 18.

Method 2:

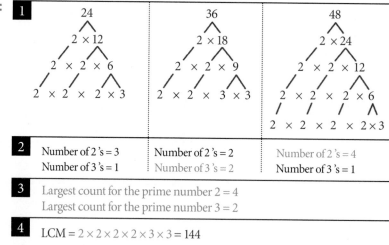

1	3	6 $\;2 \times 3$	18 $\;2 \times 9$ $\;2 \times 3 \times 3$
	3 is a prime number.		
2	Number of 3's = 1	Number of 2's = 1 Number of 3's = 1	Number of 2's = 1 Number of 3's = 2
3	Largest count for the prime number 2 = 1 Largest count for the prime number 3 = 2		
4	LCM = $2 \times 3 \times 3 = 18$		

Example 1.3-i **Finding the Least Common Multiple**

Find the LCM of 24, 36, and 48.

Solution

Method 1: The largest number, 48, is divisible by 24 but **not** by 36.
Multiples of 48 are: 48, 96, 144...
144 is divisible by both 24 and 36.
Therefore, the LCM of 24, 36, and 48 is 144.

Method 2:

1	24 $\;2 \times 12$ $\;2 \times 2 \times 6$ $\;2 \times 2 \times 2 \times 3$	36 $\;2 \times 18$ $\;2 \times 2 \times 9$ $\;2 \times 2 \times 3 \times 3$	48 $\;2 \times 24$ $\;2 \times 2 \times 12$ $\;2 \times 2 \times 2 \times 6$ $\;2 \times 2 \times 2 \times 2 \times 3$
2	Number of 2's = 3 Number of 3's = 1	Number of 2's = 2 Number of 3's = 2	Number of 2's = 4 Number of 3's = 1
3	Largest count for the prime number 2 = 4 Largest count for the prime number 3 = 2		
4	LCM = $2 \times 2 \times 2 \times 2 \times 3 \times 3 = 144$		

Example 1.3-j **Finding the Least Common Multiple to Solve a Word Problem**

Two flashing lights are turned on at the same time. One light flashes every 16 seconds and the other flashes every 20 seconds. How often will they flash together?

Solution

In this example, we are required to find the least common interval for both lights to flash together. Thereafter, both lights will continue to flash together at this interval (multiple).

Solution
continued

Method 1: The largest number, 20, is **not** divisible by 16.

Multiples of 20 are: 20, 40, 60, 80...

80 is divisble by 16.

Therefore, the LCM of 16 and 20 is 80.

Method 2:

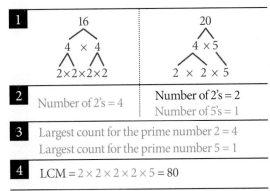

1	16	20
	4×4	4×5
	$2 \times 2 \times 2 \times 2$	$2 \times 2 \times 5$
2	Number of 2's = 4	Number of 2's = 2
		Number of 5's = 1
3	Largest count for the prime number $2 = 4$	
	Largest count for the prime number $5 = 1$	
4	LCM $= 2 \times 2 \times 2 \times 2 \times 5 = 80$	

Therefore, the two flashing lights will flash together every 80 seconds.

Greatest Common Factor (GCF)

The factors that are common to two or more numbers are called **common factors** of those numbers.

The **Greatest Common Factor (GCF)** of two or more numbers is the largest common number that divides the numbers with no remainder. In other words, the GCF is the largest of all the common factors.

> GCF is the largest integer that divides the set of numbers without remainder.

The GCF can be determined from one of the following methods:

Method 1:

First list all the factors of all the numbers. Then select all the common factors of the numbers. The highest value of the common factors is the GCF.

For example, in finding the GCF of 12 and 18:

- The factors of 12 are: 1, 2, 3, 4, 6, and 12.

- The factors of 18 are: 1, 2, 3, 6, 9, and 18.

The common factors are: 1, 2, 3, and 6.

Therefore, the GCF is 6.

Method 2:

Step 1: Find the prime factors of each of the numbers using a factor tree.

Step 2: List each of the different prime numbers that appear in each of the factorizations, including repetitions.

Step 3: Identify the prime factors that appear in the lists of **all** the numbers. If there are repeats of a factor, choose the smallest number of repeats that appear in the lists of all the numbers.

Step 4: The GCF is the product of all the prime numbers identified in Step 3.

For example, in finding the GCF of 12 and 18:

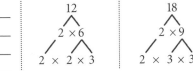

Number	Prime Factors of:	
	2	3
12	2, 2	3
18	2	3, 3

$$12$$
$$2 \times 6$$
$$2 \times 2 \times 3$$

$$18$$
$$2 \times 9$$
$$2 \times 3 \times 3$$

Therefore, the GCF is $2 \times 3 = 6$.

Note: 1 is a factor that is common to all numbers and is always included in the list of common factors. If there are no common factors other than 1, then 1 is the greatest common factor.

For example, 1 is the only common factor of 3, 5, and 7.

Example 1.3-k | **Finding the Greatest Common Factor**

Find the GCF of 36 and 60.

Solution

Method 1: Factors of 36 are 1, 2, 3, 4, 6, 9, 12, 18, and 36.

Factors of 60 are 1, 2, 3, 4, 5, 6, 10, 12, 15, 20, 30, and 60.

The common factors are 1, 2, 3, 4, 6, and 12.
Therefore, the GCF is 12.

Method 2:

Number	Prime Factors of:		
	2	3	5
36	2, 2	3, 3	
60	2, 2	3	5

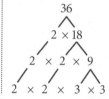 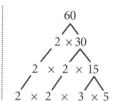

Therefore, the GCF is $2 \times 2 \times 3 = 12$.

Example 1.3-l | **Finding the Greatest Common Factor**

Find the GCF of 40 and 63.

Solution

Method 1: Factors of 40 are 1, 2, 4, 5, 8, 10, 20, and 40.

Factors of 63 are 1, 3, 7, 9, 21, and 63.

The only common factor is 1.
Therefore, the GCF is 1.

Method 2:

Number	Prime Factors of:			
	2	3	5	7
40	2, 2, 2		5	
63		3, 3		7

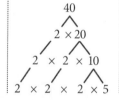

There are no common prime factors between 40 and 63.
Therefore, the GCF is 1.

Example 1.3-m | **Finding the Greatest Common Factor**

Find the GCF of 72, 126, and 216.

Solution

Method 1: The factors of 72 are 1, 2, 3, 4, 6, 8, 9, 12, 18, 24, 36, and 72.

The factors of 126 are 1, 2, 3, 6, 7, 9, 14, 18, 21, 42, 63, and 126.

The factors of 216 are 1, 2, 3, 4, 6, 8, 9, 12, 18, 24, 27, 36, 54, 72, 108, and 216.

The common factors are 1, 2, 3, 6, 9, and 18.

Therefore, the GCF is 18.

Solution
continued

Method 2:

Number	Prime Factors of:		
	2	3	7
72	2, 2, 2	3, 3	
126	2	3, 3	7
216	2, 2, 2	3, 3, 3	

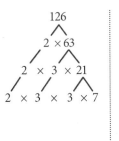

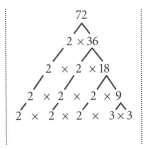

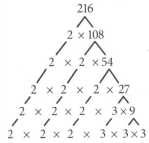

Therefore, the GCF is 2 × 3 × 3 = 18.

Example 1.3-n | **Finding the Greatest Common Factor to Solve a Word Problem**

Three pieces of timber with lengths 48 cm, 72 cm, and 96 cm are to be cut into smaller pieces of equal length without remainders.

(i)   What is the greatest possible length of each piece?

(ii)   How many total pieces of such equal lengths are possible from all three pieces of timber?

Solution

Method 1: Factors of 48 are 1, 2, 3, 4, 6, 8, 12, 16, 24, and 48.

Factors of 72 are 1, 2, 3, 4, 6, 8, 9, 12, 18, 24, 36, and 72.

Factors of 96 are 1, 2, 3, 4, 6, 8, 12, 16, 24, 32, 48, and 96.

The common factors are 1, 2, 3, 4, 6, 8, 12, and 24.

Therefore, the GCF is 24.

Method 2:

Number	Prime Factors of:	
	2	3
48	2, 2, 2, 2	3
72	2, 2, 2	3, 3
96	2, 2, 2, 2, 2	3

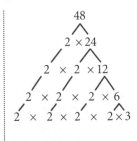

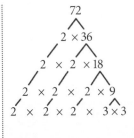

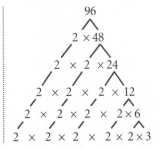

Therefore, the GCF = 2 × 2 × 2 × 3 = 24.

(i)   Therefore, the greatest possible length of each equal-sized piece is 24 cm.

(ii)   The total number of equal pieces is the sum of the number of multiples of 24 cm of each piece.

$$48 = 24 \times 2$$

$$72 = 24 \times 3$$

$$96 = 24 \times 4$$

Therefore, the total number of equal pieces of 24 cm in length that are possible is 2 + 3 + 4 = 9.

1.3 | Exercises

Answers to odd-numbered problems are available at the end of the textbook.

1.   List all the prime numbers between 20 and 40.

2.   List all the prime numbers between 40 and 60.

3.   List all the composite numbers greater than 30 and less than 50.

4. List all the composite numbers greater than 50 and less than 70.

5. Identify the prime numbers in the given sets of numbers: a. 31, 39, 41, 59, 63   b. 23, 37, 45, 51, 53

6. Identify the prime numbers in the given sets of numbers: a. 31, 33, 36, 47, 49   b. 25, 27, 29, 35, 43

For Problems 7 to 14, (i) find all the factors and (ii) list the prime factors of the numbers.

7. a. 28   b. 35   8. a. 25   b. 34

9. a. 56   b. 80   10. a. 64   b. 44

11. a. 30   b. 42   12. a. 21   b. 45

13. a. 40   b. 49   14. a. 54   b. 65

For Problems 15 to 18, find the first six multiples of the numbers.

15. a. 5   b. 12   16. a. 6   b. 8

17. a. 7   b. 15   18. a. 9   b. 10

For Problems 19 to 24, find the least common multiple (LCM) of each pair of numbers.

19. a. 12, 16   b. 21, 36   20. a. 10, 15   b. 15, 18

21. a. 10, 25   b. 45, 60   22. a. 18, 24   b. 35, 45

23. a. 12, 60   b. 25, 30   24. a. 16, 64   b. 48, 60

For Problems 25 to 32, find the least common multiple (LCM) of each set of numbers.

25. a. 8, 5, 12   b. 5, 15, 20   26. a. 2, 3, 8   b. 4, 9, 10

27. a. 4, 8, 40   b. 3, 16, 2   28. a. 10, 15, 30   b. 6, 27, 36

29. a. 4, 6, 21   b. 12, 28, 42   30. a. 14, 21, 28   b. 3, 18, 27

31. a. 5, 12, 15   b. 12, 40, 48   32. a. 6, 15, 18   b. 24, 30, 36

For Problems 33 to 38, find the (i) factors, (ii) common factors, and (iii) greatest common factor (GCF) of each pair of numbers.

33. a. 14, 35   b. 8, 36   34. a. 15, 25   b. 18, 32

35. a. 16, 30   b. 36, 42   36. a. 18, 48   b. 32, 60

37. a. 35, 75   b. 24, 72   38. a. 25, 80   b. 40, 120

For Problems 39 to 44, find the (i) factors, (ii) common factors, and (iii) greatest common factor (GCF) of each set of numbers.

39. a. 6, 8, 10   b. 10, 15, 25   40. a. 8, 12, 15   b. 6, 15, 20

41. a. 24, 36, 40   b. 12, 36, 48   42. a. 12, 18, 24   b. 12, 30, 42

43. a. 50, 75, 125   b. 60, 90, 120   44. a. 40, 50, 80   b. 30, 75, 90

45. Two cartons of milk that hold 112 fl oz and 154 fl oz are to be poured into glasses of equal volume, without wastage. Find the greatest possible volume of each glass.

46. Two IV tubings of lengths 96 cm and 160 cm are to be cut into pieces of equal length, without wastage. Find the greatest possible length of each piece.

47. Enea is enrolled in a nursing program. She has theory lessons every 8th day and practicals every 10th day. If she had theory and practical lessons on March 3rd, on which date will she have both lessons again?

48. Tahrell has nutrition classes every 6th day and respiratory therapy classes every 8th day. If he had nutrition and respiratory therapy classes on February 5th, on which date will he have both classes again? Assume the year is not a leap year.

• 49. A pharmaceutical store has 54 syringes measuring 5 mL, 72 syringes measuring 3 mL, and 90 syringes measuring 1 mL. The owner decides to package all the syringes into boxes, such that each box contains the same number of syringes. As well, each box has to contain only syringes of the same size. Find the maximum possible number of syringes in each box.

• 50. A hospital administrator orders gauze pads in three different sizes. They receive 18 boxes each containing 20 large gauze pads, 45 boxes each containing 30 medium gauze pads, and 36 boxes each containing 50 small gauze pads. If the administrator wants to stock a number of different stations, so that each station contains the same mixture of boxes of the three sizes, what is the maximum number of stations she can stock, and how many of each size will she stock in each station?

- 51. A paramedic stocks the supply room with three different types of non-prescription pain killers. If the depletion rate is at intervals of 24, 36, and 40 hours, respectively, for the three different pain-killers, how long will it take (in days) until they all need to be replenished at the same time?
- 52. Three different types of volumetric infusion devices pump at intervals of 15, 18, and 40 seconds, respectively. If they begin pumping at the same time, how long will it take (in minutes) until all three pump at the same time again?

1.4 | Powers, Square Roots, and Order of Operations

Powers of Whole Numbers

We learned previously that multiplication is a shorter way to write repeated additions of a number. Similarly, when a number is multiplied by itself repeatedly, we represent this repeated multiplication using **exponential notation**. In this section, we will learn about exponential notation and the positive powers of whole numbers.

When 2 is multiplied 5 times, in repeated multiplication, it is represented by:

$$2 \times 2 \times 2 \times 2 \times 2$$

Base 1 raised to any exponent = 1

Base 0 raised to any exponent = 0

However, when 2 is multiplied 100 times, it would be tedious to represent it using repeated multiplication. Instead, exponential notation can be used.

When 2 is multiplied 5 times, it is represented as 2^5 using exponential notation. The whole representation is read as "2 raised to the power of 5" or "2 to the 5th power".

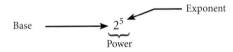

In the notation 2^5, 2 is referred to as the **base**, 5 is referred to as the **exponent**, and 2^5 is referred to as the **power**. The exponent is the number written in superscript to the right of the base, and it represents the number of times that the base is multiplied.

Notice that with this notation, 2 raised to the power of 100 (2^{100}) is just as convenient to write as 2 raised to the power of 5 (2^5).

Example 1.4-a | Simplifying Numbers in Exponential Form

Expand 8^2 to show the repeated multiplication and simplify.

Solution

In general, exponentiation is not commutative (i.e., $a^b \neq b^a$).

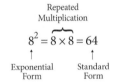

$$8^2 = 8 \times 8 = 64$$

Exponential Form   Standard Form

Note: 8^2 is not equal to 2^8.

Example 1.4-b | Writing Repeated Multiplication in Exponential Form

Express the repeated multiplication $9 \times 9 \times 9 \times 9 \times 9 \times 9$ in exponential form.

Solution

Number 9 is multiplied repeatedly 6 times.

The **base** is **9** and the **exponent** is **6**.

Therefore, $9 \times 9 \times 9 \times 9 \times 9 \times 9$ expressed as a **power** is 9^6.

| Example 1.4-c | Evaluating Expressions by Writing in Standard Form |

Express the following in standard form and then evaluate:

(i) 5×3^4 (ii) $2^3 \times 3^2$ (iii) $5^4 + 2^2$ (iv) $5^2 - 4^2$

Solution

(i) $5 \times 3^4 = 5 \times [\, 3 \times 3 \times 3 \times 3 \,] = 5 \times 81 = 405$

(ii) $2^3 \times 3^2 = [\, 2 \times 2 \times 2 \,] \times [\, 3 \times 3 \,] = 8 \times 9 = 72$

(iii) $5^4 + 2^2 = [\, 5 \times 5 \times 5 \times 5 \,] + [\, 2 \times 2 \,] = 625 + 4 = 629$

(iv) $5^2 - 4^2 = [\, 5 \times 5 \,] - [\, 4 \times 4 \,] = 25 - 16 = 9$

| Table 1.4 | Examples of Powers of Exponents of 2, 3, 4, and 5 |

Powers of 2		Powers of 3	Powers of 4	Powers of 5
$1^2 = 1$	$11^2 = 121$	$1^3 = 1$	$1^4 = 1$	$1^5 = 1$
$2^2 = 4$	$12^2 = 144$	$2^3 = 8$	$2^4 = 16$	$2^5 = 32$
$3^2 = 9$	$13^2 = 169$	$3^3 = 27$	$3^4 = 81$	$3^5 = 243$
$4^2 = 16$	$14^2 = 196$	$4^3 = 64$	$4^4 = 256$	$4^5 = 1,024$
$5^2 = 25$	$15^2 = 225$	$5^3 = 125$	$5^4 = 625$	$5^5 = 3,125$
$6^2 = 36$	$16^2 = 256$	$6^3 = 216$	$6^4 = 1,296$	$6^5 = 7,776$
$7^2 = 49$	$17^2 = 289$	$7^3 = 343$	$7^4 = 2,401$	$7^5 = 16,807$
$8^2 = 64$	$18^2 = 324$	$8^3 = 512$	$8^4 = 4,096$	$8^5 = 32,768$
$9^2 = 81$	$19^2 = 361$	$9^3 = 729$	$9^4 = 6,561$	$9^5 = 59,049$
$10^2 = 100$	$20^2 = 400$	$10^3 = 1,000$	$10^4 = 10,000$	$10^5 = 100,000$

Perfect Squares and Square Roots

Any whole number base with an exponent of 2 is called a perfect square. For example, 1, 4, 9, 16, 25, 36, 49, 64, 81, 100, ... are perfect squares.

$1^2 = 1$ $2^2 = 4$ $3^2 = 9$ $4^2 = 16$ $5^2 = 25$

$6^2 = 36$ $7^2 = 49$ $8^2 = 64$ $9^2 = 81$ $10^2 = 100$

Finding the root of a perfect square is the inverse of raising a number to the power of 2.

The square root of a number is one of two identical factors of that number.

- 2 is the **square root** of 4 because $2^2 = 4$ or $2 \times 2 = 4$
- 5 is the **square root** of 25 because $5^2 = 25$ or $5 \times 5 = 25$

That is, a whole number multiplied by itself results in a perfect square. The number multiplied by itself to get that perfect square is called the square root of that perfect square.

For example,

- 16 is a **perfect square** because it has two identical factors of 4; i.e., $16 = 4 \times 4$

  Therefore, 4 is the **square root** of 16.

The radical sign '$\sqrt{}$' indicates the root of a number (or expression). The square root of 16, using the radical sign, is represented by $\sqrt[2]{16}$, where 2 is the **index**. The index is written as a small number to the left of the radical symbol, and it indicates which root is to be taken. For square roots, the index 2 does not need to be written as it is understood to be there; i.e., $\sqrt[2]{16}$ is written as $\sqrt{16}$.

For the examples mentioned above,

$\sqrt{4} = 2$

$\sqrt{25} = 5$

$\sqrt{16} = 4$

Example 1.4-d | **Finding the Square Root of Perfect Squares**

Find the square root of the following:

(i) $\sqrt{36}$

(ii) $\sqrt{81}$

(iii) $\sqrt{144}$

Solution

(i)   Since $36 = 6^2$, therefore, $\sqrt{36} = 6$.

(ii)   Since $81 = 9^2$, therefore, $\sqrt{81} = 9$.

(iii)   Since $144 = 12^2$, therefore, $\sqrt{144} = 12$.

Order of Arithmetic Operations (BEDMAS)

So far you have learned about several different arithmetic operations: addition, subtraction, multiplication, division, and exponentiation (powers) and roots of whole numbers. In this section, you will learn the correct order (or sequence) for performing the combined arithmetic operations of whole numbers.

When there are no indicated groupings of operations within brackets or a radical sign (i.e., roots), the arithmetic operations are performed in the following sequence:

1. Exponents (Powers).

2. Division and Multiplication, in order from left to right.

3. Addition and Subtraction, in order from left to right.

Example 1.4-e | **Evaluating Expressions with Mixed Arithmetic Operations**

Solve the following arithmetic expressions:

(i) $16 \div 2^2 + 44 - 3^3$ (ii) $12 \div 3 \times 2 + 5^2$

Solution

(i) $16 \div \mathbf{2^2} + 44 - \mathbf{3^3}$ Evaluating the powers,

$= \mathbf{16 \div 4} + 44 - 27$ Dividing,

$= \mathbf{4 + 44} - 27$ Adding,

$= \mathbf{48 - 27}$ Subtracting,

$= 21$

(ii) $12 \div 3 \times 2 + \mathbf{5^2}$ Evaluating the power,

$= \mathbf{12 \div 3} \times 2 + 25$ Dividing,

$= \mathbf{4 \times 2} + 25$ Multiplying,

$= \mathbf{8 + 25}$ Adding,

$= 33$

Where there are groupings, the arithmetic operations within the groupings are to be evaluated first. Common symbols used for groupings are brackets ( ), [ ], { }, and $\sqrt{}$.

When there are groupings with more than one bracket, start with the innermost bracket and move outwards, evaluating all expressions within the brackets by following the order of operations explained earlier.

Arithmetic expressions that contain multiple operations, with brackets, exponents, divison, multiplication, addition, and subtraction, are performed in the following sequence:

1. Brackets.

2. Exponents (Powers).

3. Division and Multiplication, in order from left to right.

4. Addition and Subtraction, in order from left to right.

The above Order of Operations, <u>B</u>rackets, <u>E</u>xponents, <u>D</u>ivision, <u>M</u>ultiplication, <u>A</u>ddition, and <u>S</u>ubtraction, can be remembered by the acronym '**BEDMAS**'.

| Example 1.4-f | Evaluating Expressions by Finding the Square Roots |

Evaluate the following expressions:

(i) $\sqrt{49} + \sqrt{25}$ (ii) $\sqrt{64} - \sqrt{16}$ (iii) $\sqrt{4} \times \sqrt{9}$ (iv) $\sqrt{(4 \times 9)}$

Solution

(i) $\sqrt{49} + \sqrt{25}$ Evaluating the square roots,

$= 7 + 5$ Adding,

$= 12$

(ii) $\sqrt{64} - \sqrt{16}$ Evaluating the square roots,

$= 8 - 4$ Subtracting,

$= 4$

In general,
$\sqrt{a} \times \sqrt{b} = \sqrt{(a \times b)}$.
For example,
$\sqrt{4} \times \sqrt{9} = \sqrt{(4 \times 9)}$.

(iii) $\sqrt{4} \times \sqrt{9}$ Evaluating the square roots,

$= 2 \times 3$ Multiplying,

$= 6$

(iv) $\sqrt{(4 \times 9)}$ Multiplying,

$= \sqrt{36}$ Evaluating the square root,

$= 6$

| Example 1.4-g | Evaluating Expressions by Finding the Square Roots |

Evaluate the following expressions:

(i) $5 \times \sqrt{121}$ (ii) $\sqrt{100} \div 5$ (iii) $35 + \sqrt{49} - \sqrt{9}$

Solution

(i) $5 \times \sqrt{121}$ Evaluating the square root,

$= 5 \times 11$ Multiplying,

$= 55$

(ii) $\sqrt{100} \div 5$ Evaluating the square root,

$= 10 \div 5$ Dividing,

$= 2$

(iii) $35 + \sqrt{49} - \sqrt{9}$ Evaluating the square roots,

$= 35 + 7 - 3$ Adding and subtracting from left to right,

$= 39$

Example 1.4-h | **Evaluating Expressions with Groupings**

Solve the following arithmetic expressions:

(i) $4 \times 50 \div (8 - 3)^2 - 1$ (ii) $(100 - 3 \times 24) \div 2(6 - 3) \div 2$

(iii) $\sqrt{3^2 + 4^2} \times (7 - 4) + 2$ (iv) $35 \div 7 + \sqrt{4^2 + 9}$

(v) $4^2 - \sqrt{13^2 - 5^2} + 3^2 \sqrt{25}$

Solution

(i) $4 \times 50 \div (\mathbf{8 - 3})^2 - 1$ Evaluating the operation within the brackets,

$= 4 \times 50 \div \mathbf{5^2} - 1$ Evaluating the exponent,

$= \mathbf{4 \times 50} \div 25 - 1$

$= \mathbf{200 \div 25} - 1$ } Dividing and multiplying from left to right,

$= \mathbf{8 - 1}$ Subtracting,

$= 7$

> Two numbers written side-by-side separated using brackets are not multiplied during the Brackets phase of BEDMAS, but rather are treated as Multiplication.

(ii) $(100 - \mathbf{3 \times 24}) \div 2(\mathbf{6 - 3}) \div 2$ } Evaluating the operations within the brackets,

$= (\mathbf{100 - 72}) \div 2(3) \div 2$

$= \mathbf{28 \div 2} \times 3 \div 2$

$= \mathbf{14 \times 3} \div 2$ } Dividing and multiplying from left to right,

$= \mathbf{42 \div 2}$

$= 21$

(iii) $\sqrt{\mathbf{3^2 + 4^2}} \times (\mathbf{7 - 4}) + 2$ } Evaluating the operations within the radical sign and brackets,

$= \sqrt{\mathbf{9 + 16}} \times 3 + 2$

$= \sqrt{\mathbf{25}} \times 3 + 2$ Evaluating the square root,

$= \mathbf{5 \times 3} + 2$ Multiplying,

$= \mathbf{15 + 2}$ Adding,

$= 17$

(iv) $35 \div 7 + \sqrt{\mathbf{4^2 + 9}}$ } Evaluating the operations within the radical sign,

$= 35 \div 7 + \sqrt{\mathbf{16 + 9}}$

$= 35 \div 7 + \sqrt{\mathbf{25}}$ Evaluating the square root,

$= \mathbf{35 \div 7} + 5$ Dividing,

$= \mathbf{5 + 5}$ Adding,

$= 10$

(v) $4^2 - \sqrt{\mathbf{13^2 - 5^2}} + 3^2 \sqrt{25}$ } Evaluating the operations within the radical sign,

$= 4^2 - \sqrt{\mathbf{169 - 25}} + 3^2 \sqrt{25}$

$= 4^2 - \sqrt{\mathbf{144}} + 3^2 \sqrt{\mathbf{25}}$ Evaluating the square roots,

$= \mathbf{4^2} - 12 + \mathbf{3^2} \times 5$ Evaluating the powers,

$= 16 - 12 + \mathbf{9 \times 5}$ Multiplying,

$= \mathbf{16 - 12} + 45$

$= \mathbf{4 + 45}$ } Adding and subtracting from left to right,

$= 49$

Example 1.4-i Evaluating Expressions with More than One Bracket

Evaluate the following:

(i) $4 \times 50 \div [(8-3)^2 - 5]$ (ii) $100 - 3[24 \div 2(6-3)] \div 2$ (iii) $[10^2 \times 4 + 50] \div [(8-3)^2 - 4^2]$

Solution

(i) $4 \times 50 \div [(\mathbf{8 - 3})^2 - 5]$ Evaluating the inner bracket,

$= 4 \times 50 \div [\mathbf{5}^2 - 5]$ ⎫ Evaluating the power and then subtracting within the
$= 4 \times 50 \div [\mathbf{25 - 5}]$ ⎬ outer bracket,

$= \mathbf{4 \times 50} \div 20$ ⎫
$= \mathbf{200 \div 20}$ ⎬ Dividing and multiplying from left to right,
$= 10$

(ii) $100 - 3[24 \div 2(\mathbf{6 - 3})] \div 2$ Evaluating the inner bracket,

$= 100 - 3[\mathbf{24 \div 2} \times 3] \div 2$ ⎫ Dividing and multiplying from left to right within the outer
$= 100 - 3[\mathbf{12 \times 3}] \div 2$ ⎬ bracket,

$= 100 - \mathbf{3 \times 36} \div 2$ ⎫
$= 100 - \mathbf{108 \div 2}$ ⎬ Dividing and multiplying from left to right,

$= 100 - 54$ Subtracting,
$= 46$

(iii) $[10^2 \times 4 + 50] \div [(\mathbf{8 - 3})^2 - 4^2]$ Evaluating the inner bracket,

$= [\mathbf{10}^2 \times 4 + 50] \div [\mathbf{5}^2 - \mathbf{4}^2]$ Evaluating the powers,

$= [\mathbf{100} \times 4 + 50] \div [\mathbf{25 - 16}]$ ⎫
$= [\mathbf{400 + 50}] \div 9$ ⎬ Evaluating the outer brackets,

$= \mathbf{450 \div 9}$ Dividing,
$= 50$

1.4 | Exercises

Answers to odd-numbered problems are available at the end of the textbook.

For Problems 1 to 4, express the repeated multiplication in exponential form.

1. a. $5 \times 5 \times 5$ b. $7 \times 7 \times 7 \times 7 \times 7$ 2. a. $6 \times 6 \times 6 \times 6$ b. 12×12

3. a. $8 \times 8 \times 8 \times 8 \times 8$ b. $4 \times 4 \times 4 \times 4 \times 4$ 4. a. $3 \times 3 \times 3 \times 3 \times 3 \times 3$ b. $9 \times 9 \times 9 \times 9$

For Problems 5 to 8, write the base and exponent for the powers.

5. a. 6^2 b. 10^9 6. a. 2^9 b. 5^7

7. a. 7^5 b. 12^1 8. a. 1^{20} b. 8^3

For Problems 9 to 12, express the powers in standard form and then evaluate, without using a calculator.

9. a. 2^8 b. 5^4 10. a. 10^6 b. 3^5

11. a. 7^4 b. 4^7 12. a. 6^5 b. 5^6

For Problems 13 to 20, evaluate the expressions, without using a calculator.

13. a. $5^2 \times 2^3$ b. $4^2 \times 3^3$ 14. a. $4^2 \times 2^4$ b. $3^2 \times 2^3$

15. a. 0^{23} b. $(8-5)^4$ 16. a. 1^{20} b. $(3+2)^3$

17. a. $5^2 + 6^2$ b. $8^2 - 6^2$ 18. a. $2^3 + 3^3$ b. $5^2 - 4^2$

19. a. $5^2 \times 3 - 15$ b. $144 - 3^3 \times 4$ 20. a. $6^2 \times 2 - 2$ b. $100 - 5^2 \times 3$

For Problems 21 to 32, evaluate the expressions, without using a calculator.

21. a. $\sqrt{121} + \sqrt{36}$ b. $\sqrt{144} - \sqrt{9}$ 22. a. $\sqrt{100} + \sqrt{25}$ b. $\sqrt{81} - \sqrt{16}$

23. a. $\sqrt{25 \times 64}$ b. $\sqrt{81 \times 121}$ 24. a. $\sqrt{9 \times 16}$ b. $\sqrt{36 \times 49}$

25. a. $\sqrt{125 - 76}$ b. $\sqrt{48 - 23}$ 26. a. $\sqrt{40 - 24}$ b. $\sqrt{75 - 11}$

27. a. $\sqrt{5^2 - 4^2}$ b. $\sqrt{12^2 + 5^2}$ 28. a. $\sqrt{3^2 + 4^2}$ b. $\sqrt{13^2 - 5^2}$

29. a. $\sqrt{256 \div 4}$ b. $\sqrt{225 \div 25}$ 30. a. $\sqrt{100 \div 25}$ b. $\sqrt{196 \div 4}$

31. a. $\sqrt{12^2}$ b. $\sqrt{45^2}$ 32. a. $\sqrt{8^2}$ b. $\sqrt{29^2}$

For Problems 33 to 50, evaluate the expressions, without using a calculator.

33. a. $7 \times 5 + 20 \div 4$ b. $36 \div 4 \times 9$ 34. a. $5 \times 4 + 25 \div 25$ b. $64 \div 8 \times 2$

35. a. $80 \div 10 \times 8$ b. $50 \times 2 \times 5 + 10$ 36. a. $100 \div 25 \times 4$ b. $18 \div 2 \times 3 + 5$

37. a. $20 \div 4 \times 5 + 2$ b. $56 \div 4 \div 2 \times 5$ 38. a. $32 \div 4 \div 2 \times 4$ b. $96 \div 12 \times 2 + 4$

39. a. $40 - 3^2 \sqrt{16} + 1$ b. $6^2 \sqrt{25} + 16 - \sqrt{100}$ 40. a. $5^2 \sqrt{16} + 10 - 2$ b. $19 - 2^2 \sqrt{9} + 3$

41. a. $(9 - 6)^2 - 2^2 + 3^3$ b. $3^2 + 2^4 + (15 - 9)^2$ 42. a. $(4 + 3)^2 - 5^2 + 2^3$ b. $6^2 + 2^3 - (12 - 8)^2$

• 43. a. $16 \div 8 \times 10^2 + (12 - 7)^2 \times 2$ b. $3^2[(12^2 + 8)^2 \div 4 + 6 - 2]$ • 44. a. $12^2 - 5 \times 27 \div (5 - 2)^2 - 3$ b. $3^2[(9 - 6)^2 \div 9 + 7 - 4]$

• 45. a. $15 + (5\sqrt{9} - 8)^2$ b. $\sqrt{12^2 + 5^2} - 27 \div \sqrt{81}$ • 46. a. $7 + (3\sqrt{49} - 1)^2$ b. $16 \div \sqrt{64} + \sqrt{10^2 - 6^2}$

• 47. a. $[(6^2 \div 4) \times 5] \div (2^2 + 5)$ b. $(81 \div 9 \div 3)^2 + (9^2 + 2^2)$ • 48. a. $[(20 \div 5) \times 8] \div (2^2 + 4)$ b. $(64 \div 8 \div 4)^2 + (3^2 + 6^2)$

• 49. $(20 \div 2)^2 + [(13 - 6) + 4^2]$ • 50. $[(11 - 2)^2 + 3] + (16 \div 2)^2$

Answers to odd-numbered problems are available at the end of the textbook.

For Problems 1 and 2, write the numbers in (i) expanded form and (ii) word form.

1.   a. 9,024   b. 38,024
     c. 405,037   d. 2,601,071

2.   a. 7,502   b. 25,047
     c. 620,025   d. 3,054,705

For Problems 3 and 4, write the the numbers in (i) standard form and (ii) expanded form.

3.   a. Nine thousand, nine hundred three
     b. Fifty-nine thousand, three hundred three
     c. Seven hundred thousand, eight hundred eighty-eight
     d. Seven million, seventy-six thousand, fifty-five

4.   a. Five thousand, six hundred seven
     b. Thirty-seven thousand, forty
     c. Four hundred eight thousand, one hundred five
     d. One million, seventy thousand, fifty-five

For Problems 5 and 6, insert the proper sign of inequality (< or >) between each pair of numbers.

5.   a. 159 ☐ 139   b. 1,838 ☐ 1,868
     c. 52,109 ☐ 51,889   d. 379,847 ☐ 397,487

6.   a. 167 ☐ 176   b. 2,067 ☐ 2,097
     c. 79,084 ☐ 79,087   d. 162,555 ☐ 162,507

For Problems 7 and 8, (i) estimate the answer by rounding each number to the nearest hundred and (ii) calculate the exact answer.

7.   a. 8,655 + 348 + 75   b. 3,450 + 645 + 50
     c. 5,245 − 876   d. 2,056 − 444

8.   a. 3,495 + 276 + 85   b. 5,555 + 157 + 60
     c. 7,836 − 655   d. 6,405 − 2,769

For Problems 9 and 10, perform the arithmetic operation.

9. a. 345×34 b. 237×25
    c. $276 \div 6$ d. $4,783 \div 15$

10. a. 465×23 b. 365×24
    c. $314 \div 5$ d. $2,524 \div 12$

For Problems 11 and 12, find the LCM of the numbers.

11. a. 16 and 40   b. 36 and 54   c. 8, 24, and 32

12. a. 12 and 20   b. 16 and 72   c. 15, 18, and 30

For Problems 13 and 14, find the GCF of the numbers.

13. a. 4 and 9   b. 48 and 72   c. 12, 16, and 60

14. a. 8 and 12   b. 42 and 56   c. 24, 30, and 42

For Problems 15 to 28, perform the arithmetic operations.

15. a. $9 + 2 - 4 \times 3 \div 2$ b. $10 - (7 - 4) \div 3$

16. a. $6 + 8 - 6 \times 2 \div 4$ b. $15 - (7 - 5) \div 2$

17. a. $8 - 4(6 - 4) + 16 \div 4 + 4$ b. $10 - 4(9 - 7) \div (5 + 3)$

18. a. $12 - 2(9 - 6) + 10 \div 5 + 5$ b. $9 - 8(7 - 5) \div (6 + 2)$

19. a. $7(6 + 4) + 4^2 \div 2$ b. $9^2 \div 3 \times (8 - 5) - 4(5 + 3)$

20. a. $8(7 + 3) + 6^2 \div 4$ b. $8^2 \div 4 - 6(5 - 3)$

21. a. $64 \div 2 \times (8 - 4)^2 + 5^2$ b. $9(8 - 5) \div 3 + (7 - 4)^2$

22. a. $24 \div 2^2 \times 3 + (5 - 2)^2$ b. $8(7 - 3)^2 \div 4 - 5$

23. a. $(6 + 3 \times 2) \div (2^2 - 1)$ b. $8^2 - 3[(7 - 3)^2 + 2]$

24. a. $(16 + 4 \times 2) \div (4^2 - 8)$ b. $6^2 - 2[(6 - 3)^2 + 4]$

25. a. $\sqrt{49} - 7(6 - 4) \div (5 - 3)$
    b. $\sqrt{16} + (10 - 7) + 20 \div 4 - 3$

26. a. $\sqrt{9} - (8 - 5) + 10 \div 5 + 7$
    b. $15 - 15(8 - 6) \div \sqrt{36} + 15$

27. a. $5(12^2 - 2^2) + 48 \div 4^2$
    b. $(6 + 2)^2 - 4[(12 - 9)^2 + 3]$

28. a. $6^2 \div 9 + 6(5^2 - 2^2)$
    b. $3[(7 - 4)^2 + 4] - (2 + 3)^2$

29. Amy spent $349 and had $167 left in her bank account. How much did she have to begin with?

30. After Martha, a pharmacist, dispensed 175 pills, she had 698 pills remaining in the bottle. How many pills were in the bottle to begin with?

31. A company sold medical lab coats for $40 each. Over two weeks, $46,000 was collected in revenue from the lab coats. If 500 lab coats were sold in the first week, how many lab coats were sold in the second week?

32. Each ticket for a hospital lottery costs $25. A total of $35,000 was collected from ticket sales for Saturday and Sunday. If 550 tickets were sold on Saturday, how many were sold on Sunday?

33. A local charity held a bake-sale fundraiser. They sold 45 pies for $18 each and 63 cakes for $35 each. How much money did the fundraiser earn altogether?

34. A hospital supply company sold 245 stethoscopes for $125 each and 325 blood pressure cuffs for $68 each. How much money was collected altogether in revenue?

35. Ayesha earned $5,500 more than Beth in their respective co-op placements as part of their college's Health Sciences program. If Beth earned $13,475, how much did Ayesha earn?

36. Allan and Babar are saving up for their college tuition next semester. If Allan saved $1,675, which was $800 more than Babar, how much did they save together?

37. A delivery truck can carry a maximum of 2,000 kg. Two delivery men want to move boxes that weigh 30 kg each of lead aprons used in medical imaging. One of the delivery men weighs 85 kg and the other weighs 77 kg. What is the largest number of boxes that can be carried by the truck if both delivery men are in the truck?

38. An elevator in a medical centre can carry a maximum of 540 kg. Two delivery men are delivering water jugs, weighing 24 kg each, to all the offices. If one man weighs 72 kg and the other weighs 65 kg, what is the largest number of jugs that can be transported in the elevator if both men are in it?

39. A physiotherapist has exercise bands of four resistance levels - yellow, red, green, and blue. She has 96 metres of yellow band, 48 metres of red band, 32 metres of green band, and 72 metres of blue band. If she wishes to cut the bands into equal-sized pieces, without wastage, what is the maximum length piece that can be cut?

40. Three rolls of gauze measuring 24 feet, 60 feet, and 36 feet long are to be cut into pieces of equal lengths, without wastage. What is the maximum possible length of each piece?

41. The average times spent with each patient by three different triage nurses in the ER are 6 minutes, 8 minutes, and 10 minutes, respectively. If they call their first patients in at 7:00 AM, when will they all call a new patient again at the same time?

42. Amy, Bob, and Cathy have hospital board meetings on every 3rd, 7th, and 14th day, respectively. If they met each other on May 22nd, when will they meet again?

1 | Self-Test Exercises

In the following, (i) estimate the answer by rounding each number to the nearest hundred and (ii) calculate the exact answer.

1. a. $3{,}950 + 2{,}540 + 709 + 65$

    b. $5{,}475 + 1{,}260 + 179 - 50$

    c. $1{,}274 \times 350$

    d. $6{,}650 \div 112$

For Problems 2 to 5, evaluate the expressions.

2. a. $4(10 + 2^3) \div 3$

    b. $5(3^2 - 4) + (5^2 - 4^2)$

    c. $(5 + 4)^2 \div (5 - 2)^3$

    d. $4[12 - (6 - 3)2] \div 12$

3. a. $3^2 - 5 + 4^2 \div 8$

    b. $8 + (8 \times 5 + 4) + 11 - 7$

    c. $(5 + 1)^2 [(11 - 9)^2 - 6 \div 2]$

    d. $100 \div [5 \times 4 + (8 - 3)^2 + 5]$

4. a. $\sqrt{(12^2 \div 4)} + 3 \times 2^4$

    b. $\sqrt{(4^2 \times 5 + 1)} - \sqrt{3^2 + 4^2}$

    c. $16 \times 8 - (4^2 + 8) + \sqrt{(16 \div 4)^2}$

    d. $5(5^2 - 3^2) \div 4 \times (5 - 3)$

5. a. $4(1 + 5)^2 \div [24 - (12 + 4)]$

    b. $(4 \times 8 - 4^2) \div \sqrt{10^2 - 6^2}$

    c. $[(12^2 - 4 \times 3) + 8] \div 7$

    d. $12^2 \div 4 - 3 \times 3^2$

6. The total number of newborns in a hospital last year was 7,650. If the number of girls was two times as many as the number of boys, how many boys and girls were born last year?

7. The number of cancer-patient deaths in a hospital over each of the four quarters of last year were 9,092, 9,108, 9,102, and 9,976. Calculate:

    a. The total number of deaths due to cancer last year.

    b. The difference between the highest and the lowest number of deaths due to cancer between quarters.

8. A truck, supplying milk to the hospital, can hold 1,275 cartons. Each carton weighs 18 kg and the empty truck weighs 3,045 kg. Calculate the total weight of the truck when it is fully loaded with milk.

9. A public health nurse gets paid $24 per hour for each regular working hour and $36 per hour for every hour of overtime that she works. Last week, she worked 40 regular hours and 7 overtime hours. Calculate her total pay for last week.

10. A medical assistant's take-home pay for last year was $48,750. Calculate her pay for each week. (Assume 1 year = 52 weeks).

11. The carpark in a hospital has 9 rows and each row has 47 parking spaces. How many cars are in the carpark if there were 29 empty parking spaces?

12. On Christmas Eve, there were 1,075 patients at the Emergency Department, which was 368 more than on Christmas Day.

    a. How many patients were there on Christmas Day?

    b. If on Boxing Day there were 125 fewer patients at the Emergency Department than on Christmas Day, how many patients were there on Boxing Day?

13. 4,256 people visited the Toronto General Hospital last month. 1,968 were children and the rest were adults. How many more adults than children visited the Toronto General Hospital?

14. An obese patient with diabetes is trying to use a special diet to lose weight. In the first quarter of the year, he lost 35 pounds, and in the second quarter, he lost 39 pounds. In the third quarter, he gained back 25 pounds. If at the end of the third quarter the patient weighs 194 pounds, how many pounds did he weigh when he started the diet?

15. Four lights (red, blue, green, and yellow) flash at intervals of 12, 16, 18, and 21 seconds, respectively. If they begin flashing at the same time, when will they flash together again?

16. Four IV tubings measuring 12 m, 18 m, 24 m, and 42 m are to be cut into pieces of equal length, without wastage. What is the maximum possible length of each piece?

2 FRACTIONS AND DECIMALS

LEARNING OBJECTIVES

- Identify types of fractions and perform computations with fractions.
- Read and write decimal numbers correctly.
- Round decimal numbers to the required place values.
- Solve problems involving fractions and decimal numbers.
- Determine the relationship between fractions and decimal numbers.
- Determine the Least Common Denominator (LCD).
- Perform arithmetic operations with fractions and decimal numbers.

CHAPTER OUTLINE

2.1 Fractions

2.2 Arithmetic Operations with Fractions

2.3 Decimal Numbers

2.4 Arithmetic Operations with Decimal Numbers

2.5 Arithmetic Operations with Fractions and Decimal Numbers

Introduction

Fractions and decimal numbers are used to express numbers that are a portion of a whole number. Fractions are useful for understanding measurement, probability, and data. Decimal numbers are a type of fraction that has the denominator expressed in powers of ten. It is easier to read, write, and perform arithmetic operations with decimal numbers than with fractions. In addition, it is easier to determine the magnitude of numbers when they are expressed as decimal numbers rather than fractions. For example, it is easier to recognize that the decimal number 7.75, instead of its fractional form $\frac{31}{4}$, lies between the whole numbers 7 and 8.

In this chapter, we will learn about the different types of decimals and fractions and the methods to convert them from one form to the other. As well, we will learn to perform mathematical operations of fractions and decimal numbers combined with powers and square roots.

2.1 | Fractions

In the previous chapter, we learned about whole numbers and how to perform basic operations with whole numbers. However, measurements and calculations of quantities, values, amounts, etc., will not always be in whole numbers, but instead involve portions of whole numbers, which are represented by **fractions**. In this section, we will learn about fractions and how to perform basic mathematical operations with fractions.

If we divide one whole unit into several equal portions, then one or several of these equal portions can be represented by a fraction.

A fraction is composed of the following three parts:

1. **Numerator:** the number of equal parts of a whole unit.
2. **Fraction bar:** the division sign, meaning 'divided by'.
3. **Denominator:** the total number of equal parts into which the whole unit is divided.

For example, $\frac{3}{8}$ is a fraction.

fraction bar ⟶ $\frac{3}{8}$ ⟵ numerator
⟵ denominator

The **numerator '3'** indicates that the fraction represents 3 equal parts of a whole unit and the **denominator '8'** indicates that the whole unit is divided into 8 equal parts, as shown above. The **fraction bar** indicates that the numerator '3' is divided by the denominator '8'.

In the above example, $\frac{3}{8}$ is read as "three divided by eight", "three-eighths", or "three over eight".

All of these indicate that 3 is the numerator and that 8 is the denominator. The numerator and denominator are referred to as the **terms** of the fraction.

A fraction is also known as a **rational number**.

- For example, $\frac{2}{3}, \frac{5}{2}$, and $\frac{7}{1}$ are all rational numbers.
- We know that 7 is an integer and also a whole number. Since 7 can be written as $\frac{7}{1}$ it is also a rational number.

A whole number can be written as a fraction (or rational number) by writing the whole number as the numerator and 1 as the denominator.

The denominator of a fraction cannot be zero, since zero cannot represent the total number of equal parts in a whole unit.

Fractions can be represented on a number line, and "fill in" the gaps between whole numbers (though not entirely - there are still more numbers that we will talk about in the next chapter!).

- For example, $\frac{1}{2}$ is represented on a number line as:

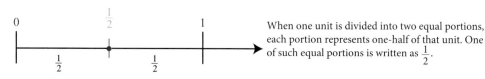

When one unit is divided into two equal portions, each portion represents one-half of that unit. One of such equal portions is written as $\frac{1}{2}$.

Example 2.1-a | **Number Line**

Represent the following fractions on a number line:

(i) $\frac{2}{3}$ (ii) $\frac{3}{5}$

Solution

(i)

When one unit is divided into three equal portions, each portion represents one-third of that unit. Two of such equal portions is two-thirds and is written as $\frac{2}{3}$.

(ii)

When one unit is divided into five equal portions, each portion represents one-fifth of that unit. Three of such equal portions is three-fifths and is written as $\frac{3}{5}$.

Proper Fractions

Fractions represent division. For example, $\frac{3}{8}$ is the same as $3 \div 8$.

A **proper fraction** is a fraction in which the numerator is less than the denominator.

For example,

- $\frac{3}{8}$ is a proper fraction because the numerator, 3, is less than the denominator, 8.

three-eighths

Improper Fractions

An **improper fraction** is a fraction in which the numerator is greater than or equal to the denominator; i.e., the value of the entire fraction is at least 1.

$\frac{4}{4}$ is also an improper fraction, because the numerator 4 is equal to the denominator 4 (i.e., $4 = 4$, or $\frac{4}{4} = 1$).

For example,

- $\frac{7}{4}$ is an improper fraction because the numerator, 7, is greater than the denominator, 4 (i.e., $7 > 4$, or $\frac{7}{4} > 1$).

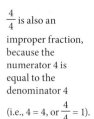

seven-quarters

Mixed Numbers (or Mixed Fractions)

Usually when two numbers are written side-by-side, the numbers are assumed to be multiplied together. However, mixed numbers represent an exception, in which the whole number and proper fraction written side-by-side are **added** together!

A **mixed number** consists of both a whole number and a proper fraction, written side-by-side, which implies that the whole number and the proper fraction are added.

For example, $3\frac{5}{8}$ is a mixed number, where 3 is the whole number and $\frac{5}{8}$ is the proper fraction.

- $3\frac{5}{8}$ implies $3 + \frac{5}{8}$

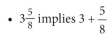

three    five-eighths

mixed number
$3\frac{5}{8}$ ← fraction
↑
whole
number

Relationship Between Mixed Numbers and Improper Fractions
Converting a Mixed Number to an Improper Fraction

Follow these steps to convert a mixed number to an improper fraction:

Example:

Convert $3\frac{5}{8}$ to an improper fraction.

Step 1: Multiply the whole number by the denominator of the fraction and add this value to the numerator of the fraction.

$$\frac{3(8)}{24 + 5 = 29}$$

Step 2: The resulting answer will be the numerator of the improper fraction.

The numerator will be 29.

Step 3: The denominator of the improper fraction is the same as the denominator of the original fraction in the mixed number.

The denominator will be 8.

Therefore, $3\frac{5}{8} = \frac{29}{8}$.

Note: You can perform the above steps in a single line of arithmetic, as follows.

- $3\frac{5}{8} = \frac{3(8) + 5}{8} = \frac{24 + 5}{8} = \frac{29}{8}$

There is a total of 29 pieces, each piece being one-eighth in size.

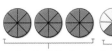

$3 \times 8 = 24$ pieces   5 pieces

Converting an Improper Fraction to a Mixed Number

Follow these steps to convert an improper fraction to a mixed number:

Example:

Convert $\frac{29}{8}$ to a mixed number.

Step 1: Divide the numerator by the denominator.

$$\begin{array}{r} 3 \leftarrow \text{Quotient} \\ 8\overline{)29} \\ -24 \\ \hline 5 \leftarrow \text{Remainder} \end{array}$$

Step 2: The quotient will be the whole number and the remainder will be the numerator of the fraction.

Step 3: The denominator of the mixed number is the same as the denominator of the original improper fraction.

Therefore, $\frac{29}{8} = 3\frac{5}{8}$.

Converting Fractions to their Equivalent Fractions

When both the numerator and denominator of a fraction are either multiplied by the same number or divided by the same number, the result is a new fraction called an **equivalent fraction**. Equivalent fractions imply that the old and new fractions have the same value; i.e., the same part (or portion) of a whole unit can be represented by different fractions.

For example,

$\frac{1}{2}$ $\frac{2}{4}$ $\frac{3}{6}$ $\frac{4}{8}$ $\frac{5}{10}$

$\frac{1}{2}, \frac{2}{4}, \frac{3}{6}, \frac{4}{8}, \frac{5}{10}, \dots$ are equivalent fractions.

Example 2.1-b | **Finding Equivalent Fractions by Raising to Higher Terms**

Find two equivalent fractions of $\dfrac{2}{5}$ by raising to higher terms.

Solution

$\dfrac{2}{5}$ ⬚ (2 portions of 5 equal parts of the whole)

$\dfrac{2}{5} = \dfrac{2 \times 2}{5 \times 2}$ Multiplying both the numerator and denominator by 2,

$= \dfrac{4}{10}$ ⬚ (4 portions of 10 equal parts of the whole)

$\dfrac{2}{5} = \dfrac{2 \times 3}{5 \times 3}$ Multiplying both the numerator and denominator by 3,

$= \dfrac{6}{15}$ ⬚ (6 portions of 15 equal parts of the whole)

Therefore, $\dfrac{4}{10}$ and $\dfrac{6}{15}$ are equivalent fractions of $\dfrac{2}{5}$.

Reducing or Simplifying Fractions

Dividing both the numerator and denominator of a fraction by the same number, which results in an equivalent fraction, is called **reducing** or **simplifying** the fraction.

We can simplify the fraction $\dfrac{18}{30}$, as shown in the following example:

Example 2.1-c | **Finding Equivalent Fractions by Reducing (or Simplifying) to Lower Terms**

Find two equivalent fractions of $\dfrac{18}{30}$ by reducing to lower terms.

Solution

$\dfrac{18}{30}$ ⬚ (18 portions of 30 equal parts of the whole)

$\dfrac{18}{30} = \dfrac{18 \div 3}{30 \div 3}$ Dividing both the numerator and denominator by 3,

$= \dfrac{6}{10}$ ⬚ (6 portions of 10 equal parts of the whole)

$= \dfrac{6 \div 2}{10 \div 2}$ Further dividing both the numerator and denominator by 2,

$= \dfrac{3}{5}$ ⬚ (3 portions of 5 equal parts of the whole)

$\dfrac{18}{30} = \dfrac{18 \div 6}{30 \div 6}$ Or, the lowest term can be found by dividing both the numerator and denominator of the original fraction, $\dfrac{18}{30}$, by 6,

$= \dfrac{3}{5}$

Therefore, $\dfrac{6}{10}$ and $\dfrac{3}{5}$ are equivalent fractions of $\dfrac{18}{30}$.

Note: The fraction $\dfrac{3}{5}$ cannot be further reduced, as 3 and 5 share no common factors. Therefore, we say $\dfrac{3}{5}$ is a fraction in its lowest (or simplest) terms.

Fractions in Lowest (or Simplest) Terms

A fraction in which the numerator and denominator have no factors in common (other than 1) is said to be a fraction in its **lowest** (or simplest) **terms**.

Any fraction can be **fully reduced** to its lowest terms by one of the following two methods:

Method 1: Dividing by the common prime factors of both the numerator and denominator.

Method 2: Dividing both the numerator and denominator by the greatest common factor (GCF).

Fully reducing fractions to their lowest terms using both methods is demonstrated in Example 2.1-d below:

| Example 2.1-d | Reducing Fractions to their Lowest Terms |

Reduce the following fractions to their lowest terms.

(i) $\dfrac{40}{45}$ (ii) $\dfrac{54}{24}$

Solution

(i) $\dfrac{40}{45}$

Method 1: Prime factors of 40 are: $2 \times 2 \times 2 \times 5$.

Prime factors of 45 are: $3 \times 3 \times 5$.

$$\frac{40}{45} = \frac{2 \times 2 \times 2 \times \cancel{5}^{\,1}}{3 \times 3 \times \cancel{5}_{\,1}} = \frac{8}{9}$$

Therefore, $\dfrac{40}{45}$ is equal to $\dfrac{8}{9}$ reduced to its lowest terms.

Method 2: The factors of 40 are: 1, 2, 4, 5, 8, 10, 20, and 40.

The factors of 45 are: 1, 3, 5, 9, 15, and 45.

The GCF is 5.

Therefore, dividing the numerator and denominator by the GCF, 5, results in the fraction in its lowest terms:

$$\frac{40}{45} = \frac{40 \div 5}{45 \div 5} = \frac{8}{9}$$

Therefore, $\dfrac{40}{45}$ is equal to $\dfrac{8}{9}$ reduced to its lowest terms.

(ii) $\dfrac{54}{24}$

Method 1: Prime factors of 54 are: $2 \times 3 \times 3 \times 3$.

Prime factors of 24 are: $2 \times 2 \times 2 \times 3$.

$$\frac{54}{24} = \frac{{}^{1}\cancel{2} \times \cancel{3}^{\,1} \times 3 \times 3}{\cancel{2}_{\,1} \times 2 \times 2 \times \cancel{3}_{\,1}} = \frac{9}{4}$$

Therefore, $\dfrac{54}{24}$ is equal to $\dfrac{9}{4}$ reduced to its lowest terms.

Solution
continued

Method 2: The factors of 54 are: 1, 2, 3, **6**, 9, 18, 27, and 54.

The factors of 24 are: 1, 2, 3, 4, **6**, 8, 12, and 24.

The GCF is 6.

Therefore, dividing the numerator and denominator by the GCF, 6, results in the fraction in its lowest terms:

$$\frac{54}{24} = \frac{54 \div 6}{24 \div 6} = \frac{9}{4}$$

Therefore, $\frac{54}{24}$ is equal to $\frac{9}{4}$ reduced to its lowest terms.

Identifying Equivalent Fractions

Identifying Equivalent Fractions By Reducing to Lowest Terms

Fully-reduced fractions are desirable for two reasons:

1. **Simplicity:** they are the simplest way of expressing fractions.

2. **Uniqueness:** there is only one way of expressing any fraction in lowest terms.

The second characteristic of fully-reduced fractions gives us a very convenient method of determining if two fractions are equivalent or not:

Reduce both fractions to lowest terms.

- If the two fully-reduced fractions are the same, the original fractions were equivalent.

- If the two fully-reduced fractions are **not** the same, the original fractions were not equivalent.

Identifying Equivalent Fractions Using Cross Products

If the **cross products** of two fractions are equal, then the two fractions are equivalent fractions, and vice versa (i.e., if the fractions are equivalent, then their cross products are equal).

i.e., If $\frac{a}{b} = \frac{c}{d}$, then $a \times d = b \times c$ $a \times d$ and $b \times c$ are called cross products.

For example, $\frac{3}{5}$ and $\frac{12}{20}$ are equivalent fractions because their cross products 3×20 and 5×12 are equal.

$$a \times d = 3 \times 20 = 60$$
$$b \times c = 5 \times 12 = 60$$

Therefore, since the cross products are equal, the fractions are equivalent.

| Example 2.1-e | Classifying Fractions as Equivalent or Not Equivalent |

Classify each of the following pairs of fractions as 'equivalent' or 'not equivalent':

(i) $\frac{4}{10}$ and $\frac{12}{30}$ (ii) $\frac{10}{8}$ and $\frac{20}{12}$ (iii) $\frac{12}{32}$ and $\frac{9}{24}$

Solution

(i) **Method 1:** $\dfrac{4}{10}$

Representing 4 and 10 as products of primes,

$= \dfrac{\cancel{2} \times 2}{\cancel{2} \times 5}$

Simplifying,

$= \dfrac{2}{5}$

$\dfrac{4}{10}$ reduced to lowest terms is $\dfrac{2}{5}$.

$\dfrac{12}{30}$

Representing 12 and 30 as products of primes,

$= \dfrac{\cancel{2} \times 2 \times \cancel{3}}{\cancel{2} \times \cancel{3} \times 5}$

Simplifying,

$= \dfrac{2}{5}$

$\dfrac{12}{30}$ reduced to lowest terms is $\dfrac{2}{5}$.

The fully-reduced fractions are the same. Therefore, $\dfrac{4}{10}$ and $\dfrac{12}{30}$ are equivalent.

Method 2: $\dfrac{4}{10}$ and $\dfrac{12}{30}$

The cross products are 4×30 and 10×12.

$4 \times 30 = 120$

$10 \times 12 = 120$

The cross products are equal.

Therefore, $\dfrac{4}{10}$ and $\dfrac{12}{30}$ are equivalent.

(ii) **Method 1:** $\dfrac{10}{8}$

Representing 10 and 8 as products of primes,

$= \dfrac{\cancel{2} \times 5}{\cancel{2} \times 2 \times 2}$

Simplifying,

$= \dfrac{5}{4}$

$\dfrac{10}{8}$ reduced to lowest terms is $\dfrac{5}{4}$.

$\dfrac{20}{12}$

Representing 20 and 12 as products of primes,

$= \dfrac{\cancel{2} \times \cancel{2} \times 5}{\cancel{2} \times \cancel{2} \times 3}$

Simplifying,

$= \dfrac{5}{3}$

$\dfrac{20}{12}$ reduced to lowest terms is $\dfrac{5}{3}$.

The fully-reduced fractions are not the same. Therefore, $\dfrac{10}{8}$ and $\dfrac{20}{12}$ are not equivalent.

Method 2: $\dfrac{10}{8}$ and $\dfrac{20}{12}$

The cross products are 10×12 and 8×20.

$10 \times 12 = 120$

$8 \times 20 = 160$

The cross products are not equal.

Therefore, $\dfrac{10}{8}$ and $\dfrac{20}{12}$ are not equivalent.

(iii) **Method 1:** $\dfrac{12}{32}$ Representing 12 and 32 as products of primes,

$$= \frac{\cancel{2} \times \cancel{2} \times 3}{\cancel{2} \times \cancel{2} \times 2 \times 2 \times 2}$$

Simplifying,

$$= \frac{3}{8}$$

$\dfrac{12}{32}$ reduced to lowest terms is $\dfrac{3}{8}$.

$$\frac{9}{24}$$

Representing 9 and 24 as products of primes,

$$= \frac{\cancel{3} \times 3}{2 \times 2 \times 2 \times \cancel{3}}$$

Simplifying,

$$= \frac{3}{8}$$

$\dfrac{9}{24}$ reduced to lowest terms is $\dfrac{3}{8}$.

The fully-reduced fractions are the same. Therefore, $\dfrac{12}{32}$ and $\dfrac{9}{24}$ are equivalent.

Method 2: $\dfrac{12}{32}$ and $\dfrac{9}{24}$ The cross products are 12×24 and 32×9.

$12 \times 24 = 288$

$32 \times 9 = 288$ The cross products are equal.

Therefore, $\dfrac{12}{32}$ and $\dfrac{9}{24}$ are equivalent.

Reciprocals of Fractions

Two numbers whose products are equal to 1 are called **reciprocals** of each other. Every non-zero real number has a unique reciprocal.

For example,

- $\dfrac{2}{3}$ and $\dfrac{3}{2}$ are reciprocals of each other (because $\dfrac{2}{3} \times \dfrac{3}{2} = 1$).

When the numerator and denominator of a fraction are interchanged, the resulting fraction is the reciprocal of the original fraction.

For example,

- 5 and $\dfrac{1}{5}$ are reciprocals (5 can also be written as $\dfrac{5}{1}$).

- Similarly, the reciprocal of $\dfrac{-2}{5}$ is $\dfrac{5}{-2} = -\dfrac{5}{2}$

The reciprocal of a number is always positive and the reciprocal of a negative number is always negative.

The reciprocal of a number has the same sign as that number.

Note:

(i) *The reciprocal of a number is not the negative of that number.*

    (The reciprocal of 3 ≠ − 3. The reciprocal of 3 = $\dfrac{1}{3}$.)

(ii) *The reciprocal of a fraction is not the equivalent fraction of that fraction.*

    (The reciprocal of $\dfrac{2}{5} \neq \dfrac{4}{10}$. The reciprocal of $\dfrac{2}{5} = \dfrac{5}{2}$.)

Table 2.1	Examples of Numbers with their Negatives and Reciprocals

When any number is multiplied by its reciprocal, the answer is always 1.

When any number is added to its negative, the answer is always 0.

Number	5	-3	$\dfrac{2}{3}$	$-\dfrac{3}{8}$
Negative of the Number	-5	3	$-\dfrac{2}{3}$	$\dfrac{3}{8}$
Reciprocal of the Number	$\dfrac{1}{5}$	$-\dfrac{1}{3}$	$\dfrac{3}{2}$	$-\dfrac{8}{3}$

2.1 | Exercises

Answers to odd-numbered problems are available at the end of the textbook.

For Problems 1 to 6, classify the fractions as proper fractions, improper fractions, or mixed numbers.

1. a. $\dfrac{16}{35}$ b. $3\dfrac{2}{9}$ 2. a. $15\dfrac{12}{13}$ b. $\dfrac{29}{30}$

3. a. $\dfrac{19}{16}$ b. $9\dfrac{7}{8}$ 4. a. $\dfrac{21}{22}$ b. $\dfrac{52}{25}$

5. a. $4\dfrac{2}{5}$ b. $\dfrac{7}{3}$ 6. a. $6\dfrac{1}{2}$ b. $\dfrac{20}{75}$

For Problems 7 to 10, convert the mixed numbers to improper fractions.

7. a. $2\dfrac{2}{7}$ b. $3\dfrac{1}{8}$ 8. a. $3\dfrac{2}{5}$ b. $7\dfrac{5}{8}$

9. a. $5\dfrac{4}{5}$ b. $6\dfrac{3}{4}$ 10. a. $4\dfrac{3}{7}$ b. $9\dfrac{5}{6}$

For Problems 11 to 14, convert the improper fractions to mixed numbers.

11. a. $\dfrac{19}{7}$ b. $\dfrac{45}{8}$ 12. a. $\dfrac{23}{7}$ b. $\dfrac{34}{3}$

13. a. $\dfrac{23}{3}$ b. $\dfrac{31}{6}$ 14. a. $\dfrac{26}{4}$ b. $\dfrac{29}{5}$

For Problems 15 to 22, classify the pairs of fractions as 'equivalent' or 'not equivalent' by first converting the mixed numbers to improper fractions.

15. $\dfrac{44}{5}$ and $8\dfrac{4}{5}$ 16. $\dfrac{47}{8}$ and $5\dfrac{7}{8}$ 17. $\dfrac{51}{7}$ and $7\dfrac{5}{7}$ 18. $\dfrac{41}{4}$ and $10\dfrac{3}{4}$

19. $\dfrac{54}{7}$ and $7\dfrac{5}{7}$ 20. $\dfrac{17}{8}$ and $2\dfrac{3}{8}$ 21. $\dfrac{37}{9}$ and $4\dfrac{1}{9}$ 22. $\dfrac{45}{11}$ and $4\dfrac{3}{11}$

For Problems 23 to 30, classify the pairs of fractions as 'equivalent' or 'not equivalent' by first converting the improper fractions to mixed numbers.

23. $\dfrac{15}{4}$ and $3\dfrac{1}{4}$ 24. $\dfrac{43}{6}$ and $7\dfrac{5}{6}$ 25. $\dfrac{18}{5}$ and $3\dfrac{3}{5}$ 26. $\dfrac{45}{7}$ and $6\dfrac{3}{7}$

27. $3\dfrac{8}{9}$ and $\dfrac{35}{9}$ 28. $\dfrac{34}{8}$ and $4\dfrac{1}{8}$ 29. $\dfrac{41}{12}$ and $3\dfrac{5}{12}$ 30. $7\dfrac{3}{9}$ and $\dfrac{67}{9}$

For Problems 31 to 36, (i) reduce the fractions to their lowest terms and (ii) write their reciprocals.

31. a. $\dfrac{32}{20}$ b. $\dfrac{48}{84}$ 32. a. $\dfrac{44}{12}$ b. $\dfrac{42}{70}$

33. a. $\dfrac{56}{48}$ b. $\dfrac{84}{21}$ 34. a. $\dfrac{75}{105}$ b. $\dfrac{144}{48}$

35. a. $\dfrac{36}{63}$ b. $\dfrac{60}{96}$ 36. a. $\dfrac{132}{84}$ b. $\dfrac{54}{126}$

For Problems 37 to 44, classify the pair of fractions as 'equivalent' or 'not equivalent'.

37. $\dfrac{6}{12}$ and $\dfrac{15}{30}$ 38. $\dfrac{6}{10}$ and $\dfrac{9}{15}$ 39. $\dfrac{8}{10}$ and $\dfrac{15}{12}$ 40. $\dfrac{12}{18}$ and $\dfrac{18}{27}$

41. $\dfrac{15}{12}$ and $\dfrac{36}{45}$ 42. $\dfrac{35}{15}$ and $\dfrac{28}{12}$ 43. $\dfrac{20}{25}$ and $\dfrac{24}{30}$ 44. $\dfrac{16}{24}$ and $\dfrac{25}{30}$

For Problems 45 to 50, find the missing values needed to make the pairs of fractions equivalent and satisfy the equation.

45. a. $\dfrac{4}{9} = \dfrac{?}{27}$ b. $\dfrac{4}{9} = \dfrac{20}{?}$ 46. a. $\dfrac{42}{36} = \dfrac{14}{?}$ b. $\dfrac{42}{36} = \dfrac{?}{30}$

47. a. $\dfrac{9}{12} = \dfrac{18}{?}$ b. $\dfrac{9}{12} = \dfrac{?}{4}$ 48. a. $\dfrac{3}{2} = \dfrac{12}{?}$ b. $\dfrac{3}{2} = \dfrac{?}{12}$

49. a. $\dfrac{45}{75} = \dfrac{?}{25}$ b. $\dfrac{45}{75} = \dfrac{18}{?}$ 50. a. $\dfrac{25}{15} = \dfrac{?}{3}$ b. $\dfrac{25}{15} = \dfrac{35}{?}$

For Problems 51 to 58, express the answers as a fraction reduced to its lowest terms.

51. What fraction of 1 year is 4 months?

52. What fraction of 1 hour is 25 minutes?

53. Karen cut a PVC tube into 16 equal pieces and used 12 pieces of it. What fraction of the PVC tube was used?

54. Out of 35 students in a biology class, 15 received an 'A' on their final exam. What fraction of the students in the class received an 'A' grade?

55. In a scientific study of 272 people, 68 people responded 'yes' and the remaining responded 'no'. What fraction of the people responded 'no'?

56. In a Health Sciences Statistics course with 490 students, 70 students failed the final exam. What fraction of the students passed the final exam in this course?

57. Out of the 480 hospital beds in a hospital wing, 182 are rented. What fraction of the beds are not rented?

58. In a community of 6,000 people, 1,800 were 60 years or older. What fraction of the people were below the age of 60 years?

2.2 | Arithmetic Operations with Fractions

Least or Lowest Common Denominator (LCD)

The **Least Common Denominator (LCD)** of a set of two or more fractions is the smallest whole number that is a common multiple of each of the denominators - i.e., it is the least common multiple (LCM) of the denominators of the fractions. There are two methods of finding the LCM as explained in Chapter 1, Section 1.3.

In performing addition and subtraction of fractions, it is necessary to determine equivalent fractions with common denominators. The best choice for a common denominator is the LCD, because it makes any further simplification easier.

| Example 2.2-a | Finding the Least Common Denominator |

Find the LCD of $\frac{4}{9}$ and $\frac{7}{15}$.

Solution

The LCD of the fractions $\frac{4}{9}$ and $\frac{7}{15}$ is the same as the LCM of the denominators 9 and 15.

Using one of the methods you had learned in Chapter 1, Section 1.3:

- The largest number, 15, is **not** divisible by 9.
- Multiples of 15 are: 15, 30, 45, ...
- 45 is divisible by both 9 and 15 (and no lesser number than 45 is divisible by both numbers).

Therefore, the LCD of $\frac{4}{9}$ and $\frac{7}{15}$ is 45.

Comparing Fractions

> It is best to convert a mixed number into an improper fraction before performing any basic arithmetic operations.

Fractions can easily be compared when they have the same denominator. If they do not have the same denominator, determine the LCD of the fractions, then convert them into equivalent fractions with that LCD as their denominator.

When the denominators are the same, the larger fraction is the one with the greater numerator.

For example, $\frac{5}{8} > \frac{3}{8}$.

Also, when the numerators are the same, the larger fraction is the one with the smaller denominator.

For example, $\frac{3}{4} > \frac{3}{5}$.

| Example 2.2-b | Comparing Fractions |

Determine which of the following fractions is greater:

(i) $\frac{5}{12}$ or $\frac{3}{8}$ (ii) $\frac{9}{25}$ or $\frac{11}{25}$ (iii) $\frac{7}{9}$ or $\frac{7}{11}$

Solution

(i) $\dfrac{5}{12}$ or $\dfrac{3}{8}$

Step 1: Since the fractions do not have the same denominator, we need to first find the LCD of the fractions, which is the same as the LCM of the denominators. The LCM of 12 and 8 is 24.

Step 2: Convert each of the fractions to its equivalent fraction with 24 as the denominator.

To convert $\dfrac{5}{12}$ to its equivalent fraction with 24 as the denominator, multiply the denominator by 2 to obtain the LCD of 24 and multiply the numerator by 2 as well to maintain an equivalent fraction.

$$\frac{5}{12} = \frac{5 \times 2}{12 \times 2} = \frac{10}{24}$$

5 portions of 12 equal parts of a whole is equivalent to 10 portions of 24 equal parts of that whole.

Similarly, convert $\dfrac{3}{8}$ to an equivalent fraction with 24 as the denominator:

$$\frac{3}{8} = \frac{3 \times 3}{8 \times 3} = \frac{9}{24}$$

3 portions of 8 equal parts of a whole is equivalent to 9 portions of 24 equal parts of that whole.

Step 3: Since the denominators are now the same, we can compare the numerators of the fractions to identify the greater fraction.

Since 10 > 9, it implies: $\dfrac{10}{24} > \dfrac{9}{24}$.

Therefore, $\dfrac{5}{12} > \dfrac{3}{8}$.

(ii) $\dfrac{9}{25}$ or $\dfrac{11}{25}$

Since the fractions have the same denominator 25, we can compare the numerators to identify the larger fraction.

11 > 9, therefore, $\dfrac{11}{25} > \dfrac{9}{25}$.

(iii) $\dfrac{7}{9}$ or $\dfrac{7}{11}$

Since the fractions have the same numerator 7, we can compare the denominators to identify the larger fraction.

9 < 11, therefore, $\dfrac{7}{9} > \dfrac{7}{11}$.

Addition of Fractions

The denominator of a fraction indicates the number of parts into which an item is divided. Therefore, addition of fractions requires that the denominators of every fraction be the same. If the denominators are different, they must be made the same, by determining the LCD and changing each fraction to its equivalent fraction with that denominator.

When the fractions have the same denominator, add the numerators of each of the fractions. The resulting fraction will have the common denominator, and its numerator will be the sum of the numerators of the equivalent fractions.

Express the final answer reduced to its lowest terms and as a mixed number, where applicable.

Example 2.2-c — Adding Fractions That Have the Same Denominator

Add $\dfrac{2}{9}$ and $\dfrac{5}{9}$.

Solution

$\dfrac{2}{9} + \dfrac{5}{9}$

The denominators of the fractions are the same. Adding the numerators and writing the common denominator,

$= \dfrac{2+5}{9}$

$= \dfrac{7}{9}$

$$\dfrac{2}{9} \quad + \quad \dfrac{5}{9} \quad = \quad \dfrac{7}{9}$$

Therefore, the result from adding $\dfrac{2}{9}$ and $\dfrac{5}{9}$ is $\dfrac{7}{9}$.

Example 2.2-d — Adding Fractions That Have Different Denominators

Add $\dfrac{3}{4}$ and $\dfrac{2}{3}$.

Solution

$\dfrac{3}{4} + \dfrac{2}{3}$

The LCM of 4 and 3 is 12 (i.e., LCD = 12). Determining the equivalent fractions using the LCD of 12,

$= \dfrac{9}{12} + \dfrac{8}{12}$

Adding the numerators and writing the common denominator,

$= \dfrac{9+8}{12}$

$= \dfrac{17}{12}$

Converting the improper fraction to a mixed number,

$= 1\dfrac{5}{12}$

$$\dfrac{3}{4} \quad + \quad \dfrac{2}{3} \quad = \quad \dfrac{9}{12} \quad + \quad \dfrac{8}{12} \quad = \quad \dfrac{17}{12} = 1\dfrac{5}{12}$$

Therefore, the result from adding $\dfrac{3}{4}$ and $\dfrac{2}{3}$ is $1\dfrac{5}{12}$.

Example 2.2-e — Adding Fractions That Have Different Denominators

Add $3\dfrac{5}{6}$ and $\dfrac{4}{9}$.

Solution

Method 1: $3\dfrac{5}{6} + \dfrac{4}{9}$

$= \dfrac{(3 \times 6) + 5}{6} + \dfrac{4}{9} = \dfrac{23}{6} + \dfrac{4}{9}$

$= \dfrac{69}{18} + \dfrac{8}{18} = \dfrac{77}{18}$

$= 4\dfrac{5}{18}$

Converting the mixed number to an improper fraction,
The LCM of 6 and 9 is 18 (i.e., LCD = 18). Determining the equivalent fractions using the LCD of 18,
Converting the improper fraction to a mixed number,

Therefore, the result from adding $3\dfrac{5}{6}$ and $\dfrac{4}{9}$ is $4\dfrac{5}{18}$.

Method 2: $3\frac{5}{6} + \frac{4}{9}$ Separating the whole number and the fractions,

$$= 3 + \left(\frac{5}{6} + \frac{4}{9}\right)$$ The LCM of 6 and 9 is 18 (i.e., LCD = 18). Determining the equivalent fractions using the LCD of 18,

$$= 3 + \left(\frac{15}{18} + \frac{8}{18}\right)$$ Adding the fractions,

$$= 3 + \frac{23}{18}$$ Converting the improper fraction to a mixed number,

$$= 3 + 1\frac{5}{18}$$

$$= 3 + 1 + \frac{5}{18}$$ Adding the whole numbers and then the fraction,

$$= 4\frac{5}{18}$$

Therefore, the result from adding $3\frac{5}{6}$ and $\frac{4}{9}$ is $4\frac{5}{18}$.

Example 2.2-f   **Adding Mixed Numbers**

Add:

(i) $2\frac{1}{6}$ and $4\frac{3}{4}$ (ii) $15\frac{2}{3}$ and $3\frac{3}{5}$.

Solution

(i) $2\frac{1}{6} + 4\frac{3}{4}$ The LCM of 6 and 4 is 12 (i.e., LCD = 12). Determining the equivalent mixed numbers using the LCD of 12,

$$= 2\frac{2}{12} + 4\frac{9}{12}$$

$$= (2 + 4) + \left(\frac{2}{12} + \frac{9}{12}\right)$$ Adding the whole numbers and then the fractions,

$$= 6\frac{11}{12}$$

Therefore, the result from adding $2\frac{1}{6}$ and $4\frac{3}{4}$ is $6\frac{11}{12}$.

(ii) $15\frac{2}{3} + 3\frac{3}{5}$ The LCM of 3 and 5 is 15 (i.e., LCD = 15). Determining the equivalent mixed numbers using the LCD of 15,

$$= 15\frac{10}{15} + 3\frac{9}{15}$$

$$= (15 + 3) + \left(\frac{10}{15} + \frac{9}{15}\right)$$ Adding the whole numbers and then the fractions,

$$= 18 + \frac{19}{15}$$ Converting $\frac{19}{15}$ to a mixed number,

$$= 18 + 1\frac{4}{15}$$

$$= 18 + 1 + \frac{4}{15}$$ Adding the whole numbers and then the fraction,

$$= 19\frac{4}{15}$$

Therefore, the result from adding $15\frac{2}{3}$ and $3\frac{3}{5}$ is $19\frac{4}{15}$.

Subtraction of Fractions

The process for subtraction of fractions is the same as that of addition of fractions. First, determine a common denominator, then change each fraction to its equivalent fraction with the common denominator. The resulting fraction will have that denominator and its numerator will be the difference of the numerators of the equivalent fractions.

Express the final answer reduced to its lowest terms and as a mixed number, where applicable.

Example 2.2-g **Subtracting Fractions That Have the Same Denonimators**

Subtract $\dfrac{3}{8}$ from $\dfrac{7}{8}$.

Solution

$\dfrac{7}{8} - \dfrac{3}{8}$

The denominators of the fractions are the same. Subtracting the numerators and writing the common denominator,

$= \dfrac{7 - 3}{8}$

$= \dfrac{4}{8} = \dfrac{\cancel{4}^{1}}{\cancel{8}_{2}}$

Reducing to lowest terms,

$= \dfrac{1}{2}$

$\dfrac{7}{8}$ − $\dfrac{3}{8}$ = $\dfrac{4}{8} = \dfrac{1}{2}$

Therefore, the result from subtracting $\dfrac{3}{8}$ from $\dfrac{7}{8}$ is $\dfrac{1}{2}$.

Example 2.2-h **Subtracting Fractions that have Different Denominators**

Subtract $\dfrac{2}{8}$ from $\dfrac{7}{10}$.

Solution

$\dfrac{7}{10} - \dfrac{2}{8}$

The LCM of 10 and 8 is 40 (i.e., LCD = 40). Determining the equivalent fractions using the LCD of 40,

$= \dfrac{28}{40} - \dfrac{10}{40}$

Subtracting the numerators and writing the common denominator,

$= \dfrac{28 - 10}{40}$

$= \dfrac{18}{40} = \dfrac{\cancel{18}^{9}}{\cancel{40}_{20}}$

Reducing to lowest terms,

$= \dfrac{9}{20}$

Therefore, the result from subtracting $\dfrac{2}{8}$ from $\dfrac{7}{10}$ is $\dfrac{9}{20}$.

Example 2.2-i **Subtracting Mixed Numbers**

Subtract $7\frac{2}{3}$ from $12\frac{1}{2}$.

Solution

Method 1:

$$12\frac{1}{2} - 7\frac{2}{3}$$

Converting the mixed numbers to improper fractions,

$$= \frac{(12 \times 2) + 1}{2} - \frac{(7 \times 3) + 2}{3}$$

$$= \frac{25}{2} - \frac{23}{3}$$

The LCM of 2 and 3 is 6 (i.e., LCD = 6). Determining the equivalent fractions using the LCD of 6,

$$= \frac{75}{6} - \frac{46}{6}$$

Subtracting the numerators and writing the common denominator,

$$= \frac{75 - 46}{6}$$

$$= \frac{29}{6}$$

Converting the improper fraction to a mixed number,

$$= 4\frac{5}{6}$$

Therefore, the result from subtracting $7\frac{2}{3}$ from $12\frac{1}{2}$ is $4\frac{5}{6}$.

Method 2:

$$12\frac{1}{2} - 7\frac{2}{3}$$

The LCM of 2 and 3 is 6 (i.e., LCD = 6). Determining the equivalent mixed numbers using the LCD of 6,

$$= 12\frac{3}{6} - 7\frac{4}{6}$$

The fraction $\frac{4}{6}$ is greater than $\frac{3}{6}$. Therefore, we have to regroup the mixed number $12\frac{3}{6}$.

Regrouping $12\frac{3}{6} = \underbrace{11 + 1}_{} + \frac{3}{6} = 11 + \underbrace{\frac{6}{6} + \frac{3}{6}}_{} = 11\frac{9}{6}$

$$= 11\frac{9}{6} - 7\frac{4}{6}$$

Subtracting the whole numbers and then the fractions,

$$= 4\frac{9 - 4}{6}$$

$$= 4\frac{5}{6}$$

Therefore, the result from subtracting $7\frac{2}{3}$ from $12\frac{1}{2}$ is $4\frac{5}{6}$.

Multiplication of Fractions

When multiplying two or more fractions, first convert any mixed number to its improper fraction, then simply multiply the numerators together to get the new numerator and multiply the denominators together to get the new denominator.

Reduce as much as possible *before* multiplying the numerators together and the denominators together. You may reduce any numerator with any denominator in a product of fractions; this is known as **cross-reducing**.

Express the final answer reduced to its lowest terms as a mixed number, where applicable.

Note: When multiplying mixed numbers, it is incorrect to multiply the whole number parts and fractional parts separately to arrive at the answer.

Example 2.2-j **Multiplying Fractions**

Multiply:

(i) $\frac{3}{2} \times \frac{4}{11}$ (ii) $15 \times \frac{2}{5}$ (iii) $3\frac{1}{8} \times 2\frac{4}{5}$

Solution

(i) $\dfrac{3}{2} \times \dfrac{4}{11} = \dfrac{3}{{}_{1}2} \times \dfrac{\overset{2}{4}}{11}$ Cross-reducing the fractions to lowest terms,

$= \dfrac{3}{1} \times \dfrac{2}{11}$ Multiplying the numerators together and the denominators together to get a new fraction,

$= \dfrac{6}{11}$

Therefore, the result of $\dfrac{3}{2} \times \dfrac{4}{11}$ is $\dfrac{6}{11}$.

(ii) $15 \times \dfrac{2}{5} = \dfrac{\overset{3}{15}}{1} \times \dfrac{2}{{}_{1}5}$ Cross-reducing the fractions to lowest terms,

$= \dfrac{3}{1} \times \dfrac{2}{1}$ Multiplying the numerators together and the denominators together to get a new fraction,

$= \dfrac{6}{1} = 6$

Therefore, the result of $15 \times \dfrac{2}{5}$ is 6.

(iii) $3\dfrac{1}{8} \times 2\dfrac{4}{5}$ Converting the mixed numbers to improper fractions,

$= \dfrac{(3 \times 8) + 1}{8} \times \dfrac{(2 \times 5) + 4}{5}$

$= \dfrac{25}{8} \times \dfrac{14}{5} = \dfrac{\overset{5}{25}}{{}_{4}8} \times \dfrac{\overset{7}{14}}{{}_{1}5}$ Cross-reducing the fractions to lowest terms,

$= \dfrac{5}{4} \times \dfrac{7}{1}$ Multiplying the numerators together and the denominators together to get the new fraction,

$= \dfrac{35}{4}$ Converting the improper fraction to a mixed number,

$= 8\dfrac{3}{4}$

Therefore, the result of $3\dfrac{1}{8} \times 2\dfrac{4}{5}$ is $8\dfrac{3}{4}$.

Division of Fractions

> When a fraction is inverted, the resulting fraction is called the 'reciprocal' of the original fraction.

When dividing fractions, as in multiplication, first convert any mixed number to its improper fraction. The division of fractions is done by multiplying the first fraction by the reciprocal of the second fraction. Then, follow the procedure used in multiplication to get the final result.

Note:

- *Dividing by 2 is the same as multiplying by the reciprocal of 2, which is $\dfrac{1}{2}$.*

- *When multiplying or dividing mixed numbers, it is incorrect to multiply or divide the whole number parts separately from the fractional parts to arrive at the answer.*

Example 2.2-k	**Dividing Fractions**

Divide $\dfrac{15}{16}$ by $\dfrac{9}{20}$.

Solution

$\dfrac{15}{16} \div \dfrac{9}{20}$ Multiplying $\dfrac{15}{16}$ by the reciprocal of $\dfrac{9}{20}$, which is $\dfrac{20}{9}$,

$= \dfrac{15}{16} \times \dfrac{20}{9} = \dfrac{\overset{5}{15}}{{}_{4}16} \times \dfrac{\overset{5}{20}}{{}_{3}9}$ Cross-reducing the fractions to lowest terms,

$$= \frac{5}{4} \times \frac{5}{3}$$ Multiplying the numerators together and the denominators together to get the new fraction,

$$= \frac{25}{12}$$ Converting the improper fraction to a mixed number,

$$= 2\frac{1}{12}$$

Therefore, the result of $\frac{15}{16}$ divided by $\frac{9}{20}$ is $2\frac{1}{12}$.

| Example 2.2-I | **Dividing Mixed Numbers** |

Divide $3\frac{3}{20}$ by $1\frac{4}{5}$.

Solution

$$3\frac{3}{20} \div 1\frac{4}{5}$$ Converting the mixed numbers to improper fractions,

$$= \frac{3(20) + 3}{20} \div \frac{1(5) + 4}{5}$$

$$= \frac{63}{20} \div \frac{9}{5}$$ Multiplying $\frac{63}{20}$ by the reciprocal of $\frac{9}{5}$, which is $\frac{5}{9}$,

$$= \frac{63}{20} \times \frac{5}{9} = \frac{^7 \cancel{63}}{_4 \cancel{20}} \times \frac{\cancel{5}^1}{\cancel{9}_1}$$ Cross-reducing the fractions to lowest terms,

$$= \frac{7}{4} \times \frac{1}{1}$$ Multiplying the numerators together and the denominators together to get the new fraction,

$$= \frac{7}{4}$$ Converting the improper fraction to a mixed number,

$$= 1\frac{3}{4}$$

Therefore, the result of $3\frac{3}{20}$ divided by $1\frac{4}{5}$ is $1\frac{3}{4}$.

Complex Fractions

A **complex fraction** is a fraction in which one or more fractions are found in the numerator or denominator.

For example,

$$\frac{1}{\left(\frac{3}{4}\right)}$$ is a complex fraction because it has a fraction in the denominator.

$$\frac{\left(\frac{2}{3}\right)}{6}$$ is a complex fraction because it has a fraction in the numerator.

$$\frac{\left(\frac{2}{5} + \frac{1}{4}\right)}{3}$$ is a complex fraction because it has two fractions in the numerator.

$$\frac{\left(\frac{5}{6}\right)}{\left(\frac{1}{8}\right)}$$ is a complex fraction because it has a fraction in both the numerator and the denominator.

A complex fraction can be converted into a proper or an improper fraction by dividing the numerator by the denominator and then simplifying the expression.

For example,

- $$\frac{\left(\dfrac{7}{2}\right)}{5} = \frac{7}{2} \div 5 = \frac{7}{2} \times \frac{1}{5} = \frac{7}{10}$$

- $$\frac{8}{\left(\dfrac{9}{2}\right)} = 8 \div \left(\frac{9}{2}\right) = \frac{8}{1} \times \frac{2}{9} = \frac{16}{9}$$

2.2 | Exercises

Answers to odd-numbered problems are available at the end of the textbook.

For Problems 1 to 8, identify the greater fraction in each pair.

1. $\dfrac{2}{5}$ or $\dfrac{3}{8}$
2. $\dfrac{4}{3}$ or $\dfrac{6}{5}$
3. $\dfrac{12}{15}$ or $\dfrac{35}{45}$
4. $\dfrac{25}{20}$ or $\dfrac{28}{24}$

5. $\dfrac{8}{7}$ or $\dfrac{13}{12}$
6. $\dfrac{5}{13}$ or $\dfrac{16}{39}$
7. $\dfrac{8}{9}$ or $\dfrac{39}{45}$
8. $\dfrac{3}{8}$ or $\dfrac{25}{48}$

9. Which of the following fractions are less than $\dfrac{2}{3}$?

$$\frac{5}{8}, \frac{6}{7}, \frac{3}{5}, \frac{7}{9}$$

10. Which of the following fractions are greater than $\dfrac{3}{4}$?

$$\frac{4}{5}, \frac{7}{9}, \frac{5}{7}, \frac{9}{11}$$

For Problems 11 to 16, perform the addition, reduce to lowest terms, and express the answer as a mixed number, whenever possible.

11. a. $\dfrac{5}{8} + \dfrac{7}{8}$ b. $\dfrac{7}{12} + \dfrac{3}{4}$
12. a. $\dfrac{5}{9} + \dfrac{7}{9}$ b. $\dfrac{7}{10} + \dfrac{9}{20}$

13. a. $\dfrac{4}{3} + \dfrac{5}{6}$ b. $12\dfrac{4}{5} + 5\dfrac{1}{3}$
14. a. $\dfrac{23}{12} + \dfrac{1}{3}$ b. $18\dfrac{5}{7} + 2\dfrac{2}{5}$

15. a. $9\dfrac{3}{4} + 6\dfrac{1}{6}$ b. $8\dfrac{2}{3} + 5\dfrac{3}{4}$
16. a. $11\dfrac{1}{4} + 5\dfrac{2}{3}$ b. $7\dfrac{1}{10} + 5\dfrac{3}{4}$

For Problems 17 to 22, perform the subtraction, reduce to lowest terms, and express the answer as a mixed number, whenever possible.

17. a. $\dfrac{2}{3} - \dfrac{1}{9}$ b. $\dfrac{9}{10} - \dfrac{3}{5}$
18. a. $\dfrac{1}{6} - \dfrac{1}{8}$ b. $\dfrac{19}{20} - \dfrac{8}{10}$

19. a. $\dfrac{5}{3} - \dfrac{3}{8}$ b. $16\dfrac{1}{8} - 1\dfrac{1}{2}$
20. a. $\dfrac{17}{9} - \dfrac{5}{6}$ b. $5\dfrac{2}{3} - 1\dfrac{5}{12}$

21. a. $8\dfrac{5}{6} - 5\dfrac{3}{9}$ b. $9\dfrac{2}{5} - 7\dfrac{3}{10}$
22. a. $8\dfrac{1}{12} - 4\dfrac{1}{6}$ b. $5\dfrac{5}{8} - 4\dfrac{5}{6}$

For Problems 23 to 28, perform the multiplication, reduce to lowest terms, and express the answer as a mixed number, whenever possible.

23. a. $\dfrac{16}{5} \times \dfrac{5}{4}$ b. $3 \times \dfrac{7}{9}$
24. a. $\dfrac{12}{5} \times \dfrac{25}{3}$ b. $6 \times \dfrac{19}{12}$

25. a. $\dfrac{3}{8} \times \dfrac{5}{11}$ b. $9\dfrac{3}{5} \times 1\dfrac{29}{96}$
26. a. $\dfrac{4}{5} \times \dfrac{23}{9}$ b. $11\dfrac{4}{3} \times 1\dfrac{1}{74}$

27. a. $\dfrac{9}{38} \times \dfrac{19}{63}$ b. $2\dfrac{2}{9} \times 1\dfrac{1}{2}$
28. a. $\dfrac{15}{27} \times \dfrac{18}{45}$ b. $2\dfrac{7}{9} \times 1\dfrac{1}{5}$

For Problems 29 to 36, perform the division, reduce to lowest terms, and express the answer as a mixed number, whenever possible.

29. a. $\dfrac{2}{3} \div \dfrac{4}{9}$ b. $\dfrac{3}{8} \div 4$ 30. a. $\dfrac{3}{5} \div \dfrac{3}{4}$ b. $\dfrac{5}{6} \div 3$

31. a. $\dfrac{7}{15} \div \dfrac{14}{3}$ b. $23\dfrac{1}{2} \div 8\dfrac{13}{16}$ 32. a. $\dfrac{9}{16} \div \dfrac{3}{4}$ b. $10\dfrac{1}{4} \div 2\dfrac{27}{48}$

33. a. $5\dfrac{1}{5} \div 13$ b. $18 \div 4\dfrac{4}{5}$ 34. a. $4\dfrac{1}{4} \div 7$ b. $15 \div 3\dfrac{1}{3}$

35. a. $\dfrac{1}{2\frac{1}{4}}$ b. $\dfrac{4\frac{3}{4}}{\frac{3}{8}}$ 36. a. $\dfrac{1}{5\frac{1}{2}}$ b. $\dfrac{8\frac{4}{9}}{\frac{14}{3}}$

For Problems 37 to 46, perform the indicated arithmetic operations, reduce to lowest terms, and express the answer as a mixed number, whenever possible.

37. a. $\dfrac{1}{10} + \dfrac{17}{100} + \dfrac{39}{1,000}$ b. $\dfrac{3}{5} + \dfrac{7}{10} + \dfrac{9}{15}$ 38. a. $\dfrac{3}{10} + \dfrac{47}{100} + \dfrac{241}{1,000}$ b. $\dfrac{2}{3} + \dfrac{3}{4} + \dfrac{5}{8}$

39. a. $\dfrac{32}{100} - \dfrac{8}{1,000}$ b. $\dfrac{5}{8} + \dfrac{13}{16} - \dfrac{3}{4}$ 40. a. $\dfrac{3}{10} - \dfrac{4}{1,000}$ b. $\dfrac{7}{12} + \dfrac{5}{6} - \dfrac{2}{3}$

41. a. $\left(2\dfrac{1}{6} + 1\dfrac{2}{3}\right) \div 5\dfrac{3}{4}$ b. $5\dfrac{1}{2} \div \left(2\dfrac{1}{2} + 2\right)$ 42. a. $\left(5\dfrac{1}{3} + 2\dfrac{5}{6}\right) \div 3\dfrac{1}{2}$ b. $2\dfrac{2}{3} \div \left(1\dfrac{7}{15} + \dfrac{2}{3}\right)$

43. $10\dfrac{1}{2} \div 4\dfrac{1}{5} + \dfrac{9}{10} \times 2\dfrac{1}{2} - \dfrac{3}{4}$ 44. $13\dfrac{3}{7} \times \dfrac{5}{94} + 6\dfrac{2}{5} \div \dfrac{4}{15} + 7\dfrac{1}{5}$ 45. $4\dfrac{2}{3} \div 2\dfrac{1}{3} + \dfrac{3}{5} \times 4\dfrac{2}{3} - \dfrac{2}{5}$ 46. $2\dfrac{1}{6} \div \dfrac{26}{45} + 2\dfrac{1}{4} \times 2\dfrac{1}{3} - \dfrac{3}{8}$

For Problems 47 to 74, express your answers as a proper fraction reduced to lowest terms or a mixed number, where appropriate.

47. Peter, a college student, spent $\dfrac{5}{12}$ of his money on rent and $\dfrac{1}{4}$ on food. What fraction of his money did he spend on rent and food?

48. Alan walked $\dfrac{3}{5}$ km to his physics class, and from there he walked another $\dfrac{3}{4}$ km to his biology class. How far did Alan walk?

49. Last night, Amy spent $3\dfrac{1}{6}$ hours on her math project and $2\dfrac{3}{10}$ hours on her biology project. How much time did she spend on both projects?

50. A package contains $2\dfrac{3}{5}$ kg of trachea tubes and $1\dfrac{1}{8}$ kg of Peri-strips dry. What is the total weight of the package?

51. Thomas had a $2\dfrac{1}{2}$ pound package of surgical staples and gave $1\dfrac{5}{8}$ pounds of it to the surgical wing of a hospital. How much was left?

52. Alexander bought $4\dfrac{2}{5}$ litres of milk and drank $1\dfrac{2}{3}$ litres of it. How much milk was left?

53. Sarah had $\dfrac{3}{4}$ kg of bandages and dressings. She used $\dfrac{2}{7}$ kg of the bandages and dressings while treating patients. How many kilograms of bandages and dressings were left?

54. Cassidy had $\dfrac{5}{8}$ litres of formaldehyde and used $\dfrac{1}{3}$ litres of the solution while disinfecting equipment. What quantity of formaldehyde was left?

55. David spent $\dfrac{7}{10}$ of his money on books and $\dfrac{1}{3}$ of the remainder on food. What fraction of his money was spent on food?

56. Mary spent $\dfrac{2}{5}$ of her money on a school bag. She then spent $\dfrac{1}{3}$ of the remainder on hospital scrubs. What fraction of her money was spent on hospital scrubs?

57. After selling $\dfrac{2}{5}$ of its textbooks, a college bookstore had 810 books left. How many textbooks were in the bookstore initially?

58. Rose travelled $\dfrac{3}{5}$ of her journey to a private clinic by car and the remaining 20 km by bus. How far did she travel in total?

59. A prescription requires two, $\frac{3}{4}$ mL doses per day for seven-and-a-half days. How many mL are required to fill the prescription?

60. How many millilitres do you need to fill a prescription that requires four, $\frac{4}{5}$ mL doses per day for nine-and-a-half days?

61. Cheng can walk $5\frac{1}{4}$ km in $1\frac{1}{2}$ hours. How many kilometres can he walk in 1 hour?

62. $1\frac{3}{4}$ litres of isopropyl alcohol weighs $4\frac{2}{3}$ kg. Find the weight (in kilograms) of 1 litre of isopropyl alcohol.

63. An elastic bandage of $\frac{7}{8}$ metres in length is cut into pieces measuring $\frac{1}{16}$ metres each. How many pieces are there?

64. A box of tongue depressors for a doctor's office that weighs $\frac{2}{3}$ kg is divided into smaller boxes weighing $\frac{1}{12}$ kg each. How many small boxes are there?

65. A bottle of medicine contains 80 mg of medicine. Each dose of the medicine is $\frac{2}{5}$ mg. How many doses are there in the bottle?

66. A package of anticoagulants weighs 100 mg. How many tablets will there be in the package if each tablet weighs 0.75 mg?

67. You have 20 mL of medicine. If each dose is $\frac{5}{8}$ mL, and three doses are required per day, how many days will the medicine last?

68. $35\frac{5}{12}$ mL of medication is expected to last eight and a half days. If each dose is $\frac{5}{6}$ mL, how many doses are required per day?

69. Out of 320 bulbs delivered to a hospital, $\frac{1}{20}$ are defective. How many of them are **not** defective?

70. If $\frac{4}{15}$ of the 1,800 students enrolled for a Health Sciences Mathematics course, how many students did **not** enroll for the course?

71. 9 litres of IV fluid solution are used to fill $3\frac{3}{4}$ IV bags. What is the capacity of one of the IV bags?

72. A PVC tube that is $33\frac{3}{4}$ cm long is cut into several $2\frac{1}{4}$ cm equal pieces and are placed in a box. The cut pieces fill the box $\frac{3}{4}$ of the way full. How many pieces can the box hold when it is filled to capacity?

73. A mixture requires $1\frac{1}{2}$ mL of ingredient A and $3\frac{4}{5}$ mL of ingredient B. How many mL of A and B are in 265 mL of the mixture?

74. A mixture requires $2\frac{5}{6}$ mL of ingredient A and $5\frac{1}{3}$ mL of ingredient B. How many mL of A and B are in 245 mL of the mixture?

2.3 | Decimal Numbers

In the previous sections, we saw how we can use fractions to represent values that are parts or portions of a whole number. However, we saw that the methods involved in performing arithmetic with fractions is significantly different than those used for arithmetic with whole numbers. This is primarily because of the base-10, place-value system used with whole numbers that is not used with fractions.

However, there is a system, known as **decimal fractions**, more commonly known as **decimal numbers** or just **decimals**, that is used to represent partial values in the same base-10, place-value system used to express whole numbers.

Fractions whose denominators are a power of 10 (such as 10, 100, 1,000, etc.) are called decimal fractions. For example, $\frac{3}{10}, \frac{7}{100}, \frac{9}{1,000}$, etc. are decimal fractions and 0.3, 0.07, and 0.009 are their equivalent decimal number representations.

Decimal numbers are used in many real-life situations that require more precision than whole numbers can provide - money is a good example: 5¢ = $0.05, 10¢ = $0.10, 25¢ = $0.25, etc.

A decimal number has both a whole number portion and a decimal portion. The decimal point (.) separates the whole number portion and the decimal portion of a decimal number. The whole number portion of a decimal is comprised of those digits to the left of the decimal point. The decimal portion is represented by the digits to the right of the decimal point. It represents a number less than 1.

> When a number is less than 1, it is usually expressed in its decimal form with 0 in its ones place. For example, .25 is expressed as 0.25.

For example,

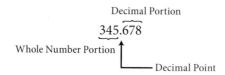

Whole Number Portion — 345.678 — Decimal Portion — Decimal Point

The decimal portion of 345.678 written as a decimal fraction: $\dfrac{678}{1,000}$.

When decimal numbers are expressed as a fraction using 10 or powers of 10, we do not reduce to their lowest terms.

For example, $\dfrac{678}{1,000}$ if reduced to $\dfrac{339}{500}$ is no longer expressed as a power of 10, and hence, is no longer a decimal fraction.

Similarly,

$$1.2 = 1\tfrac{2}{10}$$

$$23.45 = 23\tfrac{45}{100}$$

$$75.378 = 75\tfrac{378}{1,000}$$

Every whole number can be written as a decimal number by placing a decimal point to the right of the units digits.

For example, 5 in **decimal form** is 5. or 5.0 or 5.00.

The number of decimal places in a decimal number depends on the number of digits written to the right of the decimal point.

For example,

5.	No decimal place
17.2	One decimal place
4.17	Two decimal places
1.250	Three decimal places
0.0083	Four decimal places

Types of Decimal Numbers

There are three different types of decimal numbers.

> Decimal numbers of the first two types are called **rational numbers**, as every fraction can be expressed as a decimal number in one of these two forms.
>
> Decimal numbers of the third type are called **irrational numbers**, as they cannot be expressed as fractions.

(i)   Non-repeating, terminating decimal numbers:

For example, 0.2, 0.3767, 0.86452

(ii)   Repeating, non-terminating decimal numbers:

For example, 0.222222..., 0.4555555..., 0.867867...

Repeating, non-terminating decimal numbers are often expressed more simply by writing an overline bar above the repeating digits:

For example, $0.222222... = 0.\overline{2}$, $0.4555555... = 0.4\overline{5}$, $0.867867... = 0.\overline{867}$

(iii)   Non-repeating, non-terminating decimal numbers:

For example, 0.453740..., π (3.141592...), e (2.718281...)

Place Value of Decimal Numbers

The position of each digit in a decimal number determines the place value of the digit. Exhibit 2.3 illustrates the place values of the five-digit decimal number: 0.35796.

The place value of each digit as you move right from the decimal point is found by decreasing powers of 10. The first place value to the right of the decimal point is the tenths place, the second place value is the hundredths place, and so on, as shown in Table 2.3.

Table 2.3	**Place Value Chart of Decimal Numbers**

$10^{-1} = \dfrac{1}{10}$	$10^{-2} = \dfrac{1}{100}$	$10^{-3} = \dfrac{1}{1,000}$	$10^{-4} = \dfrac{1}{10,000}$	$10^{-5} = \dfrac{1}{100,000}$
0.1	0.01	0.001	0.0001	0.00001
Tenths	Hundredths	Thousandths	Ten-thousandths	Hundred-thousandths

When written in **standard form**, the five-digit number in Exhibit 2.3 is written as 0.35796.

0		3	5	7	9	6
		Tenths	Hundredths	Thousandths	Ten-thousandths	Hundred-thousandths

The above can be written in **expanded form** as follows:

$0.3 + 0.05 + 0.007 + 0.0009 + 0.00006$

Or,

3 tenths + 5 hundredths + 7 thousandths + 9 ten-thousandths + 6 hundred-thousandths

Or,

$$\frac{3}{10} + \frac{5}{100} + \frac{7}{1,000} + \frac{9}{10,000} + \frac{6}{100,000}$$ (0.35796 in decimal fraction is $\dfrac{35,796}{100,000}$)

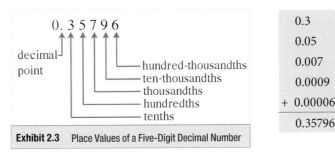

Exhibit 2.3   Place Values of a Five-Digit Decimal Number

Reading and Writing Decimal Numbers

The word 'and' is used to represent the decimal point (.).

Follow these steps to read and write decimal numbers:

Step 1:   Read or write the numbers to the left of a decimal point as a whole number.

Step 2:   Read or write the decimal point as "and".

Step 3:   Read or write the number to the right of the decimal point also as a whole number, but followed by the name of the place value occupied by the right-most digit of the decimal portion.

For example, 745.023 is written in word form as:

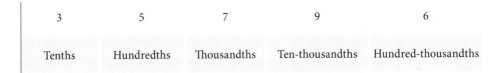

Seven hundred forty-five and twenty-**three** thousandths

| Whole Number Portion | Decimal Point | Decimal Portion |

The last digit, three, ends in the thousandths place. Therefore, the decimal fraction is $\dfrac{23}{1,000}$.

There are other ways of reading and writing decimal numbers as noted below:

(i) Use the word "point" to indicate the decimal point, and thereafter read or write each digit individually.

For example,

745.023 can also be read or written as: Seven hundred forty-five point zero, two, three.

(ii) Ignore the decimal point of the decimal number and read or write the number as a whole number, and include the place occupied by the right-most digit of the decimal portion.

For example,

745.023 can also be read or written as: Seven hundred forty-five thousand, twenty-three thousandths. (i.e., $\dfrac{745,023}{1,000}$).

Note: The above two representations are not used in the examples and exercise questions within this chapter.

Use of Hyphens to Express Numbers in Word Form

- Hyphens (-) are used to express the two digit numbers, 21 to 29, 31 to 39, 41 to 49, … 91 to 99, in each group in their word form.

- Hyphens (-) are also used while expressing the place value portion of a decimal number, such as ten-thousandths, hundred-thousandths, ten-millionths, hundred-millionths, etc.

The following examples illustrate the use of hyphens to express numbers in their word form:

0.893   Eight hundred ninety-three thousandths.

0.0506   Five hundred six ten-thousandths.

0.00145   One hundred forty-five hundred-thousandths.

| Example 2.3-a | Writing Decimal Numbers in Standard Form |

Express the following in decimal numbers in their standard form:

(i) Two hundred and thirty-five thousandths

(ii) Three and seven tenths

(iii) Eighty-four ten-thousandths

Solution

(i)

Whole Number Portion		Decimal Portion	
Two hundred	and	thirty-five <u>thousandths</u>	The last digit, five, ends in the thousandths place.
200	.	$\dfrac{35}{1,000} = 0.035$	

Therefore, the number is written in standard form as **200.035.**

*Note: This is **not** the same as the number "two hundred thirty-five thousandths", which is the decimal number 0.235. This demonstrates the importance of only using the word "and" to indicate the decimal point, not as a joining word between the hundreds and tens (for example, the number 235 should be expressed as two hundred thirty-five, **not** as two hundred **and** thirty-five).*

(ii)

Whole Number Portion		Decimal Portion	
Three	and	seven <u>tenths</u>	The last digit, seven, ends in the tenths place.
3	.	$\dfrac{7}{10} = 0.7$	

Therefore, the number is written in standard form as **3.7.**

Solution *continued*	(iii)	**Whole Number Portion**	**Decimal Portion**

| No whole number portion is mentioned, so we write a zero ("0") in the whole number spot. | 0 | . | Eighty-four <u>ten-thousandths</u>   The last digit, four, ends in the ten-thousandths place.
 $$\frac{84}{10,000} = 0.0084$$ |

Therefore, the number is written in standard form as **0.0084**.

Example 2.3-b   **Writing Decimal Numbers in Word Form**

Express the following decimal numbers in their word form:

(i)   23.125   (ii)   7.43

(iii)   80.3   (iv)   0.2345

Solution

(i)   23.12**5**   The last digit, 5, is in the thousandths place.

$$= 23\frac{125}{1,000}$$

Twenty-three and one hundred twenty-five thousandths.

(ii)   7.4**3**   The last digit, 3, is in the hundredths place.

$$= 7\frac{43}{100}$$

Seven and forty-three hundredths.

(iii)   80.**3**   The last digit, 3, is in the tenths place.

$$= 80\frac{3}{10}$$

Eighty and three tenths.

(iv)   0.234**5**   The last digit, 5, is in the ten-thousandths place.

$$= \frac{2,345}{10,000}$$

Since there is no whole number portion, we omit any reference to the whole number portion or the decimal point, and only write the decimal portion.

Two thousand, three hundred forty-five ten-thousandths.

Rounding Decimal Numbers

Rounding Decimal Numbers to the Nearest Whole Number, Tenth, Hundredth, etc.

Rounding decimal numbers refers to changing the value of the decimal number to the nearest whole number, tenth, hundredth, thousandth, etc. It is also referred to as "rounding to a specific number of decimal places", indicating the number of decimal places that will be left when the rounding is complete.

For example,

Rounding to the nearest cent refers to rounding the amount to the nearest hundredth or to two decimal places.

- Rounding to the nearest whole number is the same as rounding without any decimals.
- Rounding to the nearest tenth is the same as rounding to one decimal place.
- Rounding to the nearest hundredth is the same as rounding to two decimal places.
- Rounding to the nearest thousandth is the same as rounding to three decimal places.

Follow these steps to round decimal numbers:

Step 1: Identify the digit to be rounded (this is the place value for which the rounding is required).

Step 2: If the digit to the immediate right of the identified rounding digit is less than 5 (0, 1, 2, 3, 4), do not change the value of the rounding digit.

If the digit to the immediate right of the identified rounding digit is 5 or greater than 5 (5, 6, 7, 8, 9), increase the value of the rounding digit by one (i.e., round up by one number).

Step 3: Drop all digits that are to the right of the rounding digit.

| Example 2.3-c | **Rounding Decimal Numbers** |

Round the following decimal numbers to the indicated place value:

(i)   268.143 to the nearest tenth

(ii)   489.679 to the nearest hundredth

(iii) $39.9985 to the nearest cent

Solution

(i)   Rounding 268.143 to the nearest tenth:

1 is the rounding digit in the tenths place: 268.143.

The digit to the immediate right of the rounding digit is less than 5; therefore, do not change the value of the rounding digit. Drop all of the digits to the right of the rounding digit. This will result in 268.1.

Therefore, 268.143 rounded to the nearest tenth is 268.1.

(ii)   Rounding 489.679 to the nearest hundredth:

7 is the rounding digit in the hundredths place: 489.679.

The digit to the immediate right of the rounding digit is greater than 5; therefore, increase the value of the rounding digit by one, from 7 to 8. Drop all digits that are to the right of the rounding digit. This will result in 489.68.

Therefore, 489.679 rounded to the nearest hundredth is 489.68.

(iii)   Rounding $39.9985 to the nearest cent:

9 is the rounding digit in the hundredths place: $39.9985.

The digit to the immediate right of the rounding digit is greater than 5; therefore, increase the value of the rounding digit by one, from 9 to 10, carrying the one to the tenths place, then to the ones, and then to the tens, to increase 3 to 4. Finally, drop all digits that are to the right of the hundredths place. This will result in $40.00

Therefore, $39.9985 rounded to the nearest cent is $40.00.

2.3 | Exercises

Answers to odd-numbered problems are available at the end of the textbook.

For Problems 1 to 8, express the numbers in decimal notation.

1. a. $\dfrac{6}{10}$ b. $\dfrac{7}{1,000}$ 2. a. $\dfrac{9}{10,000}$ b. $\dfrac{41}{1,000}$

3. a. $\dfrac{12}{100}$ b. $\dfrac{29}{10,000}$ 4. a. $\dfrac{75}{100}$ b. $\dfrac{3}{10}$

5. a. $7\dfrac{5}{10}$ b. $9\dfrac{503}{1,000}$ 6. a. $9\dfrac{3}{10}$ b. $6\dfrac{207}{1,000}$

7. a. $\dfrac{367}{100}$ b. $\dfrac{2,972}{100}$ 8. a. $\dfrac{475}{10}$ b. $\dfrac{2,567}{1,000}$

For Problems 9 to 24, write the numbers in (i) standard form and (ii) expanded form.

9. Eighty-seven and two tenths

10. Thirty-five and seven tenths

11. Three and four hundredths

12. Nine and seven hundredths

13. Four hundred one ten-thousandths

14. Two hundred eight thousandths

15. Eighty-nine and six hundred twenty-five ten-thousandths

16. Fifty-two and three hundred five thousandths

17. One thousand, seven hundred eighty-seven and twenty-five thousandths

18. Nine hundred eighty-seven and twenty hundredths

19. Four hundred twelve and sixty-five hundredths

20. Seven thousand, two hundred sixty and fifteen thousandths

21. One million, six hundred thousand and two hundredths

22. Six million, two hundred seventeen thousand and five hundredths

23. Five hundred and twenty-three thousandths

24. One thousand, eight hundred and twenty-nine ten-thousandths

For Problems 25 to 32, express the decimal numbers in their word form.

25. a. 42.55   b. 734.125
26. a. 7.998   b. 12.77

27. a. 0.25   b. 9.5
28. a. 0.987   b. 311.2

29. a. 7.07   b. 15.002
30. a. 11.09   b. 9.006

31. a. 0.062   b. 0.054
32. a. 0.031   b. 0.073

33. Arrange the following numbers from least to greatest:

    a. 0.034, 0.403, 0.043, 0.304   b. 5.67, 5.607, 5.076, 5.7

34. Arrange the following numbers from greatest to least:

    a. 1.014, 1.011, 1.104, 1.041   b. 23.809, 23.9, 23.098, 23.89

For Problems 35 to 38, round the numbers to the nearest whole number (i.e., no decimal places).

35. 415.1654   36. 264.1545   37. 7.8725   38. 25.5742

For Problems 39 to 42, round the numbers to the nearest tenth (i.e., one decimal place).

39. 24.1575   40. 112.1255   41. 10.3756   42. 0.9753

For Problems 43 to 46, round the numbers to the nearest hundredth (i.e., two decimal places).

43. 14.3585   44. 0.0645   45. 181.1267   46. 19.6916

For Problems 47 to 50, round the numbers to the nearest cent (i.e., two decimal places).

47. $16.775   48. $10.954   49. $9.9987   50. $24.995

2.4 | Arithmetic Operations with Decimal Numbers

Addition of Decimal Numbers

Addition of decimal numbers (finding the **total** or **sum**) refers to combining numbers. It is similar to adding whole numbers.

Follow these steps to add one decimal number to another decimal number:

Step 1: Write the numbers with the same place values under one another, by aligning the decimal points of these numbers.

Step 2: Add zeros to the right of any numbers with fewer decimal places than the other numbers, if necessary, to have the same number of decimal places, and then draw a horizontal line underneath all the numbers.

Step 3: Starting from the right, add all the numbers in that column and continue towards the left.

- If the total is less than 10, write the total under the horizontal line in the same column.
- If the total is 10 or more, write the 'ones' digit of the total under the horizontal line in the same column and write the 'tens' digit above the next column to the left.

Step 4: Follow this procedure for each column going from right to left. Write the decimal point in the answer, lined up with the decimal points in all the other numbers in the sum.

| Example 2.4-a | **Adding Decimal Numbers** |

Perform the following additions:

(i) 25.125 + 7.14

(ii) 741.87 + 135.456

(iii) 127 + 68.8 + 669.95

Solution

(i) 25.125 + 7.14

$$
\begin{array}{r}
\overset{1}{2}5.125 \\
+7.140 \\
\hline
32.265
\end{array}
$$ ⟵ Add one zero to match the number of decimal places.

Therefore, adding 25.125 and 7.14 results in 32.265.

(ii) 741.87 + 135.456

$$
\begin{array}{r}
74\overset{1}{1}.8\overset{1}{7}0 \\
+135.456 \\
\hline
877.326
\end{array}
$$ ⟵ Add one zero to match the number of decimal places.

Therefore, adding 741.87 and 135.456 results in 877.326.

(iii) 127 + 68.8 + 669.95

$$
\begin{array}{r}
1\overset{1}{2}\overset{2}{7}.\overset{1}{0}0 \\
68.80 \\
+669.95 \\
\hline
865.75
\end{array}
$$
⟵ Add two zeros to match the number of decimal places.
⟵ Add one zero to match the number of decimal places.

Therefore, adding 127, 68.8 and 669.95 results in 865.75.

Subtraction of Decimal Numbers

Subtraction of decimal numbers refers to finding the **difference** between decimal numbers. It is similar to subtracting whole numbers.

Follow these steps to subtract one decimal number from another decimal number:

Step 1: Write the numbers with the same place values under one another, by aligning the decimal points of these numbers.

Step 2: Add zeros to the right of any numbers with fewer decimal places than the other numbers, if necessary, to have the same number of decimal places, and then draw a horizontal line underneath the numbers.

Step 3: Ensure that the subtraction is being done in the right order, with the initial value being written on top and the number being subtracted from that value being written underneath.

Step 4: Starting from the right, subtract the bottom number from the top number.

- If the top digit is greater than the bottom digit, subtract and write the difference under the horizontal line.
- If the top digit is smaller than the bottom digit, borrow from the digit to the left of this top digit, by adding ten to the digit on the top and subtracting one from the digit that was borrowed from. Find the difference and write it under the horizontal line.

Step 5: Follow this procedure for each column going from right to left. Write the decimal point in the answer, lined up with the decimal points of the other numbers in the difference.

Example 2.4-b	Subtracting Decimal Numbers

Perform the following subtractions:

(i)　　Subtract 29.02 from 135.145　　　　(ii)　　Subtract 38.7 from 457

Solution

(i)　　Subtract 29.02 from 135.145

$$
\begin{array}{r}
1\overset{2}{3}\overset{15}{5}.145 \\
-\quad 29.020 \\
\hline
106.125
\end{array}
$$

Therefore, subtracting 29.02 from 135.145 results in 106.125.

(ii)　　Subtract 38.7 from 457

$$
\begin{array}{r}
4\overset{16}{5}\overset{}{7}.\overset{10}{0} \\
-\quad 38.7 \\
\hline
418.3
\end{array}
$$

Therefore, subtracting 38.7 from 457 results in 418.3.

Multiplication of Decimal Numbers

Multiplication of decimal numbers refers to finding the **product** of two decimal numbers. It is similar to multiplying whole numbers.

Follow these steps to multiply one decimal number with another decimal number:

Step 1: Line up the numbers on the right **without** aligning the decimal points.

Step 2: Multiply the numbers assuming that there are no decimal points; i.e., multiply each digit in the top number by each digit in the bottom number and add the products, similar to the process of multiplying whole numbers.

Step 3: Count the total number of decimal places in the original numbers that are being multiplied.

Step 4: Count out the number of decimal places in the answer, starting at the right and moving towards the left by the total number of decimal places from Step 3, and place the decimal point there.

Example 2.4-c	Multiplying Decimal Numbers

(i)　　Multiply 12.56 and 1.8

(ii)　　Multiply 15,000 and 0.0004

Solution

(i)

$$
\begin{array}{r}
12.56 \quad \text{(2 Decimal places)} \\
\times \quad 1.8 \quad \text{(1 Decimal places)} \\
\hline
10048 \\
12560 \\
\hline
22.608 \quad \text{(3 Decimal places)}
\end{array}
$$

Total of 3 Decimal places

Therefore, multiplying 12.56 and 1.8 results in 22.608.

(ii)

$$
\begin{array}{r}
15{,}000 \\
\times\ 0.0004 \\
\hline
6.0000
\end{array}
\left.\begin{array}{l}
\text{(0 Decimal places)} \\
\text{(4 Decimal places)} \\
\text{(4 Decimal places)}
\end{array}\right\}\ \text{Total of 4 Decimal places}
$$

Therefore, multiplying 15,000 and 0.0004 results in 6.

Note: When multiplying very large numbers by very small decimal numbers, the product can often be arrived at more quickly using our knowledge of powers of ten:

$$15{,}000 \times 0.0004 = 1.5 \times 4 = 6$$

Division of Decimal Numbers

Division of decimal numbers is the process of determining how many times one decimal number is contained in another decimal number.

Follow these steps to divide a decimal number:

Step 1: If the divisor is not a whole number, convert it to a whole number by moving the decimal point to the right. Move the decimal point in the dividend by the same number of places.

Step 2: Divide by following a similar process to the process of dividing whole numbers.

- Add zeros to the right of the last digit of the dividend (after the decimal point) and keep dividing until there is no remainder or a repeating pattern shows up in the quotient, or until you've reached one digit more than the indicated number of decimal places which you should round to.

Example 2.4-d | **Dividing Decimal Numbers**

Perform the following divisions:

(i) Divide 8.25 by 0.6   (ii) Divide 0.166 by 0.03   (iii) Divide $29 by 1.7 (round to the nearest cent)

(i)   **Step 1:** $8.25 \div 0.6$

Since the denominator contains one decimal place, move the decimal point by one decimal place to the right for both the numerator and the denominator.

$$= \frac{8.25}{0.6}$$

This is the same as multiplying both the numerator and the denominator by 10.

$$= \frac{82.5}{6} \qquad\qquad \frac{8.25 \times 10}{0.6 \times 10} = \frac{82.5}{6}$$

Step 2:

$$
\begin{array}{r}
13.75 \\
6\,\overline{)\,82.50} \\
-6 \\
\hline
22 \\
-18 \\
\hline
45 \\
-42 \\
\hline
30 \\
-30 \\
\hline
0
\end{array}
$$

← Add a Zero

Position the decimal point within the quotient directly above the decimal point within the dividend.

Therefore, when 8.25 is divided by 0.6, the quotient is 13.75.

Solution
continued

(ii)   Step 1: $0.166 \div 0.03$

$$= \frac{0.166}{0.03}$$

$$= \frac{16.6}{3}$$

Since the denominator contains two decimal places, move the decimal point by two decimal places to the right for both the numerator and the denominator.

This is the same as multiplying both the numerator and the denominator by 100.

$$\frac{0.166 \times 100}{0.03 \times 100} = \frac{16.6}{3}$$

Step 2:

```
      5.533
3 | 16.600
   -15↓
    16
   -15
     10  ←——————— Add a Zero
     -9
     10  ←——————— Add a Zero
     -9
      1
```

Position the decimal point within the quotient directly above the decimal point within the dividend.

> Remember, repeating decimals are usually represented by a horizontal bar on top of the repeating decimal; i.e., 5.533333... is written as $5.5\overline{3}$.

Therefore, when 0.166 is divided by 0.03, the quoitent is $5.5\overline{3}$.

(iii)   Step 1: $\$29 \div 1.7$

$$= \frac{29}{1.7}$$

$$= \frac{290}{17}$$

Since the denominator contains one decimal place, move the decimal point by one decimal place to the right for both the numerator and the denominator.

This is the same as multiplying both the numerator and the denominator by 10.

$$\frac{29 \times 10}{1.7 \times 10} = \frac{290}{17}$$

Step 2:

```
       17.058
17 | 290.000
    -17↓
    120
   -119
     10  ←——————— Add a Zero
     -0
    100  ←——————— Add a Zero
    -85
    150  ←——————— Add a Zero
   -136
     14
```

Position the decimal point within the quotient directly above the decimal point within the dividend.

> To round to the nearest cent (hundredth), we need to calculate the quotient to the thousandth.

Therefore, when $29 is divided by 1.7, the quotient (rounded to the nearest cent) is $17.06.

Estimating with Decimal Numbers

Often we need to decide if the answer to a problem is reasonable or not. We can make this decision by **estimating** the answer.

To estimate an **addition**, **subtraction**, **multiplication**, or **division** problem with decimal numbers, we round each number in the problem to the level of precision of the place value of the first digit in the number; i.e., to the nearest one, ten, hundred, or thousand, or nearest tenth, hundredth, thousandth, etc. This is known as **front-end rounding**.

For example, to estimate the product of 9.761 × 0.125, we would first round 9.761 to the nearest one (place value of the digit 9), and round 0.125 to the nearest tenth (place value of the digit 1). Therefore, we estimate that 9.761 × 0.125 = 10 × 0.1 = 1 (compare to the exact answer 1.220125).

This is demonstrated in Example 2.4-e below.

| Example 2.4-e | **Estimating with Decimal Numbers** |

Estimate the answers to the following arithmetic operations.

(i)   7.25 + 8.95

(ii)   39.8 – 22.1

(iii)   0.018 + 0.072 – 0.066

(iv)   0.345 + 0.789 – 0.212

(v)   3.9 × 6.2

(vi)   198.12 ÷ 111.93

(vii)   294.3 × 31.5 ÷ 2.1

Solution

(i)   7.25 + 8.95

= 7 + 9   Estimated by rounding to the nearest one.

= 16   (Compare to the exact answer 7.25 + 8.95 = 16.20).

(ii)   39.8 – 22.1

= 40 – 20   Estimated by rounding to the nearest ten.

= 20   (Compare to the exact answer 39.8 – 22.1 = 17.7).

(iii)   0.018 + 0.072 – 0.066

= 0.02 + 0.07 – 0.07   Estimated by rounding to the nearest hundredth.

= 0.02   (Compare to the exact answer 0.018 + 0.072 – 0.066 = 0.024).

(iv)   0.345 + 0.789 – 0.212

= 0.3 + 0.8 – 0.2   Estimated by rounding to the nearest tenth.

= 0.9   (Compare to the exact answer 0.345 + 0.789 – 0.212 = 0.922).

(v)   3.9 × 6.2

= 4 × 6   Estimated by rounding to the nearest one.

= 24   (Compare to the exact answer 3.9 × 6.2 = 24.18).

(vi)   198.12 ÷ 111.93

= 200 ÷ 100   Estimated by rounding to the nearest hundred.

= 2   (Compare to the exact answer 198.12 ÷ 111.93 = 1.770034...).

(vii)   294.3 × 31.5 ÷ 2.1

= 300 × 30 ÷ 2   Estimated by rounding to the nearest hundred, ten, and one, respectively.

= 4,500   (Compare to the exact answer 294.3 × 31.5 ÷ 2.1 = 4,414.5).

2.4 | Exercises

For Problems 1 to 8, perform the additions.

1. 927.896 + 659.50 + 128.649
2. 619.985 + 52.82 + 3.187
3. 74 + 129.258 + 0.32 + 666.015
4. 17 + 3.48 + 0.278 + 78.24
5. 292.454 + 121.69 + 65.3
6. 396.716 + 191.68 + 90.6
7. 948.684 + 15.17 + 0.717
8. 625.365 + 27.97 + 0.613

9. Find the sum of the following numbers:

    Twenty and ninety-five hundredths; Two hundred and seventy-two thousandths; and Nineteen and nine tenths.

10. Find the sum of the following numbers:

    Six and thirty-nine thousandths; Eighty and fourteen hundredths; and Sixteen and eight tenths.

For Problems 11 to 18, perform the subtractions.

11. 423.92 – 185.728
12. 9.555 – 7.18
13. 29.28 – 13.4
14. 15.7 – 7.92
15. 539.64 – 258.357
16. 848.62 – 495.476
17. 409.5 – 179.832
18. 475.3 – 281.375

19. Subtract three hundred five and thirty-nine hundredths from seven hundred twenty and four tenths.

20. Subtract eight hundred twenty and four hundredths from one thousand, one hundred one and six tenths.

For Problems 21 to 28, perform the multiplications.

21. 137.89 × 5.4
22. 189.945 × 6.3
23. 62.095 × 4.18
24. 92.74 × 3.25
25. 0.43 × 0.8
26. 0.59 × 0.9
27. 109.78 × 2.91
28. 145.75 × 3.74

For Problems 29 to 36, perform the divisions.

29. 732.6 ÷ 8
30. 261.31 ÷ 7
31. 67.78 ÷ 9
32. 413.9 ÷ 6
33. 14.6 ÷ 0.6
34. 9.155 ÷ 0.7
35. 3.1 ÷ 0.25
36. 2.7 ÷ 0.15

Estimate the answers for Problems 37 to 46 by rounding each number to its first non-zero place value and compare with the exact answer.

37. 223 + 158.2
38. 189 + 123.8
39. 0.76 – 0.39
40. 5.43 – 0.49
41. 3.72 × 2.1
42. 9.3 × 4.2
43. 214.55 ÷ 111.2
44. 489.11 ÷ 231.4
45. 11.6 × 19.8 + 18.8 ÷ 2.1
46. 12 × 21.7 + 31.2 ÷ 1.8

For Problems 47 to 54, formulate arithmetic expressions and evaluate.

47. Find the amount that is $248.76 less than $627.40.

48. Find the amount that is $45.27 less than $90.75.

49. Find the difference between the amounts $30.75 and $15.89.

50. Find the difference between the amounts $235.62 and $115.75.

51. Find the sum of $52.43 and $23.95.

52. Find the sum of $252.34 and $297.90.

53. Find the amount that is $38.89 more than $25.67.

54. Find the amount that is $412.78 more than $634.25.

55. A dental assistant bought one etch-prep kit for $88.46. If he gave a $100 bill to the cashier, how much change would he receive?

56. The cost of one container of amalgam alloy capsules is $125.69. If Arun gave a $100 bill and a $50 bill to the cashier, how much change would Arun receive?

57. Bill, a smoking cessation hypnotist, holds two online seminars. The first online seminar was viewed by 8.50 thousand people. He had 4.85 thousand more viewers in his second online seminar than his first. How many viewers did Bill have in total for both of his seminars?

58. Carol, a nursing student, spent $96.75 more on lab supplies than on her nursing uniform. She spent $223.15 on lab supplies. How much did Carol spend on the nursing uniform?

59. The normal selling price of a stethoscope is $237.75. When this item was on sale, Dave paid $49.89 less for it. How much did Dave pay for the stethoscope?

60. It was found that 35,894.9 gallons of milk were served in school cafeterias last year. This year, it is found that 39,894.4 gallons of milk were served. How many more gallons of milk were served this year compared to last year, rounded to the nearest gallon?

61. After spending $38.96 on a nursing lab manual and $1.75 on a mechanical pencil, Ann still had $45.75. How much money did Ann have initially?

62. After paying $515.09 for lab resources and $379.92 for medical textbooks, the bank balance for a third year medical residency student was $675.45. How much money did this student have initially?

63. An orthodontist charges $799.99 for a complete set of braces. However, he offers an installment plan, which allows one of his patients to pay $70.35 every month for 12 months. How much more will his patient have to pay for the braces with the installment plan?

64. As the athletic trainer for a college hockey team, you ordered an electrical muscle-stimulation machine for knee rehabilitation. The machine costs $2,249.95. You agreed to pay $130.45 every month for 18 months. How much more than the selling price did you end up paying for the machine?

65. A pharmaceutical representative earns a salary of $725.35 every week. During the past 3 weeks, he also received commissions of $375.68, $578.79, and $338.57. Calculate his total income for the past 3 weeks.

66. An EMT vehicle is on a 4-year term lease at $694.38 per month. At the end of the lease period, the hospital paid an additional $18,458.74 to purchase the EMT vehicle. Find the total amount the hospital paid for the vehicle.

67. John bought two sets of IV tubing at $20.95 each and three lab coats at $34.55 each. He gave $200 to the cashier. Calculate the balance he should receive from the cashier.

68. I bought two packs of aspirin at $5.60 per pack and four bottles of Benadryl at $6.77 per bottle. I gave the pharmacist a $50 bill. How much change should I receive from the pharmacist?

69. A piece of nasal cannula tubing that measured 0.875 m was cut into pieces of 0.0625 m each. How many pieces did this result in?

70. A doctor prescribes 0.75 mg of a medication for a patient. The medication is in tablet form and contains 0.125 mg of medication per tablet. How many tablets were ordered?

71. A radiologic technologist earns an average salary of $22.49 per hour for a regular 40-hour work week. This rate increases to $37.99 per hour on the weekend. Find the total wages earned by the technologist for a week if he works a 40-hour week and 7 hours on the weekend.

72. A student nurse earns a salary of $440 for a regular 40-hour work week. This week she worked 12 hours of overtime at a rate of $17.89 for each hour of overtime worked. Find her total income for the week.

2.5 | Arithmetic Operations with Fractions and Decimal Numbers

Converting Decimal Numbers to Fractions

It is possible to convert **terminating** decimal numbers (e.g., 0.275) and **repeating** decimal numbers (e.g., 0.333333...) to fractions. However, there are no exact equivalent fractions for **non-repeating**, **non-terminating** decimal numbers (e.g., 0.837508...).

Converting Terminating Decimal Numbers to Fractions

Any non-repeating, terminating decimal number can be converted to a fraction or mixed number by following these steps:

Step 1: Separate the whole number and decimal portions. If the whole number portion is not equal to zero, this will become the whole number portion of the mixed number.

Step 2: Write the decimal portion as a whole number over the power of 10 that represents the place value of the right-most digit.

Step 3: Simplify (i.e., reduce) the fraction.

Example 2.5-a   Converting Terminating Decimal Numbers to Fractions

Convert the following decimal numbers to their fractional equivalent:

(i)   3.75   (ii)   0.015

Solution

(i)   3.75   Separating the whole number and decimal portions,

$= 3 + 0.75$ The place value of the right-most digit is hundredths.

                                Expressing the decimal portion as a whole number over 100,

$= 3 + \dfrac{75}{100}$ Simplifying the fraction,

$= 3\dfrac{3}{4}$

Therefore, 3.75 converted to a mixed number is $3\dfrac{3}{4}$.

(ii)   0.015   The place value of the right-most digit is thousandths.

                                Expressing the decimal portion as a whole number over 1,000,

$= \dfrac{15}{1,000}$ Simplifying the fraction,

$= \dfrac{3}{200}$

Therefore, 0.015 converted to a fraction is $\dfrac{3}{200}$.

Converting Repeating Decimal Numbers to Fractions

Any repeating decimal number can be converted to a fraction by following the procedure given below:

Step 1: Let x represent the unknown fraction, and set it equal to the repeating decimal.

Step 2: Multiply both sides of the equation by a power of 10 until the decimal portion is the same in two equations.

Step 3: Subtract the first equation from the second equation and solve for x.

Example 2.5-b | **Converting Repeating Decimal Numbers to Fractions**

Convert 0.777777... to a fraction.

Solution

Let 0.777777... be equal to a fraction x.

(a) $x = 0.777777... = 0.\overline{7}$ Multiplying both sides of (a) by 10,

(b) $10x = 7.777777... = 7.\overline{7}$ The decimal portion is the same as in (a).

Subtracting (a) from (b),

$$10x - x = 7.\overline{7} - 0.\overline{7}$$
$$9x = 7$$
$$x = \frac{7}{9}$$

Therefore, $0.777777... = \frac{7}{9}$.

Example 2.5-c | **Converting Repeating Decimal Numbers to Fractions**

Convert 0.353535... to a fraction.

Solution

Let 0.353535... be equal to a fraction x.

(a) $x = 0.353535... = 0.\overline{35}$ Multiplying both sides of (a) by 10,

(b) $10x = 3.535353... = 3.\overline{53}$ The decimal portion is not the same as in (a).

     Multiplying both sides of (a) by 100,

(c) $100x = 35.353535... = 35.\overline{35}$ The decimal portion is the same as in (a).

Subtracting (a) from (c),

$$100x - x = 35.\overline{35} - 0.\overline{35}$$
$$99x = 35$$
$$x = \frac{35}{99}$$

Therefore, $0.353535... = \frac{35}{99}$.

Example 2.5-d | **Converting Repeating Decimal Numbers to Fractions**

Convert 0.655555... to a fraction.

Solution

Let 0.655555... be equal to a fraction x.

(a) $x = 0.655555... = 0.6\overline{5}$ Multiplying both sides of (a) by 10,

(b) $10x = 6.555555... = 6.\overline{5}$ The decimal portion is not the same as in (a).

     Multiplying both sides of (a) by 100,

(c) $100x = 65.555555... = 65.\overline{5}$ The decimal portion is the same as in (b).

Solution
continued

Subtracting ⓑ from ⓒ,

$$100x - 10x = 65.\overline{5} - 6.\overline{5}$$
$$90x = 59$$
$$x = \frac{59}{90}$$

Therefore, $0.655555... = \frac{59}{90}$.

Rational numbers can be represented by $\frac{a}{b}$, while irrational numbers cannot be represented by $\frac{a}{b}$, where 'a' and 'b' are integers and $b \neq 0$.

From Examples 2.5-a to 2.5-d, you have now learned that it is possible to convert non-repeating, terminating decimal numbers (e.g., 0.015) and repeating decimal numbers (e.g., $0.6\overline{5}$) into fractions. Therefore, such decimal numbers are called **rational numbers**.

However, it is not possible to convert non-repeating and non-terminating numbers (e.g., $\sqrt{2}$, π, 5.81271...) to fractions. Such decimal numbers are called **irrational numbers**.

These rational numbers and irrational (non-rational) numbers together form the **real numbers**.

Converting Fractions to Decimal Numbers

Converting Proper and Improper Fractions to Decimal Numbers

A proper or improper fraction can be converted to its equivalent decimal number by dividing the numerator by the denominator, as shown in the following examples.

Example 2.5-e | **Converting Proper and Improper Fractions to Decimal Numbers**

Convert the following fractions to their decimal equivalents:

(i) $\dfrac{3}{8}$　　　　　　　　　　(ii) $\dfrac{15}{11}$

Solution

(i) $\dfrac{3}{8}$

$= 3 \div 8$

$= 0.375$

$$
\begin{array}{r}
0.375 \\
8\,\overline{)\,3.000} \\
-24 \\
\hline
60 \\
-56 \\
\hline
40 \\
-40 \\
\hline
0
\end{array}
$$

Therefore, 0.375 is the decimal equivalent of $\dfrac{3}{8}$.

(ii) $\dfrac{15}{11}$

$= 15 \div 11$

$= 1.363636...$

$= 1.\overline{36}$

$$
\begin{array}{r}
1.36\overline{36} \\
11\,\overline{)\,15.0000} \\
-11 \\
\hline
40 \\
-33 \\
\hline
70 \\
-66 \\
\hline
40 \\
-33 \\
\hline
70 \\
-66 \\
\hline
4
\end{array}
$$

Therefore, $1.\overline{36}$ is the decimal equivalent of $\dfrac{15}{11}$.

Converting Mixed Numbers to Decimal Numbers

A mixed number can be converted to its decimal form by dividing the numerator by the denominator of the fraction portion, and adding the quotient to the whole number portion, as shown in the following example.

| Example 2.5-f | Converting Mixed Numbers to Decimal Numbers |

Convert the following mixed numbers to their decimal number equivalents, rounded to two decimal places as needed:

(i) $3\frac{1}{2}$ (ii) $11\frac{3}{7}$

Solution

(i) $3\frac{1}{2}$ Separating the whole number and fractional portions,

$= 3 + \dfrac{1}{2}$ Dividing the numerator by the denominator,

$= 3 + 0.5$

$= 3.5$

Therefore, the decimal number equivalent of $3\frac{1}{2}$ is 3.5.

(ii) $11\frac{3}{7}$ Separating the whole number and fractional portions,

$= 11 + \dfrac{3}{7}$ Dividing the numerator by the denominator,

$= 11 + 0.428571...$

$= 11.428571... = 11.43$

Therefore, the decimal number equivalent of $11\frac{3}{7}$, rounded to two decimal places, is 11.43.

Powers of Fractions and Decimal Numbers

Powers of fractions and decimal numbers are expressed the same way as whole numbers. The fractions and decimal numbers are usually writtten within brackets when they are raised to a power.

For example, $\left(\dfrac{2}{3}\right)^2$ is read as "two-thirds squared".

Exponents indicate the number of times the base is to be multiplied.

This means that $\left(\dfrac{2}{3}\right)$ is used as a factor 2 times.

i.e., $\left(\dfrac{2}{3}\right)^2 = \dfrac{2}{3} \times \dfrac{2}{3} = \dfrac{4}{9}$

Similarily, $(0.12)^3$ is read as "twelve hundredths raised to the power 3".

This means that (0.12) is used as a factor 3 times.

i.e., $(0.12)^3 = (0.12)(0.12)(0.12) = 0.001728$

A mixed number that is raised to a power is evaluated by first converting it into an improper fraction and then following the same procedure explained earlier.

For example, $\left(1\frac{2}{3}\right)^4$ is evaluated by first converting $\left(1\frac{2}{3}\right)$ into an improper fraction.

i.e., $\left(1\frac{2}{3}\right)^4 = \left(\dfrac{1(3) + 2}{3}\right)^4 = \left(\dfrac{5}{3}\right)^4$ Then, expand by using $\left(\dfrac{5}{3}\right)$ as a factor 4 times.

$= \left(\dfrac{5}{3}\right)\left(\dfrac{5}{3}\right)\left(\dfrac{5}{3}\right)\left(\dfrac{5}{3}\right)$

$= \dfrac{625}{81}$

Example 2.5-g **Evaluating Powers of Fractions and Decimal Numbers**

Evaluate the following powers:

(i) $\left(\dfrac{4}{5}\right)^4$ (ii) $\left(1\dfrac{1}{2}\right)^5$ (iii) $(1.12)^3$

Solution

(i) $\left(\dfrac{4}{5}\right)^4$ Expanding by using $\left(\dfrac{4}{5}\right)$ as a factor 4 times,

$= \left(\dfrac{4}{5}\right)\left(\dfrac{4}{5}\right)\left(\dfrac{4}{5}\right)\left(\dfrac{4}{5}\right) = \dfrac{256}{625}$

(ii) $\left(1\dfrac{1}{2}\right)^5$ Converting to an improper fraction,

$= \left(\dfrac{1(2)+1}{2}\right)^5 = \left(\dfrac{3}{2}\right)^5$ Expanding by using $\left(\dfrac{3}{2}\right)$ as a factor 5 times,

$= \left(\dfrac{3}{2}\right)\left(\dfrac{3}{2}\right)\left(\dfrac{3}{2}\right)\left(\dfrac{3}{2}\right)\left(\dfrac{3}{2}\right) = \dfrac{243}{32}$ Converting to a mixed number,

$= 7\dfrac{19}{32}$

(iii) $(1.12)^3$ Expanding by using (1.12) as a factor 3 times,

$= (1.12)\,(1.12)\,(1.12) = 1.404928$

Roots of Fractions and Decimal Numbers

In this section, you will learn about the **square roots** of **fractions** and **decimals** that have exact roots.

Square roots of fractions are calculated the same way as the square roots of whole numbers, but the numerators and denominators are evaluated separately. The answers are expressed in simplified or reduced form.

$\sqrt{\dfrac{a}{b}}$ is equal to $\dfrac{\sqrt{a}}{\sqrt{b}}$ For example, $\sqrt{\dfrac{9}{16}}$ is the same as $\dfrac{\sqrt{9}}{\sqrt{16}} = \dfrac{3}{4}$

Finding roots of decimals becomes easy if the decimal number is converted to a fraction having an even power of ten, i.e., $10^2 = 100$, $10^4 = 10,000$, etc., and then following the procedure for finding the square roots of fractions.

For example, $\sqrt{0.25} = \sqrt{\dfrac{25}{100}} = \dfrac{\sqrt{25}}{\sqrt{100}} = \dfrac{5}{10} = \dfrac{1}{2}$ or 0.5

Example 2.5-h **Evaluating Square Roots of Fractions and Decimal Numbers**

Evaluate the following square roots:

(i) $\sqrt{\dfrac{25}{144}}$ (ii) $\sqrt{0.49}$

Solution

(i) $\sqrt{\dfrac{25}{144}} = \dfrac{\sqrt{25}}{\sqrt{144}} = \dfrac{5}{12}$ (ii) $\sqrt{0.49} = \sqrt{\dfrac{49}{100}} = \dfrac{\sqrt{49}}{\sqrt{100}} = \dfrac{7}{10} = 0.7$

Combined Order of Operations

The Order of Operations (BEDMAS) learned in Chapter 1, Section 1.4, is also used in evaluating expressions with fractions and decimal numbers.

Follow these steps to evaluate expressions with fractions and decimal numbers:

Step 1: Evaluate the expressions within the grouping symbols (Brackets and radical signs; i.e., roots).

Step 2: Evaluate powers (i.e., Exponents).

Step 3: Perform Division and Multiplication in order from left to right.

Step 4: Perform Addition and Subtraction in order from left to right.

Note: For mutliplication, division, powers, and roots of mixed numbers, fractions must first be converted to improper fractions before proceeding with the Order of Operations.

Example 2.5-i | **Evaluating Expressions Using Order of Operations (BEDMAS)**

Evaluate the following expressions:

(i) $\left(1\frac{1}{3}\right)^2 + \sqrt{\frac{5}{16} + \frac{20}{16}}$

(ii) $\left(\frac{2}{3}\right)^2 + \frac{1}{2}\left(4\frac{1}{2}\right)^2 \div \sqrt{0.81}$

(iii) $\left(\frac{4}{5}\right)^2 + \left(\frac{11}{9} + \sqrt{\frac{49}{81}}\right) \times \frac{3}{25}$

(iv) $\sqrt{1.69} + \sqrt{0.09} + \sqrt{\frac{64}{25}}$

Solution

(i) $\left(1\frac{1}{3}\right)^2 + \sqrt{\frac{5}{16} + \frac{20}{16}}$

$= \left(\frac{4}{3}\right)^2 + \sqrt{\frac{25}{16}}$

$= \left(\frac{4}{3}\right)\left(\frac{4}{3}\right) + \frac{\sqrt{25}}{\sqrt{16}}$

$= \frac{16}{9} + \frac{5}{4}$

$= \frac{64 + 45}{36}$

$= \frac{109}{36} = 3\frac{1}{36}$

(ii) $\left(\frac{2}{3}\right)^2 + \frac{1}{2}\left(4\frac{1}{2}\right)^2 \div \sqrt{0.81}$

$= \left(\frac{2}{3}\right)^2 + \frac{1}{2}\left(\frac{9}{2}\right)^2 \div \frac{\sqrt{81}}{\sqrt{100}}$

$= \left(\frac{2}{3}\right)\left(\frac{2}{3}\right) + \frac{1}{2}\left(\frac{9}{2}\right)\left(\frac{9}{2}\right) \div \frac{9}{10}$

$= \frac{4}{9} + \frac{81\cancel{9}}{\cancel{8}4} \times \frac{\cancel{10}5}{\cancel{9}1}$

$= \frac{4}{9} + \frac{45}{4}$

$= \frac{16 + 405}{36}$

$= \frac{421}{36} = 11\frac{25}{36}$

(iii) $\left(\frac{4}{5}\right)^2 + \left(\frac{11}{9} + \sqrt{\frac{49}{81}}\right) \times \frac{3}{25}$

$= \left(\frac{4}{5}\right)^2 + \left(\frac{11}{9} + \frac{\sqrt{49}}{\sqrt{81}}\right) \times \frac{3}{25}$

$= \left(\frac{4}{5}\right)^2 + \left(\frac{11}{9} + \frac{7}{9}\right) \times \frac{3}{25}$

$= \left(\frac{4}{5}\right)^2 + \frac{18}{9} \times \frac{3}{25}$

$= \left(\frac{4}{5}\right)\left(\frac{4}{5}\right) + \frac{2}{1} \times \frac{3}{25}$

$= \frac{16}{25} + \frac{6}{25}$

$= \frac{22}{25}$

(iv) $\sqrt{1.69} + \sqrt{0.09} + \sqrt{\frac{64}{25}}$

$= \sqrt{\frac{169}{100}} + \sqrt{\frac{9}{100}} + \sqrt{\frac{64}{25}}$

$= \frac{\sqrt{169}}{\sqrt{100}} + \frac{\sqrt{9}}{\sqrt{100}} + \frac{\sqrt{64}}{\sqrt{25}}$

$= \frac{13}{10} + \frac{3}{10} + \frac{8}{5}$

$= \frac{13 + 3 + 16}{10}$

$= \frac{32}{10}$

$= \frac{16}{5} = 3\frac{1}{5}$

Example 2.5-j Evaluating Expressions Using Order of Operations (BEDMAS)

Evaluate: $\dfrac{4}{2^3}[(0.5 \times 5^2 + 2.5)^2 \div 3^2] + \sqrt{25}$

Solution

$$\dfrac{4}{2^3}[(0.5 \times 5^2 + 2.5)^2 \div 3^2] + \sqrt{25}$$

$$= \dfrac{4}{2^3}[(0.5 \times 25 + 2.5)^2 \div 3^2] + 5$$

$$= \dfrac{4}{2^3}[(12.5 + 2.5)^2 \div 3^2] + 5$$

$$= \dfrac{4}{2^3}[15^2 \div 3^2] + 5$$

$$= \dfrac{4}{2^3}[225 \div 9] + 5$$

$$= \dfrac{4}{2^3} \times 25 + 5$$

$$= \dfrac{4}{8} \times 25 + 5$$

$$= 0.5 \times 25 + 5$$

$$= 12.5 + 5$$

$$= 17.5$$

2.5 | Exercises

Answers to odd-numbered problems are available at the end of the textbook.

For Problems 1 to 8, convert the decimal numbers to proper fractions in lowest terms and the proper fractions to decimal numbers.

1.

	Decimal Number	Proper Fraction
a.	0.2	?
b.	?	$\dfrac{3}{4}$
c.	0.06	?

2.

	Decimal Number	Proper Fraction
a.	0.26	?
b.	?	$\dfrac{41}{50}$
c.	0.92	?

3.

	Decimal Number	Proper Fraction
a.	?	$\dfrac{9}{25}$
b.	0.004	?
c.	?	$\dfrac{7}{50}$

4.

	Decimal Number	Proper Fraction
a.	?	$\dfrac{16}{25}$
b.	0.225	?
c.	?	$\dfrac{19}{20}$

5.

	Decimal Number	Proper Fraction
a.	?	$\dfrac{1}{2}$
b.	0.4	?
c.	?	$\dfrac{3}{50}$

6.

	Decimal Number	Proper Fraction
a.	?	$\dfrac{13}{20}$
b.	0.425	?
c.	?	$\dfrac{14}{25}$

7.

	Decimal Number	Proper Fraction
a.	0.005	?
b.	?	$\dfrac{9}{25}$
c.	0.01	?

8.

	Decimal Number	Proper Fraction
a.	0.66	?
b.	?	$\dfrac{43}{50}$
c.	0.78	?

For Problems 9 to 12, convert the decimal numbers to improper fractions in lowest terms and the improper fractions to decimal numbers.

9.

	Decimal Number	Improper Fraction
a.	3.5	?
b.	?	$\dfrac{8}{5}$
c.	5.6	?

10.

	Decimal Number	Improper Fraction
a.	7.2	?
b.	?	$\dfrac{37}{5}$
c.	8.4	?

11.

	Decimal Number	Improper Fraction
a.	?	$\dfrac{101}{20}$
b.	6.8	?
c.	?	$\dfrac{11}{4}$

12.

	Decimal Number	Improper Fraction
a.	?	$\dfrac{107}{50}$
b.	4.8	?
c.	?	$\dfrac{22}{4}$

For Problem 13 to 16, convert the decimal numbers to mixed numbers in lowest terms and the mixed numbers to decimal numbers.

13.

	Decimal Number	Mixed Number
a.	2.25	?
b.	?	$1\dfrac{3}{4}$
c.	4.02	?

14.

	Decimal Number	Mixed Number
a.	5.04	?
b.	?	$12\dfrac{3}{5}$
c.	14.025	?

15.

	Decimal Number	Mixed Number
a.	?	$8\frac{7}{20}$
b.	16.005	?
c.	?	$15\frac{1}{2}$

16.

	Decimal Number	Mixed Number
a.	?	$3\frac{5}{8}$
b.	4.75	?
c.	?	$5\frac{9}{20}$

For Problems 17 to 20, convert the repeating decimal numbers to proper fractions and the proper fractions to repeating decimal numbers.

17.

	Decimal Number	Proper Fraction
a.	$0.\overline{6}$	?
b.	?	$\frac{23}{90}$
c.	$0.\overline{25}$	?

18.

	Decimal Number	Proper Fraction
a.	$0.\overline{27}$	?
b.	?	$\frac{4}{7}$
c.	$0.8\overline{3}$	?

19.

	Decimal Number	Proper Fraction
a.	?	$\frac{4}{9}$
b.	$0.\overline{2}$	?
c.	?	$\frac{2}{7}$

20.

	Decimal Number	Proper Fraction
a.	?	$\frac{4}{99}$
b.	$0.\overline{75}$	?
c.	?	$\frac{11}{15}$

For Problems 21 to 30, evaluate the powers of the fractions.

21. a. $\left(\frac{3}{5}\right)^2$ b. $\left(\frac{6}{7}\right)^2$ 22. a. $\left(\frac{3}{4}\right)^2$ b. $\left(\frac{2}{9}\right)^2$

23. a. $\left(\frac{3}{4}\right)^3$ b. $\left(\frac{5}{3}\right)^4$ 24. a. $\left(\frac{2}{7}\right)^3$ b. $\left(\frac{6}{5}\right)^4$

25. a. $\left(1\frac{1}{3}\right)^2$ b. $\left(3\frac{1}{2}\right)^3$ 26. a. $\left(2\frac{1}{4}\right)^2$ b. $\left(1\frac{2}{3}\right)^3$

27. a. $\left(\frac{3}{5}\right)^2\left(\frac{2}{3}\right)^3$ b. $\left(\frac{3}{4}\right)^3\left(\frac{1}{6}\right)^2$ 28. a. $\left(\frac{5}{2}\right)^3\left(\frac{4}{3}\right)^2$ b. $\left(\frac{3}{8}\right)^2\left(\frac{4}{3}\right)^3$

29. a. $\left(\frac{1}{4}\right)^2 \div \left(\frac{1}{8}\right)^2$ b. $\left(\frac{5}{3}\right)^2 \div \left(\frac{10}{9}\right)^2$ 30. a. $\left(\frac{1}{6}\right)^2 \div \left(\frac{1}{3}\right)^2$ b. $\left(\frac{2}{3}\right)^2 \div \left(\frac{4}{9}\right)^2$

For Problems 31 to 40, evaluate the roots of the fractions.

31. a. $\sqrt{\frac{1}{9}}$ b. $\sqrt{\frac{1}{49}}$ 32. a. $\sqrt{\frac{1}{16}}$ b. $\sqrt{\frac{1}{36}}$

33. a. $\sqrt{\frac{4}{25}}$ b. $\sqrt{\frac{81}{16}}$ 34. a. $\sqrt{\frac{36}{100}}$ b. $\sqrt{\frac{9}{49}}$

35. a. $\sqrt{\frac{100}{121}}$ b. $\sqrt{\frac{1}{100}}$ 36. a. $\sqrt{\frac{144}{81}}$ b. $\sqrt{\frac{1}{10,000}}$

37. a. $\sqrt{\dfrac{5}{9} + \dfrac{4}{9}}$ b. $\sqrt{\dfrac{2}{25} + \dfrac{14}{25}}$ 38. a. $\sqrt{\dfrac{15}{36} + \dfrac{10}{36}}$ b. $\sqrt{\dfrac{1}{16} + \dfrac{8}{16}}$

39. a. $\sqrt{5\dfrac{1}{16}}$ b. $\sqrt{6\dfrac{1}{4}}$ 40. a. $\sqrt{1\dfrac{11}{25}}$ b. $\sqrt{2\dfrac{23}{49}}$

For Problems 41 to 44, evaluate the powers of the decimal numbers.

41. a. $(0.1)^3$ b. $(1.1)^3$ 42. a. $(0.3)^2$ b. $(1.2)^3$

43. a. $(0.4)^2$ b. $(0.02)^3$ 44. a. $(0.9)^2$ b. $(0.05)^3$

For Problems 45 to 50, evaluate the roots of the decimal numbers.

45. a. $\sqrt{0.25}$ b. $\sqrt{0.49}$ 46. a. $\sqrt{0.36}$ b. $\sqrt{0.64}$

47. a. $\sqrt{1.21}$ b. $\sqrt{1.69}$ 48. a. $\sqrt{2.56}$ b. $\sqrt{1.44}$

49. a. $\sqrt{0.01}$ b. $\sqrt{0.0049}$ 50. a. $\sqrt{0.09}$ b. $\sqrt{0.0016}$

For Problems 51 to 64, evaluate the expressions.

51. a. $\left(\dfrac{3}{5}\right)^2 + \left(1\dfrac{1}{5}\right)\left(\sqrt{144}\right)$ b. $\left(\dfrac{2}{5}\right)^2 + \left(\dfrac{3}{10}\right)^2$ 52. a. $\left(\dfrac{2}{3}\right)^2 + \sqrt{\dfrac{3}{9} + \dfrac{1}{9}}$ b. $\left(\dfrac{3}{8}\right)^2 + \left(\dfrac{1}{2}\right)^3$

53. a. $\sqrt{4\dfrac{21}{25}} + \left(\dfrac{5}{3}\right)^2$ b. $\left(\dfrac{1}{4}\right)^2 \div \left(\dfrac{1}{8}\right)^2$ 54. a. $\sqrt{1\dfrac{9}{16}} \times \left(\dfrac{4}{5}\right)^2$ b. $\left(\dfrac{1}{3}\right)^2 + \left(\dfrac{1}{6}\right)^2$

55. a. $(1.3)^2 \times \sqrt{0.04}$ b. $(0.1)^3 \div \sqrt{\dfrac{1}{100}}$ 56. a. $(1.5)^2 \times \sqrt{0.09}$ b. $(0.5)^3 + \sqrt{\dfrac{1}{25}}$

57. $\left(\dfrac{5}{8}\right)^2 + \dfrac{3}{16} + \dfrac{5}{12} + 1\dfrac{2}{3}$ 58. $\left(\dfrac{7}{6}\right)^2 + 1\dfrac{5}{9} + \dfrac{5}{6} + 4\dfrac{1}{2}$

59. $\sqrt{\dfrac{7}{9} - \dfrac{2}{3}} \div \left(\dfrac{1}{12} + \dfrac{1}{9}\right)$ 60. $\left(\dfrac{5}{12} + \dfrac{3}{8}\right) \div \sqrt{\dfrac{2}{9} + \dfrac{1}{36}}$

61. $[0.8 - (7.2 - 6.5)] \div [3 \div (3.4 - 0.4)]$ 62. $(9.9 \div 1.1) \div (8.1 \div 1.5) + (9.2 - 7.7 + 1.5)$

63. $(9.2 + 2.8)\,0.25 \div (5.6 - 2.3 + 1.7)$ 64. $(9.1 - 7.3)\,0.5 \div (5.8 + 8.6 - 5.4)$

2 | Review Exercises

Answers to odd-numbered problems are available at the end of the textbook.

For Problems 1 and 2, find the missing values.

1. a. $\dfrac{6}{12} = \dfrac{?}{6} = \dfrac{24}{?}$ b. $\dfrac{12}{45} = \dfrac{?}{15} = \dfrac{16}{?}$

   c. $\dfrac{20}{25} = \dfrac{?}{5} = \dfrac{12}{?}$ d. $\dfrac{36}{48} = \dfrac{?}{36} = \dfrac{18}{?}$

2. a. $\dfrac{9}{15} = \dfrac{?}{45} = \dfrac{15}{?}$ b. $\dfrac{18}{27} = \dfrac{?}{18} = \dfrac{10}{?}$

   c. $\dfrac{21}{35} = \dfrac{?}{25} = \dfrac{12}{?}$ d. $\dfrac{12}{28} = \dfrac{?}{70} = \dfrac{15}{?}$

For Problems 3 and 4, place the appropriate symbol ($<$, $>$, $=$) between each of the fractions.

3. a. $\dfrac{24}{21} \,\square\, \dfrac{6}{5}$ b. $\dfrac{20}{48} \,\square\, \dfrac{6}{15}$

   c. $\dfrac{40}{48} \,\square\, \dfrac{35}{42}$ d. $\dfrac{15}{25} \,\square\, \dfrac{63}{105}$

4. a. $\dfrac{15}{18} \,\square\, \dfrac{30}{42}$ b. $\dfrac{21}{24} \,\square\, \dfrac{35}{40}$

   c. $\dfrac{18}{45} \,\square\, \dfrac{16}{36}$ d. $\dfrac{8}{38} \,\square\, \dfrac{12}{57}$

For Problems 5 and 6, change the improper fractions to mixed numbers in simplest form.

5. a. $\dfrac{16}{10}$ b. $\dfrac{39}{26}$

    c. $\dfrac{88}{12}$ d. $\dfrac{102}{9}$

6. a. $\dfrac{18}{8}$ b. $\dfrac{98}{12}$

    c. $\dfrac{88}{10}$ d. $\dfrac{48}{15}$

For Problems 7 and 8, reduce the fractions to their lowest terms.

7. a. $\dfrac{75}{345}$ b. $\dfrac{124}{48}$

    c. $\dfrac{70}{15}$ d. $\dfrac{292}{365}$

8. a. $\dfrac{36}{144}$ b. $\dfrac{68}{10}$

    c. $\dfrac{80}{12}$ d. $\dfrac{305}{366}$

For Problems 9 to 12, express the decimal numbers in their word form.

9. a. 0.5   b. 0.007
    c. 0.12   d. 0.029

10. a. 0.75   b. 0.3
    c. 0.008   d. 0.04

11. a. 32.04   b. 200.2
    c. 45,005.001   d. 1,005,071.25

12. a. 27.602   b. 470.5
    c. 32,010.07   d. 3,500,007.45

For Problems 13 and 14, perform the indicated arithmetic operations.

13. a. 478.82 + 85.847   b. 65.09 − 24.987
    c. 54.37 × 1.46   d. 77.09 ÷ 6

14. a. 716.03 + 49.936   b. 15.71 − 3.509
    c. 15.71 × 3.26   d. 39.83 ÷ 9

For Problems 15 and 16, estimate the answer to the following problems by rounding each number to its first non-zero place value and compare with the exact answer.

15. a. 322.3 + 178.2   b. 0.77 − 0.39
    c. 3.7 × 9.1   d. 59.55 ÷ 18.2

16. a. 172 + 78.3   b. 7.99 − 4.62
    c. 4.2 × 2.3   d. 62.1 ÷ 10.9

17. What is the difference between the smallest and the largest numbers of the following?

    0.012, 0.201, 0.02, 0.102

18. What is the sum of the smallest and the largest numbers of the following?

    0.041, 0.011, 0.14, 0.1

19. Which of the following is closest to 2?

    2.011, 2.05, 1.996, 1.995

20. Which of the following is closest to 1?

    0.011, 0.4, 1.997, 1.996

For Problems 21 and 22, convert the decimal numbers to proper fractions in lowest terms and the fractions to decimal numbers.

21.

	Decimal Number	Proper Fraction
a.	0.025	?
b.	?	$\dfrac{5}{8}$
c.	0.08	?
d.	?	$\dfrac{7}{25}$
e.	0.002	?
f.	?	$\dfrac{39}{50}$

22.

	Decimal Number	Proper Fraction
a.	0.06	?
b.	?	$\dfrac{23}{50}$
c.	0.075	?
d.	?	$\dfrac{27}{40}$
e.	0.004	?
f.	?	$\dfrac{17}{25}$

23. Find the total weight of three newborns that weigh $3\dfrac{2}{3}$ kg, $4\dfrac{1}{2}$ kg, and $3\dfrac{3}{8}$ kg.

24. A patient lost $2\dfrac{1}{5}$ pounds in the first week, $1\dfrac{1}{4}$ pounds in the second week, and $3\dfrac{1}{3}$ pounds in the third week. How many pounds did the patient lose in total over the three weeks?

25. A hospital is sponsoring a 10-mile run to raise money for the pediatric wing. The first checkpoint is $2\frac{5}{12}$ miles from the starting point. The second checkpoint is $8\frac{1}{4}$ miles from the starting point. How many miles are between the first and second checkpoints?

26. A hospital chef purchased a turkey that weighed $12\frac{1}{10}$ pounds. After removing $4\frac{4}{5}$ pounds of the fat and bone, what was the weight of the trimmed turkey?

27. A car can travel $8\frac{3}{4}$ km with one litre of gas. How many kilometres can it travel using $45\frac{3}{5}$ litres of gas?

28. Samantha can walk $5\frac{5}{8}$ km in one hour. How far can she walk in $5\frac{1}{3}$ hours?

29. A radiologist purchased a portable digital radiography x-ray machine and portable x-ray cassettes for a combined total of $58,000. Two-fifths of the portable x-ray cassettes cost is $14,400. How much did the portable digital radiography x-ray machine cost?

30. The value of a small medical office building and the land on which it was built is $1,280,000. One-third of the land value is $250,000. How much did the medical office building cost?

31. Lakshmi had $2,675.68 in her chequing account. She deposited two cheques in the amounts of $729.27 and $72.05 and withdrew $1,275.60 for college tuition. How much did she have in her account after the transactions?

32. An ambulance had 12.47 litres of gas at the start of its trip. The ambulance driver added the following quantities of gas during the trip: 34.25 litres, 15.2 litres, and 20.05 litres. At the end of the trip, there were 7.9 litres of gas left in the ambulance. How much gas was used during the trip?

33. Barbie's hourly pay as a lab technician is $23.07. If Barbie worked 37.75 hours last week, calculate her gross pay for last week.

34. Carol's overtime rate of pay as a registered nurse is $57.45 per hour. If Carol worked 12.5 hours overtime last week, calculate her gross overtime pay for last week.

35. Three-fourths of the number of men at a retirement home is equal to half of the number of women. The retirement home has 480 residents in total. How many more women are there than men?

36. There are 34 surgical residents at a certain hospital. Three-fifths of the number of men equals six-sevenths of the number of women. How many residents are women?

For Problems 37 to 48, evaluate the expressions.

37. $5 + \left(\dfrac{3}{4}\right)^3 + \sqrt{6^2 + 8^2}$

38. $\left(\dfrac{5}{7}\right)^2 + 5 + \sqrt{3^2 + 4^2}$

39. $\sqrt{1.21} - (0.5)^2 + \sqrt{\dfrac{4}{25}}$

40. $\sqrt{0.81} - (0.2)^2 + \sqrt{\dfrac{9}{36}}$

41. $\left(\dfrac{1}{5}\right)^3 + \left(\dfrac{4}{25}\right)^2$

42. $\left(\dfrac{2}{3}\right)^3 + \left(\dfrac{2}{9}\right)^2$

43. $\left(\dfrac{5}{12}\right)^3 + \left(\dfrac{4}{5}\right)^2$

44. $\left(\dfrac{4}{9}\right)^2 + \left(\dfrac{3}{4}\right)^3$

45. $\left(2\dfrac{4}{5} - \dfrac{7}{10}\right) + 2\dfrac{4}{5}$

46. $\left(2\dfrac{3}{8} + 1\dfrac{5}{12}\right) \div 3\dfrac{1}{2}$

47. $3\dfrac{1}{5} + 2\left(\dfrac{3}{5} + \dfrac{1}{2}\right)$

48. $2\dfrac{2}{5} + 3\left(\dfrac{2}{5} + 1\dfrac{1}{10}\right)$

2 | Self-Test Exercises

Answers to all problems are available at the end of the textbook.

1. Find the missing values:

   a. $\dfrac{8}{5} = \dfrac{?}{20} = \dfrac{24}{?}$ b. $\dfrac{12}{22} = \dfrac{6}{?} = \dfrac{?}{55}$

   c. $\dfrac{48}{72} = \dfrac{12}{?} = \dfrac{?}{144}$ d. $\dfrac{11}{12} = \dfrac{?}{72} = \dfrac{22}{?}$

2. Reduce the following fractions to their lowest terms:

   a. $\dfrac{225}{30}$ b. $\dfrac{156}{18}$

   c. $\dfrac{256}{144}$ d. $\dfrac{135}{825}$

3. Perform the indicated operations:

   a. $7\frac{1}{2} + 6\frac{1}{4}$ b. $5\frac{1}{3} - 3\frac{7}{15}$

   c. $\frac{3}{4} \times \frac{26}{27} \times \frac{9}{13}$ d. $2\frac{1}{4} + \frac{3}{8}$

4. Perform the indicated operations:

   a. $0.165 + 10.8478 + 14.7 + 2.19$
   b. $34.09 - 25.957$
   c. 0.524×4.08
   d. $6.893 \div 3$

5. Express the following numbers in word from:

   a. 0.004   b. 6.05

   c. 300.02   d. 7.071

6. Convert the decimal numbers to fractions in lowest terms:

	Decimal Number	Fraction
a.	0.625	?
b.	3.2	?
c.	3.4	?
d.	$0.\overline{72}$	?
e.	$2.\overline{3}$	?
f.	$1.7\overline{3}$	?

7. Convert the fractions to decimal numbers:

	Fraction	Decimal Number
a.	$\frac{7}{20}$	?
b.	$\frac{11}{5}$	?
c.	$1\frac{4}{5}$	?
d.	$\frac{8}{9}$	?
e.	$\frac{16}{15}$	?
f.	$2\frac{1}{3}$	?

8. On a certain map, 1 cm represents 125 km. How many km are represented by 4.75 cm? How many cm on the map will represent a distance of 4,725 km?

9. Henry took 3 days to make 69 medical supply deliveries. On the first day, he completed one-third of the deliveries. On the second day, he made 10 more deliveries than on the first day. How many deliveries did he make on the third day?

10. Kyle had $4,000 and gave half of it to Bob. Bob spent a quarter of the money he received from Kyle. How much money does Bob have left?

11. Niveda spent one-third of her money on stationary supplies and half of the remainder on college textbooks. What fraction of her money did she spend on textbooks? If she has $40 left, how much did she spend in total?

12. Adrian's annual salary as a clinical research assistant is $52,000. Calculate his hourly rate if he works 37.5 hours per week. (Hint: 1 year = 52 weeks)

13. 1,000 blood collection tubes sell for $279.75. The same items are sold online for $245.99. How much cheaper are the tubes online?

14. The cost per day to rent a ventilator is $25 per day used, in addition to the $900 charged upfront. What would be the cost to rent a ventilator for 5 days?

15. I walked for $\frac{3}{4}$ hour at $5\frac{1}{3}$ km per hour and jogged for $\frac{1}{2}$ hour at 10 km per hour. What was the total distance that I covered?

For Problems 16 to 24, evaluate the expressions.

16. $\sqrt{0.0025} - \left(\frac{2}{5}\right)^2 + \sqrt{\frac{49}{16}}$

17. $\sqrt{\frac{81}{64}} - \left(\frac{5}{4}\right)^3 \div \left(\frac{25}{16}\right)^2 + \sqrt{7^2 + 24^2}$

18. $\sqrt{\frac{1}{9}} + \sqrt{\frac{4}{36}} - \left(\frac{2}{3}\right)^2$

19. $\left(\frac{3}{5}\right)^3 \left(\frac{25}{6}\right)^2 + (\sqrt{0.25})\sqrt{100}$

20. $\sqrt{5^2 + 12^2} - (\sqrt{0.49})\sqrt{\frac{25}{144}}$

21. $\left(4\frac{9}{10} + \frac{7}{15} \times 1\frac{3}{5}\right) + 1\frac{2}{5}$

22. $3\frac{1}{2} + 1\frac{2}{5} + \frac{9}{10} \div 2\frac{2}{5} - \frac{3}{4}$

23. $\left(3\frac{4}{15} + 2\frac{3}{5}\right) \times \left(\frac{1}{6} + \frac{1}{9}\right) - 1\frac{1}{2}$

24. $\left(\frac{1}{2} \times \frac{3}{4} + \frac{4}{5} \times \frac{5}{6}\right) + \left(\frac{1}{2} + 2\frac{7}{12}\right)$

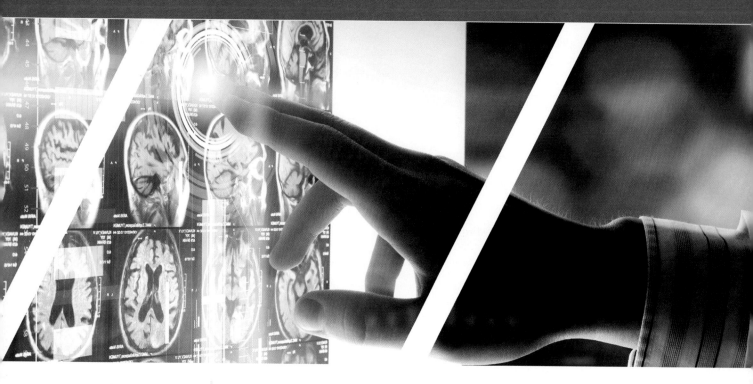

3 OPERATIONS WITH EXPONENTS AND INTEGERS

LEARNING OBJECTIVES

- Identify the types and properties of exponents.
- Perform arithmetic operations with exponents.
- Identify types of roots.
- Perform computations with roots and fractional exponents.
- Perform arithmetic operations with signed numbers.
- Apply rounding rules using significant digits.
- Perform calculations involving scientific notation.

CHAPTER OUTLINE

3.1 Exponents

3.2 Roots and Fractional Exponents

3.3 Arithmetic Operations with Signed Numbers

3.4 Significant Digits and Scientific Notation

Introduction

An exponent is a notation that demonstrates the number of times a number or expression is multiplied by itself. It allows us to represent extremely large and extremely small numbers and perform arithmetic operations more easily than having to use the standard form of a number. An example in which exponents are used is in equations to calculate compound interest on loans and investments.

Roots (or radicals) and exponents are the opposites of each other. For example, if 3 raised to the power of 2 (3^2) equals 9, then the square root of 9 ($\sqrt{9}$) is 3. Fractional exponents simplify calculations involving radicals, such as square roots, cubic roots, etc.

In this chapter, we will learn about the properties and rules associated with exponents, roots, fractional exponents, and signed numbers, as well as perform calculations involving scientific notation and round numbers using significant digits.

3.1 | Exponents

In Section 1.4 (Chapter 1) and Section 2.5 (Chapter 2), you learned about powers and roots of whole numbers, fractions, and decimal numbers.

Recall that when a number is raised to a whole number exponent, we can think of it as a repeated multiplication. Exponentiation (or 'powers') is a shorter way to indicate repeated multiplication, similar to how multiplication is a shorter way to indicate repeated addition. Powers are expressed using exponential notation.

For example, the number 2 multiplied by itself 5 times, $2 \times 2 \times 2 \times 2 \times 2$, is written in exponential notation as 2^5:

Base $\longrightarrow 2^5 \longleftarrow$ Exponent

Power

Recall from Chapter 1 that 2 is known as the base, 5 is known as the exponent, and the whole representation, 2^5, is known as the power.

$$2^5 = 2 \times 2 \times 2 \times 2 \times 2 = 32$$

Exponential Form   Expanded Form   Standard Form

Similarly, the fraction $\left(\dfrac{4}{5}\right)$ multiplied by itself 4 times, $\left(\dfrac{4}{5}\right) \times \left(\dfrac{4}{5}\right) \times \left(\dfrac{4}{5}\right) \times \left(\dfrac{4}{5}\right)$, is written in exponential notation as $\left(\dfrac{4}{5}\right)^4$:

Base $\longrightarrow \left(\dfrac{4}{5}\right)^4 \longleftarrow$ Exponent

Power

The whole representation, $\left(\dfrac{4}{5}\right)^4$, is the power.

$$\left(\frac{4}{5}\right)^4 = \frac{4}{5} \times \frac{4}{5} \times \frac{4}{5} \times \frac{4}{5} = \frac{256}{625}$$

Exponential Form   Expanded Form   Standard Form

Similarily, the decimal number 1.2 multiplied by itself 3 times, $(1.2) \times (1.2) \times (1.2)$, is written in exponential notation as $(1.2)^3$:

base $\longrightarrow (1.2)^3 \longleftarrow$ exponent

Power

The whole representation, $(1.2)^3$, is the power.

$$(1.2)^3 = 1.2 \times 1.2 \times 1.2 = 1.728$$

Exponential Form   Expanded Form   Standard Form

Properties (Rules) of Exponents

The following properties of exponents, known as the **rules** or **laws** of exponents, are used to simplify expressions that involve exponents:

Product of Powers (Product Rule)

When multiplying powers of the same bases, add the exponents.

To multiply powers with the same base, add their exponents.

For example, $7^5 \times 7^3 = (7 \times 7 \times 7 \times 7 \times 7) \times (7 \times 7 \times 7)$

5 Factors of 7   3 Factors of 7

$$= 7 \times 7 \times 7 \times 7 \times 7 \times 7 \times 7 \times 7$$

8 Factors of 7

$$= 7^8, \text{ which is the same as } 7^{(5+3)}$$

You will note that the resulting exponent, 8, is obtained by adding the exponents 5 and 3. That is, the exponents are added when powers with the same base are multiplied.

In general, to multiply a number *'a'* raised to the power *'m'* by *'a'* raised to the power *'n'*, raise the power of the number *'a'* to the sum of the exponents *'m'* and *'n'*,

$$a^m \times a^n = a^{(m+n)}$$

Note: $a^{(m+n)} \neq a^m + a^n$

Example 3.1-a | **Simplifying in Exponential Form Using the Product Rule**

Express the following as a single power:

(i) $\quad 2^3 \times 2^4 \times 2^2$

(ii) $\quad \left(\dfrac{3}{5}\right)^6 \times \left(\dfrac{3}{5}\right)^2$

(iii) $\quad (0.2)^3 \times (0.2)^2$

Solution

(i) $\quad 2^3 \times 2^4 \times 2^2$

$\quad = 2^{(3+4+2)}$

$\quad = 2^9$

(ii) $\quad \left(\dfrac{3}{5}\right)^6 \times \left(\dfrac{3}{5}\right)^2$

$\quad = \left(\dfrac{3}{5}\right)^{(6+2)}$

$\quad = \left(\dfrac{3}{5}\right)^8$

(iii) $\quad (0.2)^3 \times (0.2)^2$

$\quad = (0.2)^{(3+2)}$

$\quad = (0.2)^5$

Quotient of Powers (Quotient Rule)

When dividing powers with the same bases, subtract the exponent of the denominator from that of the numerator.

To divide two powers with the same base, subtract their exponents.

For example, $4^7 \div 4^2 = \dfrac{\overbrace{4 \times 4 \times 4 \times 4 \times 4 \times 4 \times 4}^{7 \text{ Factors of 4}}}{\underbrace{4 \times 4}_{2 \text{ Factors of 4}}}$

$$= \frac{4 \times 4}{4 \times 4} \times 4 \times 4 \times 4 \times 4 \times 4$$

$$= 1 \times \underbrace{4 \times 4 \times 4 \times 4 \times 4}_{5 \text{ Factors of 4}}$$

$$= 4^5, \text{ which is the same as } 4^{(7-2)}$$

You will note that the resulting exponent, 5, is obtained by subtracting the exponent of the denominator from the exponent of the numerator (7 − 2 = 5). That is, the exponents are subtracted when powers with the same base are divided.

In general, to divide a non-zero number *'a'* raised to the power *'m'* by *'a'* raised to the power *'n'*, raise the power of the number *'a'* to the difference of the exponents *'m'* and *'n'*,

$$\frac{a^m}{a^n} = a^{(m-n)}, \text{ where } a \neq 0$$

Note: $a^{(m-n)} \neq a^m - a^n$

| Example 3.1-b | Simplifying in Exponential Form Using the Quotient Rule |

Express the following as a single power:

(i) $3^9 \div 3^5$ (ii) $\left(\dfrac{2}{3}\right)^6 \div \left(\dfrac{2}{3}\right)^4$ (iii) $(1.15)^5 \div (1.15)^2$

Solution

(i) $3^9 \div 3^5$
$= 3^{(9-5)}$
$= 3^4$

(ii) $\left(\dfrac{2}{3}\right)^6 \div \left(\dfrac{2}{3}\right)^4$
$= \left(\dfrac{2}{3}\right)^{(6-4)}$
$= \left(\dfrac{2}{3}\right)^2$

(iii) $(1.15)^5 \div (1.15)^2$
$= (1.15)^{(5-2)}$
$= (1.15)^3$

Power of a Product (Power of a Product Rule)

To raise the product of factors 'a' and 'b' to the power 'n', raise each factor to the nth power.

To find the **Power of a Product**, each factor of the product is raised to the indicated power.

For example, $(3 \times 5)^4 = (3 \times 5)(3 \times 5)(3 \times 5)(3 \times 5)$

$$= \underbrace{3 \times 3 \times 3 \times 3}_{\text{4 Factors of 3}} \times \underbrace{5 \times 5 \times 5 \times 5}_{\text{4 Factors of 5}}$$

$$= 3^4 \times 5^4$$

You will note from the result that each factor of the product is raised to the power of 4.

In general, if any product of factors '**a**' and '**b**' is raised to a power '**n**', it means that each factor of the product is raised to the same power,

$$(a \times b)^n = a^n \times b^n$$

| Example 3.1-c | Simplifying in Exponential Form Using the Power of a Product Rule |

Express the following in expanded form using the Power of a Product Rule:

(i) $(8 \times 6)^3$ (ii) $\left(\dfrac{3}{5} \times \dfrac{2}{7}\right)^4$ (iii) $(1.12 \times 0.6)^2$

Solution

(i) $(8 \times 6)^3$
$= 8^3 \times 6^3$

(ii) $\left(\dfrac{3}{5} \times \dfrac{2}{7}\right)^4$
$= \left(\dfrac{3}{5}\right)^4 \times \left(\dfrac{2}{7}\right)^4$

(iii) $(1.12 \times 0.6)^2$
$= (1.12)^2 \times (0.6)^2$

Power of a Quotient (Power of a Quotient Rule)

To raise a fraction to the power 'n', raise both the numerator and denominator to the nth power.

This is similar to the power of a product rule. To find the **Power of a Quotient**, raise the numerator to the indicated power and divide by the denominator raised to the indicated power.

For example, $\left(\dfrac{5}{8}\right)^3 = \underbrace{\left(\dfrac{5}{8}\right) \times \left(\dfrac{5}{8}\right) \times \left(\dfrac{5}{8}\right)}_{\text{3 Factors of } \left(\frac{5}{8}\right)}$

$$= \frac{5 \times 5 \times 5}{8 \times 8 \times 8} \quad \begin{matrix} \leftarrow \text{3 factors of 5} \\ \leftarrow \text{3 factors of 8} \end{matrix}$$

$$= \frac{5^3}{8^3}$$

You will note from the result that both the numerator and the denominator of the expression are raised to the power of 3.

In general, if any quotient with numerator 'a' and a non-zero denominator 'b' is raised to a power 'n', it means that the numerator 'a' and denominator 'b' are both raised to the same power,

$$\left(\frac{a}{b}\right)^n = \frac{a^n}{b^n}, \text{ where } b \neq 0$$

| Example 3.1-d | Simplifying in Exponential Form Using Power of a Quotient Rule |

Express the following in expanded form using the Power of a Quotient Rule:

(i) $\left(\dfrac{7}{4}\right)^3$ (ii) $\left[\dfrac{\left(\dfrac{2}{3}\right)}{\left(\dfrac{3}{5}\right)}\right]^4$ (iii) $\left(\dfrac{1.05}{0.05}\right)^2$

Solution

(i) $\left(\dfrac{7}{4}\right)^3$

$= \dfrac{7^3}{4^3}$

(ii) $\left[\dfrac{\left(\dfrac{2}{3}\right)}{\left(\dfrac{3}{5}\right)}\right]^4$

$= \left(\dfrac{2}{3} \div \dfrac{3}{5}\right)^4$

$= \left(\dfrac{2}{3}\right)^4 \div \left(\dfrac{3}{5}\right)^4$

$= \dfrac{2^4}{3^4} \div \dfrac{3^4}{5^4}$

$= \dfrac{2^4}{3^4} \times \dfrac{5^4}{3^4}$

$= \dfrac{2^4 \times 5^4}{3^8}$

(iii) $\left(\dfrac{1.05}{0.05}\right)^2$

$= \dfrac{(1.05)^2}{(0.05)^2}$

Power of a Power (Power of a Power Rule)

To raise a power to a power, multiply the exponents.

To find the **Power of a Power** of a number, multiply the two exponents of the powers together to get the new exponent of the power.

For example, $(9^3)^2 = (9^3) \times (9^3)$

$= (9 \times 9 \times 9) \times (9 \times 9 \times 9)$

$= 9 \times 9 \times 9 \times 9 \times 9 \times 9$

$= 9^6$, which is the same as $9^{(3 \times 2)}$

In general, to raise a number 'a' to a power 'm', and then to raise it to a power 'n' [i.e., $(a^m)^n$], raise the power of the number 'a' to the product of the exponents 'm' and 'n',

$$(a^m)^n = a^{mn}$$

Example 3.1-e   Simplifying in Exponential Form Using Power of a Power Rule

Express the following as a single power:

(i) $(5^4)^3$

(ii) $\left[\left(\dfrac{3}{8}\right)^3\right]^2$

(iii) $[(1.04)^4]^2$

Solution

(i) $(5^4)^3$

$= 5^{(4 \times 3)}$

$= 5^{12}$

(ii) $\left[\left(\dfrac{3}{8}\right)^3\right]^2$

$= \left(\dfrac{3}{8}\right)^{(3 \times 2)}$

$= \left(\dfrac{3}{8}\right)^6 = \dfrac{3^6}{8^6}$

(iii) $[(1.04)^4]^2$

$= (1.04)^{(4 \times 2)}$

$= (1.04)^8$

Example 3.1-f   Solving Expressions Using Several Exponent Rules

Solve the following:

(i) $(2^2)^3 \times 2^7 \div 2^9$

(ii) $7^5 \div (7^3)^2 \times 7^2$

Solution

(i) $(2^2)^3 \times 2^7 \div 2^9$

$= 2^6 \times 2^7 \div 2^9$

$= 2^{(6 + 7 - 9)}$

$= 2^4$

$= 16$

(ii) $7^5 \div (7^3)^2 \times 7^2$

$= 7^5 \div 7^6 \times 7^2$

$= 7^{(5 - 6 + 2)}$

$= 7^1$

$= 7$

Example 3.1-g   Expressing Powers to Indicated Bases

Express the following as powers to the indicated base value:

(i) 8^5 as a power of 2

(ii) $\dfrac{9^6}{27^2}$ as a power of 3

Solution

(i) $8 = 2^3$. Therefore,

$8^5 = (2^3)^5 = 2^{15}$

(ii) $9 = 3^2$ and $27 = 3^3$. Therefore,

$\dfrac{9^6}{27^2} = \dfrac{(3^2)^6}{(3^3)^2} = \dfrac{3^{12}}{3^6} = 3^6$

Table 3.1-a summarizes the properties (rules) of exponents.

Table 3.1-a   Properties (Rules) of Exponents

Property (Rule)	Rule in Exponential Form	Example
Product Rule	$a^m \times a^n = a^{(m+n)}$	$3^5 \times 3^4 = 3^{(5+4)} = 3^9$
Quotient Rule	$\dfrac{a^m}{a^n} = a^{(m-n)}$	$\dfrac{3^7}{3^4} = 3^{(7-4)} = 3^3$
Power of a Product Rule	$(a \times b)^n = a^n \times b^n$	$(3 \times 5)^2 = 3^2 \times 5^2$
Power of a Quotient Rule	$\left(\dfrac{a}{b}\right)^n = \dfrac{a^n}{b^n}$	$\left(\dfrac{3}{5}\right)^3 = \dfrac{3^3}{5^3}$
Power of a Power Rule	$(a^m)^n = a^{(m \times n)}$	$(3^2)^3 = 3^{(2 \times 3)} = 3^6$

Properties of Exponents and Bases of One and Zero

Table 3.1-b explains the properties of exponents and bases of one and zero.

Table 3.1-b	Exponents and Bases of One (1) and Zero (0)		
Property (Rule)	**Description**	**Rule in Exponential Form**	**Example**
Base 'a' Exponent 1	Any base 'a' raised to the exponent '1' equals the base itself.	$a^1 = a$	$8^1 = 8$
Base 'a' Exponent 0	Any non-zero base 'a' raised to the exponent '0' equals 1.	$a^0 = 1, (a \neq 0)$	$8^0 = 1$
Base '1' Exponent 'n'	A base of '1' raised to any exponent 'n' equals 1.	$1^n = 1$	$1^5 = 1$
Base '0' Exponent 'n'	A base of '0' raised to any positive exponent 'n' equals 0.	$0^n = 0, (n > 0)$	$0^5 = 0$
Base '0' Exponent '0'	A base of '0' raised to the exponent '0' is indeterminate.	$0^0 = $ indeterminate	

Operations Involving Powers

Recall:

$a^{m+n} \neq a^m + a^n$

$a^{m-n} \neq a^m - a^n$

For **Addition** or **Subtraction of Powers**, there is **no** special rule for exponents, regardless of whether the powers have the same or different bases. Evaluate each power separately and then perform the addition or subtraction.

For example,

Addition of exponential expressions with the same base:

(i) $2^3 + 2^4$ Evaluating 2^3 and 2^4 separately, and then adding,

   $= 8 + 16 = 24$

Addition of exponential expressions with different bases:

(ii) $2^2 + 3^3$ Evaluating 2^3 and 3^3 separately, and then adding,

   $= 4 + 27 = 31$

Subtraction of exponential expressions with the same base:

(iii) $5^3 - 5^2$ Evaluating 5^3 and 5^2 separately, and then subtracting,

   $= 125 - 25 = 100$

Subtraction of exponential expressions with different bases:

(iv) $4^3 - 2^3$ Evaluating 4^3 and 2^3 separately, and then subtracting,

   $= 64 - 8 = 56$

There is also no special rule for the **Product** or **Quotient of Powers** having exponents of different bases. Evaluate each power separately and then perform the multipication or division.

For example,

Product of exponential expressions with different bases:

(i) $2^4 \times 3^2$ Evaluating 2^4 and 3^2 separately, and then multiplying,

$$= 16 \times 9 = 144$$

Quotient of exponential expressions with different bases:

(ii) $\dfrac{3^3}{2^4}$ Evaluating 3^3 and 2^4 separately, and then dividing,

$$= \frac{27}{16} = 1.6875$$

Example 3.1-h   **Adding and Subtracting Powers**

Evaluate the following:

(i) $3^3 + 3^2$ (ii) $5^2 + 3^2$ (iii) $5^4 - 5^2$ (iv) $6^2 - 4^2$

Solution

(i) $3^3 + 3^2$ **Note: $a^m + a^n \neq a^{(m+n)}$**

$\quad = 27 + 9$ $3^3 + 3^2 \neq 3^{(3+2)}$

$\quad = 36$

(ii) $5^2 + 3^2$ **Note: $a^n + b^n \neq (a+b)^n$**

$\quad = 25 + 9$ $5^2 + 3^2 \neq (5+3)^2$

$\quad = 34$

(iii) $5^4 - 5^2$ **Note: $a^m - a^n \neq a^{(m-n)}$**

$\quad = 625 - 25$ $5^4 - 5^2 \neq 5^{(4-2)}$

$\quad = 600$

(iv) $6^2 - 4^2$ **Note: $a^n - b^n \neq (a-b)^n$**

$\quad = 36 - 16$ $6^2 - 4^2 \neq (6-4)^2$

$\quad = 20$

Example 3.1-i   **Multiplying and Dividing Powers that have Exponents with Different Bases**

Evaluate the following:

(i) $5^3 \times 4^2$ (ii) $5^3 \div 3^2$ (iii) $9^2 \times 5^1$ (iv) $4^2 \times 5^0$

Solution

(i) $5^3 \times 4^2$ (ii) $5^3 \div 3^2$ (iii) $9^2 \times 5^1$ (iv) $4^2 \times 5^0$

$\quad = 125 \times 16$ $= 125 \div 9$ $= 81 \times 5$ $= 16 \times 1$

$\quad = 2{,}000$ $= \dfrac{125}{9}$ $= 405$ $= 16$

                           $= 13\dfrac{8}{9} = 13.\overline{8}$

Negative Exponents

In the exponential notation of a number, the base of a non-zero number may be raised to a negative exponent. When the exponent is negative, it is represented by a^{-n}. A power with a negative exponent is the reciprocal of a power with a positive exponent.

Positive Exponent: $a^n = a \times a \times a \times a \times a \times \ldots \times a$ (multiplication of 'n' factors of 'a')

Negative Exponent: $a^{-n} = \dfrac{1}{a^n} = \dfrac{1}{a \times a \times a \times a \times a \times \ldots \times a}$ (division of 'n' factors of 'a')

The rationale for this can be seen in the following exhibit:

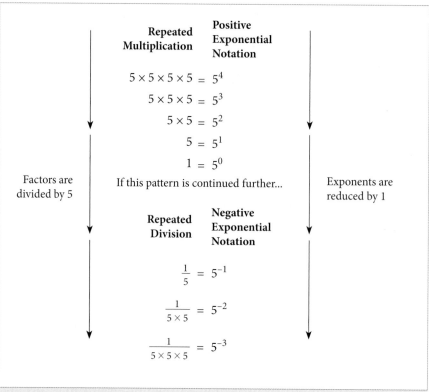

Exhibit 3.1   Repeated Multiplication/Division of a Number and its Exponential Notation

$a^{-n} = \dfrac{1}{a^n}$, or $\dfrac{1}{a^{-n}} = a^n$. Therefore, a^n and a^{-n} are reciprocals.

The properties (rules) of exponents in Section 3.1 of this chapter (summarized in Table 3.1-a) also apply to all negative exponents.

We use these properties to first simplify the negative exponents and then convert the negative exponents to positive exponents.

Example 3.1-j	**Multiplying and Dividing Powers with Negative Exponents**

Simplify the following and express the answer in exponential form with positive exponents:

(i) $2^{-2} \times 2^{-3}$ (ii) $\dfrac{3^{-4}}{3^{-2}}$ (iii) $(3 \times 5)^{-2}$ (iv) $\left(3^{-2}\right)^{3}$

Solution

(i) $2^{-2} \times 2^{-3}$ Using Product Rule,

$= 2^{-2 + (-3)}$

$= 2^{-2 - 3}$

$= 2^{-5}$ Expressing with a positive exponent,

$= \dfrac{1}{2^5}$

Arithmetic with signed numbers is covered in Section 3.3.

(ii) $\dfrac{3^{-4}}{3^{-2}}$ Using Quotient Rule,

$= 3^{-4 - (-2)}$

$= 3^{-4 + 2}$

$= 3^{-2}$ Expressing with a positive exponent,

$= \dfrac{1}{3^2}$

Solution
continued

(iii) $(3 \times 5)^{-2}$ Using Power of a Product Rule,

$= 3^{-2} \times 5^{-2}$ Expressing with positive exponents,

$= \dfrac{1}{3^2} \times \dfrac{1}{5^2}$

(iv) $\left(3^{-2}\right)^3$ Using Power of Power Rule,

$= 3^{-2(3)}$

$= 3^{-6}$ Expressing with a positive exponent,

$= \dfrac{1}{3^6}$

Recall: $a^{-n} \neq -a^n$

Note: Any positive number base with a negative exponent will always result in a positive answer. For example,

Negative Exponential Form	Positive Exponential Form	Repeated Division	Standard Notation
5^{-1}	$\dfrac{1}{5^1}$	$\dfrac{1}{5}$	$\dfrac{1}{5}$
5^{-2}	$\dfrac{1}{5^2}$	$\dfrac{1}{5 \times 5}$	$\dfrac{1}{25}$
5^{-3}	$\dfrac{1}{5^3}$	$\dfrac{1}{5 \times 5 \times 5}$	$\dfrac{1}{125}$

Calculator Method for Solving Expressions with Exponents

The exponent key on different calculators can be identified by symbols such as , y^x, x^y, etc.

In the following examples ' $\boxed{\wedge}$ ' will be used to to represent the exponent key.

Example 3.1-k   **Solving Exponential Expressions Using a Calculator**

Evaluate the following using a calculator:

(i) 5^6 (ii) $\left(\dfrac{3}{2}\right)^3$ (iii) $(1.02)^4$ (iv) 8^{-2}

Solution

(i) 5^6

(ii) $\left(\dfrac{3}{2}\right)^3$

(iii) $(1.02)^4$

Solution
continued

(iv) 8^{-2}

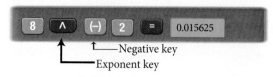

—Negative key

—Exponent key

Note: *The negative key* (−) *is also represented by* +/− *on some calculators.*

3.1 | Exercises

Answers to odd-numbered problems are available at the end of the textbook.

For Problems 1 and 2, identify the values in the empty columns for Expanded Form, Base, Exponent, and Power (Exponential Form).

1.

		Expanded Form	Base	Exponent	Power (Exponential Form)
	a.	$7 \times 7 \times 7 \times 7$	?	?	?
	b.	?	?	?	9^5
	c.	?	3	4	?
	d.	$\dfrac{2}{5} \times \dfrac{2}{5} \times \dfrac{2}{5} \times \dfrac{2}{5} \times \dfrac{2}{5} \times \dfrac{2}{5}$	?	?	?
	e.	?	?	?	$\left(\dfrac{5}{7}\right)^5$
	f.	?	$\left(\dfrac{4}{7}\right)$	3	?
	g.	$(1.15) \times (1.15) \times (1.15) \times (1.15)$	?	?	?
	h.	?	?	?	$(1.6)^3$
	i.	?	(1.25)	5	?

2.

		Expanded Form	Base	Exponent	Power (Exponential Form)
	a.	$2 \times 2 \times 2 \times 2 \times 2 \times 2 \times 2 \times 2$	?	?	?
	b.	?	?	?	6^7
	c.	?	5	3	?
	d.	$\dfrac{2}{7} \times \dfrac{2}{7} \times \dfrac{2}{7} \times \dfrac{2}{7} \times \dfrac{2}{7}$	?	?	?
	e.	?	?	?	$\left(\dfrac{3}{8}\right)^4$
	f.	?	$\left(\dfrac{2}{9}\right)$	4	?
	g.	$(2.5) \times (2.5) \times (2.5) \times (2.5) \times (2.5)$	?	?	?
	h.	?	?	?	$(1.1)^5$
	i.	?	(0.75)	4	?

Express Problems 3 to 26 as a single power and then evaluate using a calculator. Round the answer to two decimal places, wherever applicable.

3. $4^3 \times 4^6$

4. $5^5 \times 5^6$

5. $\left(\dfrac{1}{2}\right)^4 \left(\dfrac{1}{2}\right)^3$

6. $\left(\dfrac{2}{3}\right)^2 \left(\dfrac{2}{3}\right)^3$

7. $\left(\dfrac{5}{2}\right)^2 \left(\dfrac{5}{2}\right)^3$

8. $\left(\dfrac{5}{3}\right)^3 \left(\dfrac{5}{3}\right)^2$

9. $(3.25)^4 (3.25)^2$

10. $(0.75)^3 (0.75)^4$

11. $6^8 \div 6^3$

12. $3^7 \div 3^5$

13. $\left(\dfrac{2}{5}\right)^3 \div \left(\dfrac{2}{5}\right)^1$

14. $\left(\dfrac{3}{2}\right)^4 \div \left(\dfrac{3}{2}\right)^4$

15. $(1.4)^5 \div (1.4)^2$

16. $(3.25)^6 \div (3.25)^5$

17. $[(6)^2]^3$

18. $[(3)^5]^2$

19. $\left[\left(\dfrac{2}{3}\right)^4\right]^3$

20. $\left[\left(\dfrac{3}{4}\right)^4\right]^2$

21. $[(2.5)^2]^3$

22. $[(1.03)^7]^4$

23. $\dfrac{3^9 \times 3^2}{3^5}$

24. $\dfrac{2^9 \times 2^1}{2^5}$

25. $\dfrac{10^6}{10^0}$

26. $\dfrac{8^5}{8^3}$

Express Problems 27 to 34 as a power of the indicated base value.

27. 4^5 as a power of 2

28. 9^6 as a power of 3

29. $9(27)^2$ as a power of 3

30. $8(16)^2$ as a power of 2

31. $\dfrac{(2^5)^4}{8^6}$ as a power of 2

32. $\dfrac{(4^3)^4}{16^3}$ as a power of 4

33. $\dfrac{3^7}{27}$ as a power of 3

34. $\dfrac{5^6}{125}$ as a power of 5

Evaluate Problems 35 to 82.

35. $5^2 + 5^3$

36. $4^3 + 4^2$

37. $5^4 - 2^4$

38. $6^3 - 4^3$

39. $4^4 - 4^2$

40. $6^3 - 6^1$

41. $7^2 + 3^2$

42. $8^3 + 2^3$

43. $3^5 + 5^3$

44. $4^3 + 3^4$

45. $2^5 - 5^2$

46. $2^6 - 6^2$

47. $5^4 - 4^2$

48. $10^3 - 7^2$

49. $4^0 + 4^4$

50. $3^0 + 3^4$

51. $(5 \times 4)^3$

52. $(10 \times 2)^4$

53. $(1.25 \times 4)^4$

54. $(5 \times 0.8)^3$

55. $\left(\dfrac{2}{3} + 6\right)^5$

56. $\left(\dfrac{3}{5} + 4\right)^3$

57. $3^4 + 3^2 + 3^0$

58. $4^2 + 4^4 + 4^0$

59. $2^4 + 3^4 - 1^4$

60. $3^3 + 2^3 - 1^3$

61. $\left(\dfrac{1}{2}\right)^3 + \left(\dfrac{1}{2}\right)^2 + \left(\dfrac{1}{2}\right)^0$

62. $\left(\dfrac{1}{5}\right)^2 + \left(\dfrac{1}{5}\right)^0 + \left(\dfrac{1}{5}\right)^4$

63. $(2.1)^2 + (2.1)^0$

64. $(3.2)^2 + (3.2)^1$

65. $4^3 \times 3^4$

66. $7^2 \times 2^2$

67. $6^4 \div 5^4$

68. $8^2 \div 7^2$

69. $(2 \times 3^2)^4$

70. $(5 \times 2^2)^3$

71. $\dfrac{3^{-1}}{2^{-1}}$

72. $3^{-1} + 2^{-1}$

73. $\dfrac{2^{-2}}{3^{-1}}$

74. $2^{-2} + 3^{-1}$

75. $3^{-1} \times 3^2 \times 3^{-2}$

76. $[2^{-3}]^{-1}$

77. $5^{-2} \times 5^2 \times 5^3$

78. $[5^{-2}]^{-2}$

79. $\dfrac{2^{-4} + 3^0 \times 2^{-1}}{\left(\dfrac{1}{2}\right)^{-1}}$

80. $2^{-2} + \dfrac{1}{2^{-1}}$

81. $\dfrac{3^{-3} \times 2^0 \times 3^{-1}}{\left(\dfrac{1}{3}\right)^{-1}}$

82. $3^{-2} + \dfrac{1}{3^{-1}}$

3.2 | Roots and Fractional Exponents

Roots

In Chapter 1, we were introduced to the idea of square roots, as the inverse operation of raising a number to the exponent of 2.

Recall: $2^2 = 4$, so $\sqrt{4} = 2$

Now, we will examine general roots, also known as **radicals**, which are the inverse operations of powers involving any exponent:

If $2^2 = 4$, then $\sqrt[2]{4} = 2$

If $2^3 = 8$, then $\sqrt[3]{8} = 2$

If $2^4 = 16$, then $\sqrt[4]{16} = 2$

The number in front of the root symbol is called the **index** of the root and represents the exponent that is being 'undone'. In the case of the square root (which is the most common root), the index of 2 is assumed, and we do not need to write it.

For example,

The square root of 4 is denoted $\sqrt{4}$.

The cube (or third) root of 8 is denoted $\sqrt[3]{8}$.

The fourth root of 16 is denoted $\sqrt[4]{16}$.

In general, the nth root of a is denoted $\sqrt[n]{a}$.

Index of the root ⟶ $\sqrt[n]{a}$ — 'a' represents any positive number

Radical sign

Perfect Roots

Roots of a whole number may not be a whole number. If the root of a whole number is another whole number, then the root is called a **perfect root**.

For example,

4 is a perfect square root of 16 because $4^2 = 16$; i.e., $\sqrt{16} = 4$

3 is a perfect cube root of 27 because $3^3 = 27$; i.e., $\sqrt[3]{27} = 3$

| Table 3.2 | Examples of Perfect Roots |

Roots	1	2	3	4	5	6	7	8	9	10
Square Roots	$\sqrt{1}$	$\sqrt{4}$	$\sqrt{9}$	$\sqrt{16}$	$\sqrt{25}$	$\sqrt{36}$	$\sqrt{49}$	$\sqrt{64}$	$\sqrt{81}$	$\sqrt{100}$
Cube Roots	$\sqrt[3]{1}$	$\sqrt[3]{8}$	$\sqrt[3]{27}$	$\sqrt[3]{64}$	$\sqrt[3]{125}$	$\sqrt[3]{216}$	$\sqrt[3]{343}$	$\sqrt[3]{512}$	$\sqrt[3]{729}$	$\sqrt[3]{1,000}$
Fourth Roots	$\sqrt[4]{1}$	$\sqrt[4]{16}$	$\sqrt[4]{81}$	$\sqrt[4]{256}$	$\sqrt[4]{625}$	$\sqrt[4]{1,296}$	$\sqrt[4]{2,401}$	$\sqrt[4]{4,096}$	$\sqrt[4]{6,561}$	$\sqrt[4]{10,000}$

Simplifying Roots Using Perfect Roots

Just like we can simplify a power of a product, we can simplify a **root of a product** as follows:

$$\sqrt[n]{ab} = \sqrt[n]{a} \times \sqrt[n]{b}$$

For example, $\sqrt{10} = \sqrt{2 \times 5} = \sqrt{2} \times \sqrt{5}$.

The Root of a Product Rule and the knowledge of Perfect Roots are used in simplifying square roots, cube roots, etc.

For example,

(i) To simplify $\sqrt{12}$, we could write 12 as 4×3; i.e., as a combination of two factors where one of them, 4, is a perfect square.

i.e., $\sqrt{12} = \sqrt{4 \times 3} = \sqrt{4} \times \sqrt{3} = 2\sqrt{3}$

(ii) To simplify $\sqrt[3]{54}$, we could write 54 as 27×2; i.e., as a combination of two factors where one of them, 27, is a perfect cube.

i.e., $\sqrt[3]{54} = \sqrt[3]{27 \times 2} = \sqrt[3]{27} \times \sqrt[3]{2} = 3\sqrt[3]{2}$

Example 3.2-a	**Finding Perfect Roots**

Simplify using perfect roots of a number:

(i) $\sqrt{72}$ 　　　　　　　　　　　　(ii) $\sqrt[3]{40}$

Solution

(i) $\sqrt{72}$

$= \sqrt{36 \times 2}$ 　　　　$72 = 36 \times 2$

$= \sqrt{36} \times \sqrt{2}$ 　　Root of a Product Rule

$= 6\sqrt{2}$ 　　　　　　36 is a perfect square of 6.

(ii) $\sqrt[3]{40}$

$= \sqrt[3]{8 \times 5}$ 　　　　$40 = 8 \times 5$

$= \sqrt[3]{8} \times \sqrt[3]{5}$ 　　Root of a Product Rule

$= 2\sqrt[3]{5}$ 　　　　　　8 is a perfect cube of 2.

Fractional Exponents

Roots of a number represented by the radical sign and index of the root can be expressed using fractional exponents. The index of the root becomes the denominator of the fractional exponent and the numerator is 1. Fractional exponents are often easier to write than radical notations.

$$\underset{\text{the Root}}{\overset{\text{Index of}}{\longrightarrow}} \quad \sqrt[n]{a} \;=\; a^{\frac{1}{n}} \quad \underset{\text{Exponent}}{\overset{\text{Fractional}}{\longleftarrow}}$$

For example, $\sqrt{5} = 5^{\frac{1}{2}}$, and $\sqrt[3]{8} = 8^{\frac{1}{3}}$

An appropriate radical will "undo" an exponent. We can see this by using the fractional exponent notation and the Power of a Power Rule.

For example,

$$\sqrt{5^2} = (5^2)^{\frac{1}{2}} = 5$$

$$\sqrt[3]{7^3} = (7^3)^{\frac{1}{3}} = 7$$

In general, $\sqrt[n]{a^n} = a$.

Similarly, if we combine a radical with a power, we can rewrite the expression as a single power, using the Power of a Power Rule.

For example,

$$\sqrt[3]{5^2} = (5^2)^{\frac{1}{3}} = 5^{\frac{2}{3}}$$

$$(\sqrt[3]{5})^2 = (5^{\frac{1}{3}})^2 = 5^{\frac{2}{3}}$$

In general, $a^{\frac{m}{n}} = \sqrt[n]{a^m}$ or $(\sqrt[n]{a})^m$.

A number expressed using radical signs and the index of the root can be solved more easily using a calculator by first converting it into a fractional exponent.

For example,

$$\sqrt[5]{25^2}$$ First, convert the radical to a fractional exponent,

$$= (25^2)^{\frac{1}{5}} = 25^{\frac{2}{5}}$$

Then, to evalute $25^{\frac{2}{5}}$ using a calculator, it would be entered as follows:

When entering fractional exponents in a calculator, **brackets** must be used.

Exponent key

Note: *Brackets must be used around the fractional exponent* $\frac{2}{5}$. *Without the brackets, the operation will mean* $(25)^2 \div 5$, *which is incorrect.*

Example 3.2-b | **Evaluating Expressions with Fractional Exponents Using a Calculator**

Evaluate the following expressions. Round your answers to two decimal places, wherever applicable.

(i) $15^{\frac{3}{2}}$ (ii) $\left(\frac{3}{5}\right)^{\frac{1}{4}}$ (iii) $(2.5)^{\frac{3}{7}}$

Solution

(i) $15^{\frac{3}{2}} =$ [15] [∧] [(] [3] [÷] [2] [)] [=]

[58.094750] $= 58.09$

(ii) $\left(\frac{3}{5}\right)^{\frac{1}{4}} =$ [(] [3] [÷] [5] [)] [∧] [(] [1] [÷] [4] [)] [=]

[0.880111] $= 0.88$

(iii) $(2.5)^{\frac{3}{7}} =$ [2.5] [∧] [(] [3] [÷] [7] [)] [=]

[1.480968] $= 1.48$

Example 3.2-c | **Expressions in Radical Form**

Express the following in radical form:

(i) $2^{\frac{5}{6}}$ (ii) $3^{\frac{2}{5}}$ (iii) $\left(\frac{2}{3}\right)^{\frac{3}{4}}$

Solution

(i) $2^{\frac{5}{6}}$ (ii) $3^{\frac{2}{5}}$ (iii) $\left(\frac{2}{3}\right)^{\frac{3}{4}}$

$= \sqrt[6]{2^5}$ $= \sqrt[5]{3^2}$ $= \sqrt[4]{\left(\frac{2}{3}\right)^3}$

Example 3.2-d **Expressions in Exponential Form**

Express the following in exponential form:

(i) $\sqrt[4]{20}$ (ii) $\sqrt[3]{4^5}$ (iii) $\sqrt[5]{\left(\dfrac{1}{2}\right)^2}$

Solution

(i) $\sqrt[4]{20}$ (ii) $\sqrt[3]{4^5}$ (iii) $\sqrt[5]{\left(\dfrac{1}{2}\right)^2}$

$= 20^{\frac{1}{4}}$ $= 4^{\frac{5}{3}}$ $= \left(\dfrac{1}{2}\right)^{\frac{2}{5}}$

Arithmetic Operations with Fractional Exponents

All the rules of exponents (Product Rule, Quotient Rule, Power of a Product Rule, Power of a Quotient Rule, Power of a Power Rule, etc.) learned in Section 3.1 and outlined in Table 3.1-a and Table 3.1-b are applicable to fractional exponents with a positive base (i.e., $a > 0$).

Example 3.2-e **Solving Expressions with Fractional Exponents using the Product Rule**

Simplify the following using the Product Rule to express the answer in exponential form and then evaluate to two decimal places, wherever applicable.

(i) $2^{\frac{1}{2}} \times 2^{\frac{1}{3}}$ (ii) $3^{\frac{3}{4}} \times 3^{\frac{9}{4}} \times 3^0$ (iii) $\left(\dfrac{3}{5}\right)^{\frac{7}{3}} \times \left(\dfrac{3}{5}\right)^{\frac{2}{3}}$

Solution

(i) $2^{\frac{1}{2}} \times 2^{\frac{1}{3}}$ (ii) $3^{\frac{3}{4}} \times 3^{\frac{9}{4}} \times 3^0$ (iii) $\left(\dfrac{3}{5}\right)^{\frac{7}{3}} \times \left(\dfrac{3}{5}\right)^{\frac{2}{3}}$

Recall:
$a^m \times a^n = a^{m+n}$

$= 2^{\left(\frac{1}{2} + \frac{1}{3}\right)}$ $= 3^{\left(\frac{3}{4} + \frac{9}{4} + 0\right)}$ $= \left(\dfrac{3}{5}\right)^{\left(\frac{7}{3} + \frac{2}{3}\right)}$

$= 2^{\left(\frac{3+2}{6}\right)}$ $= 3^{\frac{12}{4}}$ $= \left(\dfrac{3}{5}\right)^{\frac{9}{3}}$

$= 2^{\frac{5}{6}}$ $= 3^3$ $= \left(\dfrac{3}{5}\right)^3$

$= 1.781797... = 1.78$ $= 27$ $= 0.216 = 0.22$

Example 3.2-f **Solving Expressions with Fractional Exponents Using the Quotient Rule**

Simplify the following using the Quotient Rule to express the answer in exponential form and then evaluate to two decimal places, wherever applicable.

(i) $2^{\frac{4}{3}} \div 2^{\frac{2}{3}}$ (ii) $(1.2)^{\frac{5}{2}} \div (1.2)^{\frac{1}{2}}$ (iii) $\left(\dfrac{1}{3}\right)^{\frac{6}{4}} \div \left(\dfrac{1}{3}\right)^{\frac{3}{4}}$

Solution

(i) $2^{\frac{4}{3}} \div 2^{\frac{2}{3}}$ (ii) $(1.2)^{\frac{5}{2}} \div (1.2)^{\frac{1}{2}}$ (iii) $\left(\dfrac{1}{3}\right)^{\frac{6}{4}} \div \left(\dfrac{1}{3}\right)^{\frac{3}{4}}$

Recall:
$a^m \div a^n = a^{m-n}$

$= 2^{\left(\frac{4}{3} - \frac{2}{3}\right)}$ $= 1.2^{\left(\frac{5}{2} - \frac{1}{2}\right)}$ $= \left(\dfrac{1}{3}\right)^{\left(\frac{6}{4} - \frac{3}{4}\right)}$

$= 2^{\frac{2}{3}}$ $= (1.2)^{\frac{4}{2}}$ $= \left(\dfrac{1}{3}\right)^{\left(\frac{3}{4}\right)}$

$= 1.587401... = 1.59$ $= (1.2)^2$ $= 0.438691... = 0.44$

                                              $= 1.44$

Example 3.2-g | Solving Expressions with Fractional Exponents using the Power of a Product Rule

Simplify the following using the Power of a Product Rule to express the answer in exponential form and then evaluate to two decimal places, wherever applicable.

(i) $(4^2 \times 3^2)^{\frac{1}{2}}$

(ii) $\left(7^2 \times \dfrac{1}{3^2}\right)^{\frac{1}{2}}$

(iii) $(2^6 \times 3^2)^{\frac{3}{2}}$

Solution

(i) $(4^2 \times 3^2)^{\frac{1}{2}}$

(ii) $\left(7^2 \times \dfrac{1}{3^2}\right)^{\frac{1}{2}}$

(iii) $(2^6 \times 3^2)^{\frac{3}{2}}$

Recall:
$(a \times b)^n = a^n \times b^n$

(i)
$= (4^2)^{\frac{1}{2}} \times (3^2)^{\frac{1}{2}}$

$= 4 \times 3$

$= 12$

(ii)
$= \dfrac{(7^2)^{\frac{1}{2}}}{(3^2)^{\frac{1}{2}}}$

$= \dfrac{7}{3}$

$= 2.333333... = 2.33$

(iii)
$= (2^6)^{\frac{3}{2}} \times (3^2)^{\frac{3}{2}}$

$= 2^9 \times 3^3$

$= 512 \times 27$

$= 13,824$

Example 3.2-h | Solving Expressions with Fractional Exponents using the Power of a Quotient Rule

Simplify the following using the Power of a Quotient Rule to express the answer in exponential form and then evaluate to two decimal places, wherever applicable.

(i) $\left(\dfrac{4^2}{3^2}\right)^{\frac{1}{2}}$

(ii) $\left(\dfrac{5^3}{2^6}\right)^{\frac{1}{3}}$

Solution

(i) $\left(\dfrac{4^2}{3^2}\right)^{\frac{1}{2}}$

(ii) $\left(\dfrac{5^3}{2^6}\right)^{\frac{1}{3}}$

Recall:
$\left(\dfrac{a}{b}\right)^n = \dfrac{a^n}{b^n}$

(i)
$= \dfrac{(4^2)^{\frac{1}{2}}}{(3^2)^{\frac{1}{2}}}$

$= \dfrac{4}{3}$

$= 1.333333... = 1.33$

(ii)
$= \dfrac{(5^3)^{\frac{1}{3}}}{(2^6)^{\frac{1}{3}}}$

$= \dfrac{5}{2^2}$

$= \dfrac{5}{4} = 1.25$

Example 3.2-i | Solving Expressions with Fractional Exponents Using the Power of a Power Rule

Simplify the following using the Power of a Power Rule to express the answer in exponential form and then evaluate to two decimal places, wherever applicable.

(i) $\left(6^{\frac{1}{2}}\right)^3$

(ii) $\left(18^{\frac{1}{3}}\right)^{\frac{1}{4}}$

(iii) $\left[\left(\dfrac{2}{3}\right)^3\right]^2$

Solution

(i) $\left(6^{\frac{1}{2}}\right)^3$

(ii) $\left(18^{\frac{1}{3}}\right)^{\frac{1}{4}}$

(iii) $\left[\left(\dfrac{2}{3}\right)^3\right]^2$

Recall:
$(a^m)^n = a^{m \times n}$

(i)
$= 6^{\left(\frac{1}{2} \times 3\right)}$

$= 6^{\frac{3}{2}}$

$= 14.696938... = 14.70$

(ii)
$= 18^{\left(\frac{1}{3} \times \frac{1}{4}\right)}$

$= 18^{\frac{1}{12}}$

$= 1.272348... = 1.27$

(iii)
$= \left(\dfrac{2}{3}\right)^{3 \times 2}$

$= \left(\dfrac{2}{3}\right)^6$

$= \dfrac{2^6}{3^6}$

$= \dfrac{64}{729}$

$= 0.087791... = 0.09$

| Example 3.2-j | Solving Expressions with Fractional Exponents and Different Bases |

Solve the following and round to two decimal places, wherever applicable.

(i) $16^{\frac{1}{2}} + 8^{\frac{1}{2}}$

(ii) $25^{\frac{1}{2}} - 27^{\frac{1}{3}}$

(iii) $\left(\frac{7}{8}\right)^{\frac{1}{4}} - \left(\frac{2}{3}\right)^{\frac{1}{3}}$

(iv) $5^{\frac{1}{2}} \times 3^{\frac{1}{2}}$

(v) $2^{\frac{3}{4}} \div 3^{\frac{1}{2}}$

(vi) $5^{(2\frac{2}{5})}$

Solution

(i) $16^{\frac{1}{2}} + 8^{\frac{1}{2}}$

$= 4 + 2.828427...$

$= 6.828427... = 6.83$

(ii) $25^{\frac{1}{2}} - 27^{\frac{1}{3}}$

$= 5 - 3$

$= 2$

(iii) $\left(\frac{7}{8}\right)^{\frac{1}{4}} - \left(\frac{2}{3}\right)^{\frac{1}{3}}$

$= 0.967168... - 0.873580...$

$= 0.093587... = 0.09$

(iv) $5^{\frac{1}{2}} \times 3^{\frac{1}{2}}$

$= 2.236067... \times 1.732050...$

$= 3.872983... = 3.87$

(v) $2^{\frac{3}{4}} \div 3^{\frac{1}{2}}$

$= 1.681792... \div 1.732050...$

$= 0.970983... = 0.97$

(vi) $5^{(2\frac{2}{5})}$

$= 5^{\frac{12}{5}}$

$= 47.591348... = 47.59$

Fractions with Negative Exponents

When a fraction has a negative exponent, change the fraction to its reciprocal and drop the sign of the exponent. After this change, the number in the exponent indicates the number of times the numerator and denominator should be multiplied, as before.

$$\left(\frac{a}{b}\right)^{-n} = \left(\frac{b}{a}\right)^{n}$$

For example,

$$\left(\frac{2}{5}\right)^{-3} = \left(\frac{5}{2}\right)^{3} = \left(\frac{5}{2}\right)\left(\frac{5}{2}\right)\left(\frac{5}{2}\right) = \frac{5 \times 5 \times 5}{2 \times 2 \times 2} = \frac{125}{8}$$

Note: The reciprocal of $\frac{2}{5}$ is $\frac{5}{2}$.

| Example 3.2-k | Evaluating Fractions with Negative Exponents |

Evaluate the following:

(i) $\left(\frac{5}{4}\right)^{-2} \times \left(\frac{2}{3}\right)^{-3}$

(ii) $\left(\frac{3}{5}\right)^{-3} \div \left(\frac{2}{5}\right)^{-2}$

Solution

(i) $\left(\frac{5}{4}\right)^{-2} \times \left(\frac{2}{3}\right)^{-3}$

$= \left(\frac{4}{5}\right)^{2} \times \left(\frac{3}{2}\right)^{3}$

$= \frac{4^2}{5^2} \times \frac{3^3}{2^3}$

(ii) $\left(\frac{3}{5}\right)^{-3} \div \left(\frac{2}{5}\right)^{-2}$

$= \left(\frac{5}{3}\right)^{3} \div \left(\frac{5}{2}\right)^{2}$

$= \frac{5^3}{3^3} \div \frac{5^2}{2^2}$

$$= \frac{2}{25}^{\!\!\!16} \times \frac{27}{8}_{\,1}$$

$$= \frac{2}{25} \times \frac{27}{1}$$

$$= \frac{54}{25}$$

$$= 2\frac{4}{25} = 2.16$$

$$= \frac{5}{27}^{\!\!\!125} \times \frac{4}{25}_{\,1}$$

$$= \frac{5}{27} \times \frac{4}{1}$$

$$= \frac{20}{27}$$

$$= 0.740740\ldots = 0.74$$

3.2 | Exercises

Answers to odd-numbered problems are available at the end of the textbook.

Express Problems 1 to 4 in their radical form and evaluate.

1. a. $64^{\frac{1}{2}}$ b. $\left(\frac{25}{16}\right)^{\frac{1}{2}}$ 2. a. $81^{\frac{1}{2}}$ b. $\left(\frac{36}{25}\right)^{\frac{1}{2}}$

3. a. $8^{\frac{1}{3}}$ b. $\left(\frac{27}{64}\right)^{\frac{1}{3}}$ 4. a. $64^{\frac{1}{3}}$ b. $\left(\frac{125}{8}\right)^{\frac{1}{3}}$

Express Problems 5 to 14 in their fractional exponent form and then evaluate. Round the answers to two decimal places, wherever applicable.

5. a. $\sqrt{144}$ b. $\sqrt[5]{64}$ 6. a. $\sqrt{81}$ b. $\sqrt[3]{125}$

7. a. $\sqrt{2^6}$ b. $\sqrt{40}$ 8. a. $\sqrt{3^4}$ b. $\sqrt{50}$

9. a. $\sqrt{8} \times \sqrt{12}$ b. $\sqrt{7} \times \sqrt{14}$ 10. a. $\sqrt{12} \times \sqrt{10}$ b. $\sqrt{9} \times \sqrt{27}$

11. a. $\sqrt[4]{25^2} \times \sqrt[4]{25^2}$ b. $\sqrt[4]{5^2 \times 25^3}$ 12. a. $\sqrt{3^4 \times 2^4}$ b. $\sqrt[6]{9^3 \times 27^4}$

13. a. $\sqrt{\frac{25}{81}}$ b. $\sqrt{\frac{48}{3}}$ 14. a. $\sqrt{\frac{49}{64}}$ b. $\sqrt{\frac{24}{6}}$

Simplify Problems 15 to 24 by expressing the powers using a single exponent (using the properties of exponents) and then evaluate. Round the answers to two decimal places, wherever applicable.

15. a. $5^{\frac{1}{2}} \times 5^{\frac{3}{4}}$ b. $3^{\frac{7}{8}} \times 3^{\frac{5}{9}}$ 16. a. $3^{\frac{1}{2}} \times 3^{\frac{1}{4}}$ b. $11^{\frac{3}{4}} \times 11^{\frac{2}{3}}$

17. a. $8^{\frac{4}{5}} \times 8^{\frac{2}{5}} \times 8^{\frac{1}{5}}$ b. $5^{\frac{1}{3}} \times 5^{\frac{1}{2}} \times 5^0$ 18. a. $5^{\frac{4}{7}} \times 5^{\frac{4}{7}} \times 5^{\frac{6}{7}}$ b. $9^{\frac{5}{8}} \times 9^{\frac{2}{3}} \times 9^0$

19. a. $8^{\frac{1}{3}} \times 8^{\frac{2}{3}} \times 8^1$ b. $\frac{3^{\frac{8}{3}}}{3^2}$ 20. a. $2^{\frac{2}{3}} \times 2^{\frac{1}{2}} \times 2^1$ b. $\frac{6^{\frac{7}{2}}}{6^2}$

21. a. $\frac{4^{\frac{5}{7}}}{4^{\frac{2}{7}}}$ b. $(3^2)^{\frac{1}{3}}$ 22. a. $\frac{2^{\frac{4}{5}}}{2^{\frac{3}{5}}}$ b. $(10^3)^{\frac{1}{4}}$

23. a. $\left(12^{\frac{1}{2}}\right)^4$ b. $\left(7^{\frac{1}{4}}\right)^8$ 24. a. $\left(5^{\frac{2}{3}}\right)^6$ b. $\left(4^{\frac{3}{4}}\right)^{12}$

Evaluate Problems 25 to 32 and express the answers rounded to two decimal places, wherever applicable.

25. a. $5^{\frac{1}{2}} + 7^{\frac{1}{2}}$ b. $16^{\frac{1}{2}} + 9^{\frac{1}{2}}$ 26. a. $125^{\frac{1}{3}} + 64^{\frac{1}{3}}$ b. $50^{\frac{1}{2}} - 40^{\frac{1}{2}}$

27. a. $5 \times 3^{\frac{1}{2}} + 2^{\frac{1}{2}}$ b. $(2^5)^{\frac{1}{2}} + (5^2)^{\frac{1}{5}}$ 28. a. $12 \times 10^{\frac{1}{2}} + 5^{\frac{1}{2}}$ b. $(3^4)^{\frac{1}{3}} + (4^3)^{\frac{1}{4}}$

29. a. $8^{\frac{1}{2}} \times 9^{\frac{1}{2}}$ b. $45^{\frac{1}{2}} \times 60^{\frac{1}{2}}$ 30. a. $36^{\frac{1}{2}} \times 48^{\frac{1}{2}}$ b. $24^{\frac{1}{2}} \times 75^{\frac{1}{2}}$

31. a. $\frac{5 + 4^{\frac{1}{2}}}{36^{\frac{1}{2}}}$ b. $\frac{10^{\frac{1}{2}} - 5^{\frac{1}{2}}}{25^{\frac{1}{2}}}$ 32. a. $\frac{8 + 49^{\frac{1}{2}}}{9^{\frac{1}{2}}}$ b. $\frac{7 - 7^{\frac{1}{2}}}{4^{\frac{1}{2}}}$

Simplify Problems 33 to 42 by expressing the powers using a single exponent (using the properties of exponents), and as a radical (where applicable), and then evaluate. Round the answers to two decimal places, wherever applicable.

33. a. $6^{\frac{5}{4}} \times 6^{\frac{3}{4}}$ b. $7^{\frac{4}{3}} \times 7^{\frac{2}{3}}$ 34. a. $5^{\frac{4}{9}} \times 5^{-\frac{2}{9}}$ b. $3^{-\frac{6}{7}} \times 3^{\frac{2}{7}}$

35. a. $\dfrac{10^{-\frac{3}{5}} \times 10^{\frac{4}{5}}}{10^{\frac{2}{5}}}$ b. $\dfrac{2^{\frac{5}{7}} \times 2^{-\frac{6}{7}}}{2^{\frac{8}{7}}}$ 36. a. $\dfrac{5^{\frac{2}{7}} \times 5^{\frac{4}{7}}}{5^{-\frac{6}{7}}}$ b. $\dfrac{3^{\frac{2}{3}} \times 3^{-\frac{4}{3}}}{3^{\frac{5}{3}}}$

37. a. $\dfrac{6^{-\frac{5}{9}} \times 6^{0}}{6^{-\frac{7}{9}}}$ b. $\dfrac{7^{\frac{7}{8}} \times 7^{\frac{8}{3}}}{7^{2}}$ 38. a. $\dfrac{9^{\frac{2}{5}} \times 9^{0}}{9^{-\frac{3}{5}}}$ b. $\dfrac{5^{\frac{5}{6}} \times 5^{\frac{2}{3}}}{5^{2}}$

39. a. $(5^{-2})^{\frac{4}{3}}$ b. $(6^{\frac{1}{2}})^{-6}$ 40. a. $(4^{-2})^{\frac{5}{2}}$ b. $(2^{-\frac{4}{5}})^{-5}$

41. a. $(8^{-\frac{2}{3}})^{-6}$ b. $(7^{-\frac{1}{3}})^{9}$ 42. a. $(6^{-\frac{2}{3}})^{-3}$ b. $(3^{-\frac{4}{9}})^{0}$

3.3 | Arithmetic Operations with Signed Numbers

In the previous chapters, you learned that positive real numbers can be represented by points on a number line from zero to the right of the zero. That is, whole numbers (which include positive integers and zero), positive rational numbers, and positive irrational numbers can be represented on a number line from zero to the right of the zero.

Every positive number has a negative number known as its additive opposite, which adds together with it to make a sum of zero (0). Negative numbers lie to the left of the zero on the number line. We use the negative sign, '−', to represent negative numbers, and the positive sign, '+', to represent positive numbers. We call these **signed numbers**. Zero (0) is neither positive nor negative, and so zero does not have a sign.

The following number line shows the positive numbers 0.75, 4, and 6.5 plotted to the right of the zero, and their additive opposites plotted to the left of the zero.

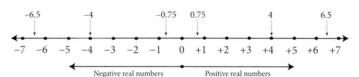

The real numbers are made up of all positive numbers, all negative numbers, and zero.

Since numbers are naturally positive, when we read or write positive numbers, we usually omit the word '**positive**' and the positive sign (**+**). However, when the number is negative, we must read it as '**negative**' or include the negative sign (**−**). For example, '**+ 7**' is usually read as just '**seven**' and written as '**7**'. But '**− 7**' should be read as '**negative seven**' and should be written with the negative sign as '**− 7**'.

Two integers that are at equal distances from the origin and in opposite directions are called opposites.

Any positive number and its negative (opposite) will be at an equal distance from zero (i.e., the origin) on the number line.

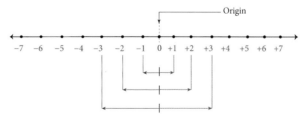

A negative number is the opposite of a positive number. For example, − 3 is the opposite of + 3.

The opposite of a positive number a is the negative value of a (i.e., the negative number that is the same distance away from 0 as a), and is denoted $-a$. Therefore, the opposite of a negative number, denoted $-(-a)$, would be equal to the positive value of a (i.e., $+a$).

$-(-a) = +a$

For example, $-(-3) = +3$

Hence we can summarize as follows:

$$-(-a) = +a \text{ for every real number } a$$

Numbers that lie to the left of a number on the number line are less than that number, and numbers that lie to the right of a number on the number line are greater than that number.

For example,

- 3 is greater than −2,   i.e., $3 > -2$

- −3 is greater than −5,   i.e., $-3 > -5$

- −5 is less than −4,   i.e., $-5 < -4$

- −1 is less than 2,   i.e., $-1 < 2$

Absolute Value

Absolute value is the magnitude of the number.

The absolute value of a number is its distance from the origin '0' on the number line. Since it is a distance, it is always positive and the direction does not matter.

For example, −5 and +5 are both 5 units from the origin '0', and so both have an absolute value of 5.

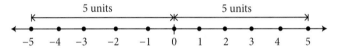

The absolute value of a number 'a' is denoted by $|a|$; e.g., $|5| = 5$ and $|-5| = 5$.

The vertical bars used in the representation of the absolute value are evaluated at the 'Brackets' step of BEDMAS, but differ from how brackets are used.

For example, $|-4| = 4$, whereas $(-4) = -4$

Example 3.3-a	Simplifying Arithmetic Expressions Involving Absolute Values

Simplify the following expressions:

(i) $-\left|\dfrac{-4}{3}\right|$

(ii) $-|8(-2)|$

Solution

(i) $-\left|\dfrac{-4}{3}\right|$ Simplifying the absolute value,

$= -\left(\dfrac{4}{3}\right)$ Simplifying the bracket,

$= -\dfrac{4}{3}$ or $\dfrac{-4}{3}$

Therefore, $-\left|\dfrac{-4}{3}\right| = \dfrac{-4}{3}$.

(ii) $-|8(-2)|$ Simplifying within the absolute value,

$= -|-16|$ Simplifying the absolute value,

$= -(16)$ Simplifying the bracket,

$= -16$

Therefore, $-|8(-2)| = -16$.

Example 3.3-b	Adding and Subtracting Arithmetic Expressions Involving Absolute Values

Simplify the following expressions:

(i) $10 - |8 - 15|$

(ii) $-5 + |-10 + 8|$

Solution

(i) $10 - |8 - 15|$ Simplifying within the absolute value,

$= 10 - |-7|$ Simplifying the absolute value,

(ii) $-5 + |-10 + 8|$ Simplifying within the absolute value,

$= -5 + |-2|$ Simplifying the absolute value,

Solution
continued

$= 10 - 7$	Subtracting,	$= -5 + 2$	Adding,
$= 3$		$= -3$	

Therefore, $10 - |8 - 15| = 3$.   Therefore, $-5 + |-10 + 8| = -3$.

Note: In the previous two examples, we performed arithmetic with signed numbers. The rules we follow when adding, subtracting, multiplying, and dividing signed numbers are explained in detail below.

Addition and Subtraction of Signed Numbers

- When adding two positive numbers, the answer is always positive (+).
  For example,

  Adding +5 and +3:

  $(+5) + (+3) = 5 + 3 = \mathbf{8}$

  This is the same as **+8**.

  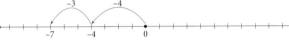

- When adding two negative numbers, the answer is always negative (−).
  For example,

  Adding −4 and −3:

  $(-4) + (-3) = -4 - 3 = \mathbf{-7}$

  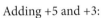

- When adding numbers that have different signs, subtract the smaller number from the larger number and the answer will have the sign of the larger, dominant number.
  For example,

  (i) Adding +8 and −12 (or −12 and +8):

  $+8 + (-12) = 8 - 12 = \mathbf{-4}$

  (ii) Adding −5 and +8 (or +8 and −5):

  $-5 + (+8) = -5 + 8 = \mathbf{3}$ (or +3)

  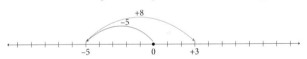

- When subtracting negative numbers, first change all the subtraction problems to addition problems, then follow the rule for the addition of signed numbers.
  For example,

  (i) Subtracting 12 from 18:

  $18 - 12 = 18 + (-12) = 6$

  (ii) Subtracting −12 from 18:

  $18 - (-12) = 18 + 12 = 30$

  (iii) Subtracting 12 from −18:

  $-18 - 12 = -18 + (-12) = -30$

  (iv) Subtracting −12 from −18:

  $-18 - (-12) = -18 + 12 = -6$

Multiplication and Division of Signed Numbers

The following are rules to be followed when multiplying or dividing **two signed numbers**:

(a) Multiplying two signed numbers:

- The product of two numbers with the **same sign** is **positive**.
  For example,

  (i) $(+5)(+4) = +20$

  (ii) $(-5)(-4) = +20$

Multiplying two signed numbers:

$(+)(+) = (+)$

$(-)(-) = (+)$

$(+)(-) = (-)$

$(-)(+) = (-)$

- The product of two numbers with **different signs** is **negative**.
  For example,
  (i) $(+5)(-4) = -20$
  (ii) $(-5)(+4) = -20$

(b) Dividing two signed numbers:

Dividing two
signed numbers:

$$\frac{(+)}{(+)} = (+)$$

$$\frac{(-)}{(-)} = (+)$$

$$\frac{(-)}{(+)} = (-)$$

$$\frac{(+)}{(-)} = (-)$$

- The quotient of two numbers with the **same sign** is **positive**.
  For example,
  (i) $\dfrac{+12}{+6} = +2$

  (ii) $\dfrac{-12}{-6} = +2$

- The quotient of two numbers with **different signs** is **negative**.
  For example,
  (i) $\dfrac{-12}{+6} = -2$

  (ii) $\dfrac{+12}{-6} = -2$

Note: When multiplying or dividing more than two signed numbers, group them into pairs and determine the sign using the rules for multiplication and division of signed numbers.

For example,

(i) $\underbrace{(-3)(-2)}\ \underbrace{(+4)(-1)}(-5)$
$= (6)(-4)(-5)$
$= (-24)(-5)$
$= 120$

(ii) $\dfrac{\overbrace{(-15)(+8)}(-50)}{\underbrace{(-25)(14)}}$

$= \dfrac{\overbrace{-(15 \times 8)(-50)}}{-(25 \times 14)}$

$= \dfrac{+(15 \times 8 \times 50)}{-(25 \times 14)} = -\dfrac{15 \times \overset{4}{8} \times \overset{2}{50}}{\underset{1}{25} \times \underset{7}{14}}$

$= -\dfrac{15 \times 4 \times 2}{7}$

$= -\dfrac{120}{7} = -17\dfrac{1}{7}$

Powers with Negative Bases

When a power has a negative base, there are four possible scenarios. These are explored in the following table:

Table 3.3-a   **Powers with Negative Bases**

Negative Base with Exponents	Example	Sign of Answer
Positive and Even	$(-2)^6 = \underbrace{(-2)(-2)}\,\underbrace{(-2)(-2)}\,\underbrace{(-2)(-2)} = 64$	+
Positive and Odd	$(-2)^5 = \underbrace{(-2)(-2)}\,\underbrace{(-2)(-2)}\,(-2) = -32$	−
Negative and Even	$(-2)^{-6} = \dfrac{1}{(-2)^6} = \dfrac{1}{(-2)(-2)(-2)(-2)(-2)(-2)} = \dfrac{1}{64} = 0.015625$	+
Negative and Odd	$(-2)^{-5} = \dfrac{1}{(-2)^5} = \dfrac{1}{(-2)(-2)(-2)(-2)(-2)} = \dfrac{1}{-32} = -0.03125$	−

From the above scenarios you will note:

- A negative number (base) with an even exponent gives a positive result (because pairs of negatives become positive).

- A negative number (base) with an odd exponent gives a negative result (because after the pairs of negatives, one negative will be left over).

However, it is important to note that a negative base of a power expressed within a bracket, as in $(-a)^n$, results in a different answer compared to a negative base expressed without a bracket, as in $-a^n$.

In $(-a)^n$, the exponent applies to both the negative sign and a.

In $-a^n$, the exponent applies only to a and the negative sign remains in the answer.

For example,

(i) In $(-5)^4$, (-5) is multiplied 4 times; i.e., $(-5)^4 = (-5)(-5)(-5)(-5) = 625$

(ii) In $(-5)^3$, (-5) is multiplied 3 times; i.e., $(-5)^3 = (-5)(-5)(-5) = -125$

(iii) In -5^4, only 5 is multiplied 4 times and the negative remains; i.e., $-5^4 = -5 \times 5 \times 5 \times 5] = -625$

(iv) In -5^3, only 5 is multiplied 3 times and the negative remains; i.e., $-5^3 = -[5 \times 5 \times 5] = -125$

Example 3.3-c | Solving Expressions using the Product Rule

Solve the following expressions:

(i) $(-5)^4 \times (-5)^{-1}$

(ii) $(-2)^5 \times (-2)^2 \times (-2)^0 \times 2$

Solution

(i) $(-5)^4 \times (-5)^{-1}$
$= (-5)^{(4-1)}$
$= (-5)^3$
$= -125$

(ii) $(-2)^5 \times (-2)^2 \times (-2)^0 \times 2$
$= (-2)^{(5+2+0)} \times 2$
$= (-2)^7 \times 2$
$= -128 \times 2$
$= -256$

Example 3.3-d | Solving Expressions using the Quotient Rule

Solve the following expressions:

(i) $(-3)^7 \div (-3)^2$

(ii) $(-5)^0 \div (-5)^3$

Solution

(i) $(-3)^7 \div (-3)^2$
$= (-3)^{(7-2)}$
$= (-3)^5$
$= -243$

(ii) $(-5)^0 \div (-5)^3$
$= (-5)^{(0-3)}$
$= (-5)^{-3}$
$= \dfrac{1}{(-5)^3}$
$= -\dfrac{1}{125}$

Example 3.3-e | Solving Expressions using the Power of a Product Rule

Solve the following expressions:

(i) $(-5 \times 2)^3$

(ii) $(-3 \times 2)^{-2}$

Solution

(i) $(-5 \times 2)^3$
$= (-5)^3 \times 2^3$
$= -125 \times 8$ or
$= -1,000$

$(-5 \times 2)^3$
$= (-10)^3$
$= -1,000$

(ii) $(-3 \times 2)^{-2}$
$= (-3)^{-2} \times 2^{-2}$
$= \dfrac{1}{(-3)^2} \times \dfrac{1}{2^2}$ or
$= \dfrac{1}{9} \times \dfrac{1}{4}$
$= \dfrac{1}{36}$

$(-3 \times 2)^{-2}$
$= (-6)^{-2}$
$= \dfrac{1}{(-6)^2}$
$= \dfrac{1}{36}$

Example 3.3-f | **Solving Expressions using the Power of a Quotient Rule**

Solve the following expressions:

(i) $(-2 \div 3)^{-2}$

(ii) $(3 \div (-2))^{-3}$

Solution

(i) $(-2 \div 3)^{-2}$
$= \left(\dfrac{-2}{3}\right)^{-2}$
$= \left(\dfrac{3}{-2}\right)^{2}$
$= \dfrac{3^2}{(-2)^2}$
$= \dfrac{9}{4}$

(ii) $(3 \div (-2))^{-3}$
$= \left(\dfrac{3}{-2}\right)^{-3}$
$= \left(\dfrac{-2}{3}\right)^{3}$
$= \dfrac{(-2)^3}{3^3}$
$= \dfrac{-8}{27} = -\dfrac{8}{27}$

Example 3.3-g | **Solving Expressions using the Power of a Power Rule**

Solve the following expressions:

(i) $[(-2)^3]^3$

(ii) $[(-3)^3]^2$

Solution

(i) $[(-2)^3]^3$
$= (-2)^{(3 \times 3)}$
$= (-2)^9$
$= -512$

(ii) $[(-3)^3]^2$
$= (-3)^{(3 \times 2)}$
$= (-3)^6$
$= 729$

Principal Roots

Roots of Positive Numbers

When the index of the root is **even**, any **positive** number will have **two solutions**, with one being the negative of the other. The positive solution is known as the principal root.

For example, $\sqrt{9}$ has two roots: +3 and –3, because $(3) \times (3) = 9$, and $(-3) \times (-3) = 9$.

This is usually written as ±3 and read as "plus or minus 3". The principal root is 3.

Similary, $\sqrt[4]{16}$ has two roots: +2 and –2, because $(2) \times (2) \times (2) \times (2) = 16$ and $(-2) \times (-2) \times (-2) \times (-2) = 16$; i.e., the roots are ±2 and the principal root is 2.

When the index of the root is **odd,** there is only **one solution** and it is **positive**. This positive solution is the principal root.

For example,

$\sqrt[3]{27} = 3$ because $(3) \times (3) \times (3) = 27$

$\sqrt[5]{32} = 2$ because $(2) \times (2) \times (2) \times (2) \times (2) = 32$

Roots of Negative Numbers

When the index of the root is **even**, there is **no real solution** to any **negative** number.

For example, $\sqrt{-4}$ and $\sqrt[4]{-81}$ both have no real roots.

When the index of the root is **odd**, there is only **one solution** and it is **negative**. This negative solution is the principal root.

For example,

$$\sqrt[5]{-32} = -2 \qquad \text{because } (-2) \times (-2) \times (-2) \times (-2) \times (-2) = -32$$

$$\sqrt[3]{-27} = -3 \qquad \text{because } (-3) \times (-3) \times (-3) = -27$$

Table 3.3-b   **Types of Real Numbers**

Type	Description	Examples
Natural Numbers	Counting numbers (numbers starting from 1).	Natural Numbers 0 1 2 3 4
Whole Numbers	Natural numbers and zero.	Whole Numbers
Integers	Natural numbers (positive integers), their negatives (negative integers), and zero.	−4 −3 −2 −1 0 1 2 3 4 Negative Integers Positive Integers Zero is neither positive nor negative
Rational Numbers	Numbers that can be expressed as one integer divided by another non-zero integer; i.e., numbers that can be written as a quotient of integers with non-zero divisors.	$-\dfrac{5}{2}, 0.75, \dfrac{3}{2}$
Irrational Numbers	Numbers that cannot be expressed as a rational number.	$\sqrt{2}, \pi, e = 2.718281\ldots$

Natural numbers are positive integers. Zero is neither positive nor negative.

Rational numbers can be expressed as $\frac{a}{b}$, where a and b are integers and $b \neq 0$.

Irrational numbers cannot be expressed as $\frac{a}{b}$, where a and b are integers and $b \neq 0$.

Note: Terminating decimals and repeating decimals are also rational numbers because they can be expressed as a quotient of integers.

- *Terminating decimals* are decimals that require only a finite number of place values after the decimal point to express.

  For example, 0.375 which can be expressed as $\dfrac{3}{8}$.

- *Repeating decimals* are decimals that do not terminate (i.e., they require an infinite number of place values after the decimal point to express), but show a repeating pattern.

  For example, 0.185185... is usually written as $0.\overline{185}$ and can be expressed as $\dfrac{5}{27}$.

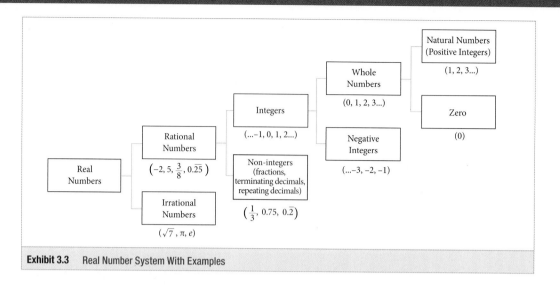

Exhibit 3.3 Real Number System With Examples

3.3 | Exercises

Answers to odd-numbered problems are available at the end of the textbook.

For Problems 1 to 6, place the correct sign, '<' or '>', in the space between the given pairs of numbers.

1. a. $-5 \;\square\; 0$ b. $-2 \;\square\; +6$ 2. a. $0 \;\square\; -3$ b. $-5 \;\square\; +3$

3. a. $+8 \;\square\; -3$ b. $+1 \;\square\; -2$ 4. a. $-5 \;\square\; +4$ b. $+3 \;\square\; -7$

5. a. $-6 \;\square\; -8$ b. $-5 \;\square\; -2$ 6. a. $-7 \;\square\; -9$ b. $-8 \;\square\; -4$

For Problems 7 to 10, arrange the numbers in order from smallest to largest.

7. a. $5, -6, 8, -8, -5, 2$ b. $-8, 4, -6, 3, -9, 7$ 8. a. $-2, -3, 5, 2, -1, 4$ b. $13, 6, -4, 4, -6, -5$

9. a. $9, -5, -8, 3, 7, 10$ b. $12, -13, 15, 2, -8, -3$ 10. a. $-3, 6, 1, -7, -1, 7$ b. $-12, 0, 12, -16, 15, -5$

Evaluate Problems 11 to 20.

11. a. $|-16|$ b. $-|3|$ 12. a. $|-8|$ b. $-|12|$

13. a. $-|-5|$ b. $-[-|-9|]$ 14. a. $-|-7|$ b. $-[-|-3|]$

15. a. $|-4| - |-7|$ b. $-|-8| + |-3|$ 16. a. $-|-15| - |-3|$ b. $|-5| + |-4|$

17. a. $|-10| \times |-5|$ b. $|-15| \div |-3|$ 18. a. $|-10| \times |-2|$ b. $|-12| \div |-4|$

19. a. $-|6| \times |-3|$ b. $-|-20| \div |-5|$ 20. a. $-|8| \times |-4|$ b. $-|-24| \div |-6|$

Evaluate Problems 21 to 38.

21. a. $-8 + (-5 - 7)$ b. $2 - (-3) + 1$ 22. a. $-9 + (-3 - 8)$ b. $5 - (-7) + 8$

23. a. $-3 - (-7) + 8$ b. $(-4 + 9) - (-3 - 6)$ 24. a. $-7 - (-9) - 1$ b. $(-5 + 3) + (-4 - 9)$

25. a. $4 + (-3) - [5 + (-11)]$ b. $-6 + (-4) - [-(15 - 8)]$ 26. a. $5 + (-4) - [7 + (-9)]$ b. $-8 + (-15) - [-(6 - 7)]$

27. a. $2(-3)(-5)$ b. $-4(-3)(-2)$ 28. a. $6(-2)(-4)$ b. $-5(-3)(-2)$

29. a. $-64 \div (-8)$ b. $45 \div (-5)$ 30. a. $-48 \div (-6)$ b. $36 \div (-4)$

31. a. $-5 + (-2)(-5) - (6 - 3)$ b. $7(2 - 3) - 4(-7 + 1)$ 32. a. $-8(5 - 6) - 3(-6 + 2)$ b. $-7 + (-3)(-4) - (-8 - 3)$

33. a. $(5 + 7)^2 - 5^2 - 7^2$ b. $2^2 - 2^4 - 20 \times 3$ 34. a. $(9 - 12)^2 - 9^2 - 12^2$ b. $7 \times 8 - 3^2 - 2^3$

35. a. $(20 \times 4 - 8^2)^2 + 9$ b. $(3 \times 9 - 3^2) + 12$ 36. a. $(-12^2 \div 4^2) - 3 \times 2^4$ b. $-5 \times 3^3 \div 9 + 5^2$

37. a. $-11^2 - 4 \times 54 \div (5 - 2)^3 - 3$ b. $-31 - [(15 \div 3) \times 32] \div 2^2 \times (26 \div 13)$ 38. a. $[(1 - 12)(1 - 5)]^2 \div (5 - 3 \times 2^2 - 4)$ b. $3(7^2 + 2 \times 15 \div 3) - (1 - 3 \times 4)^2$

Express Problems 39 to 42 as a single power and then evaluate.

39. a. $(-6)^5 \times (-6)^3$ b. $8^{-6} \times 8^9$ 40. a. $(-2)^5 \times (-2)^6$ b. $4^{-7} \times 4^8$

41. a. $(-4)^5 \div (-4)^3$ b. $(-2)^7 \div (-2)^4$ 42. a. $[(-2)^3]^2 \div (-2)^5$ b. $[(-3)^2]^3 \div (-3)^7$

Evaluate Problems 43 to 48.

43.　a. $-5^4 \div (-5)^2$　　　　b. $-4^6 \div (-4)^4$　　　　44.　a. $-(3^2) \div (-3)^6$　　　　b. $-(2^2)^2 \div (-2)^3$

45.　a. $(-2)^2 + (-3)^3$　　　　b. $(-3)^2 - (-2)^3$　　　　46.　a. $(-4)^2 + (-5)^3$　　　　b. $(-5)^2 - (-4)^2$

47.　a. $(-2)^3 - (-3)^2 - 1^5$　　　　b. $(-7)^1 + (5)^0 - (-3)^2$　　　　48.　a. $(-3)^0 + (-4)^1 - (-2)^3$　　　　b. $(-3)^2 - (-2)^3 - 2^2$

3.4 | Significant Digits and Scientific Notation

Significant Digits

Significant digits are critical when reporting data as they provide information on how well the data is measured or reported.

The **accuracy** of a number is determined by the number of significant digits in the number. The **precision** of a number is based on the place value of the right-most significant digit.

For example,

- 4,700 is accurate to 2 significant digits and precise to the nearest hundred.

- 12.25 is accurate to 4 significant digits and precise to the nearest hundredth.

The number of significant digits in a number is calculated by following the rules given in Table 3.4-a below.

Table 3.4-a   **Determining the Number of Significant Digits**

	General Rule	Example	
1.	All non-zero digits are significant.	$2\,7\,0$	2 significant digits
		$3\,1\,.\,4$	3 significant digits
2.	All zeros between two significant digits are significant.	$3\,0\,0\,5$	4 significant digits
		$1\,0\,5\,.\,0\,3$	5 significant digits
3.	Leading zeros are **not** significant.	$0\,.\,0\,5$	1 significant digit
		$0\,.\,0\,0\,3\,2\,5$	3 significant digits
4.	Trailing zeros in any number with a decimal point **are** significant.	$2\,5\,0\,.\,0$	4 significant digits
		$0\,.\,0\,0\,3\,8\,0$	3 significant digits
5.	Trailing zeros in a whole number are **ambiguous** and therefore should not be counted as significant.	$2\,5\,0\,0\,0$	assume 2 significant digits
		$1\,5\,8\,0$	assume 3 significant digits

Trailing zeros in a whole number with the decimal point at the end are significant.

For example, the number 250. has 3 significant digits as there is a decimal point at the end of the number.

Example 3.4-a   **Identifying Significant Digits and Precision**

Identify the number of significant digits and precision of the following numbers:

(i)　89,000　　　　(ii)　108.9　　　　(iii) 706.00　　　　(iv) 30.

(v)　0.075　　　　(vi) 0.00875　　　　(vii) 0.750　　　　(viii) 0.4070

Solution

(i) 89,000
    ↑↑↑
  Not significant

Number of significant digits = 2 (Rules 1 and 5)

Precision = Thousands

(ii) 108.9   All digits are significant
   ↑
  Significant

Number of significant digits = 4 (Rules 1 and 2)

Precision = Tenths

(iii) 706.00   All digits are significant
   ↑ ↑↑
  Significant

Number of significant digits = 5 (Rules 1, 2, and 4)

Precision = Hundredths

(iv) 30.   All digits are significant
   ↑
  Significant

Number of significant digits = 2 (Rules 1 and 4)

Precision = Units

(v) 0.075
   ↑↑
  Not significant

Number of significant digits = 2 (Rules 1 and 3)

Precision = Thousandths

(vi) 0.00875
   ↑↑↑
  Not significant

Number of significant digits = 3 (Rules 1 and 3)

Precision = Hundred-thousandths

(vii) 0.750
   ↑ ↑
     Significant
  Not significant

Number of significant digits = 3 (Rules 1, 3, and 4)

Precision = Thousandths

(viii) 0.4070
   ↑ ↑↑
     Significant
  Not significant

Number of significant digits = 4 (Rules 1, 2, 3, and 4)

Precision = Ten-thousandths

Note:

- *4,500 has 2 significant digits (Rule 1) and precision to the hundreds.*
- *4,500. has 4 significant digits (Rules 1 and 4) and precision to the units.*
- *4,500.0 has 5 significant digits (Rules 1 and 4) and precision to the tenths.*
- *4,500.00 has 6 significant digits (Rules 1 and 4) and precision to the hundredths.*

Rounding Numbers to Required Significant Digits

It is often necessary to round numbers to keep the result of calculations to the required number of significant digits.

The general methods for rounding numbers to the required number of significant digits are as follows:

Table 3.4-b	Rules for Rounding Numbers to Significant Digits

Start at the left of the number and count from left to right until the required number of significant digits is reached and identify the last significant digit.

	If the digit immediately to the right of the identified digit is:	Rounding Whole Numbers to required significant digits	Rounding Decimal Numbers to required significant digits
1.	Less than 5	Leave the identified digit unchanged and replace all digits to the right of it with zeros.	Leave the identified digit unchanged and drop all digits to the right of it.

	Example:
	(Rounding to 3 significant digits)
		278,312 = 278,000
		      ↑
		     <5
			3.0723 = 3.07
			   ↑
			   <5

	If the digit immediately to the right of the identified digit is:	Rounding Whole Numbers to required significant digits	Rounding Decimal Numbers to required significant digits
2.	Greater than 5, or equal to 5 but followed by at least one non-zero digit	Add 1 to the identified digit and replace all digits to the right of it with zeros.	Add 1 to the identified digit and drop all digits to the right of it.

Example:
(Rounding to 3 significant digits)

i. $30\underset{\uparrow}{\underline{8}},765 = 309,000$
   >5

ii. $29\underline{6},572 = 297,000$
   >0
   $= 5$

i. $21.\underline{4}76 = 21.5$
   >5

ii. $13.\underline{3}502 = 13.4$
   >0
   $= 5$

| 3. a | Equal to 5, but followed by all zero digits or no other digits | If the identified digit is an even digit, leave the identified digit unchanged and replace all digits to the right of it with zeros. *Note: Zero is an even digit.* | If the identified digit is an even digit, leave the identified digit unchanged and drop all digits to the right of it. *Note: Zero is an even digit.* |

Example:
(Rounding to 3 significant digits)

i. $40\underline{8},500 = 408,000$ ⌐even
   $= 0$
   $= 5$

ii. $7,4\underline{6}5 = 7,460$ ⌐even
   $= 5$

i. $7.0\underline{4}50 = 7.04$ ⌐even
   $= 0$
   $= 5$

ii. $24.\underline{0}5 = 24.0$ ⌐even
   $= 5$

| 3. b | Equal to 5, but followed by all zero digits or no other digits | If the identified digit is an odd digit, add 1 to the identified digit to make it even and replace all digits to the right of it with zeros. | If the identified digit is an odd digit, add 1 to the identified digit to make it even and drop all digits to the right of it. |

Example:
(Rounding to 3 significant digits)

i. $38\underline{3},500 = 384,000$ ⌐odd
   $= 0$
   $= 5$

ii. $7,4\underline{1}5 = 7,420$ ⌐odd
   $= 5$

i. $43.\underline{7}500 = 43.8$ ⌐odd
   $= 0$
   $= 5$

ii. $9.3\underline{9}5 = 9.40$ ⌐odd
   $= 5$

Example 3.4-b   Rounding Whole Numbers to Indicated Significant Digits

Round the following numbers to the indicated significant digits:

(i)   62,578 to 3 significant digits   (ii)   124,390 to 2 significant digits

(iii) 704,534 to 3 significant digits   (iv)   8,047,500 to 4 significant digits

(v)   340,650 to 4 significant digits   (vi)   500,067 to 4 significant digits

Solution

(i)   Rounding 62,578 to 3 significant digits

   $62,\underline{5}78 = 62,600$
   >5

Solution
continued

(ii) Rounding 124,390 to 2 significant digits

$$124,390 = 120,000$$

↑
<5

(iii) Rounding 704,534 to 3 significant digits

$$704,534 = 705,000$$

>0
=5

(iv) Rounding 8,047,500 to 4 significant digits

odd
$$8,047,500 = 8,048,000$$

=0
=5

(v) Rounding 340,650 to 4 significant digits

even
$$340,650 = 340,600$$

=0
=5

(vi) Rounding 500,067 to 4 significant digits

$$500,067 = 500,100$$

↑
>5

Example 3.4-c	**Rounding Decimal Numbers to Indicated Significant Digits**

Round the following numbers to the indicated significant digits:

(i) 0.8090 to 2 significant digits   (ii) 1.0621 to 3 significant digits   (iii) 0.0635 to 2 significant digits

(iv) 0.08250 to 2 significant digits   (v) 0.043517 to 2 significant digits   (vi) 4,257.25 to 3 significant digits

Solution

(i) Rounding 0.8090 to 2 significant digits

$$0.8090 = 0.81$$

↑
>5

(ii) Rounding 1.0621 to 3 significant digits

$$1.0621 = 1.06$$

↑
<5

(iii) Rounding 0.0635 to 2 significant digits

odd
$$0.0635 = 0.064$$

↑
=5

(iv) Rounding 0.08250 to 2 significant digits

even
$$0.08250 = 0.082$$

=0
=5

(v) Rounding 0.043517 to 2 significant digits

$$0.043517 = 0.044$$

>0
=5

(vi) Rounding 4,257.25 to 3 significant digits

$$4,257.25 = 4,260$$

↑
>5

Rounding Rules for Addition and Subtraction of Decimal Numbers

When adding or subtracting decimal numbers, the final answer should have the same number of decimal places as the number with the least number of decimal places. The rules for rounding to a given precision are the same as the rules for rounding decimal numbers. For a review of these rules, refer back to Chapter 2.

Example 3.4-d | Rounding to a Number with the Least Number of Decimal Places

(i)   Add 565.346 and 6.35   (ii)   Subtract 3.9 from 34.45   (iii) 43.38 − 24.2 + 1.355

Solution

(i)
$$\begin{array}{r} \overset{1}{565.346} \\ +\ \ 6.35 \\ \hline 571.696 \end{array}$$
⟵ 3 decimal places
⟵ 2 decimal places

565.346 has 3 decimal places and 6.35 has 2 decimal places. The least number of decimal places is 2. Therefore, rounding the answer 571.696 to 2 decimal places results in 571.70.

(ii)
$$\begin{array}{r} \overset{3\ 14}{34.45} \\ -\ \ 3.9 \\ \hline 30.55 \end{array}$$
⟵ 2 decimal places
⟵ 1 decimal place

34.45 has 2 decimal places and 3.9 has 1 decimal place. The least number of decimal places is 1. Therefore, rounding the answer 30.55 to 1 decimal place results in 30.6.

(iii)
$$\begin{array}{r} \overset{3\ 13}{43.38} \\ -24.2 \\ \hline 19.18 \end{array}$$
⟵ 2 decimal places
⟵ 1 decimal place

$$\begin{array}{r} \overset{1\ \ \ 1}{19.18} \\ +\ 1.355 \\ \hline 20.535 \end{array}$$
⟵ 3 decimal places

43.38 has 2 decimal places, 24.2 has 1 decimal place, and 1.355 has 3 decimal places. The least number of decimal places is 1. Therefore, rounding the answer 20.535 to 1 decimal place results in 20.5.

Rounding Rules for Multiplication and Division of Decimal Numbers

When multiplying or dividing decimal numbers, the final answer should have the same number of significant digits as the number with the least number of significant digits in any of the numbers being multiplied or divided. Here, we must use the rules for rounding with significant digits introduced earlier in Table 3.4-b.

Example 3.4-e | Rounding to a Number with the Least Number of Significant Digits

(i)   Multiply 10.46 and 1.2   (ii)   Divide 370.25 by 10.5   (iii) 3.142 × 115.2 ÷ 14.4

Solution

(i)
$$\begin{array}{r} 10.46 \\ \times\ \ 1.2 \\ \hline 2092 \\ 10460 \\ \hline 12.552 \end{array}$$
⟵ 4 significant digits
⟵ 2 significant digits

10.46 has 4 significant digits and 1.2 has 2 significant digits. The least number of significant digits is 2. Therefore, rounding the answer 12.552 to 2 significant digits results in 13.

Solution
continued

(ii)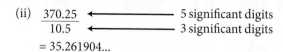

$$\frac{370.25}{10.5} \longleftarrow \text{5 significant digits}$$
$$\text{3 significant digits}$$

= 35.261904...

370.25 has 5 significant digits and 10.5 has 3 significant digits. The least number of significant digits is 3. Therefore, rounding the answer 35.261904... to 3 significant digits results in 35.3.

(iii)

$$\begin{array}{r} 3.142 \longleftarrow \text{4 significant digits} \\ \times 115.2 \longleftarrow \text{4 significant digits} \\ \hline 6284 \\ 157100 \\ 314200 \\ 3142000 \\ \hline 361.9584 \end{array}$$

$$\frac{361.9584}{14.4} \longleftarrow \text{3 significant digits}$$

= 25.136

3.142 has 4 significant digits, 115.2 has 4 significant digits, and 14.4 has 3 significant digits. The least number of significant digits is 3. Therefore, rounding the answer 25.136 to 3 significant digits results in 25.1.

*Note: In calculations that require both addition/subtraction **and** multiplication/division to be performed, there are different approaches which can be taken when rounding the final answer. In this textbook, we will not cover these scenarios.*

Special Situation in Rounding to Indicated Significant Digits

Consider the multiplication: 3,125 × 144

3,125 has 4 significant digits and 144 has 3 significant digits. Therefore, the answer should be rounded to 3 significant digits. However, when we multiply these numbers, the answer is 450,000, which has only 2 significant digits.

To indicate that the answer has 3 significant digits, place the symbol '~' above the first zero that is to be included as a significant digit to have a total of 3 significant digits; i.e., place the symbol '~' above the 3rd digit (zero), to indicate it as a significant digit.

450,000   45~0,000
↑   ↑
2 significant digits   3 significant digits

Similarly, consider the multiplication: 3,906.25 × 115.2

3,906.25 has 6 significant digits and 115.2 has 4 significant digits. Therefore, the answer should be rounded to 4 significant digits. However, when we multiply these numbers, the answer is 450,000, which has only 2 significant digits.

To indicate that the answer has 4 significant digits, place the symbol '~' above the second zero that is to be included as a significant digit to have a total of 4 significant digits; i.e., place the symbol '~' above the 4th digit (second zero), to indicate it as a significant digit.

450,000   450,~000
↑   ↑
2 significant digits   4 significant digits

This is a tedious method of expressing significant digits. We will learn next about scientific notation, which is a much more efficient and clear way of expressing the number of significant digits.

Scientific Notation

Scientific notation is a method of expressing numbers using decimal numbers with one non-zero digit to the left of the decimal point multiplied by the power of 10 corresponding to the place value of the leading digit of the original number.

For example, 52,500 in scientific notation is written as 5.25×10^4, since the leading 5 represents the ten thousands (i.e., 10^4) place value.

$$52,500 = \underset{\text{Coefficient}}{\underline{5.25}} \times 10^{4} \quad \begin{array}{l} \text{Exponent} \\ \text{Base} \end{array}$$

Note:

- *The base is always 10.*
- *The exponent is always an integer.*
- *The coefficient should always be greater than or equal to 1, and less than 10.*

Converting Numbers from Standard Notation to Scientific Notation

Any number raised to the power of 0 is 1. Therefore, $10^0 = 1$.

	Converting Numbers from Standard Notation to Scientific Notation	Example
1.	For numbers 1 up to 10, the exponent will be 0.	9.5
	For example, to convert 9.5 to scientific notation, multiply 9.5 by the factor $10^0 = 1$.	9.5×10^0
2.	For numbers 10 and above, the exponent will be positive.	525.6
	For example, to convert 525.6 to scientific notation, follow these steps:	
	Move the decimal point to the left and place it after the first non-zero digit in the number. This will be the coefficient.	525.6
		Coefficient = 5.256
	Count the number of places the decimal point moved to the left. This will be the exponent on the power of 10, and it will be positive.	2 decimal places to the left
		Exponent = 2
	Write the number in scientific notation as:	
	Coefficient $\times 10^{\text{Exponent}}$	5.256×10^2
3.	For numbers less than 1, the exponent will be negative.	0.00752
	For example, to convert 0.00752 to scientific notation, follow these steps:	
	Move the decimal point to the right and place it after the first non-zero digit in the number. This will be the coefficient.	0.00752
		Coefficient = 7.52
	Count the number of places the decimal point moved to the right. This will be the exponent on the power of 10, and it will be negative.	3 decimal places to the right
		Exponent = –3
	Write the number in scientific notation as:	
	Coefficient $\times 10^{\text{Exponent}}$	7.52×10^{-3}

Example 3.4-f | Converting Numbers from Standard Notation to Scientific Notation

Convert the following to numbers from standard notation to scientific notation:

(i) 6,526 | (ii) 135.275 | (iii) 0.000058 | (iv) 7.2

Solution

(i) $6526 = 6.526 \times 10^3$ | (ii) $135.275 = 1.35275 \times 10^2$

(iii) $0.000058 = 5.8 \times 10^{-5}$ | (iv) $7.2 = 7.2 \times 10^0$

Converting Numbers from Scientific Notation to Standard Notation

	Converting Numbers from Scientific Notation to Standard Notation	Example
1.	When the exponent of base 10 is 0: To convert to standard notation, simply drop the factor 10^0.	8.75×10^0 $= 8.75$
2.	When the exponent of base 10 is a postive number: The answer will be a larger number. To convert to standard notation, move the decimal point to the right by the same number of places of the exponent.	3.45×10^4 Exponent of base 10 = 4 $= 3.45$ 4 places to the right $= 34,500$
3.	When the exponent of base 10 is a negative number: The answer will be a smaller number. To convert to standard notation, move the decimal point to the left by the same number of places of the exponent.	2.45×10^{-3} Exponent of base 10 = −3 $= 2.45$ 3 places to the left $= 0.00245$

Example 3.4-g | Converting Numbers from Scientific Notation to Standard Notation

Convert the following numbers from scientific notation to standard notation:

(i) 2.07×10^3 | (ii) 5.18×10^{-4} | (iii) 9×10^1 | (iv) 7.29×10^0

Solution

(i) 2.07×10^3 — Moving the decimal point 3 places to the right, $= 2.07$ $= 2,070$

(ii) 5.18×10^{-4} — Moving the decimal point 4 places to the left, $= 5.18$ $= 0.000518$

(iii) 9×10^1 — Moving the decimal point 1 point to the right, $= 9$ $= 90$

(iv) 7.29×10^0 — Dropping the factor 10^0, $= 7.29$

Using Scientific Notation to Express Significant Digits

Recall the example from earlier in this section where we needed to express the number 450,000 using 3 or 4 significant digits. We may use scientific notation to more easily express this:

$$450\tilde{0},000 = \underline{4.50} \times 10^5$$

3 significant digits

$$450,\tilde{0}00 = \underline{4.500} \times 10^5$$

4 significant digits

Example 3.4-h	Rounding Numbers to Indicated Significant Digits

Round the number 50,040.365 first to 6 significant digits, then to 5, 4, and 3 significant digits.

Solution

$$50,040.365 \quad = \underline{50,040.4} \qquad\qquad = 5.00404 \times 10^4$$

6 significant digits

$$50,040.365 \quad = \underline{50,040}, \;\; \text{or} \quad \underline{50,04\tilde{0}} \qquad = 5.0040 \times 10^4$$

5 significant digits

$$50,040.365 \quad = \underline{50,040} \qquad\qquad\qquad = 5.004 \times 10^4$$

4 significant digits

$$50,040.365 \quad = \underline{50,\tilde{0}00} \qquad\qquad\qquad = 5.00 \times 10^4$$

3 significant digits

Addition and Subtraction of Numbers in Scientific Notation

Numbers in scientific notation are multiplied by powers with the same base of 10. However, they may or may not have the same exponent.

1. To add or subtract numbers in scientific notation whose exponents are the same, factor out the power and add or subtract the coefficients within the brackets.

For example,

(i) $4 \times 10^5 + 3 \times 10^5$ Taking 10^5 as common factor,

        $= (4 + 3) \times 10^5$ Adding coefficients within the bracket,

        $= 7 \times 10^5$

(ii) $9 \times 10^6 - 5 \times 10^6$ Taking 10^6 as common factor,

        $= (9 - 5) \times 10^6$ Subtracting coefficients within the bracket,

        $= 4 \times 10^6$

2. To add or subtract numbers in scientific notation whose exponents are the not the same, they must be converted to have the same exponent. It is easier to convert the lesser exponent to make it equal with the greater exponent.

Follow these steps to add (or subtract) numbers in scientific notation (with different exponents):

Steps	Example
1. Determine the number by which the lesser exponent needs to be increased to make it equal with the greater exponent.	$9.8 \times 10^5 + 6.2 \times 10^4$ Greater exponent = 5 Lesser exponent = 4 $5 - 4 = 1$
2. Increase the lesser exponent by this number and move the decimal point of the coefficient of the number to the left by the same number of places.	$9.8 \times 10^5 + 6.2 \times 10^{(4+1)}$ $= 9.8 \times 10^5 + 0.62 \times 10^5$
3. Add (or subtract) the new coefficient and factor out the common exponent in power of 10.	$(9.8 + 0.62) \times 10^5$ $= 10.42 \times 10^5$ (This answer is not in scientific notation.)
4. If the answer is not in scientific notation (i.e., if the coefficient is not between 1 and 10), then convert it to scientific notation. To convert to scientific notation, move the decimal point to the left or to the right until the coefficient is between 1 and 10. For each place the decimal point is moved to the left, increase the exponent by 1; for each place it is moved to the right, decrease the exponent by 1.	$10.42 \times 10^{(5+1)}$ $= 1.042 \times 10^6$

Example 3.4-i   Adding Numbers in Scientific Notation

Add the following:

(i) $5.1 \times 10^{-2} + 6.3 \times 10^{-2}$ (ii) $8.74 \times 10^{-3} + 5.28 \times 10^{-1}$ (iii) $7.41 \times 10^2 + 2.6 \times 10^{-3}$

Solution

(i) $5.1 \times 10^{-2} + 6.3 \times 10^{-2}$
    Exponents are equal. Taking common factor 10^{-2},

$= (5.1 + 6.3) \times 10^{-2}$
    Adding numbers within the bracket,

$= 11.4 \times 10^{-2}$
    Answer **not** in scientific notation.

$= 11.4 \times 10^{(-2+1)}$
    Converting to scientific notation by increasing the exponent by 1 and moving the decimal point 1 place to the left,

$= 1.14 \times 10^{-1}$
    Answer in scientific notation.

(ii) $8.74 \times 10^{-3} + 5.28 \times 10^{-1}$
    Exponents are not equal; greater exponent = –1, lesser exponent = –3.

    Greater exponent – lesser exponent = $-1 - (-3) = -1 + 3 = 2$

$= 8.74 \times 10^{(-3+2)} + 5.28 \times 10^{-1}$
    Increasing the lesser exponent by 2 and moving the decimal point of its coefficient to the left by 2 places,

$= 0.0874 \times 10^{-1} + 5.28 \times 10^{-1}$
    Taking common factor 10^{-1},

$= (0.0874 + 5.28) \times 10^{-1}$
    Adding numbers within the bracket,

$= 5.3674 \times 10^{-1}$
    Answer in scientific notation.

Solution
continued

(iii) $7.41 \times 10^2 + 2.6 \times 10^{-3}$ — Exponents are not equal; greater exponent = 2, lesser exponent = –3.

Greater exponent – lesser exponent = 2 – (–3) = 2 + 3 = 5

$= 7.41 \times 10^2 + 2.6 \times 10^{(-3+5)}$ — Increasing the lesser exponent by 5 and moving the decimal point of its coefficient to the left by 5 places,

$= 7.41 \times 10^2 + 0.000026 \times 10^2$ — Taking common factor 10^2,

$= (7.41 + 0.000026) \times 10^2$ — Adding numbers within the bracket,

$= 7.410026 \times 10^2$ — Answer in scientific notation.

Example 3.4-j | **Subtracting Numbers in Scientific Notation**

Subtract the following:

(i) $7.24 \times 10^{-4} - 6.5 \times 10^{-4}$ (ii) $5.28 \times 10^{-2} - 9.59 \times 10^{-5}$ (iii) $4.78 \times 10^3 - 6.5 \times 10^{-2}$

Solution

(i) $7.24 \times 10^{-4} - 6.5 \times 10^{-4}$ — Exponents are equal. Taking common factor 10^{-4},

$= (7.24 - 6.5) \times 10^{-4}$ — Subtracting numbers within the bracket,

$= 0.74 \times 10^{-4}$ — Answer **not** in scientific notation.

$= 0.74 \times 10^{(-4-1)}$ — Converting to scientific notation by decreasing the exponent by 1 and moving the decimal point 1 place to the right.

$= 7.4 \times 10^{-5}$ — Answer in scientific notation.

(ii) $5.28 \times 10^{-2} - 9.59 \times 10^{-5}$ — Exponents are not equal; greater exponent = –2, lesser exponent = –5.

Greater exponent – lesser exponent = –2 – (–5) = –2 + 5 = 3

$= 5.28 \times 10^{-2} - 9.59 \times 10^{(-5+3)}$ — Increasing the lesser exponent by 3 and moving the decimal point of its coefficient to the left by 3 places,

$= 5.28 \times 10^{-2} - 0.00959 \times 10^{-2}$ — Taking common factor 10^{-2},

$= (5.28 - 0.00959) \times 10^{-2}$ — Subtracting numbers within the bracket,

$= 5.27041 \times 10^{-2}$ — Answer in scientific notation.

(iii) $4.78 \times 10^3 - 6.5 \times 10^{-2}$ — Exponents are not equal; greater exponent = 3, lesser exponent = –2.

Greater exponent – lesser exponent = 3 – (–2) = 3 + 2 = 5

$= 4.78 \times 10^3 - 6.5 \times 10^{(-2+5)}$ — Increasing the lesser exponent by 5 and moving the decimal point of its coefficient to the left by 5 places,

$= 4.78 \times 10^3 - 0.000065 \times 10^3$ — Taking common factor 10^3,

$= (4.78 - 0.000065) \times 10^3$ — Subtracting numbers within the bracket,

$= 4.779935 \times 10^3$ — Answer in scientific notation.

Example 3.4-k | **Combined Addition and Subtraction of Numbers in Scientific Notation**

Evaluate: $2.5 \times 10^5 + 8.2 \times 10^4 - 4.7 \times 10^3$

Solution

$2.5 \times 10^5 + 8.2 \times 10^4 - 4.7 \times 10^3$ — Greatest exponent = 5. Converting all exponents to 5 by moving the decimal places to the left and increasing the exponents,

$= 2.5 \times 10^5 + 8.2 \times 10^{(4+1)} - 4.7 \times 10^{(3+2)}$

<table>
<tr><td>Solution
continued</td><td>$= 2.5 \times 10^5 + 0.82 \times 10^5 - 0.047 \times 10^5$</td><td>Taking common factor 10^5,</td></tr>
<tr><td></td><td>$= (2.5 + 0.82 - 0.047) \times 10^5$</td><td>Performing arithmetic operations within the bracket,</td></tr>
<tr><td></td><td>$= 3.273 \times 10^5$</td><td>Answer in scientific notation.</td></tr>
</table>

Multiplication of Numbers in Scientific Notation

We have already seen that multiplying two powers together that have the same base is equivalent to adding their exponents together.

Numbers in scientific notation are coefficients multiplied by powers of the same base: 10.

Therefore, to multiply numbers in scientific notation, multiply their coefficients and add their exponents on the power of 10. If the answer is not in scientific notation (i.e., the coefficient is not between 1 and 10), convert it to scientific notation.

For example,

$(6.02 \times 10^3) \times (4 \times 10^5)$	Multiplying the coefficients and adding the exponents,
$= (6.02 \times 4) \times 10^{(3+5)}$	Performing arithmetic operation within brackets,
$= 24.08 \times 10^8$	Answer **not** in scientific notation.
$= 24.08 \times 10^{(8+1)}$	Converting to scientific notation,
$= 2.408 \times 10^9$	Answer in scientific notation.

Note: When the decimal point is moved to the left, the coefficient is decreased by a power of 10; as a result, the exponent on the 10 must be increased by 1 for every place value that the decimal point was moved to the left in the coefficient.

Example 3.4-I	**Multiplying Numbers in Scientific Notation**

Multiply the following:

(i) $(5.4 \times 10^{-3}) \times (2.2 \times 10^{-5})$ (ii) $(4.75 \times 10^6) \times (1.5 \times 10^{-2})$ (iii) $(7.5 \times 10^{-6}) \times (5.0 \times 10^4)$

Solution		
	(i) $(5.4 \times 10^{-3}) \times (2.2 \times 10^{-5})$	Multiplying the coefficients and adding the exponents,
	$= (5.4 \times 2.2) \times 10^{[-3 + (-5)]}$	Performing arithmetic operation within brackets,
	$= 11.88 \times 10^{-8}$	Answer **not** in scientific notation.
	$= 11.88 \times 10^{(-8+1)}$	Converting to scientific notation,
	$= 1.188 \times 10^{-7}$	Answer in scientific notation.
	(ii) $(4.75 \times 10^6) \times (1.5 \times 10^{-2})$	Multiplying the coefficients and adding the exponents,
	$= (4.75 \times 1.5) \times 10^{[6 + (-2)]}$	Performing arithmetic operation within brackets,
	$= 7.125 \times 10^4$	Answer in scientific notation.
	(iii) $(7.5 \times 10^{-6}) \times (5.0 \times 10^4)$	Multiplying the coefficients and adding the exponents,
	$= (7.5 \times 5.0) \times 10^{(-6 + 4)}$	Performing arithmetic operation within brackets,
	$= 37.5 \times 10^{-2}$	Answer **not** in scientific notation.
	$= 37.5 \times 10^{(-2+1)}$	Converting to scientific notation,
	$= 3.75 \times 10^{-1}$	Answer in scientific notation.

Division of Numbers in Scientific Notation

We have already seen that dividing a power by another power of the same base is equivalent to subtracting their exponents.

Numbers in scientific notation are coefficients multiplied by powers of the same base: 10.

Therefore, to divide two numbers in scientific notation, divide their coefficients and subtract their exponents on the power of 10. If the answer is not in scientific notation (i.e., the coefficient is not between 1 and 10), convert it to scientific notation.

For example,

$(2.48 \times 10^6) \div (8.0 \times 10^2)$	Dividing the coefficients and subtracting the exponents,
$= \dfrac{2.48}{8.0} \times 10^{(6-2)}$	Performing arithmetic operations,
$= 0.31 \times 10^4$	Answer **not** in scientific notation.
$= 0.31 \times 10^{(4-1)}$	Converting to scientific notation,
$= 3.1 \times 10^3$	Answer in scientific notation.

Note: When the decimal point is moved to the right, the coefficient is increased by a power of 10; as a result, the exponent on the 10 must be decreased by 1 for every place value that the decimal point was moved to the right in the coefficient.

Example 3.4-m **Dividing Numbers in Scientific Notation**

Divide the following:

(i) $(4.68 \times 10^{-3}) \div (6.5 \times 10^{-5})$ (ii) $(3.5 \times 10^8) \div (4.0 \times 10^{-4})$ (iii) $(9.2 \times 10^{-3}) \div (1.15 \times 10^2)$

Solution

(i)
$(4.68 \times 10^{-3}) \div (6.5 \times 10^{-5})$	Dividing the coefficients and subtracting the exponents,
$= \dfrac{4.68}{6.5} \times 10^{[-3-(-5)]}$	Performing arithmetic operations,
$= 0.72 \times 10^2$	Answer **not** in scientific notation.
$= 0.72 \times 10^{(2-1)}$	Converting to scientific notation,
$= 7.2 \times 10^1$	Answer in scientific notation.

(ii)
$(3.5 \times 10^8) \div (4.0 \times 10^{-4})$	Dividing the coefficients and subtracting the exponents,
$= \dfrac{3.5}{4.0} \times 10^{[8-(-4)]}$	Performing arithmetic operations,
$= 0.875 \times 10^{12}$	Answer **not** in scientific notation.
$= 0.875 \times 10^{(12-1)}$	Converting to scientific notation,
$= 8.75 \times 10^{11}$	Answer in scientific notation.

(iii)
$(9.2 \times 10^{-3}) \div (1.15 \times 10^2)$	Dividing the coefficients and subtracting the exponents,
$= \dfrac{9.2}{1.15} \times 10^{(-3-2)}$	Performing arithmetic operations,
$= 8 \times 10^{-5}$	Answer in scientific notation.

Example 3.4-n | **Combined Multiplication and Division of Numbers in Scientific Notation**

Evaluate:

(i) $\dfrac{(7.4 \times 10^6) \times (3.75 \times 10^5)}{2.5 \times 10^4}$

(ii) $\dfrac{(3.5 \times 10^{-8}) \times (1.2 \times 10^{-3})}{5.6 \times 10^{-7}}$

Solution

(i) $\dfrac{(7.4 \times 10^6) \times (3.75 \times 10^5)}{2.5 \times 10^4}$ Multiplying the coefficients within the numerator and dividing it by the coefficient in the denominator, then adding the exponents within the numerator and subtracting the exponent of the denominator,

$= \dfrac{(7.4 \times 3.75)}{2.5} \times 10^{(6 + 5 - 4)}$ Performing arithmetic operations within brackets,

$= 11.1 \times 10^7$ Answer **not** in scientific notation.

$= 11.1 \times 10^{(7 + 1)}$ Converting to scientific notation,

$= 1.11 \times 10^8$ Answer in scientific notation.

(ii) $\dfrac{(3.5 \times 10^{-8}) \times (1.2 \times 10^{-3})}{5.6 \times 10^{-7}}$ Multiplying the coefficients within the numerator and dividing it by the coefficient in the denominator, then adding the exponents within the numerator and subtracting the exponent of the denominator,

$= \dfrac{(3.5 \times 1.2)}{5.6} \times 10^{[-8 + (-3) - (-7)]}$ Performing arithmetic operations within brackets,

$= 0.75 \times 10^{-4}$ Answer **not** in scientific notation.

$= 0.75 \times 10^{(-4 - 1)}$ Converting to scientific notation,

$= 7.5 \times 10^{-5}$ Answer in scientific notation.

3.4 | Exercises

Answers to odd-numbered problems are available at the end of the textbook.

For Problems 1 to 10, determine the number of significant digits in each of the numbers.

1. a. 700   b. 9,070   2. a. 46,000   b. 10,200

3. a. 5.70   b. 30.40   4. a. 9.00   b. 20.80

5. a. 6.250   b. 70.0164   6. a. 4.530   b. 20.325

7. a. 0.4700   b. 24.805   8. a. 0.2010   b. 15.407

9. a. 0.008   b. 0.0224   10. a. 0.000004   b. 0.0825

For Problems 11 to 20, round the numbers to (i) 3 significant digits and (ii) 2 significant digits.

11. a. 5,065   b. 1,982   12. a. 5,465   b. 1,978

13. a. 589.025   b. 57.3892   14. a. 821.782   b. 40.9055

15. a. 48.4848   b. 25.859   16. a. 99.0999   b. 91.555

17. a. 0.7750   b. 6.07344   18. a. 0.8150   b. 9.0085

19. a. 0.098901   b. 6.6666   20. a. 0.05555   b. 7.7777

For Problems 21 to 26, perform the indicated arithmetic operations and round the answer to the same number of decimal places as the number with the least number of decimal places.

21. a. 142.135 + 9.12   b. 324.761 + 28.4   22. a. 215.241 + 6.37   b. 532.863 + 59.9

23. a. 287.657 − 6.42   b. 466.945 − 54.8   24. a. 354.657 − 7.89   b. 465.976 − 99.7

25. a. 30.6 + 4.703 − 9.09   b. 44.9 − 1.906 − 0.61   26. a. 50.7 + 9.856 − 21.05   b. 27.02 − 9.5 − 0.081

For Problems 27 to 32, perform the indicated arithmetic operations and round the answer to the same number of significant digits as the number with the least number of significant digits.

27. a. 67.86×9.8 b. 152.92×45.5 28. a. 59.43×8.2 b. 253.15×38.4

29. a. $99.33 \div 9.9$ b. $225.25 \div 25.5$ 30. a. $46.66 \div 0.6$ b. $315.15 \div 15.15$

31. a. $54.75 \times 1.21 \times 4,500$ b. $1.90 \times 380 \div 0.95$ 32. a. $25.5 \times 1.825 \times 3,600$ b. $5.07 \times 4,500 \div 13.5$

For Problems 33 to 42, write the numbers in scientific notation.

33. a. 235   b. 42,300   34. a. 745   b. 15,700

35. a. 12.75   b. 78.91   36. a. 18.25   b. 90.54

37. a. 0.58   b. 0.048   38. a. 0.74   b. 0.089

39. a. 0.0038   b. 0.0002   40. a. 0.0096   b. 0.0007

41. a. 0.06×10^8 b. 0.0025×10^{-9} 42. a. 0.03×10^5 b. 0.0046×10^{-10}

For Problems 43 to 52, write the numbers in standard notation.

43. a. 4.6×10^4 b. 2.9×10^0 44. a. 3.7×10^3 b. 4.75×10^1

45. a. 3.09×10^6 b. 4.654×10^4 46. a. 7.54×10^4 b. 8.015×10^5

47. a. 8.9×10^{-1} b. 2.16×10^{-4} 48. a. 6.8×10^{-2} b. 4.65×10^{-3}

49. a. 3.15×10^{-3} b. 6.15×10^{-5} 50. a. 1.29×10^{-4} b. 9.17×10^{-3}

51. a. 0.0056×10^3 b. 406.5×10^{-6} 52. a. 0.0076×10^4 b. 675.7×10^{-5}

For Problems 53 to 72, perform the arithmetic operations and write the answers in scientific notation. Do not round the answers.

53. $(8.5 \times 10^5) + (3.84 \times 10^4)$

54. $(6.35 \times 10^6) + (5.07 \times 10^7)$

55. $(9.82 \times 10^{-3}) + (1.58 \times 10^{-4})$

56. $(7.92 \times 10^{-5}) + (9.72 \times 10^{-3})$

57. $(3.1 \times 10^9) - (2.6 \times 10^8)$

58. $(8.2 \times 10^7) - (4.7 \times 10^6)$

59. $(7.54 \times 10^{-2}) - (3.25 \times 10^{-3})$

60. $(2.58 \times 10^{-2}) - (1.99 \times 10^{-4})$

61. $(2.5 \times 10^4) + (8.9 \times 10^2) - (1.5 \times 10^3)$

62. $(6.7 \times 10^3) + (7.4 \times 10^2) - (8.6 \times 10^1)$

63. $(1.1 \times 10^5) \times (8.6 \times 10^8)$

64. $(4.75 \times 10^4) \times (2.0 \times 10^6)$

65. $(7.5 \times 10^{-12}) \times (4.2 \times 10^5)$

66. $(8.25 \times 10^3) \times (4 \times 10^{-6})$

67. $(4.8 \times 10^5) \div (1.5 \times 10^8)$

68. $(9.25 \times 10^{10}) \div (5.0 \times 10^4)$

69. $(3.84 \times 10^{-2}) \div (7.68 \times 10^{-4})$

70. $(6.48 \times 10^{-4}) \div (9.72 \times 10^{-6})$

71. $(9.8 \times 10^{-4}) \times (5 \times 10^{-3}) \div (3.5 \times 10^{-9})$

72. $(3.6 \times 10^{-5}) \times (1.8 \times 10^{-6}) \div (7.2 \times 10^{-14})$

3 | Review Exercises

1. Find the difference between 2^5 and 5^2.

2. Find the difference between 3^4 and 4^3.

3. Express 243 as a power of 3 and then evaluate $243^{\frac{3}{5}}$.

4. Express 512 as a power of 2 and then evaluate $512^{\frac{4}{9}}$.

For Problems 5 to 8, express the expression as a single exponent using laws of exponents, and evaluate.

5. a. $(2^6)^{\frac{1}{3}}$

   b. $\left(\dfrac{3^9}{3^3}\right)^{\frac{1}{3}}$

6. a. $(5^{15})^{\frac{1}{5}}$

   b. $\left(\dfrac{2^{12}}{2^4}\right)^{\frac{1}{4}}$

7. a. $(3^2)^{\frac{1}{2}} \times (3^3)^{\frac{2}{3}}$ b. $(6^2)^{\frac{1}{3}} \times (6^3)^{\frac{2}{9}}$

8. a. $(2^2)^{\frac{1}{4}} \times (2^5)^{\frac{3}{10}}$ b. $(5^3)^{\frac{2}{3}} \times (5^2)^{\frac{1}{2}}$

For Problems 9 to 16, simplify using laws of exponents and then evaluate.

9. a. $\dfrac{2^3 \times 3^4 \times 2^2}{3 \times 2^5}$ b. $\dfrac{(5^2)^3 \times 5^4}{5^7}$

10. a. $\dfrac{5^2 \times 7^3 \times 5^4}{7 \times 5^6}$ b. $\dfrac{(2^5)^4 \times 2^2}{2^{17}}$

11. a. $(-5)^2 \times (4)^2$ b. $-10^4 \times 10^3$

12. a. $(-2)^2 \times (3)^2$ b. $-2^4 \times 2^2$

13. a. $(125)^{-\frac{1}{3}}$ b. $(49)^{-\frac{1}{2}}$ c. $\sqrt{\dfrac{64}{81}}$

14. a. $(16)^{-\frac{1}{4}}$ b. $(27)^{-\frac{1}{3}}$ c. $\sqrt{\dfrac{25}{4}}$

15. a. $\sqrt{7^4}$ b. $\sqrt{\dfrac{25}{36}}$ c. $\sqrt[3]{\dfrac{216}{125}}$

16. a. $\sqrt{5^6}$ b. $\sqrt{\dfrac{64}{81}}$ c. $\sqrt[3]{\dfrac{64}{27}}$

Evaluate Problems 17 to 32 and express the answers rounded to two decimal places wherever applicable.

17. a. $\dfrac{16 + 4(-3)}{10 - 4 + 1} + \dfrac{(16 + 4) - 3}{10 - (4 + 1)}$

    b. $14 - 3[(6 - 9)(-4) + 12] \div (-2)$

18. a. $\dfrac{2(-6) + 4}{24 - (7 + 3)} + \dfrac{2(-6 + 4)}{24 - 7 + 3}$

    b. $5(-4) - 3[(-9 + 6) + (-3) - 4]$

19. a. $[(1 + 11)(1 - 5)]^2 \div [(5 + 3) \times 2^2 - (-2)^2]$

    b. $2^2[(9 - 7) \div 2 + 9 - 4]$

20. a. $8 \div 4 + (4 - 6^2) \div (13 - 5) \times (-2)^6$

    b. $6 \div [4 \times (2 - 8) \div (3^2 + 3)] \div 4$

21. a. $64 \div (-2)^4 + 4(-3^2) \div 2 - 5$

    b. $(-6)^2 - 9^2 \div 3^3 - (-3)(-2)$

22. a. $8 \div (-2)^3(-9) + 6(-5)^3 \div (-5)^2$

    b. $(-8)^2 - 4^3 \div 2^2 - (-6)(-2)$

23. a. $6{,}000\left(1 + \dfrac{0.06}{12}\right)^{36}$

    b. $2{,}000(1 + 0.004)^{-24}$

24. a. $4{,}000\left(1 + \dfrac{0.075}{12}\right)^{60}$

    b. $5{,}000(1 + 0.003)^{-48}$

25. $\dfrac{3{,}000[(1.06)^{25} - 1]}{0.06}$

26. $\dfrac{1{,}400[(1.03)^{30} - 1]}{0.03}$

27. $\dfrac{950[1 - (1.03)^{15}]}{0.03}$

28. $\dfrac{1{,}200[1 - (1.04)^{-20}]}{0.04}$

29. a. $-15 - (-15)$

    b. $-14 - (-7)$

30. a. $13 - (-11)$

    b. $22 - (-4) - 6$

31. a. $8 + |2 - 7|$

    b. $-|-23| - |10 - 15|$

32. a. $15 - |3 - 9|$

    b. $-|-42| - |35 - 18|$

33. Determine the number of significant digits in each of the following numbers and write them in scientific notation:

    a. 7,100   b. 54.001   c. 0.0072

34. Determine the number of significant digits in each of the following numbers and write them in scientific notation:

    a. 54,020   b. 0.250   c. 0.09081

35. Write the numbers in standard form.

    a. 8.9×10^2 b. 5.6×10^{-2} c. 9.64×10^{-4}

36. Write the numbers in standard form.

    a. 5.1×10^3 b. 6.8×10^{-4} c. 4.75×10^{-4}

131

For Problems 37 to 46, perform the arithmetic operations and write the answers in scientific notation. Do not round the answer.

37. a. $4.65 \times 10^{14} + 9.95 \times 10^{12}$

    b. $7.02 \times 10^{-2} + 6.95 \times 10^{-3}$

38. a. $7.28 \times 10^{6} + 4.35 \times 10^{5}$

    b. $1.64 \times 10^{-12} + 5.5 \times 10^{-10}$

39. a. $4.01 \times 10^{6} - 3.56 \times 10^{4}$

    b. $3.56 \times 10^{-3} - 8.01 \times 10^{-4}$

40. a. $1.25 \times 10^{7} - 9.75 \times 10^{5}$

    b. $2.85 \times 10^{-1} - 7.45 \times 10^{-3}$

41. a. $(6.0 \times 10^{4}) \times (4.0 \times 10^{7})$

    b. $(7.5 \times 10^{-6}) \times (6.0 \times 10^{-5})$

42. a. $(7.75 \times 10^{6}) \times (2.0 \times 10^{8})$

    b. $(9.45 \times 10^{-5}) \times (3.0 \times 10^{-7})$

43. a. $(2.0 \times 10^{5}) \div (4.0 \times 10^{8})$

    b. $(1.45 \times 10^{-9}) \div (5.8 \times 10^{-3})$

44. a. $(1.75 \times 10^{4}) \div (3.50 \times 10^{-6})$

    b. $(1.61 \times 10^{-7}) \div (4.83 \times 10^{-2})$

45. $\dfrac{(4.3 \times 10^{8}) \times (7.8 \times 10^{3})}{1.2 \times 10^{4}}$

46. $\dfrac{(1.6 \times 10^{-6}) \times (2.4 \times 10^{-9})}{4.8 \times 10^{-2}}$

3 | Self-Test Exercises

Answers to all problems are available at the end of the textbook.

For the following problems, simplify and express the answers rounded to two decimal places wherever applicable.

1. Express the following as a power of the indicated bases:

    a. 625 as a power of 5.

    b. 729 as a power of 3.

    c. 128 as a power of 2.

2. Express the following as a power of the indicated bases:

    a. $(9)^{\frac{3}{2}}$ as a power of 3

    b. $(16)^{\frac{3}{4}}$ as a power of 2

3. Express the following as a single power:

    a. $3^{4} \times 3^{(4 + 2)}$

    b. $10^{4} \times 10^{(3 + 2)}$

4. Simplify using laws of exponents and then evaluate:

    a. $\dfrac{2^{3} \times (3^{2})^{3} \times 3^{4}}{2^{3} \times (2^{3})^{2} \times 3^{5}}$ b. $\dfrac{2^{4} \times (3^{2})^{4} \times 2^{2}}{2^{3} \times (3^{3})^{2} \times 2^{0}}$

Evaluate Problems 5 to 19.

5. a. $(2^{2} \times 3 \times 5^{0})^{-1}$ b. $(3^{2} \times 2^{-2} \times 5)^{0}$

6. a. $\left(\dfrac{3}{2}\right)^{2} + \dfrac{3}{8}$

    b. $\dfrac{3}{2} \div \dfrac{15}{8} \times \sqrt{16}$

    c. $4 \times \dfrac{8}{5} \div \dfrac{4}{3} + \sqrt{4} - 1$

7. a. $\dfrac{2}{5} \times \sqrt{100} + 2^{4} + \dfrac{5}{3}$

    b. $\dfrac{3}{4} + \left(\dfrac{2}{5}\right)^{3}$

    c. $\sqrt{36} \times \dfrac{4}{3} \div \dfrac{8}{6} - 7 + 2$

8. a. $\left(\dfrac{2}{3} + \dfrac{4}{3}\right)^{5}$ b. $\left(\dfrac{5^{-\frac{1}{3}}}{2^{-2}}\right)^{3}$

9. a. $\left(\dfrac{9^{\frac{2}{5}}}{9^{\frac{3}{5}}}\right) \times 3^{2}$ b. $\left(\dfrac{8^{-\frac{5}{9}}}{9^{-\frac{7}{9}}}\right) \times 2^{3}$

10. a. $-5^{3} \times (-25)^{3}$ b. $-100^{2} \times (-10)^{4}$

11. a. $3^{-2} \times 3^{3}$ b. $12^{-8} \times 12^{9}$

12. a. $(-3)^{3} - (-1)^{3}$

    b. $(-2)^{5} \times (4 - 5)^{3} - (-10)$

    c. $1,250 \times \left(1 + 0.02 \times \dfrac{136}{365}\right)^{-1}$

13. a. $(-5)^{3} - (-4)^{3}$

    b. $(-4)^{5} \div (-2)^{6}$

    c. $5,600 \times \left(1 + 0.04 \times \dfrac{219}{365}\right)^{-1}$

14. a. $200(1.08)^{7}$

    b. $450(1.03)^{-2}$

15. a. $2,000\left[1 + \dfrac{0.075}{12}\right]^{-60}$

    b. $4,500\left[1 + \dfrac{0.048}{4}\right]^{-15}$

16. $\dfrac{3,600[(1.06)^{5} - 1]}{0.06}$

17. $\dfrac{4,400[1 - (1.03)^{-20}]}{0.03}$

18. a. $-9 + |(-4) + (-2)|$

    b. $|8 - (-5) - (-3)|$

    c. $|12 - 8 \times 2| - |-4|$

19. a. $\dfrac{16^{\frac{1}{2}} \times 6}{81^{\frac{1}{2}}}$ b. $\dfrac{9^{\frac{1}{2}} \times 81^{\frac{1}{2}}}{13^2 - 5^2}$

20. Write the numbers in scientific notation:

   a. 10.09   b. 0.005   c. 60,200

21. Write the numbers in standard form:

   a. 2.7×10^3 b. 4.15×10^{-3} c. 3.0405×10^{-2}

Perform the arithmetic operations and express the answers in scientific notation. Do not round the answers.

22. a. $4.01 \times 10^4 + 9.99 \times 10^3$

   b. $2.004 \times 10^{-6} + 8.95 \times 10^{-5}$

23. a. $3.04 \times 10^6 - 2.512 \times 10^5$

   b. $4.06 \times 10^{-8} - 9.94 \times 10^{-7}$

24. a. $(6.50 \times 10^7) \times (8.0 \times 10^{-9})$

   b. $(1.225 \times 10^{14}) \div (8.75 \times 10^{-6})$

4 BASIC ALGEBRA

LEARNING OBJECTIVES

- Perform basic arithmetic operations on algebraic expressions.
- Setup basic linear equations with one variable.
- Solve linear equations with one variable using various arithmetic operations.
- Create, rearrange, and use equations to solve for unknown variables.

CHAPTER OUTLINE

4.1 Algebraic Expressions

4.2 Simple Algebraic Equations and Word Problems

4.3 Rearranging Equations and Formulas

Introduction

Algebra is a branch of mathematics that introduces the concept of using variables to represent numbers. These variables, together with numbers, use rules of operations to express statements and equations. Algebra provides a framework from which formulas are derived to solve general problems and will help develop logical-thinking and problem-solving skills in a systematic and analytical way. The study of algebra is required in any occupational field, including the health sciences.

4.1 | Algebraic Expressions

Algebraic expressions consist of one or more **terms** involving a combination of variables, numbers, and operations. In order to solve most problems in mathematics, the use of equations and formulas is necessary. These equations and formulas are formed using algebraic expressions.

In arithmetic, we use only numbers in expressions. For example,

$$25 + 15, \qquad 75 - 22, \qquad 8 \times 9, \qquad \frac{9}{5}$$

Algebra is a branch of mathematics that is used to analyze and solve practical problems by using letters and symbols to represent numbers, values, etc.

In algebra, we use both numbers and **variables** (letters and symbols that represent various numbers) in expressions. For example,

$$2x + 5, \qquad 30 - 5y, \qquad 6(2a + 5), \qquad \frac{b + 3}{2}$$

Also, in algebra, we use variables, numbers, and operations to translate word problems into equations.

For example, if the sum of two numbers is 100, it can be represented by the equation:

$x + y = 100$

If $x = 40$, then $y = 60$.

If $x = 10$, then $y = 90$.

Note: In algebraic expressions involving multiplication, the number and the variable(s) can be written together without the operation sign for multiplication.

For example, 5a means $5 \times a$, or 5(a), or $5 \cdot a$. Similarly, xy means $x \times y$, or x(y), or $x \cdot y$.

The following key words will help in translating word problems into algebraic expressions and forming equations:

Table 4.1-a **Arithmetic Operations and their Meanings**

Operations	Key Words
Addition (+)	add, sum, total, and, plus, more than, increased by, appreciate, rise
Subtraction (–)	subtract, difference, minus, less than, decreased by, depreciate, fall
Multiplication (×), (·)	multiply, product, times, of
Division (÷), (/)	divide, ratio, divided by, quotient, per
Equal (=)	is, was, gives, given by

The examples below illustrate how to translate word problems into algebraic expressions using the key words above:

In words	In algebraic expression
• Ten more than a number	$x + 10$
• A number more than ten	$10 + x$
• Twenty less than a number	$x - 20$
• A number less than twenty	$20 - x$
• Product of five and a number	$5x$
• Divide a number by 20	$\dfrac{x}{20}$
• Divide 20 by a number	$\dfrac{20}{x}$
• Half of a number	$\dfrac{1}{2}x$ or $\dfrac{x}{2}$
• Twice a number	$2x$
• Ten more than the product of two numbers	$xy + 10$
• 'x' less than 'y' or 'y' minus 'x'	$y - x$
• 'y' less than 'x' or 'x' minus 'y'	$x - y$
• Seventy decreased by 3 times a number	$70 - 3x$
• 'm' subtracted from 'n'	$n - m$

Terminology used in Algebraic Expressions

Terminology	Description	Examples
Variable	A letter or symbol used in expressions and equations to represent a varying or unknown quantity.	x, y, a, b In the expression $2m + 5n - 6$, m and n are variables.
Term	A number, variable, or a combination of numbers and variables which are multiplied or divided together.	$5, x, 5x^2y, 2xy, \dfrac{4}{a}, \dfrac{b}{3}$ are all single terms. The expression $5x + y$ has 2 terms. The expression $\dfrac{x}{4} - y^2 + \dfrac{x}{y} - \dfrac{1}{x}$ has 4 terms.
Constant	A term that only has a number with no variables.	In the expression $2x + 3y + 5$, the 3rd term, $+5$, is a constant. In the expression $5x^2 - 8$, the 2nd term, -8, is a constant.
Coefficient	The product of all numerical factors in a single term involving a variable.	Coefficient of x^2 is 1, the coefficient of $\dfrac{7}{4}x$ is $\dfrac{7}{4}$, and the coefficient of $-3x(2y^3)$ is -6. In the expression $5x^2 - 2y + 3$, the coefficient of the 1st term is 5, and the coefficient of the 2nd term is -2. The third term ($+3$) is a constant term that does not involve a variable, so it does not have a coefficient.

Terminology	Description	Examples
Expression	A mathematical phrase made up of a combination of terms and operations.	Expressions with one variable: $(2x + 5)$, $(9x - 3)$ Expressions with two variables: $(5x - 7y + 5)$, $(xy + 3x + 7)$
Like terms	Terms that have the same variables and exponents. They differ only in their numerical coefficient. Constant terms are like terms.	$5x$ and $9x$ are like terms. $30a^2$, $-4a^2$, and $9a^2$ are like terms. 5, -9 are like terms.
Unlike terms	Terms that have different variables or the same variables with different exponents.	$12y$ and $3y^2$ are unlike terms. x, y, and 1 are unlike terms. $5xy$, $-3x^2y$, and $7xy^2$ are unlike terms.
Factors	Refer to each of the combinations of variables and/or numbers multiplied together in a term.	5 and x are factors of the term $5x$. 3, x, and y are factors of the term $3xy$.
Monomial	An algebraic expression that has only one term.	8, $7x$, $4y$, and $2xy$ are monomials.
Polynomial	An algebraic expression that has two or more terms.	$(8x^2 - 5x + 3)$ is a polynomial with 3 terms, where the 1st term is $8x^2$, the 2nd term is $-5x$, and the 3rd term is 3. The coefficient of the 1st term is 8, and the coefficient of the 2nd term is -5. The 3rd term is a constant.
Binomial	A polynomial with 2 terms.	$(4x - 3y)$, $(x - 5)$, $(4xy + 7x)$ are binomials.
Trinomial	A polynomial with 3 terms.	$(2x + 3y + 5)$, $(xy + x - 2)$, $(2x + xy + 3z)$ are trinomials.

Evaluating Algebraic Expressions

In an algebraic expression, the process of replacing all the variables with numerical values and simplifying the expression is referred to as evaluating the algebraic expression. The simplified answer is the value of the expression.

Example 4.1-a Evaluating Algebraic Expressions

Evaluate the following expressions:

(i) $2x + y$, where $x = 10$ and $y = 5$

(ii) $\dfrac{3xy + 3x}{2y + 5}$, where $x = 3$ and $y = 2$

Solution

(i) $2x + y$ Substituting $x = 10$ and $y = 5$,

        $= 2(10) + 5$ [Recall: $2x$ means $2(x)$]

        $= 20 + 5 = 25$

(ii) $\dfrac{3xy + 3x}{2y + 5}$ Substituting $x = 3$ and $y = 2$,

        $= \dfrac{3(3)(2) + 3(3)}{2(2) + 5}$

        $= \dfrac{18 + 9}{4 + 5} = \dfrac{27}{9} = 3$

Example 4.1-b **Evaluating Algebraic Expressions with Exponents**

Evaluate the following expressions:

(i) $\dfrac{(5x)^2 \times 4y}{50}$, where $x = 2$ and $y = 3$ 　　　(ii) 　$2(x^2 + 3x) - 5y$, where $x = 4$ and $y = -3$

Solution

(i) $\dfrac{(5x)^2 \times 4y}{50}$ 　　　　　　　　Substituting $x = 2$ and $y = 3$,

$= \dfrac{[5(2)]^2 \times 4(3)}{50}$

$= \dfrac{10^2 \times 12}{50} = \dfrac{100 \times 12}{50} = 24$

(ii) $2(x^2 + 3x) - 5y$ 　　　　　Substituting $x = 4$ and $y = -3$,

$= 2[(4)^2 + 3(4)] - 5(-3)$

$= 2(16 + 12) + 15 = 56 + 15 = 71$

Basic Arithmetic Operations with Algebraic Expressions

All arithmetic operations can be applied to algebraic expressions by following the applicable rules (BEDMAS, exponents, signed numbers, etc.). Arithmetic operations can be commutative, associative, or distributive, which are properties discussed in the following table:

Table 4.1-b **Commutative, Associative, and Distributive Properties**

Property	Algebraic Definition	Example
Commutative: The order of the numbers does not alter the final result.	Addition: $a + b = b + a$ Multiplication: $a \times b = b \times a$	$2 + 3 = 5$ and $3 + 2 = 5$ $6 \times 2 = 12$ and $2 \times 6 = 12$
Associative: The grouping of the numbers does not alter the final result.	Addition: $a + (b + c) = (a + b) + c$ Multiplication: $(a \times b) \times c = a \times (b \times c)$	$8 + (2 + 4) = (8 + 2) + 4$ $(10 \times 5) \times 9 = 10 \times (5 \times 9)$
Distributive: An operation on an expression in brackets can be expanded and applied to each term within the brackets.	Multiplication over Addition: $a \times (b + c) = ab + ac$ Multiplication over Subtraction: $a \times (b - c) = ab - ac$	$5 \times (1 + 4) = (5 \times 1) + (5 \times 4)$ $3 \times (7 - 2) = (3 \times 7) - (3 \times 2)$

Addition and Subtraction

Addition and Subtraction of Monomials

Addition and subtraction of like monomials (i.e., the same variables with the same exponents) can be performed by adding or subtracting the coefficients according to the rules of signed numbers. Unlike monomials can be added and subtracted, but the resulting expression cannot be simplified.

Note: If a coefficient of a term is not written, it is 1.

Example 4.1-c

Adding and Subtracting Monomials

(i)   Add $6x$ and $3x$

(ii) Add $4x^2y$ and x^2y

(iii) Subtract $5x^3$ from $7x^3$

(iv) Subtract $8x$ from the sum of $7x$ and $4x$

(v)   Add $5x$ and $6y$

(vi) Subtract $2y^2$ from $7y^3$

Solution

(i) $6x + 3x$ Adding like terms,

    $= 9x$

(ii) $4x^2y + x^2y$ Adding like terms,

    $= 5x^2y$

(iii) $7x^3 - 5x^3$ Subtracting like terms,

    $= 2x^3$

(iv) $(7x + 4x) - (8x)$ Adding like terms inside the brackets

    $= 11x - 8x$ Subtracting like terms,

    $= 3x$

(v) $5x + 6y$ Since these are not like terms, we cannot simplify the expression at all.

(vi) $7y^3 - 2y^2$ Since these are not like terms, we cannot simplify the expression at all.

Addition and Subtraction of Polynomials

When grouping like terms, the sign of the term moves with the term.

When adding or subtracting algebraic expressions, first collect the like terms and group them, then add or subtract the coefficients of the like terms.

Addition of Polynomials, Indicated by a Plus '+' Sign Outside the Brackets

Brackets can be removed without changing any of the signs of the terms within the brackets.

Subtraction of Polynomials, Indicated by a Negative '–' Sign Outside the Brackets

Brackets can be removed by distributing the negative sign to terms within the brackets, which is equivalent to multiplying every term within the brackets by –1, resulting in the signs changing on each term within the brackets.

Example 4.1-d

Adding and Subtracting Algebraic Expressions

(i)   Add $(3x + 7)$ and $(5x + 3)$

(ii) Add $(4y^2 - 8y - 9)$ and $(2y^2 + 6y - 2)$

(iii) Subtract $(x^2 + 5x - 7)$ from $(2x^2 - 2x + 3)$

(iv) Subtract $[5x - (x + 8)]$ from $(x - 3)$

Solution

(i) $(3x + 7) + (5x + 3)$ Removing brackets,

When a bracket is preceded by a positive sign (+), then drop the brackets.

    $= 3x + 7 + 5x + 3$ Grouping like terms,

    $= \underline{3x + 5x} + \underline{7 + 3}$ Adding like terms,

    $= 8x + 10$

(ii) $(4y^2 - 8y - 9) + (2y^2 + 6y - 2)$ Removing brackets,

$\qquad = 4y^2 - 8y - 9 + 2y^2 + 6y - 2$ Grouping like terms,

$\qquad = \underline{4y^2 + 2y^2} \; \underline{- 8y + 6y} \; \underline{- 9 - 2}$ Adding and subtracting like terms,

$\qquad = 6y^2 - 2y - 11$

> When a bracket is preceded by a negative sign (−), change the sign of every term within the brackets, then drop the brackets.

(iii) $(2x^2 - 2x + 3) - (x^2 + 5x - 7)$ Removing brackets by distributing the negative sign to all the terms within the bracket,

$\qquad = 2x^2 - 2x + 3 - x^2 - 5x + 7$ Grouping like terms,

$\qquad = \underline{2x^2 - x^2} \; \underline{- 2x - 5x} \; \underline{+ 3 + 7}$ Adding and subtracting like terms,

$\qquad = x^2 - 7x + 10$

(iv) $(x - 3) - [5x - (x + 8)]$ Removing brackets by distributing the negative sign to all the terms within the bracket,

$\qquad = x - 3 - [5x - x - 8]$

$\qquad = x - 3 - 5x + x + 8$ Grouping like terms,

$\qquad = \underline{x - 5x + x} \; \underline{- 3 + 8}$ Adding and subtracting like terms,

$\qquad = -3x + 5$

Multiplication

Multiplying Monomials by Monomials

When multiplying a monomial by a monomial, multiply the coefficients together and multiply the variables together, grouping and simplifying like variables following the exponent rules from Chapter 3.1.

Example 4.1-e   **Multiplying Monomials by Monomials**

(i)   Multiply $6x^2y$ and $5xy$

(ii)   Multiply $(3a^3)$, $(-4a^2b^5)$, and $(2b^2)$

(iii)   Multiply $(-12pr)$, $(\frac{2}{3}q^2r^3)$, and $(-\frac{3}{4}p^3q)$

(i) $(6x^2y)(5xy)$ Grouping coefficients and variables,

$\qquad = (6)(5)(x^2)(x)(y)(y)$ Multiplying the coefficients, and multiplying the variables by adding the exponents of like variables (Product Rule from Chapter 3.1),

$\qquad = 30x^3y^2$

(ii) $(3a^3)(-4a^2b^5)(2b^2)$ Grouping coefficients and variables,

$\qquad = (3)(-4)(2)(a^3)(a^2)(b^5)(b^2)$ Multiplying the coefficients, and multiplying the variables by adding the exponents of like variables,

$\qquad = -24a^5b^7$

(iii) $(-12pr), (\frac{2}{3}q^2r^3)(-\frac{3}{4}p^3q)$ Grouping coefficients and variables,

$\qquad = (-12)(\frac{2}{3})(-\frac{3}{4})(p)(p^3)(q^2)(q)(r)(r^3)$ Multiplying the coefficients, and multiplying the variables by adding the exponents of like variables,

$\qquad = 6p^4q^3r^4$

Multiplying Polynomials by Monomials

When multiplying a polynomial by a monomial, multiply the monomial by **each term** of the polynomial. This is also known as the distributive property of multiplication, as shown below.

$$a(b + c) = ab + ac$$

Then, group the like terms and simplify using addition and subtraction.

Example 4.1-f

Multiplying Polynomials by Monomials

(i)   Multiply: $2x^3$ and $(3x^2 + 2x - 5)$

(ii) Expand and simplify: $8x\,(x + 3) + 4x\,(x - 4)$

(iii) Expand and simplify: $\dfrac{1}{5}\{5y - 15[2 - 3(y - 2)] + 25\}$

Solution

(i) $2x^3\,(3x^2 + 2x - 5)$ Expanding, by following the Product Rule from Chapter 3.1

    $= 6x^5 + 4x^4 - 10x^3$

(ii) $8x\,(x + 3) + 4x\,(x - 4)$ Expanding,

    $= 8x^2 + 24x + 4x^2 - 16x$ Grouping like terms,

    $= \underline{8x^2 + 4x^2} + \underline{24x - 16x}$ Adding and subtracting like terms,

    $= 12x^2 + 8x$

(iii) $\dfrac{1}{5}\{5y - 15[2 - 3(y - 2)] + 25\}$ Expanding the inner brackets,

    $= \dfrac{1}{5}\{5y - 15[2 - 3y + 6] + 25\}$

    $= \dfrac{1}{5}\{5y - 30 + 45y - 90 + 25\}$ Grouping like terms,

    $= \dfrac{1}{5}\,\{\underline{5y + 45y} \;\underline{- 30 - 90 + 25}\}$ Adding and subtracting like terms,

    $= \dfrac{1}{5}\,\{50y - 95\}$ Expanding the outer brackets,

    $= 10y - 19$

Multiplying a Binomial by a Binomial

When multiplying two binomials, multiply each term of the first binomial by each term of the second binomial. This is the same as adding the product of the **F**irst terms, **O**utside terms, **I**nside terms, and **L**ast terms of each binomial, which can be remembered by the acronym "**FOIL**".

$$(a + b)(c + d) = a \cdot c + a \cdot d + b \cdot c + b \cdot d$$

The same result is obtained by using the distributive property to expand.

$$(a + b)\,(c + d) = a(c + d) + b(c + d)$$

$$= a \cdot c + a \cdot d + b \cdot c + b \cdot d$$

Then, group the like terms and simplify using addition and subtraction.

Example 4.1-g **Multiplying Two Binomials**

(i)   Multiply $(x + 5)$ and $(x + 6)$

(ii) Multiply $(2x + 3)$ and $(3x - 4)$

Solution

(i) $(x + 5)(x + 6)$

$(x + 5)(x + 6)$

$= x^2 \underline{+ 6x + 5x} + 30$

$= x^2 + 11x + 30$

or

$x(x + 6) + 5(x + 6)$

$= x^2 \underline{+ 6x + 5x} + 30$

$= x^2 + 11x + 30$

(ii) $(2x + 3)(3x - 4)$

$(2x + 3)(3x - 4)$

$= 6x^2 \underbrace{- 8x + 9x} - 12$

$= 6x^2 + x - 12$

or

$2x(3x - 4) + 3(3x - 4)$

$= 6x^2 \underline{- 8x + 9x} - 12$

$= 6x^2 + x - 12$

Special Products of Binomials

- **Squaring a binomial:** the product of a binomial with itself

$(a + b)^2 = a^2 + 2ab + b^2$

$(a - b)^2 = a^2 - 2ab + b^2$

$(a + b)^2 = (a + b)(a + b)$

$= a^2 \underline{+ ab + ab} + b^2$

$= a^2 + 2ab + b^2$

| Square of the first term $(a)^2$ | Twice the product of the first and second terms $2(a)(b) = 2ab$ | Square of the second term $(b)^2$ |

$(a - b)^2 = (a - b)(a - b)$

$= a^2 \underline{- ab - ab} + (-b)^2$

$= a^2 - 2ab + b^2$

| Square of the first term $(a)^2$ | Twice the product of the first and second terms $2(a)(-b) = -2ab$ | Square of the second term $(-b)^2 = b^2$ |

- **Difference of squares:** the product of two binomials having the same two terms but opposite signs separating the terms; i.e., the product of the sum and difference of two terms.

$(a + b)(a - b) = a^2 - b^2$

$(a + b)(a - b) = a^2 \underline{- ab + ab} - b^2$

$= a^2 - b^2$

| Square of the first term | Minus | Square of the second term |

Example 4.1-h **Squaring a Binomial**

Multiply the following expressions using the special product of binomials.

(i) $(2x + y)(2x + y)$

(ii) $(3x + 4)(3x + 4)$

(iii) $(3x - 2y)(3x - 2y)$

(iv) $(5x - 6)(5x - 6)$

Solution

(i) $(2x + y)(2x + y)$

$= (2x + y)^2$ Using $(a + b)^2 = a^2 + 2ab + b^2,$

Note: Common error $(a + b)^2 \neq a^2 + b^2$

$= (2x)^2 + 2(2x)(y) + (y)^2$

$= 4x^2 + 4xy + y^2$

(ii) $(3x + 4)(3x + 4)$

$= (3x + 4)^2$ Using $(a + b)^2 = a^2 + 2ab + b^2,$

$= (3x)^2 + 2(3x)(4) + (4)^2$

$= 9x^2 + 24x + 16$

(iii) $(3x - 2y)(3x - 2y)$

$= (3x - 2y)^2$ Using $(a - b)^2 = a^2 - 2ab + b^2,$

Note: Common error $(a - b)^2 \neq a^2 - b^2$

$= (3x)^2 - 2(3x)(2y) + (2y)^2$

$= 9x^2 - 12xy + 4y^2$

(iv) $(5x - 6)(5x - 6)$

$= (5x - 6)^2$ Using $(a - b)^2 = a^2 - 2ab + b^2,$

$= (5x)^2 - 2(5x)(6) + (6)^2$

$= 25x^2 - 60x + 36$

Example 4.1-i **Multiplying the Sum and Difference of Two Terms (Difference of Squares)**

Multiply the following expressions using the special product of binomials.

(i) $(3x + y)(3x - y)$

(ii) $(2x + 5)(2x - 5)$

Solution

(i) $(3x + y)(3x - y)$ Using $(a + b)(a - b) = a^2 - b^2,$

$= (3x)^2 - (y)^2$

$= 9x^2 - y^2$

(ii) $(2x + 5)(2x - 5)$ Using $(a + b)(a - b) = a^2 - b^2,$

$= (2x)^2 - (5)^2$

$= 4x^2 - 25$

Multiplying Polynomials by Polynomials

When multiplying a polynomial by a polynomial, multiply each term of the first polynomial by each term of the second polynomial. Then, expand using the distributive property, group the like terms, and simplify using addition and subtraction.

| Example 4.1-j | Multiplying Polynomials by Polynomials |

(i)   Multiply: $(x^2 + 7)$ and $(2x^2 + 5x + 2)$

(ii) Multiply: $(x - 4)$ and $(2x^2 - x - 3)$

(iii) Expand and simplify: $(x + 5)(2x - 6) + (3x - 4)(x - 5)$

(iv) Expand and simplify: $(x - 3)(3x - 1) - (2x - 3)(x + 4)$

Solution

(i) $(x^2 + 7)(2x^2 + 5x + 2)$

$= x^2(2x^2 + 5x + 2) + 7(2x^2 + 5x + 2)$ Expanding,

$= 2x^4 + 5x^3 \underline{+ 2x^2 + 14x^2} + 35x + 14$ Adding like terms,

$= 2x^4 + 5x^3 + 16x^2 + 35x + 14$

(ii) $(x - 4)\ (2x^2 - x - 3)$

$= x(2x^2 - x - 3) - 4(2x^2 - x - 3)$ Expanding,

$= 2x^3 - x^2 - 3x - 8x^2 + 4x + 12$ Grouping like terms,

$= 2x^3 \underline{- x^2 - 8x^2} \underline{- 3x + 4x} + 12$ Adding and subtracting like terms,

$= 2x^3 - 9x^2 + x + 12$

(iii) $(x + 5)(2x - 6) + (3x - 4)(x - 5)$

$= [x(2x - 6) + 5(2x - 6)] + [3x(x - 5) - 4(x - 5)]$ Expanding,

$= (2x^2 - 6x + 10x - 30) + (3x^2 - 15x - 4x + 20)$ Removing brackets,

$= 2x^2 - 6x + 10x - 30 + 3x^2 - 15x - 4x + 20$ Grouping like terms,

$= \underline{2x^2 + 3x^2} \underline{- 6x + 10x - 15x - 4x} \underline{- 30 + 20}$ Adding and subtracting like terms,

$= 5x^2 - 15x - 10$

(iv) $(x - 3)(3x - 1) - (2x - 3)(x + 4)$

$= [x(3x - 1) - 3(3x - 1)] - [2x(x + 4) - 3(x + 4)]$ Expanding,

$= (3x^2 - x - 9x + 3) - (2x^2 + 8x - 3x - 12)$ Removing brackets by distributing the negative sign,

$= 3x^2 - x - 9x + 3 - 2x^2 - 8x + 3x + 12$ Grouping like terms,

$= \underline{3x^2 - 2x^2} \underline{- x - 9x - 8x + 3x} \underline{+ 3 + 12}$ Adding and subtracting like terms,

$= x^2 - 15x + 15$

Division

Dividing a Monomial by a Monomial

When dividing a monomial by a monomial, group the coefficients and each of the variables separately and simplify them by canceling common factors.

Example 4.1-k | **Dividing Monomials by Monomials**

  (i)   Divide $8x^2y$ by $6x$
  (ii) Divide $-9x^2$ by $3x^3$

Solution

  (i) $\dfrac{8x^2y}{6x} = \dfrac{8}{6} \cdot \dfrac{x^2}{x} \cdot y = = \dfrac{4}{3}xy$ or $\dfrac{4xy}{3}$

  (ii) $\dfrac{-9x^2}{3x^3} = \dfrac{-9}{3} \cdot \dfrac{x^2}{x^3} = \dfrac{-3}{1} \cdot \dfrac{1}{x} = \dfrac{-3}{x}$

Dividing a Polynomial by a Monomial

When dividing a polynomial by a monomial, divide **each term** of the polynomial by the monomial. The process is similar to dividing a monomial by a monomial.

Example 4.1-l | **Dividing Polynomials by Monomials**

  (i)   Divide $(9x^3 + 12x^2)$ by $6x$
  (ii) Divide $(4x^4 + 2x^3 - 7x)$ by $4x^4$

Solution

  (i) $\dfrac{9x^3 + 12x^2}{6x} = \dfrac{9x^3}{6x} + \dfrac{12x^2}{6x} = \dfrac{3x^2}{2} + 2x$

  (ii) $\dfrac{4x^4 + 2x^3 - 7x}{4x^4} = \dfrac{4x^4}{4x^4} + \dfrac{2x^3}{4x^4} - \dfrac{7x}{4x^4} = 1 + \dfrac{1}{2x} - \dfrac{7}{4x^3}$

Factoring Algebraic Expressions with Common Factors

Factoring algebraic expressions involves finding the greatest common factor for both the coefficients and variables in all the terms. Once the greatest common factor is found, the expression will become a product of a monomial and a polynomial (or a combination of both). The purpose of factoring is to simplify the multiplication and division of algebraic expressions. Once factored, we can simplify algebraic expressions by canceling out common terms.

Example 4.1-m | **Factoring Algebraic Expressions**

Factor the following:
  (i) $12x + 18y$ (ii) $8y^2 + 20y$
  (iii) $3x^2y^3 + 6xy^4 - 15x^3y^5$ (iv) $x(x + 4) - y(4 + x)$

Solution

  (i) $12x + 18y$

   $12x = 2 \cdot 2 \cdot 3 \cdot x$

   $18y = 2 \cdot 3 \cdot 3 \cdot y$

   The GCF is $2 \cdot 3 = 6$.

   Divide the original expression by the GCF of 6 to determine the second factor:

   $\dfrac{12x + 18y}{6} = \dfrac{12x}{6} + \dfrac{18y}{6} = 2x + 3y$

   i.e., the second factor is $(2x + 3y)$.

   Therefore, $12x + 18y = 6(2x + 3y)$.

(ii) $8y^2 + 20y$

$8y^2 = 2 \cdot 2 \cdot 2 \cdot y \cdot y$

$20y = 2 \cdot 2 \cdot 5 \cdot y$

The GCF is $2 \cdot 2 \cdot y = 4y$.

Divide the original expression by the GCF of $4y$ to determine the second factor:

$$\frac{8y^2 + 20y}{4y} = \frac{8y^2}{4y} + \frac{20y}{4y} = 2y + 5$$

i.e., the second factor is $(2y + 5)$.

Therefore, $8y^2 + 20y = 4y(2y + 5)$.

(iii) $3x^2y^3 + 6xy^4 - 15x^3y^5$

The GCF is $3xy^3$.

Divide the original expression by the GCF of $3xy^3$ to determine the second factor:

$$\frac{3x^2y^3 + 6xy^4 - 15x^3y^5}{3xy^3} = \frac{3x^2y^3}{3xy^3} + \frac{6xy^4}{3xy^3} - \frac{15x^3y^5}{3xy^3} = x + 2y - 5x^2y^2$$

i.e., the second factor is $(x + 2y - 5x^2y^2)$.

Therefore, $3x^2y^3 + 6xy^4 - 15x^3y^5 = 3xy^3(x + 2y - 5x^2y^2)$.

(iv) $x(x + 4) - y(4 + x)$

The GCF is $(x + 4)$. [By the commutative property, $(x + 4) = (4 + x)$.]

Divide the original expression by the GCF of $(x + 4)$ to obtain the second factor:

$$\frac{x(x + 4) - y(4 + x)}{(x + 4)} = \frac{x(x + 4)}{(x + 4)} - \frac{y(4 + x)}{(x + 4)} = x - y$$

i.e., the second factor is $(x - y)$.

Therefore, $x(x + 4) - y(4 + x) = (x + 4)(x - y)$.

Example 4.1-n	Simplifying Algebraic Expressions by Factoring

Simplify the following expressions:

(i) $[14(2x + y) - 7x(2x + y)] \div (2x + y)$

(ii) $\dfrac{(x^2 + xy)}{(7x - 14)} \times \dfrac{(14x - 28)}{(x + y)}$

Solution

(i) $[14(2x + y) - 7x(2x + y)] \div (2x + y)$ — Rewriting the question,

$$= \frac{14(2x + y) - 7x(2x + y)}{(2x + y)}$$ — The GCF of the numerator is $7(2x + y)$. Factoring,

$$= \frac{7(2x + y)(2 - x)}{(2x + y)}$$ — Cancelling out common terms,

Alternatively, when there is a common binomial, such as $(2x + y)$, it may be simpler to factor it out first.

$$= 7(2 - x)$$

Therefore, $[14(2x + y) - 7x(2x + y)] \div (2x + y) = 7(2 - x)$.

(ii) $\dfrac{(x^2 + xy)}{(7x - 14)} \times \dfrac{(14x - 28)}{(x + y)}$ — The GCF of the first numerator is x. Factoring,

$$= \frac{x(x + y)}{(7x - 14)} \times \frac{(14x - 28)}{(x + y)}$$ — The GCF of the second numerator is 14. Factoring,

$$= \frac{x(x+y)}{(7x-14)} \times \frac{14(x-2)}{(x+y)}$$ The GCF of the first denominator is 7. Factoring,

$$= \frac{x(x+y)}{7(x-2)} \times \frac{14(x-2)}{(x+y)}$$ Cancelling out common terms,

$$= \frac{14x}{7}$$ Simplifying,

$$= 2x$$

Therefore, $\frac{(x^2+xy)}{(7x-14)} \times \frac{(14x-28)}{(x+y)} = 2x$.

4.1 | Exercises

Answers to odd-numbered problems are available at the end of the textbook.

For Problems 1 and 2, write the algebraic expression for the following:

1. a. Three less than twice a number.

   b. Two times a number divided by five.

   c. Twenty-five increased by three times a number.

2. a. Seven less than four times a number.

   b. Fifteen divided by three times a number.

   c. Twenty increased by twice a number.

For Problems 3 to 6, (i) identify the number of terms in each expression, (ii) identify the constant term (if applicable), and (iii) state the coefficients of each of the variable terms.

3. a. $3x^2 + 7xy - 4y$ b. $x^2 - 5x$ c. $9xy + 7x - 6y + 2$

4. a. $-x^2 + 9xy + y + 7$ b. $7xy$ c. $10x^2 + 5xy - 7y^2$

5. a. $5x^2 - 3xy + 5$ b. $-2y^2 + 3x + 1$ c. $-2xy^2 - 2x^2y + 7$

6. a. $-2y^2 + 3y - 4$ b. $y^5 - 2y^7 - 2$ c. $2x^3 - 3x^2 + 1$

For Problems 7 to 10, identify the like terms, group them, and simplify.

7. a. $12A + 4B - 7A - B$ b. $6x + 8y - 5x - 3y + 7$

8. a. $6B + 8A - A - 2B$ b. $14 - 3x + 10y - 11 + 4y$

9. a. $-2x + 5x - 12x + 8y + 7y$ b. $6xy^2 - 2x^2y - 4x^2 + 2xy^2 + 3x^2y + 2x^2 + 4$

10. a. $3x + 6x - 20x + 8y + 8y + 5x$ b. $3x^2y - 12xy^2 - 6x^2y - 5xy - 2xy - 4xy^2$

For Problems 11 to 14, simplify and evaluate the expressions.

11. a. $6y + 4y - 7y$, where $y = 10$ b. $2z - z + 7z$, where $z = 7$

12. a. $3x + 5x - 8x$, where $x = 4$ b. $3A - A + 6A$, where $A = 10$

13. a. $(6x)(3x) - (5x)(4x)$, where $x = 3$ b. $(2x)(0.5x + 4x)(5x + x)$, where $x = 5$

14. a. $(10x \times 4.5x) - (11x \times 4x)$, where $x = 50$ b. $(4x)(12x + 0.25x)(0.5x + x)$, where $x = 3$

For Problems 15 to 18, identify the like terms, group them, simplify, and evaluate.

15. $3a + 6b - 16c - a + 8b + 4c + 2$, where $a = 3$, $b = 2$, $c = 1$

16. $3x - 60y - 17z - 2x + 62y + 4z + 1$, where $x = 5$, $y = 8$, $z = 2$

17. $x^2 - x + 2x^2 - x$, where $x = 5$

18. $-a^2 - 3a + 3a^2 + 4a$, where $a = 15$

For Problems 19 to 22, evaluate the following expressions, given $x = 2$ and $y = 3$:

19. a. $\dfrac{19x - 5y}{9}$
    b. $x^2 + 6x + 8$

20. a. $\dfrac{7x - 5y}{3}$
    b. $-x^2 + 10x + 7$

21. a. $\dfrac{(3x)^2(5y)}{6y}$
    b. $-2x^2 + 3x + 8y$

22. a. $\dfrac{(2x)^2(2y)}{5y}$
    b. $4x^2 + 10x - 4y$

For Problems 23 to 42, simplify the following expressions:

23. a. $13x^2 + 8x - 2x^2 + 9x$
    b. $-18y - 5y^2 + 19y - 2y^2$

24. a. $7x + 12x^2 - 4x + 5x^2$
    b. $-14y - 2y^2 + 7y + 7y^2$

25. a. $6x - 3x + 2y^2 + y^2$
    b. $4xy^2 - x^2y^2 - 3xy^2 + 2x^2y^2$

26. a. $9x^2 - 6x^2 + 7y - 6y$
    b. $3x^2y^2 - 2xy^2 - 8x^2y^2 + xy^2$

27. a. $\dfrac{3x + 5x}{5y}$
    b. $\dfrac{12y - 3y}{4y + 2y}$

28. a. $\dfrac{8x}{x + 5x}$
    b. $\dfrac{20y - 5y}{-4y + 7y}$

29. a. $\dfrac{(16y)(8x)}{(4x)(8y)}$
    b. $\dfrac{(6x)(-18y)}{(3x)(-24y)}$

30. a. $\dfrac{(20y)(4x)}{(2x)(5y)}$
    b. $\dfrac{(7x)(18y)}{(14x)(-27y)}$

31. $3[(5 - 3)(4 - x)] - 2 - 5[3(5x - 4) + 8] - 9x$

32. $(5 - 14)\{x - 8[3 - 5(2x - 3) + 3x] - 3\}$

33. $6[4(8 - y) - 5(3 + 3y)] - 21 - 7[3(7 + 4y) - 4] + 198y$

34. $\dfrac{1}{2}\{y - 15[2 - 3(3y - 2) - 7y] - 4\}$

35. $y - \{4x - [y - (2y - 9) - x] + 2\}$

36. $2y + \{-6y - [3x + (-4x + 3)] + 5\}$

37. $(x - 1) - \{[x - (x - 3)] - x\}$

38. $9x - \{3y + [4x - (y - 6x)] - (x + 7y)\}$

39. $5\{-2y + 3[4x - 2(3 + x)]\}$

40. $4\{-7y + 8[5x - 3(4x + 6)]\}$

41. $2y + \{8[3(2y - 5) - (8y + 9) + 6]\}$

42. $7x - \{5[4(3x - 8) - (9x + 10)] + 14\}$

For Problems 43 to 52, expand and simplify the following expressions:

43. $(2y - 1)(y - 4) - (3y + 2)(3y - 1)$

44. $(y + 4)(y - 3) + (y - 2)(y - 3)$

45. $(2x + 3)(2x - 1) - 4(x^2 - 7)$

46. $4(2x - 1)(x + 3) - 3(x - 2)(3x - 4)$

47. $3(x - 2)(4 - 3x) + 4(2x - 1)(3 - x)$

48. $2(3x + 2)(1 - 3x) + 3(2x - 1)(4 - x)$

49. $4(3x^2 + 4) - 2(x + 3)(x + 5)$

50. $3(5x^2 - 1) - (2x - 4)(3x + 5)$

51. $3(2 - 3x)(2 + x) - (1 - x)(x - 3)$

52. $(x - 2)(3x + 2) - (3x + 2)(x - 5)$

For Problems 53 to 60, expand the following expressions by using special products of binomials:

53. a. $(x + 5)^2$ b. $(2x + 3y)^2$

54. a. $(x + 7)^2$ b. $(3x + 4y)^2$

55. a. $(3 - x)^2$ b. $(3x - 2y)^2$

56. a. $(7 - x)^2$ b. $(2x - 3y)^2$

57. a. $(1 - 3x)^2$ b. $(3 - 2x)^2$

58. a. $(6x - 1)^2$ b. $(2y - 1)^2$

59. a. $(x + 5)(x - 5)$ b. $(3 + 7x)(3 - 7x)$

60. a. $(12x - 1)(12x + 1)$ b. $(2a + 9b)(2a - 9b)$

For Problems 61 to 68, expand and simplify the following expressions:

61. $(x + 3)^2 + (x - 2)^2$ 62. $(x + 5)^2 + (x - 4)^2$

63. $(4 + x)^2 - (x - 3)(x + 3)$ 64. $(3 + x)^2 + (x + 5)(x - 5)$

65. $(3x - 2)^2 + (2x - 3)(2x + 3)$ 66. $(2x + 5)(2x - 5) + (1 - 4x)^2$

67. $(2x - 4)^2 - (y + 3)^2$ 68. $(5x - 6)^2 - (x + 5)^2$

For Problems 69 to 74, simplify the following expressions:

69. $\dfrac{-x^2y - xy^2}{xy}$ 70. $\dfrac{x^2y - 3xy^2}{xy}$

71. $\dfrac{x^2y - 3xy^2 + 4x^2y + xy}{xy}$ 72. $\dfrac{3x^3y^3 - 6x^2y + 3xy^2 + 3xy}{3xy}$

73. $\dfrac{6xy^2}{7} \cdot \dfrac{21x^2}{y} \cdot \dfrac{1}{36xy^2}$ 74. $\dfrac{12x^2y^3}{5} \cdot \dfrac{15x^2}{4xy} \cdot \dfrac{1}{30x^3y}$

For Problems 75 to 102, factor the following expressions:

75. $6xy - 9yz$ 76. $12a^2b - 16ab - 24b$

77. $15y^4 - 12y^2 - 3y$ 78. $8a^3 - 4a^2 + 20a$

79. $-120y^2 - 40y$ 80. $4xy - 12yz + 3xz + 15zy$

81. $6x^2y - 3xy - 9y$ 82. $10ab - 8bc$

83. $10x^3 - 4x^2$ 84. $22x^2 - 3x$

85. $6ab - 8bc$ 86. $6x^2 - 6x$

87. $5x(y + 2) + 3(y + 2)$ 88. $7x(m - 4) + 3(m - 4)$

89. $4y(x - 5) - x^2 + 5x$ 90. $3y(x - 1) + 2x^2 - 2x$

91. $xy - 2y + 5x - 10$ 92. $4x - xy - 20y + 5y^2$

93. $x^2 + x - xy - y$ 94. $2x^2 + 3y + 2x + 3xy$

95. $x^2 - 4y + 4x - xy$ 96. $5x^2y - 10x^2 + y^2 - 2y$

97. $\dfrac{(3x^2 + 9)}{14} \cdot \dfrac{(7x + 21)}{x + 3}$ 98. $\dfrac{16}{(3x^2y + 4x)} \cdot \dfrac{(6x^2y + 8x)}{12}$

99. $\dfrac{(x^2 - 5x)}{(2x + 10)} \cdot \dfrac{(3x + 15)}{4x}$ 100. $\dfrac{(3xy - 5x)}{8x} \cdot \dfrac{12y^2}{(9y - 15)}$

101. $\dfrac{(15xy - 5x)}{(4x + 12)} \cdot \dfrac{(3x - 9)}{(4x - 12)}$ 102. $\dfrac{(x^2 - xy)}{(7x - 14)} \cdot \dfrac{(14x - 28)}{(x + y)}$

An algebraic equation is a mathematical sentence expressing equality between two algebraic expressions (or an algebraic expression and a number).

All equations have an equal (=) sign that separates the equation into two equal parts: the left side (LS) and right side (RS).

When two expressions are joined by an equal (=) sign, it indicates that the expression to the left of the equal sign is identical in value to the expression to the right of the equal sign.

For example, when two algebraic expressions, such as $5x + 7$ and $x + 19$, are equal, the two expressions are joined by an equal (=) sign and the equation is written as:

$$\underbrace{5x + 7} = \underbrace{x + 19}$$

'Left side' (LS) = 'Right side' (RS)

The value of the variable that makes both sides (LS and RS) equal is the solution to the equation.

The **solution** to the equation is the value of the variable that makes the left side (LS) evaluate to the same number as the right side (RS).

Note: You need an equation to solve for an unknown variable - you cannot solve for a variable in an algebraic expression that is not part of an equation.

- *If you have an **expression**, it needs to be **simplified**.*
- *If you have an **equation**, it needs to be **solved**.*

In algebra, there are a variety of equations. In this section, you will learn one category of equations, known as **linear equations with one variable**.

Examples of linear equations with one variable are:

$$2x = 8, \qquad 3x + 5 = 14, \qquad 5x + 7 = x + 19$$

An equation is either true or false depending on the value of the variable.

For example, consider the equation $2x = 8$:

- If $x = 4$, LS = 2(4) = 8, RS = 8; therefore, the equation is true.
- If $x = 3$, LS = 2(3) = 6, RS = 8; therefore, the equation is false.

Equations may be classified into the following three types:

1. **Conditional Equation** - these equations are only true when the variable has a specific value.

   For example, $2x = 8$ is a conditional equation, true if and only if $x = 4$.

2. **Identity** - these equations are true for any value for the variable.

   For example, $2x + 10 = 2(x + 5)$ is an identity, true for any value of x.

3. **Contradiction** - these equations are not true for any value of the variable.

   For example, $x + 5 = x + 4$ is a contradiction, not true for any value of x.

Equivalent Equations

Equations with the same solutions are called **equivalent equations**.

For example, $2x + 5 = 9$ and $2x = 4$ are equivalent equations because the solution $x = 2$ satisfies each equation. Similarly, $3x - 4 = 5$, $2x = x + 3$, and $x + 1 = 4$ are equvialent equations because the solution $x = 3$ satisfies each equation.

Properties of Equality

If $a = b$, then,

Performing the same operation on both sides of an equation will result in an equivalent equation.

$b = a$	Symmetric Property	Interchanging LS and RS.
$a + \mathbf{c} = b + \mathbf{c}$	Addition Property	Adding the same quantity to both sides.
$a - \mathbf{c} = b - \mathbf{c}$	Subtraction Property	Subtracting the same quantity from both sides.
$a \cdot \mathbf{c} = b \cdot \mathbf{c}$	Multiplication Property	Multiplying by the same quantity on both sides.
$\dfrac{a}{\mathbf{c}} = \dfrac{b}{\mathbf{c}}$	Division Property, $c \neq 0$	Dividing by the same quantity on both sides.

The above properties are used to solve equations.

Equations with Fractional Coefficients

If an equation contains fractional coefficients, then the fractional coefficients can be changed to whole numbers by multiplying each term by the least common denominator (LCD) of all the fractions.

For example,

$$\frac{2}{3}x = \frac{5}{2} + 4$$

Since the LCD of the denominators 3 and 2 is 6, multiply each term by 6,

$$6\left(\frac{2}{3}x\right) = 6\left(\frac{5}{2}\right) + 6(4)$$

Simplifying,

$$4x = 15 + 24$$

Now, the equation has only whole number coefficients.

$$4x = 39$$

Equations with Decimal Coefficients

If an equation contains decimal coefficients, then the decimal coefficients can be changed to whole numbers by multiplying each term by the power of 10 with an exponent equal to the greatest number of decimal places in any of the coefficients or constants (e.g., if all coefficients and constants have 3 decimal places or less, multiply the entire equation by 10^3).

For example,

$$1.25x = 0.2 + 4$$

Since there is at most 2 decimal places in any of the coefficients or constants, multiply each term in the equation by $10^2 = 100$,

$$100(1.25x) = 100(0.2) + 100(4)$$

Simplifying,

$$125x = 20 + 400$$

Now, the equation has only whole number coefficients.

$$125x = 420$$

Steps to Solve Algebraic Equations with One Variable

Step 1: If the equation contains fraction and/or decimal coefficients, it is possible to work with them as they are - in that case, proceed onto Step 2. Alternatively, the equation may be rewritten in whole numbers, as explained above, to make calculations and rearrangements easier.

Step 2: Expand and clear brackets in the equation, if present, by following the order of arithmetic operations (BEDMAS).

Step 3: Use the addition and subtraction properties to collect and group all **variable** terms on the **left side** of the equation and all **constants** on the right side of the equation. Then, simplify both sides.

Note: If it is more convenient to gather all the variable terms on the right side and the constants on the left side, you may do so, and then use the symmetric property and switch the sides of the equation to bring the variables over to the left side and the constants to the right side.

Step 4: Use the division and multiplication properties to ensure that the coefficient of the variable is +1.

Step 5: After completing Step 4, there should be a single variable with coefficient of +1 on the left side and a single constant term on the right side - that constant term is the solution to the equation.

Step 6: Verify the answer by substituting the solution from Step 5 back into the original problem.

Step 7: State the answer.

Example 4.2-a Solving Equations Using the Addition and Subtraction Properties

Solve the following equations and verify the solutions:

(i) $x - 11 = 4$
(ii) $8 + x = 20$

Solution

(i) $x - 11 = 4$ Adding **11** to both sides,   Verify by substituting $x = 15$:

$x - 11 + \mathbf{11} = 4 + \mathbf{11}$

$x = \mathbf{15}$

$$\begin{array}{c|c} \text{LS} = x - 11 & \text{RS} = 4 \\ = \mathbf{15} - 11 & \\ = 4 & \end{array}$$

$$\text{LS} = \text{RS}$$

Therefore, the solution is $x = 15$.

(ii) $8 + x = 20$ Subtracting **8** from both sides,   Verify by substituting $x = 12$:

$8 - \mathbf{8} + x = 20 - \mathbf{8}$

$x = \mathbf{12}$

$$\begin{array}{c|c} \text{LS} = 8 + x & \text{RS} = 20 \\ = 8 + \mathbf{12} & \\ = 20 & \end{array}$$

$$\text{LS} = \text{RS}$$

Therefore, the solution is $x = 12$.

Example 4.2-b Solving Equations Using the Multiplication and Division Properties

Solve the following equations and verify the solutions:

(i) $5x = 20$
(ii) $\dfrac{3}{8}x = 12$

Solution

(i) $5x = 20$ Dividing both sides by **5**,   Verify by substituting $x = 4$:

$\dfrac{5x}{5} = \dfrac{20}{5}$

$x = \mathbf{4}$

$$\begin{array}{c|c} \text{LS} = 5x & \text{RS} = 20 \\ = 5(\mathbf{4}) & \\ = 20 & \end{array}$$

$$\text{LS} = \text{RS}$$

Therefore, the solution is $x = 4$.

(ii) $\dfrac{3}{8}x = 12$ Multiplying both sides by $\dfrac{8}{3}$

(the reciprocal of $\dfrac{3}{8}$),

$\left(\dfrac{\mathbf{8}}{\mathbf{3}}\right) \cdot \dfrac{3}{8}x = \left(\dfrac{\mathbf{8}}{\mathbf{\cancel{3}}}\right)_1 \cdot \cancel{12}^{\,4}$

$x = 8 \times 4$

$x = \mathbf{32}$

or

$\dfrac{3}{8}x = 12$ Multiplying both sides by **8**,

$(\mathbf{8}) \cdot \dfrac{3}{8}x = (\mathbf{8}) \cdot 12$

$3x = 96$ Dividing both sides by **3**,

$\dfrac{3x}{3} = \dfrac{96}{3}$

$x = \mathbf{32}$

Verify by substituting $x = 32$:

$$\begin{array}{c|c} \text{LS} = \dfrac{3}{8}x & \text{RS} = 12 \\[2mm] = \dfrac{3}{8} \times \mathbf{32} & \\[2mm] = 12 & \end{array}$$

$$\text{LS} = \text{RS}$$

Therefore, the solution is $x = 32$.

Example 4.2-c

Solving Equations with Variables on Both Sides

Solve the following equations and verify the solutions:

(i)　$3x - 8 = 12 - 2x$

(ii)　$15 + 6x - 4 = 3x + 31 - x$

Solution

(i)

$$3x - 8 = 12 - 2x$$ 　　　Adding **2x** to both sides,

$$3x + 2x - 8 = 12 - 2x + 2x$$

$$5x - 8 = 12$$ 　　　Adding **8** to both sides,

$$5x - 8 + 8 = 12 + 8$$

$$5x = 20$$ 　　　Dividing both sides by **5**,

$$\frac{5x}{5} = \frac{20}{5}$$

$$x = 4$$

Verify by substituting $x = 4$ back into the original equation:

LS $= 3x - 8$	RS $= 12 - 2x$
$= 3(4) - 8$	$= 12 - 2(4)$
$= 12 - 8$	$= 12 - 8$
$= 4$	$= 4$

$$LS = RS$$

Therefore, the solution is $x = 4$.

(ii)

$$15 + 6x - 4 = 3x + 31 - x$$ 　　Combining like terms (LS: $15 - 4 = 11$, and RS: $3x - x = 2x$),

$$11 + 6x = 2x + 31$$ 　　Subtracting **2x** from both sides,

$$11 + 6x - 2x = 2x - 2x + 31$$

$$11 + 4x = 31$$ 　　Subtracting **11** from both sides,

$$11 - 11 + 4x = 31 - 11$$

$$4x = 20$$ 　　Dividing both sides by **4**,

$$\frac{4x}{4} = \frac{20}{4}$$

$$x = 5$$

Verify by substituting $x = 5$ back into the original equation:

LS $= 15 + 6x - 4$	RS $= 3x + 31 - x$
$= 15 + 6(5) - 4$	$= 3(5) + 31 - 5$
$= 15 + 30 - 4$	$= 15 + 31 - 5$
$= 41$	$= 41$

$$LS = RS$$

Therefore, the solution is $x = 5$.

Example 4.2-d

Solving Equations with Fractions

Solve the following equation and verify the solution:

$$\frac{x}{3} - \frac{1}{12} = \frac{1}{6} + \frac{x}{4}$$

$$\frac{x}{3} - \frac{1}{12} = \frac{1}{6} + \frac{x}{4}$$

LCD of 3, 4, 6, and 12 is 12. Multiplying each term by **12**,

$$12 \cdot \frac{x}{3} - 12 \cdot \frac{1}{12} = 12 \cdot \frac{1}{6} + 12 \cdot \frac{x}{4}$$

$$4x - 1 = 2 + 3x$$

Subtracting **3x** from both sides,

$$4x - \mathbf{3x} - 1 = 2 + 3x - \mathbf{3x}$$

$$x - 1 = 2$$

Adding **1** to both sides,

$$x - 1 + \mathbf{1} = 2 + \mathbf{1}$$

$$x = 3$$

Verify by substituting $x = 3$ back into the original equation:

$$LS = \frac{x}{3} - \frac{1}{12} \qquad\qquad RS = \frac{1}{6} + \frac{x}{4}$$

$$= \frac{3}{3} - \frac{1}{12} \qquad\qquad = \frac{1}{6} + \frac{3}{4}$$

$$= \frac{12}{12} - \frac{1}{12} \qquad\qquad = \frac{2}{12} + \frac{9}{12}$$

$$= \frac{11}{12} \qquad\qquad = \frac{11}{12}$$

$$LS = RS$$

Therefore, the solution is $x = 3$.

Example 4.2-e **Solving Equations with Decimals**

Solve the following equation and verify the solution:
$0.15x + 1.2 = 0.4x - 0.8$

Solution

$$0.15x + 1.2 = 0.4x - 0.8$$

Greatest number of decimal places is 2
(i.e., hundredths). Multiplying all the terms by $10^2 = \mathbf{100}$,

$$\mathbf{100}(0.15x) + \mathbf{100}(1.2) = \mathbf{100}(0.4x) - \mathbf{100}(0.8)$$

$$15x + 120 = 40x - 80$$

Subtracting **40x** from both sides,

$$15x - \mathbf{40x} + 120 = 40x - \mathbf{40x} - 80$$

$$-25x + 120 = -80$$

Subtracting **120** from both sides,

$$-25x + 120 - \mathbf{120} = -80 - \mathbf{120}$$

$$-25x = -200$$

Dividing both sides by **–25**,

$$\frac{-25x}{\mathbf{-25}} = \frac{-200}{\mathbf{-25}}$$

$$x = 8$$

Verify by substituting $x = 8$ back into the original equation:

$$LS = 0.15x + 1.2 \qquad\qquad RS = 0.4x - 0.8$$

$$= 0.15(\mathbf{8}) + 1.2 \qquad\qquad = 0.4(\mathbf{8}) - 0.8$$

$$= 1.2 + 1.2 \qquad\qquad = 3.2 - 0.8$$

$$= 2.4 \qquad\qquad = 2.4$$

$$LS = RS$$

Therefore, the solution is $x = 8$.

Note: For the rest of the examples in this section, we will not show the verification by substitution step.

Example 4.2-f   **Solving Equations Using All the Properties**

Solve the following equations by using the properties of equations, and express the answer as a fraction in its lowest terms, or as a mixed number, wherever applicable:

(i) $8x + 7 - 3x = -6x - 15 + x$

(ii) $2(3x - 7) = 28 - 3(x + 1)$

(iii) $\frac{1}{4}(x + \frac{2}{3}) = \frac{1}{2}(x - 3) + x$

(iv) $0.45(2x + 3) - 2.55 = 0.6(3x - 5)$

(v) $\frac{x + 2}{3} = \frac{5 - 2x}{7}$

Solution

(i) $8x + 7 - 3x = -6x - 15 + x$ Grouping like terms on both sides,

$8x - 3x + 7 = -6x + x - 15$

$5x + 7 = -5x - 15$ Adding **5x** to both sides,

$5x + \mathbf{5x} + 7 = -5x + \mathbf{5x} - 15$

$10x + 7 = -15$ Subtracting **7** from both sides,

$10x + 7 - \mathbf{7} = -15 - \mathbf{7}$

$10x = -22$ Dividing both sides by **10**,

$\frac{10x}{\mathbf{10}} = -\frac{22}{\mathbf{10}}$

$x = -\frac{11}{5} = -2\frac{1}{5}$

(ii) $2(3x - 7) = 28 - 3(x + 1)$ Expanding both sides,

$6x - 14 = 28 - 3x - 3$ Grouping like terms,

$6x - 14 = 28 - 3 - 3x$

$6x - 14 = 25 - 3x$ Adding **3x** to both sides,

$6x + \mathbf{3x} - 14 = 25 - 3x + \mathbf{3x}$

$9x - 14 = 25$ Adding **14** to both sides,

$9x - 14 + \mathbf{14} = 25 + \mathbf{14}$

$9x = 39$ Dividing both sides by **9**,

$\frac{9x}{\mathbf{9}} = \frac{39}{\mathbf{9}}$

$x = \frac{13}{3} = 4\frac{1}{3}$

(iii) $\frac{1}{4}(x + \frac{2}{3}) = \frac{1}{2}(x - 3) + x$ Expanding both sides,

$\frac{1}{4}x + \frac{1}{6} = \frac{1}{2}x - \frac{3}{2} + x$ Multiplying each term by the LCD **12**,

$\mathbf{12}\left(\frac{1}{4}x\right) + \mathbf{12}\left(\frac{1}{6}\right) = \mathbf{12}\left(\frac{1}{2}x\right) - \mathbf{12}\left(\frac{3}{2}\right) + \mathbf{12}\,(x)$

$3x + 2 = 6x - 18 + 12x$ Grouping like terms,

$3x + 2 = 6x + 12x - 18$

$3x + 2 = 18x - 18$ Subtracting **18x** from both sides,

$3x - \mathbf{18x} + 2 = 18x - \mathbf{18x} - 18$

$$-15x + 2 = -18$$

Subtracting **2** from both sides,

$$-15x + 2 - 2 = -18 - 2$$

$$-15x = -20$$

Dividing both sides by **−15**,

$$\frac{-15x}{-15} = \frac{-20}{-15}$$

$$x = \frac{4}{3} = 1\frac{1}{3}$$

(iv) $0.45(2x + 3) - 2.55 = 0.6(3x - 5)$

Expanding both sides,

$$0.90x + 1.35 - 2.55 = 1.8x - 3.0$$

Greatest number of decimal places is 2 (i.e., hundredths). Multiplying all the terms by $10^2 = $ **100**,

$$100(0.90x) + 100(1.35) - 100(2.55) = 100(1.8x) - 100(3.0)$$

$$90x + \underline{135 - 255} = 180x - 300$$

Grouping like terms,

$$90x - 120 = 180x - 300$$

Subtracting **180x** from both sides,

$$90x - 180x - 120 = 180x - 180x - 300$$

$$-90x - 120 = -300$$

Adding **120** to both sides,

$$-90x - 120 + 120 = -300 + 120$$

$$-90x = -180$$

Dividing both sides by **−90**,

$$\frac{-90x}{-90} = \frac{-180}{-90}$$

$$x = 2$$

(v) $\dfrac{x + 2}{3} = \dfrac{5 - 2x}{7}$

Cross multiplying,

$$7(x + 2) = 3(5 - 2x)$$

Expanding both sides,

$$7x + 14 = 15 - 6x$$

Adding **6x** to both sides,

$$7x + 6x + 14 = 15 - 6x + 6x$$

$$13x + 14 = 15$$

Subtracting **14** from both sides,

$$13x + 14 - 14 = 15 - 14$$

$$13x = 1$$

Dividing both sides by **13**,

$$\frac{13x}{13} = \frac{1}{13}$$

$$x = \frac{1}{13}$$

Steps to Solve Word Problems

Step 1:   Read the entire problem and ensure you understand the situation.

Step 2:   Identify the given information and the question to be answered.

Step 3:   Look for key words. Some words indicate certain mathematical operations (see Table 4.1-a on page 135).

Step 4:   Choose a variable to represent the unknown(s) and state what that variable represents, including the unit of measure.

> *Note: For now, if there is more than one unknown, try to identify all the unknowns in terms of one variable, as all the questions in this chapter can be solved with only one variable.*

Step 5: Where necessary, draw a simple sketch to identify the information. This helps with envisioning the question more clearly.

Step 6: Create an equation (or set of equations) to describe the relationship between the variables and the constants in the question.

Step 7: Group like terms, isolate the variable, and solve for the unknown(s).

Example 4.2-g **Solving a Word Problem Using Algebraic Equations**

If Harry will be 65 years old in 5 years, how old is he today?

Solution

Let Harry's age today be x years.

Therefore, in 5 years, Harry's age will be:

$$x + 5 = 65$$

Solving for x,

$$x = 65 - 5$$
$$= 60$$

Therefore, Harry is 60 years old today.

Example 4.2-h **Solving a Word Problem Using Algebraic Equations**

The perimeter of a hospital building is 50 metres. The length is 5 metres more than the width. Find the dimensions of the hospital building. *Hint: Perimeter = 2(length) + 2(width)*

Solution

Let the width be w metres.

Therefore, the length is: $(w + 5)$ metres.

$$Perimeter = 2(length) + 2(width)$$
$$50 = 2(w + 5) + 2w$$
$$50 = 2w + 10 + 2w$$
$$2w + 10 + 2w = 50$$
$$4w + 10 = 50$$
$$4w = 50 - 10$$
$$4w = 40$$
$$w = \frac{40}{4}$$
$$w = 10$$

Diagram labels: $w + 5$ (top), w (left), w (right), $w + 5$ (bottom), Perimeter = 50 m

Therefore, the width of the hospital building is 10 metres, and the length = 10 + 5 = 15 metres.

Example 4.2-i **Solving a Word Problem Using Algebraic Equations**

A stethoscope costs $190 more than a box of endotracheal tubes. The total cost to purchase one stethoscope and five boxes of endotracheal tubes is $688. Calculate the cost of the stethoscope and the cost of a single box of endotracheal tubes.

Let the cost of the box of endotracheal tubes be $x.

Therefore, the cost of a stethoscope is $(x + 190.00).

The total cost is $688.00.

$$5x + (x + 190.00) = 688.00$$

$$5x + x + 190.00 = 688.00$$

$$6x + 190.00 = 688.00$$

$$6x = 688.00 - 190.00$$

$$6x = 498.00$$

$$x = \frac{498.00}{6}$$

$$x = \$83.00$$

The cost of the stethoscope = $x + 190.00$

$$= 83.00 + 190.00 = \$273.00$$

Therefore, the cost of a box of endotracheal tubes is $83.00 and the cost of a stethoscope is $273.00.

Example 4.2-j	Solving a Word Problem Using Algebraic Equations

How many litres of water need to be added to 30 litres of a 15% saline solution to make a saline solution that is 10% saline?

	# of Litres	% Saline	Total Litres of Saline
Water	x	0	0
15% Saline Solution	30	0.15	$0.15 \times 30 = 4.5$
10% Saline Solution	$30 + x$	0.10	$0.10 \times (30 + x)$

From the last column, you get the equation for the saline mix. The number of litres of saline in the 15% solution must be the same as the number of litres in the final 10% solution, as only water is being added, which does not contribute any additional saline to the solution. Therefore,

$$4.5 = 0.10 \times (30 + x)$$

$$4.5 = 3 + 0.10x$$

$$1.5 = 0.10x$$

$$x = 15$$

Therefore, 15 litres of water need to be added to the 15% saline solution to make the solution 10% saline.

4.2 | Exercises

Answers to odd-numbered problems are available at the end of the textbook.

For Problems 1 to 8, write and solve the algebraic equations for the following:

1. The sum of a number and six is ten.

2. A number decreased by fifteen is five.

3. Six times a number is seventy-two.

4. The product of a number and four is twenty-eight.

5. A number divided by five is four.

6. A number divided by three is three.

7. Two-thirds of a number is twelve.

8. Two-fifths of a number is six.

For Problems 9 to 30, solve the following algebraic equality using properties of equality, and express the answer as a fraction in its lowest terms, or as a mixed number, wherever applicable.

9. $x - 20 = 10$

10. $x - 25 = 17$

11. $22 = 40 - x$

12. $54 = 23 - x$

13. $21 + x = 4$

14. $50 + x = 45$

15. $16 + x = 22$

16. $12 + x = 38$

17. $11x + 4 = 17$

18. $7x - 16 = 22$

19. $x - \dfrac{4}{5} = \dfrac{3}{5}$

20. $x - \dfrac{1}{6} = \dfrac{5}{6}$

21. $\dfrac{3x}{4} - 11 = 7$

22. $\dfrac{x}{7} + 15 = 24$

23. $x + \dfrac{2}{5} = \dfrac{1}{4}$

24. $2x - \dfrac{2}{3} = \dfrac{5}{6}$

25. $5x = 20$

26. $4x = 24$

27. $\dfrac{2x}{3} + 1 = \dfrac{5x}{8} + 2$

28. $\dfrac{x}{2} - \dfrac{1}{6} = \dfrac{1}{3} + \dfrac{3x}{5}$

29. $\dfrac{7x}{8} - 4 = \dfrac{x}{4} + 6$

30. $\dfrac{8x}{3} - 5 = \dfrac{x}{3} + 2$

For Problems 31 to 54, solve the algebraic equations using properties of equality, and round the answer to 2 decimal places, wherever applicable.

31. $10y - 0.09y = 17$

32. $x + 0.13x = 70$

33. $0.3x - 3.2 = 0.4 - 0.6x$

34. $4 + 0.2x = 0.7x - 0.5$

35. $0.4x - 1.38 = 0.3x - 1.2$

36. $1.2x - 0.7 = 2.7 - 0.5x$

37. $0.43x + 0.25 = 0.29x - 0.03$

38. $1.5x - 1.2 = 0.9 - 0.6x$

39. $8x + 7 - 3x = -6x - 15 + x$

40. $x - 2 - 4x = -3x - 8 + 5x$

41. $2(5x - 7) = 28 - 3(x + 1)$

42. $4(2x - 5) = 32 - 4(x - 2)$

43. $(4 + 6)(2 + 4x) = 45 - 2.5(x + 3)$

44. $(5 + 0.5x)(1 + 3) = -1.2(2x + 4) + 25$

45. $15 + 5(x - 10) = 3(x - 1)$

46. $2(x - 3) + 3(x - 5) = 4$

47. $4(y + 7) - 2(y - 4) = 3(y - 2)$

48. $8(2y + 4) - 6(3y + 7) = 3y$

49. $\dfrac{y + 4}{5} = \dfrac{y - 2}{3}$

50. $\dfrac{x + 1}{3} = \dfrac{x - 3}{2}$

51. $\dfrac{5x - 3}{7} = \dfrac{4x}{5}$

52. $\dfrac{y + 2}{5} = \dfrac{y}{3}$

53. $\dfrac{1}{2}(x - 7) + \dfrac{1}{3}(x + 2) = 41$

54. $\dfrac{7}{12}(2x + 1) + \dfrac{3}{4}(x + 1) = 3$

For Problems 55 to 72, solve the following word problems using algebraic equations.

55. If three times a number plus twenty is seven times that number, what is the number?

56. Fifteen less than five times a number is twice that number. What is the number?

57. A 25-metre long PVC tube is cut into 2 pieces. One piece is 7 metres longer than the other. Find the length of each piece.

58. A 39-metre long PVC tube is cut into 3 pieces. The longest piece is twice the length of the shortest piece, and the remaining piece is 7 metres longer than the shortest piece. Find the length of each piece.

59. 100 patients are treated by three residents, Andy, Billy and Catherine. Billy treated 9 more patients than Andy. Catherine treated 8 patients less than Andy. Calculate the number of patients treated by each resident.

60. 60 patients are treated by two residents, Alice and Carol. Carol treated 8 more patients than Alice. Calculate the number of patients treated by each resident.

61. There are six times as many nurses as physicians at a hospital. If the hospital has a total of 84 staff on duty at a certain time, how many of these staff members are attending physicians?

62. Giri had twice as many inpatient procedures as outpatient procedures. If he had a total of 237 procedures, how many of them were outpatient procedures?

63. A children's waiting room, which is a square with sides of length x metres, is widened by 4 metres and lengthened by 3 metres.
    a. Write the equation for the area (A) of the expanded waiting room.

    b. If each side was originally 10 metres in length, find the new area. (Hint: Area of a Rectangle = Length × Width)

64. A square garden at a nursing home, with sides of length x metres, has had its width reduced by 4 metres and its length reduced by 2 metres.
    a. Write the equation for the area (A) of the smaller garden.

    b. If each side was originally 20 metres in length, find the new area.

65. Aran bought a scrub shirt and a surgical cap for $34.75. The shirt cost $9.75 more than the cap. Calculate the cost of the cap.

66. Mythili bought a box of wrap bandages and a bottle of hand sanitizer for $30.45. The box of wrap bandages cost $5.45 more than the hand sanitizer. Calculate the cost of the box of wrap bandages.

67. Sam is paid $720 a week as a radiology technician. He worked 9 hours of overtime last week and received $954. Calculate his overtime rate of pay per hour.

68. Lisa is paid $840 a week as a registered nurse. Her overtime rate is $28 per hour. Last week she received $1,036. How many hours of overtime did she work last week?

69. After completing a weight-loss program, a patient weighs 160 lb. His dietician finds that the patient has lost 15% of his original weight. What was the patient's starting weight?

70. A beaker in a chemistry lab contains 3 litres of water. While conducting an experiment, the chemistry professor removes three-fifths of the water from the beaker. He then adds three-fifths of the remaining volume to the beaker. How much water is left in the beaker at the end of the experiment?

71. A researcher wants to make 4 L of a 7% acid solution. She has a beaker of 15% acid solution in stock. How much of the 15% solution does she need to use and how much water must she add in order to prepare her desired solution?

72. A chemist wants to make a 10% acid solution. She has 5 L of 25% acid solution. How many litres of water should she add to the 25% solution in order to prepare her desired solution?

4.3 | Rearranging Equations and Formulas

Equations are mathematical statements formed by placing an equal (=) sign between two expressions to indicate that the expression on the left side of the equal sign is equal to the expression on the right side of the equal sign.

For example, $5x + 3 = y - x$

Formulas are similar to equations. In formulas, the relationship between one variable and several other variables is expressed as a rule for performing calculations. Formulas are written so that a single variable, known as the subject of the formula, is on the left side of the equation, and everything else is on the right side.

For example, $I = Prt$

Isolating Variables

To isolate a particular variable in an equation or a formula, rearrange the terms and simplify so that the required variable is on the left side of the equation and all the other variables and numbers are on the right side of the equation. When rearranging and simplifying an equation or formula, be sure to follow the rules for algebraic manipulation learned in the previous sections of this chapter:

- Expand brackets and collect like terms.

- Remove fractions by multiplying both sides by the LCD.

- Add or subtract the same quantity to or from both sides.
- Multiply or divide both sides by the same quantity.
- Take powers or roots on both sides.

  Note: If taking a square root of a squared variable, the resulting expression on the other side of the equation must always be proceeded with a ± sign, as the answer can be either positive or negative (e.g., if $x^2 = 9$, then solving for x, we get x = +3 or –3).

For example, consider the formula for simple interest: $I = Prt$.

To solve for any of the variables, 'P', 'r', or 't', in this formula, we can rearrange the variables as shown below:

$$I = Prt \qquad \text{is the same as} \quad Prt = I$$

Solving for 'P':

$$\frac{Prt}{rt} = \frac{I}{rt} \qquad \text{Dividing both sides by 'rt',}$$

$$P = \frac{I}{rt}$$

Solving for 'r':

$$\frac{Prt}{Pt} = \frac{I}{Pt} \qquad \text{Dividing both sides by 'Pt',}$$

$$r = \frac{I}{Pt}$$

Solving for 't':

$$\frac{Prt}{Pr} = \frac{I}{Pr} \qquad \text{Dividing both sides by 'Pr',}$$

$$t = \frac{I}{Pr}$$

Example 4.3-a **Rearranging Formulas to Isolate Variables**

Rearrange the following formulas to isolate the variables indicated in the brackets (i.e., the subjects):

(i) $S = C + M$ $\qquad\qquad\qquad\qquad$ (M)

(ii) $P = RB$ $\qquad\qquad\qquad\qquad\quad$ (R)

(iii) $y = mx + b$ $\qquad\qquad\qquad\qquad$ (m)

(iv) $F = \left(\dfrac{9}{5}\right)C + 32$ $\qquad\qquad\qquad$ (C)

Solution

(i) $\qquad S = C + M$ $\qquad\qquad$ Subtracting 'C' from both sides,

$\qquad S - C = C - C + M$

$\qquad\quad M = S - C$

(ii) $\qquad P = RB$ $\qquad\qquad\qquad$ Dividing both sides by 'B',

$\qquad \dfrac{P}{B} = \dfrac{RB}{B}$

$\qquad R = \dfrac{P}{B}$

(iii) $\qquad y = mx + b$ $\qquad\qquad$ Subtracting 'b' from both sides,

$\qquad y - b = mx + b - b$

$\qquad y - b = mx$ $\qquad\qquad\quad$ Dividing both sides by 'x',

$\qquad \dfrac{y - b}{x} = \dfrac{mx}{x}$

$\qquad\quad m = \dfrac{y - b}{x}$

(iv) $F = \left(\dfrac{9}{5}\right)C + 32$ Subtracting 32 from both sides,

$F - 32 = \dfrac{9}{5}C + 32 - 32$

$F - 32 = \dfrac{9}{5}C$ Multiplying both sides by $\dfrac{5}{9}$(the reciprocal of $\dfrac{9}{5}$),

$\dfrac{5}{9}(F - 32) = \dfrac{5}{9}\left(\dfrac{9}{5}C\right)$

$C = \dfrac{5}{9}(F - 32)$

Example 4.3-b Rearranging Formulas Involving Fractions

Rearrange to isolate the variables indicated in the brackets.

(i) $R = \dfrac{Vd}{t}$ (*t*)

(ii) $\dfrac{P_1 V_1}{T_1} = \dfrac{P_2 V_2}{T_2}$ (*V₂*)

(iii) $M = \dfrac{1}{3}S + \dfrac{2}{3}D$ (*D*)

Solution

(i) $R = \dfrac{Vd}{t}$ Multiplying both sides by '*t*',

$Rt = Vd$ Dividing both sides by '*R*',

$t = \dfrac{Vd}{R}$

(ii) $\dfrac{P_1 V_1}{T_1} = \dfrac{P_2 V_2}{T_2}$ Cross multiplying,

$T_2(P_1 V_1) = T_1(P_2 V_2)$ Removing brackets,

$T_2 P_1 V_1 = T_1 P_2 V_2$ Dividing each side by '$(T_1 P_2)$',

$V_2 = \dfrac{T_2 P_1 V_1}{T_1 P_2}$

(iii) $M = \dfrac{1}{3}S + \dfrac{2}{3}D$ Multiplying both sides by the LCD 3,

$3M = S + 2D$ Subtracting '*S*' from both sides,

$3M - S = 2D$ Dividing both sides by 2,

$D = \dfrac{3M - S}{2}$

Example 4.3-c   Rearranging Formulas Involving Powers and Roots

Rearrange to isolate the variables indicated in the brackets.

(i) $F = \dfrac{mV^2}{r}$ (V)

(ii) $r = \sqrt{x^2 + y^2}$ (x)

(iii) $F = 11.18r\left(\dfrac{V}{100}\right)^2$ (V)

Solution

> Recall: A square root has two solutions: a positive (+) solution and negative (−) solution. We represent this using a ± sign when rearranging formulas.

(i) $F = \dfrac{mV^2}{r}$ Multiplying both sides by 'r',

$Fr = mV^2$ Dividing both sides by 'm',

$\dfrac{Fr}{m} = V^2$ Taking the square root of both sides, and adding a ± sign in front of the radical,

$V = \pm\sqrt{\dfrac{Fr}{m}}$

(ii) $r = \sqrt{x^2 + y^2}$ Squaring both sides,

$r^2 = x^2 + y^2$ Subtracting 'y^2' from both sides,

$r^2 - y^2 = x^2$ Taking the square root of both sides, and adding a ± sign in front of the radical,

$x = \pm\sqrt{r^2 - y^2}$

(iii) $F = 11.18r\left(\dfrac{V}{100}\right)^2$ Dividing both sides by '11.18r',

$\dfrac{F}{11.18r} = \left(\dfrac{V}{100}\right)^2$ Taking the square root of both sides, and adding a ± sign in front of the radical,

$\pm\sqrt{\dfrac{F}{11.18r}} = \dfrac{V}{100}$ Multiplying both sides by 100,

$V = \pm100\sqrt{\dfrac{F}{11.18r}}$

Example 4.3-d   Rearranging Formulas Involving Factors

Rearrange to isolate the variables indicated in the brackets.

(i) $y = \dfrac{x + a}{x - a}$ (x)

(ii) $\dfrac{1}{f} = \dfrac{1}{u} + \dfrac{1}{v}$ (u)

Solution

(i) $y = \dfrac{x + a}{x - a}$ Multiplying both sides by '$x - a$',

$y(x - a) = x + a$ Expanding,

$xy - ay = x + a$ Subtracting 'x' from both sides and adding 'ay' to both sides,

$xy - x = ay + a$ Factoring 'x' on the left side and 'a' on the right side,

$$x(y - 1) = a(y + 1)$$ Dividing both sides by '$(y - 1)$',

$$x = \frac{a(y + 1)}{(y - 1)}$$

(ii) $\frac{1}{f} = \frac{1}{u} + \frac{1}{v}$ Multiplying both sides by the common denominator 'fuv',

$$uv = fv + fu$$ Subtracting 'fu' from both sides,

$$uv - fu = fv$$ Factoring 'u' on the left side,

$$u(v - f) = fv$$ Dividing both sides by '$(v - f)$',

$$u = \frac{fv}{v - f}$$

| Example 4.3-e | Rearranging a Formula and Evaluating to Find the Value of a Subject |

The formula for the volume of a right cylinder is $V = \pi r^2 h$.

(i)   Rearrange the formula to find 'h' as the subject.

(ii) Calculate the height (h) of a rectangle if $V = 200$ cm^3 and $r = 5$ cm. (Round the answer to two decimal places).

Solution

(i) $V = \pi r^2 h$ Dividing both sides by 'πr^2',

$$h = \frac{V}{\pi r^2}$$

(ii) Substituting the values for 'V' and 'r' into the rearranged formula,

$$h = \frac{200}{\pi \times 5^2}$$

$$h = \frac{200}{25\pi}$$

$$h = \frac{8}{\pi} = 2.546479... = 2.55 \text{ cm}$$

| Example 4.3-f | Rearranging a Formula and Evaluating to Find the Value of a Subject |

The area 'A' of a circle is given by the formula $A = \pi r^2$, where r is the radius of the circle.

(i)   Rearrange the formula to find 'r' as the subject.

(ii) Find the radius (r) of a circle whose area is 400 cm^2.
      (Round the answer to two decimal places).

Solution

(i) $A = \pi r^2$ Dividing both sides by π,

$$\frac{A}{\pi} = r^2$$ Taking the square root on both sides,

Since the radius of a circle must be positive, we can omit the ± sign.

$$r = \sqrt{\frac{A}{\pi}}$$

(ii) Substituting the value for 'A' in the rearranged formula,

$$r = \sqrt{\frac{400}{\pi}}$$

$$= 11.283791... = 11.28 \text{ cm}$$

For Problems 1 to 46, rearrange to isolate the variables indicated in the brackets:

1. $4x + 5 = y$ (x) 2. $x + 6y = 15$ (y)

3. $3x - y = 7$ (x) 4. $2y - x = 5$ (y)

5. $S = C + M$ (C) 6. $L - N = dL$ (d)

7. $N = L(1 - d)$ (L) 8. $C = 2\pi r$ (r)

9. $C + E + P = S$ (P) 10. $S = P + I$ (P)

11. $5x - 6 = 2x + y$ (x) 12. $3 - 5x = x + y$ (x)

13. $b = \dfrac{ac}{c + a}$ (a) 14. $b = \dfrac{ac}{c - a}$ (c)

15. $c = \dfrac{a - c}{b}$ (b) 16. $c = \dfrac{a + c}{b}$ (a)

17. $b = \dfrac{c + ac}{a - 2}$ (a) 18. $b = \dfrac{c - ac}{a + 2}$ (c)

19. $c = \dfrac{ab - b}{4 + a}$ (b) 20. $c = \dfrac{ab + b}{4 - a}$ (a)

21. $6(a - x) = y$ (x) 22. $4(x + a) = y$ (x)

23. $3(a + x) = x$ (x) 24. $5(y + a) = y$ (y)

25. $V^2 = u^2 + 2as$ (u) 26. $x^2 + y^2 = r^2$ (y)

27. $V^2 = u^2 + 2as$ (s) 28. $S = ut + at^2$ (u)

29. $5(x + 2y) = 3(x - 7y)$ (x) 30. $4(9y - 5x) = 5(y + 4x)$ (y)

31. $x - y = xy$ (x) 32. $x - xy = y$ (y)

33. $y = \dfrac{x + 5}{x - 5}$ (x) 34. $x = \dfrac{y + 1}{y - 2}$ (y)

35. $y = \sqrt{2x + 5}$ (x) 36. $y = \sqrt{7 - 5x}$ (x)

37. $y = 8 - \sqrt{x}$ (x) 38. $y = \sqrt{x} + 4$ (x)

39. $r = \sqrt{\dfrac{A}{4\pi}}$ (A) 40. $C = \sqrt{a^2 + b^2}$ (a)

41. $\dfrac{x}{y} + 5 = x$ (y) 42. $7 - \dfrac{x}{y} = x$ (y)

43. $A = \dfrac{(a + b)h}{2}$ (a) 44. $A = \dfrac{(a + b)h}{2}$ (h)

45. $y = (x - 4)(x + 4)$ (x) 46. $y = (3 - x)(3 + x)$ (x)

47. The formula for the volume, 'V', of a right cylinder is $V = \pi r^2 h$, where r is the radius of the base and h is the perpendicular height.

    a. Rearrange the formula to find r as the subject.

    b. Find the base radius of a cylinder whose volume is 900 cm^3 and whose perpendicular height is 10 cm. (Round the answer to two decimal places.)

48. The formula for the volume, 'V', of a right cone is $V = \dfrac{1}{3}\pi r^2 h$, where r is the radius of the base of the cone and h is the perpendicular height.

    a. Rearrange the formula to find h as the subject.

    b. Find the perpendicular height of a cone whose volume is 120 cm^3 and whose base diameter is 15 cm. (Round the answer to two decimal places.)

For Problems 1 to 6, simplify the following expressions, then evaluate for the given value of the variables in the brackets.

1. a. $-4x^2 + 3x - 5 + 7x^2 - 2x + 3$ $(x = 2)$

    b. $4x^2 - 5 + 7x - 2x^2 - x - 3$ $(x = -1)$

2. a. $3x^2 - x + 2 + x^2 - 5x - 2$ $(x = 3)$

    b. $-5y^2 - 7y + 3 + y^2 - 5y + 2$ $(y = -2)$

3. a. $-y^2 + 4xy + x^2 - 6y^2 - xy - 11x^2$ $(x = 1, y = 2)$

    b. $(x - 4)(x + 2) + 3(x + 2)$ $(x = 3)$

4. a. $-4x^2 + 6xy - 6y^2 + 6x^2 - 2xy + 3y^2$ $(x = 2, y = 1)$

    b. $(y - 2)(y - 3) + 2(y - 2)$ $(y = 4)$

5. a. $(2x + 1)^2 - (x - 2)^2$ $(x = 1)$

    b. $(3 - x)^2 + (x - 3)(x + 3)$ $(x = 2)$

6. a. $(2x - 1)^2 - (x + 2)^2$ $(x = 1)$

    b. $(4 - x)^2 + (x + 4)(x - 4)$ $(x = 2)$

For Problems 7 to 10, factor the following expressions, then evaluate for the given value of the variables in the brackets.

7. a. $6x^2 - 4x$ $(x = 1)$

    b. $3y^3 - 12y^2$ $(y = -2)$

8. a. $8y^2 - 64y$ $(y = 2)$

    b. $16x^2 - 4x^3$ $(x = -1)$

9. a. $7xy + 14x^2$ $(x = 3, y = 2)$

    b. $9x^3 - 6x^2 + 3x$ $(x = 1)$

10. a. $15y^2 + 10xy$ $(x = -1, y = 2)$

    b. $16x^3 + 8x^2 - 4x$ $(x = 2)$

For Problems 11 to 14, write an algebraic expression for each of the following:

11. a. Twelve increased by three times a number.

    b. The difference between a number and five.

12. a. Eight decreased by twice a number.

    b. Six less than the total of a number and ten.

13. a. The sum of ten times a number and fifteen.

    b. The product of three more than a number and the number.

14. a. The sum of fifteen and half of a number.

    b. The product of two times a number and seven more than the number.

For Problems 15 to 18, write an algebraic equation for each of the following and solve:

15. a. Seventeen more than five times a number is forty-two.

    b. A number divided by fifteen is forty-five.

16. a. The product of five and a number is seventy-five.

    b. Three more than two times a number is nine.

17. a. The difference between a number and ten is ten.

    b. The product of four times a number and three is thirty-six.

18. a. The sum of two times a number and eight is one hundred.

    b. A number divided by three is seven.

For Problems 19 to 22, solve for the unknown variable, 'x', using the properties of equality.

19. a. $5x - 5 = 10$ b. $\dfrac{x}{3} + 4 = 10$

20. a. $3x - 5 = -17$ b. $\dfrac{x}{4} - 2 = 1$

21. a. $12 - 3x = 3 - 4x$ b. $4(x + 4) = 24$

22. a. $4x - 2 = 13 - 6x$ b. $3(2x - 5) = 3$

23. The formula for the circumference of a circle is $C = 2\pi r$.

    a. Rearrange to isolate the variable 'r'.

    b. Find 'r' to 2 decimal places when $C = 75$ cm.

    c. Find the area 'A' of the above circle (from part b) to the nearest cm^2, using the formula $A = \pi r^2$. (Use the rounded 'r' value from part b.)

24. The formula for the volume of a cylinder is $V = \pi r^2 h$.

    a. Isolate the variable 'r'.

    b. Find 'r' when $V = 300$ cm^3 and $h = 15$ cm. Round to 2 decimal places.

    c. Find the surface area 'SA' of the above cylinder (from part b) to the nearest cm^2, using the formula $SA = 2\pi r^2 + 2\pi rh$. (Use the rounded 'r' value from part b.)

25. The formula for the volume of a cone is $V = \dfrac{1}{3}\pi r^2 h$.

    a. Isolate the variable 'h'.

    b. Find 'h', when $r = 11$ cm and $V = 4,560$ cm^3. Round the answer to 2 decimal places.

26. The formula for the volume of a cone is $V = \dfrac{1}{3}\pi r^2 h$.

    a. Isolate the variable 'r'.

    b. Find 'r', when $V = 2{,}280$ cm^3 and $h = 15$ cm. Round the answer to 2 decimal places.

27. A patient currently weighs 240 lb, which is approximately 20% over his maximum healthy body weight. What is his maximum healthy body weight?

28. The average adult requires 7 hours of sleep, which is roughly 30% less than the amount of sleep an elementary school child needs. How many hours of sleep does an elementary school child need?

29. A chemistry student wants to create a 20% solution of HCl. How much water needs to be added to 20 L of a 35% HCl concentration to create a 20% solution of HCl?

30. Determine the volumes of a 7% saline solution and water that should be mixed together to get 400 mL of a 3% saline solution?

4 | Self-Test Exercises

Answers to all problems are available at the end of the textbook.

Simplify the following expressions, then evaluate for the given value of the variables in the brackets:

1.   a. $2x^2 + 5x + 1 - 4 - 3x - x^2$ $(x = 2)$

     b. $-3x^2 + 2x + 2x^2 - 8x + 10$ $(x = -3)$

2.   a. $9x^2 - 4xy + y^2 - 6y^2 - 3xy + 10x^2$ $(x = 1, y = 2)$

     b. $5(2x - 3y) - 2(3x - 2y) + 7$ $(x = 2 \text{ and } y = 1)$

3. $(x + 3)^2 - (x + 2)(x - 2)$ $(x = 3)$

4. $(2x + 5)^2 - (3x - 1)^2$ $(x = 1)$

Factor the following expressions, then evaluate for the given value of the variables in the brackets:

5.   a. $18y^2 - 12y$ $(y = -2)$

     b. $15y^3 + 12y^2 + 3y$ $(y = 1)$

6.   a. $14xy - 21x^2$ $(x = 2, y = -1)$

     b. $8xy^2 - 6x^2y$ $(x = 1, y = -1)$

Write an algebraic expression for each of the following:

7.   a. Twenty-five less than three times a number.

     b. A number increased by eighteen.

8.   a. The difference between twice a number and six.

     b. A number divided by three more than the number.

Write the following as algebraic equations and solve:

9.   a. Nine less than twice a number is twenty-one.

     b. Twenty-two is three less than five times a number.

10. a. Four times nine more than a number is sixteen times the number.

     b. Thirty is twelve less than the product of six and a number.

Solve for the unknown variable 'x', using the properties of equality:

11. a. $24 - 5x = 4$ b. $\dfrac{x}{3} - 2 = 4$

12. a. $8 + 2x = 36 - 5x$ b. $3(3x - 5) = 33$

13. a. $\dfrac{x + 1}{6} = \dfrac{2x - 3}{2}$ b. $\dfrac{x - 5}{3} = \dfrac{x + 3}{15}$

14. a. $1.2(4x + 1) = 0.8(x - 6)$ b. $0.02(100x + 60) = 0.05(80x - 20)$

15. Given the formula $C = \dfrac{5}{9}(F - 32)$:

    a. Isolate 'F'.

    b. Find the value of 'F' when $C = 30$ °C. Round to two decimal places, as needed.

16. Given the formula $C = 2\pi r$:

    a. Isolate 'r'.

    b. Find the value of 'r' when $C = 1{,}200$ cm. Round to two decimal places.

17. A defibrillator costs $2,120 after a 15% discount. What was the original price?

18. A pharmacist uses a markup rate of 115% for over-the-counter medications. If he purchased a shipment of Tylenol from a wholesaler for a unit price of $3.72 per bottle, for what price should he sell each bottle of Tylenol?

19. Alice has 20 L of a 5% acid solution. How much water should she add to make a 2% acid solution?

20. How much water must be evaporated from 1,000 L of an 8% salt solution to form a 19% salt solution?

5 RATIOS, PROPORTIONS, PERCENTS, AND PERCENT CHANGES

LEARNING OBJECTIVES

- Identify ratios and rates to compare quantity.
- Set up ratios and use them to solve problems involving allocation and sharing of quantities.
- Solve problems by finding unknown quantities using proportions as equivalent sets of ratios.
- Allocate quantities on a proportional basis using pro-ration as an application of proportions.
- Convert percents to equivalent fractions and decimal numbers.
- Solve percent problems using different methods.
- Calculate base, rate, or portion of quantities, expressed in percents.
- Identify the terminology used in percent change.
- Use percents to measure percent increase and decrease.

CHAPTER OUTLINE

5.1 Ratios

5.2 Proportions

5.3 Percents

5.4 Percent Changes

Introduction

One of the ways in which we use mathematics in health sciences is through the comparison of quantities, amounts, or values using ratios, rates, proportions, and percents. We use ratios to compare two or more quantities, amounts, or values of the same unit, and rates to compare quantities, amounts, or values involving different units. We use proportions to calculate unknown quantities or to determine precise values, such as finding the unit price of items, like medical supplies, to determine the best deal. And we use percents to express the ratio of the part to the whole, on a scale out of 100. Due to their simplicity, percents are a widely accepted measure for expressing fractions or decimal numbers. Some examples of the use of percents include the concentration of dosages of medication, the strength of solutions, the proportion of patients who are successfully treated by a certain drug therapy, etc.

5.1 | Ratios

Ratio is a comparison or relationship between two or more quantities.

A **ratio** is a comparison or relationship between two or more quantities with the same unit. Therefore, ratios are not expressed with units.

For example, if a solution contains 375 mL of water and 150 mL of iodine, the comparison of the volume of water to the volume of iodine, in the same order, is called the ratio of their quantities, and can be expressed in three different ways, as discussed below.

Expressing a Ratio of Two Quantities

When comparing two quantities, there are different ways to express the ratio. In the example above, the ratio of the quantity of water to that of iodine may be expressed in any of the following forms:

375 to 150	(separate the quantities using the word 'to')
375 : 150	(using a colon and read as '375 is to 150')
$\dfrac{375}{150}$	(as a fraction and read as '375 over 150')

Note: *When representing a ratio as a fraction, if the denominator is 1, the denominator (1) must still be written.*

For example, if the ratio of two quantities is $\dfrac{3}{1}$ then it is incorrect to say that the ratio is 3. It should be stated as $\dfrac{3}{1}$ or 3 : 1.

Expressing a Ratio of More than Two Quantities

When comparing more than two quantities, we always use a colon to represent the ratio.

For example, if an electrolyte solution contains 600 mg of sodium chloride, 40 mg of potassium chloride, and 30 mg of calcium chloride, then the ratio of these quantities is expressed as:

Sodium chloride : Potassium chloride : Calcium chloride = 600 : 40 : 30

Terms of a Ratio

The quantities in a ratio are called the **terms** of the ratio.

In the examples above, the terms are 375 and 150 (in the first ratio), and 600, 40, and 30 (in the second ratio).

Equivalent Ratios

When all the terms of the ratio are multiplied by the same number or divided by the same number, the result will be an **equivalent ratio**.

For example, when the terms of the ratio 12 : 15 are multiplied by 2, we obtain an equivalent ratio of 24 : 30.

$$12 : 15$$
$$12 \times \mathbf{2} : 15 \times \mathbf{2}$$
$$24 : 30$$

When the terms of the ratio 12 : 15 are divided by the common factor 3, we obtain the equivalent ratio of 4 : 5.

$$12 : 15$$
$$12 \div \mathbf{3} : 15 \div \mathbf{3}$$
$$4 : 5$$

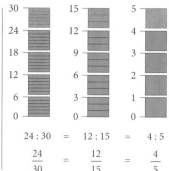

Therefore, the ratios 12 : 15, 24 : 30, and 4 : 5 are equivalent ratios.

Reducing a Ratio to its Simplest or Lowest Terms

When two ratios are equivalent, they result in the same answer when reduced to their lowest terms.

Comparisons are easier when ratios are reduced to their lowest terms. When all the terms of a ratio are integers, the ratio can be reduced to its lowest terms by dividing all the terms by their common factors.

For example, if a medical assistant earns $3,000 per month, a nursing assistant earns $4,500, and a nurse earns $6,000, then the equivalent ratio of their monthly earnings, reduced to their lowest terms, is calculated as follows:

A ratio is in its simplest form when the terms have no common factor (other than 1).

Medical assistant : Nursing assistant : Nurse

3,000 :	4,500	: 6,000	Dividing each term by the common factor 100,
30 :	45	: 60	Dividing each term by the common factor 15,
2 :	3	: 4	Now, the ratio is in its lowest terms.

By reducing the ratio to lowest terms, we can say that the monthly earnings of a medical assistant, a nursing assistant, and a nurse are in the ratio of 2 : 3 : 4.

Example 5.1-a **Determining Equivalent Ratios**

Determine whether the given pairs of ratios are equivalent by reducing to their lowest terms.

(i)   18 : 12 and 12 : 8

(ii)   20 : 24 and 15 : 20

Solution

(i)   18 : 12   12 : 8
    $18 \div 6 : 12 \div 6$ $12 \div 4 : 8 \div 4$
           3 : 2   3 : 2

Therefore, the given pair of ratios are equivalent.

(ii)   20 : 24   15 : 20
    $20 \div 4 : 24 \div 4$ $15 \div 5 : 20 \div 5$
           5 : 6   3 : 4

Therefore, the given pair of ratios are not equivalent.

Reducing Ratios When One or More of the Terms of the Ratio Are Fractions

To reduce a ratio containing at least one fraction, first convert all the terms to integers by multiplying all the terms by the least common denominator (LCD), and then reduce to its lowest terms.

For example,

$\dfrac{2}{3}$	:	$\dfrac{4}{5}$	:	2	Multiplying each term by the least common denominator 15,

$\dfrac{2}{3}$: $\dfrac{4}{5}$: 2   Multiplying each term by the least common denominator 15,

10 : 12 : 30   Dividing each term by the common factor 2,

5 : 6 : 15

Reducing Ratios When One or More of the Terms of the Ratio Are Decimal Numbers

To reduce a ratio containing at least one decimal number, first convert all the terms to integers by moving the decimal of all the terms to the right by the same number of places in order to eliminate all the decimal places, and then reduce to its lowest terms.

For example,

2.25 : 3.5 : 5   Moving the decimal point of each term two places to the right,

225 : 350 : 500   Dividing each term by the common factor 25,

9 : 14 : 20

Reducing Ratios When the Terms of the Ratio Are a Combination of Fractions and Decimals

To reduce a ratio containing both fractions and decimals, first convert all the fractional terms to integers, then convert all the decimal terms to integers. Finally, reduce to its lowest terms.

For example,

5.25 : $\dfrac{9}{2}$: 3   Multiplying each term by the common denominator 2,

10.5 : 9 : 6   Moving the decimal point of each term one place to the right,

105 : 90 : 60   Dividing each term by the common factor 15,

7 : 6 : 4

Example 5.1-b   **Reducing Ratios to Lowest Terms**

Express the following ratios as equivalent ratios in their lowest terms:

(i) $2\dfrac{7}{9} : 3\dfrac{1}{3} : 5$ (ii) $2.5 : 1.75 : 0.625$ (iii) $1.25 : \dfrac{5}{6} : 2$

Solution

(i) $2\dfrac{7}{9}$: $3\dfrac{1}{3}$: 5   Converting the terms with mixed numbers to improper fractions,

$\dfrac{25}{9}$: $\dfrac{10}{3}$: 5   Multiplying each term by the least common denominator 9,

25 : 30 : 45   Dividing each term by the common factor 5,

5 : 6 : 9

Therefore, $2\dfrac{7}{9} : 3\dfrac{1}{3} : 5$ reduced to its lowest terms is $5 : 6 : 9$

(ii) $2.5 : 1.75 : 0.625$ Moving the decimal point of each term three places to the right,

2,500 : 1,750 : 625   Dividing each term by the common factor 125,

20 : 14 : 5

Therefore, $2.5 : 1.75 : 0.625$ reduced to its lowest terms is $20 : 14 : 5$.

(iii) $1.25 : \dfrac{5}{6} : 2$ Multiplying each term by the common denominator 6,

   $7.5 : 5 : 12$ Moving the decimal point of each term one place to the right,

   $75 : 50 : 120$ Dividing each term by the common factor 5,

   $15 : 10 : 24$

Therefore, $1.25 : \dfrac{5}{6} : 2$ reduced to its lowest terms is $15 : 10 : 24$.

Reducing Ratios to an Equivalent Ratio Where the Smallest Term is 1

To make the comparison of quantities easier, we can also reduce a ratio to its equivalent ratio where the smallest term is equal to 1, by dividing all the terms of the ratio by the smallest term.

For example, if the number of hours that 3 radiologist technicians, A, B, and C, worked in one week were 32, 40, and 48, respectively, then the equivalent ratio of the times worked, where the smallest term is 1, is calculated as follows:

A : B : C

32 : 40 : 48   Dividing each term by the smallest term, 32,

1 : 1.25 : 1.5   Now, the ratio is reduced to its equivalent ratio with the smallest term equal to 1.

By reducing it so that the smallest term is equal to 1, we can state that B worked 1.25 times more than A, and C worked 1.5 times more than A.

Example 5.1-c | **Reducing Ratios to an Equivalent Ratio where the Smallest Term is 1**

Three registered nurses, A, B, and C, earn salaries of \$64,000, \$50,000, and \$40,000, respectively. By expressing their salaries in a ratio where the smallest term is 1, determine how many times greater A's and B's salaries are than C's.

A : B : C

64,000 : 50,000 : 40,000   Dividing each term by the smallest term, 40,000,

1.6 : 1.25 : 1

Therefore, A's salary is 1.6 times greater than C's salary, and B's salary is 1.25 times greater than C's salary.

Order of a Ratio

The order of presenting terms in a ratio is important. For example, if we order a shipment of 20 boxes of masks, 30 boxes of surgical gloves, and 50 boxes of IV tubing, then the ratio of the boxes of masks, gloves, and IV tubing is:

Masks : Gloves : IV tubing = 20 : 30 : 50   Dividing each term by the common factor 10,
   = 2 : 3 : 5

In the previous example, the ratio of the boxes of IV tubing, gloves, and masks is:

IV tubing : Gloves : Masks = 50 : 30 : 20   Dividing each term by the common factor 10,
   = 5 : 3 : 2

Note that the ratio Masks : Gloves : IV tubing is not the same as the ratio IV tubing : Gloves : Masks.

Ratios compare numbers in a specific order. The ratio $5 : 3 : 2$ expresses a different comparison than the ratio $2 : 3 : 5$.

Comparing Quantities

When using ratios to compare quantities of items that have the **same kind of measure**, the measures need to be expressed in the same unit before they can be expressed via a ratio. It is often easiest to do this by expressing the value with the larger unit in terms of the smaller unit to avoid decimals and fractions. This is shown in the following example.

| Example 5.1-d | Comparing Quantities with the Same Kind of Measure |

Express each of the following ratios in its simplest form:

   (i)   5 dollars to 10 quarters   (ii)   16 weeks to 2 years

Solution

   (i)   5 dollars : 10 quarters   Converting 5 dollars to quarters: 5 dollars = 5 × 4 quarters = 20 quarters,

         20 quarters : 10 quarters   Dividing both terms by the common factor 10,

              2 : 1

       Therefore, the ratio of 5 dollars to 10 quarters is 2 : 1.

   (ii)   16 weeks : 2 years   Converting 2 years to weeks: 2 years = 2 × 52 weeks = 104 weeks,

        16 weeks : 104 weeks   Dividing both terms by the common factor 8,

             2 : 13

       Therefore, the ratio of 16 weeks to 2 years is 2 : 13.

When using ratios to compare quantities of items that have **different kinds of measure**, the units of measurement of each quantity must be included in the ratio.

For example, to prepare a banana bag (rally pack), Maggie uses 1,000 mL of normal saline, 100 mg of thiamine, and 2 mg of folic acid.

saline	:	thiamine	:	folic acid	
(mL)		(mg)		(mg)	
1,000	:	100	:	2	Dividing each term by the common factor 2,
500	:	50	:	1	500 mL of saline to 50 mg of thiamine to 1 mg of of folic acid

Therefore, the ratio of normal saline to thiamine to folic acid in the banana bag is 500 mL : 50 mg : 1 mg.

Rate, Unit Rate, and Unit Price

Rate

A rate is a special ratio that is used to compare two quantities or amounts that have different units of measure. Rate is used to describe the strength of a solution, medicine dosage amounts, and other scientific calculations.

For example, if a saline solution contains 1.8 g of sodium chloride (NaCl) and 200 mL of water, then the rate of grams per millilitres is 1.8 g : 200 mL. The first term of the ratio is measured in grams and the second term is measured in millilitres.

The word 'per' indicates that it is a rate and is usually denoted by a slash '/'. Therefore, 1.8 g : 200 mL is usually written as 1.8 g per 200 mL or 1.8g/200mL.

Rates are used in our day-to-day activities such as travelling, working, shopping, etc.

For example,

- Travelled 90 km in 1.5 hours (90km/1.5h)
- Worked 75 hours in 2 weeks (75h/2 weeks)
- Paid $4.80 for 4 L of milk ($4.80/4L)

Unit Rate

Unit rate represents the number of units of the first quantity (or measurement) that corresponds to one unit of the second quantity (or measurement). That is, unit rate is a rate expressed as a ratio which has a denominator of 1.

If the denominator of a **ratio** is 1, the 1 must be written in the denominator.
If the denominator of a **rate** is 1, we usually do not write the 1 in the denominator.

Rates can be converted to unit rates simply by dividing the first term by the second term.

For example,

An employee works 75 hours over 2 weeks. Writing this rate of work as a unit rate in hours per week:

$$= \frac{75 \text{ hours}}{2 \text{ weeks}}$$

$$= \frac{37.5 \text{ hours}}{1 \text{ week}}$$

$$= 37.5 \text{ hours/week}$$

Similarly,

9 mg of medication is to be administered over 1.5 hours. Writing this rate of drug infusion as a unit rate in mg per hour:

$$= \frac{9 \text{ mg}}{1.5 \text{ hours}}$$

$$= \frac{6 \text{ mg}}{1 \text{ hour}}$$

$$= 6 \text{ mg/hour}$$

Example 5.1-e — Calculating Hourly Rate of Pay

Peter worked 9 hours and earned $247.50. Calculate his hourly rate of pay.

Solution

$247.50 is earned over 9 hours.

$$\text{Therefore, the hourly rate of pay} = \frac{\$247.50}{9 \text{ h}}$$

$$= \$27.50/\text{h}$$

Therefore, his hourly rate of pay is $27.50 per hour or $27.50/h.

Example 5.1-f — Calculating Unit Rate of Flow

A 1,500 mL normal saline solution is infused over 12 hours. What is the unit rate of flow in mL/h?

Solution

A volume of 1,500 mL needs to be infused over a time period of 12 hours.

$$\text{Therefore, the unit rate of flow} = \frac{1,500 \text{ mL}}{12 \text{ h}}$$

$$= 125 \text{ mL/h}$$

Therefore, the solution will infuse at a rate of 125 mL/h.

Example 5.1-g — Comparing Drug/Dosage Rates

Solution *A* contains 2 mg of a drug per 20 mL of water. Solution *B* contains 4 mg of a drug per 50 mL of water. Which solution has a lower concentration of the drug?

Solution

Solution A: 2 mg of the drug per 20 mL of water.

$$\text{Concentration of Solution } A \text{ (in mg/mL)} = \frac{2 \text{ mg}}{20 \text{ mL}}$$
$$= 0.1 \text{ mg/mL}$$

Solution B: 4 mg of the drug per 50 mL of water.

$$\text{Concentration of Solution } B \text{ (in mg/mL)} = \frac{4 \text{ mg}}{50 \text{ mL}}$$
$$= 0.08 \text{ mg/mL}$$

Therefore, Solution B has a lower concentration of the drug.

Unit Price

Unit price is the unit rate when it is expressed per unit currency (dollars, cents, etc.). Unit price indicates the cost of one unit of a particular good or service. The price is always the numerator and the unit is the denominator. That is, price is expressed per quantity of 1 unit.

For example, the price of gas is $1.18 per litre ($1.18/L), the price of grapes is $2 per kilogram ($2/kg), the price of juice is $0.75 per can ($0.75/can), etc.

If the total price for a given quantity of an item is known, to find its unit price, divide the total price of the item by its quantity.

The unit price is used in comparing and making decisions in purchasing items when various options are available. We save money when we compare the unit price of the same item in different-sized containers or different packages to determine the cheaper price per unit for our purchases.

Example 5.1-h | **Calculating the Unit Price of an Item**

If 1,000 disposable syringes cost $140, then what is the unit price of a syringe?

Solution

Divide the total price ($140) by the total quantity of syringes (1,000) to determine the unit price of a syringe:

$$\frac{\$140}{1,000 \text{ syringes}} = \$0.14/\text{syringe}$$

Therefore, the unit price is $0.14 per syringe ($0.14/syringe).

Example 5.1-I | **Comparing Unit Prices**

Andrea paid $360 for 4 cases of cotton swabs, whereas Sam paid $286.50 for 3 cases of cotton swabs. Which buyer received a better (cheaper) unit price?

Solution

Andrea paid $360 for 4 cases of cotton swabs.

$$\text{Unit price} = \frac{\$360.00}{4 \text{ cases}}$$
$$= \$90.00/\text{case}$$

Sam paid $286.50 for 3 cases of cotton swabs.

$$\text{Unit price} = \frac{\$286.50}{3 \text{ cases}}$$
$$= \$95.50/\text{case}$$

Therefore, based on the unit price, Andrea paid a better price for the cotton swabs.

Note: Unit rate and unit price problems can also be solved using the method of proportions, as will be demonstrated in the next section.

Sharing Quantities

Sharing quantities refers to the distribution of a quantity into two or more portions (or units) based on a given ratio.

For example, a supplier's budget of $10,000 needs to be allocated among three hospital departments, A, B, and C, in the ratio of $2 : 3 : 5$. To calculate the amount that each department receives, first add the terms of the ratio (i.e., 2, 3, and 5), which will result in a total of 10 units. These 10 units represent the total budget of $10,000, where A's share constitutes 2 units, B's share 3 units, and C's share 5 units, as shown in the diagram below.

Each department's share can then be calculated, as follows:

$$A\text{'s share} = \frac{2}{10} \times 10,000 = \$2,000.00$$

$$B\text{'s share} = \frac{3}{10} \times 10,000 = \$3,000.00$$

$$C\text{'s share} = \frac{5}{10} \times 10,000 = \$5,000.00$$

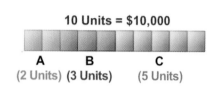

10 Units = $10,000

A (2 Units) B (3 Units) C (5 Units)

The total of the individual portions will be equal to the original amount shared.

- The total of A, B, and C's shares is equal to the budget amount of $10,000. That is, the shares of $A + B + C = \$2,000 + \$3,000 + \$5,000 = \$10,000$.

- If we reduce the ratio of the amounts shared by A, B, and C to its lowest terms, the result is the original ratio. That is, $2,000 : 3,000 : 5,000$ reduced to lowest terms is $2 : 3 : 5$.

The ratio of the individual portions, when reduced, will be equal to the original ratio.

If this year the ratio of A's share : B's share : C's share is changed to $5 : 3 : 2$ (instead of last year's $2 : 3 : 5$), and the budget amount of $10,000 remained the same, then the department shares would change as follows:

$$A\text{'s share} = \frac{5}{10} \times 10,000 = \$5,000.00$$

$$B\text{'s share} = \frac{3}{10} \times 10,000 = \$3,000.00$$

$$C\text{'s share} = \frac{2}{10} \times 10,000 = \$2,000.00$$

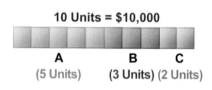

10 Units = $10,000

A (5 Units) B (3 Units) C (2 Units)

- The total of A, B, and C's shares this year is still be equal to the budget amount of $10,000. That is, the shares of $A + B + C = \$5,000 + \$3,000 + \$2,000 = \$10,000$.

- If we reduce the ratio of the amounts shared by A, B, and C to its lowest terms, the result is the original ratio. That is, $5,000 : 3,000 : 2,000$ reduced to lowest terms is $5 : 3 : 2$.

Example 5.1-j | **Sharing Quantities Using Ratios**

Three hospital departments, A, B, and C, have a supplies budget of $3,500, $2,100, and $2,800, respectively. If Department C is closed down, and its budget is allocated between Departments A and B, how much would each department receive, if the original ratio is maintained?

Solution

The initial budget of A, B, and C is in the ratio of $3,500 : 2,100 : 2,800$, which can be reduced to $5 : 3 : 4$.

If A and B want to maintain their initial budget ratio of $5 : 3$, then C's share of $2,800 has to be allocated to departments A and B in the same ratio, $5 : 3$.

By adding the reduced terms of A and B, we know that C's share is to be divided into a total of 8 units, as illustrated:

Department A would receive: $\frac{5}{8} \times 2,800.00 = \$1,750.00$

Department B would receive: $\frac{3}{8} \times 2,800.00 = \$1,050.00$

8 Units = $2,800

A (5 Units) B (3 Units)

Therefore, Department A would receive $1,750 and Department B would receive $1,050 of Department C's budget, if the original ratio is maintained.

Example 5.1-k | **Application Using Equivalent Ratios**

Andrew, Barry, and Cathy invested their savings in a bank. The investment ratio of Andrew to Barry is 2 : 3 and that of Barry to Cathy is 4 : 5. What is the investment ratio of Andrew : Barry : Cathy?

Solution

$A : B = 2 : 3$ and $B : C = 4 : 5$

Find the equivalent ratios for $A : B$ and $B : C$ so that the number of units in B is the same in both cases (i.e., we want the LCM of 3 and 4 - the terms representing Barry in the two different ratios).

This can be done for the ratio of $A : B$ by multiplying each term by 4 and that of $B : C$ by multiplying each term by 3.

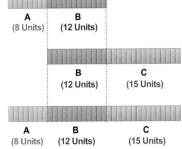

$A : B = 2 : 3$ Multiplying each term by 4,

$= 8 : 12$

$B : C = 4 : 5$ Multiplying each term by 3,

$= 12 : 15$

Therefore, the investment ratio of Andrew : Barry : Cathy is 8 : 12 : 15.

5.1 | Exercises

Answers to odd-numbered problems are available at the end of the textbook.

1. Find the ratio of the following, reduced to lowest terms:

   a. 9 months to 2 years   b. 10 quarters to 5 dimes   c. 30 minutes to 1.25 hours

2. Find the ratio of the following, reduced to lowest terms:

   a. 3 weeks to 126 days   b. 12 loonies to 10 toonies   c. 55 minutes to 2.75 hours

For Problems 3 to 6, express the ratios as equivalent ratios in their lowest whole number form.

3. a. 18 : 48 : 30   b. 175 : 50 : 125   c. 0.45 : 1 : 2

4. a. 27 : 45 : 72   b. 180 : 60 : 150   c. 2.4 : 0.75

5. a. $\dfrac{2}{3} : \dfrac{1}{5}$ b. $12 : \dfrac{5}{3} : 3$ c. $1.7 : 8.5 : \dfrac{34}{3}$

6. a. $\dfrac{3}{4} : \dfrac{2}{5}$ b. $65 : 91 : \dfrac{13}{2}$ c. $12 : 1.5 : \dfrac{3}{2}$

7. Determine if the following ratios are equivalent or not equivalent.

   a. 4 : 6 and 6 : 10   b. 8 : 10 and 28 : 35   c. 6 : 8 and 27 : 32   d. 16 : 22 and 64 : 88

8. Determine if the following ratios are equivalent or not equivalent.

   a. 16 : 20 and 24 : 30   b. 10 : 12 and 35 : 42   c. 12 : 14 and 30 : 42   d. 12 : 26 and 30 : 65

9. Determine if the following ratios are equivalent or not equivalent to the ratio 6 : 9 : 12.

   a. 4 : 6 : 8   b. 2 : 3 : 4   c. 1 : 3 : 2   d. 8 : 12 : 16

10. Determine if the following ratios are equivalent or not equivalent to the ratio 16 : 24 : 12.

    a. 20 : 30 : 15   b. 8 : 12 : 6   c. 28 : 42 : 21   d. 24 : 36 : 18

For Problems 11 to 18, find the unit rate.

11. 525 km in 7 hours = ? km/h

12. 680 km in 8 hours = ? km/h

13. 1,000 mL in 24 hours = ? mL/h

14. 2,000 mL in 12 hours = ? mL/h

15. 5 mg per 2 mL = ? mg/mL

16. 5 mg per 15 min = ? mg/min

17. 496 words typed in 8 minutes = ? words/min

18. 192 pages in 8 minutes = ? pages/min

For Problems 19 and 20, identify the option with the higher concentration, based on unit rate.

19. 5 mg of NaCl in 150 mL of compound, or 4 mg of NaCl in 100 mL?

20. 400 mg of sugar in 5 ounces of fluid, or 600 mg of sugar in 9 ounces of fluid?

For Problems 21 and 22, identify the option with the lower cost, based on unit price.

21. 12 mL of 0.2M HCl for $1.44, or 18 mL of 0.2M HCl for $2.88?

22. 300 mL of isopropyl alcohol for $5.60, or 500 mL of isopropyl alcohol for $7.25?

23. 480 mg of an antibiotic is given to a patient who weighs 80 kg. What is the ratio of the antibiotic to the patient's weight (express the ratio as mg : kg, reduced to lowest terms)? If the safe dosage rate is 5-8 mg/kg, is this dose safe for this patient?

24. Adam has a budget of $6,000 to spend on medical supplies. If he spent $800 on IV tubing, what is the ratio of the IV tubing expense to the the total expense, reduced to lowest terms? If the ratio of Adam's budget for IV tubing to his total budget is 1 : 10, was he under-budget or over-budget?

25. If employee A earns $196 for working 8 hours and employee B earns $105 for working 5 hours, who has the higher hourly rate?

26. If Ambulance A travelled 324 km in 4 hours and 15 minutes and Ambulance B travelled 280 km in 3 hours and 30 minutes, which ambulance travelled faster?

27. Jack's monthly pay as a medical secretary is $4,000. Steve's weekly pay as an optometrist technician is $1,080. Connor's bi-weekly pay as an optometrist is $3,000.

 a.   Calculate their annual salaries. (Annual Salary = 12 monthly payments = 26 bi-weekly payments = 52 weekly payments)

 b.   Express their salaries as a ratio, with the lowest term being 1. Based on this, how many times greater is the highest salary than the lowest salary?

28. Kate, a registered nurse, earns $1,200 weekly; Amy, a physician assistant, earns $2,000 bi-weekly; and Susan, a general practitioner, earns $6,500 monthly.

 a.   Calculate their annual salaries. (Annual Salary = 12 monthly payments = 26 bi-weekly payments = 52 weekly payments)

 b.   Express their salaries as a ratio, with the lowest term being 1. Based on this, how many times greater is the highest salary than the lowest salary?

29. Emily was planning to make a phosphate buffer solution. She used 10 mL of potassium phosphate dibasic (K_2HPO_4) and 14 mL of mono-potassium phosphate (KH_2PO_4).

 a.   What is the ratio of the solutions in her buffer, reduced to lowest terms?

 b.   If she decides to reduce the quantity of mono-potassium phosphate to 4.5 mL, calculate the new ratio of the solutions in her buffer solution.

30. In Murphy's MRI manufacturing company, 600 kg of gradient coils, 45 kg of RF equipment, 30 kg of magnets, and 120 kg of a display unit are used per day to make MRI machines.

 a.   What is the ratio of the raw materials used per day to make MRIs, reduced to lowest terms?

 b.   If they alter the quantity of RF equipment used in the MRI machines and utilize only 30 kg of RF equipment per day, calculate the new ratio of raw materials used per day.

5.2 | Proportions

When two ratios are equivalent, we say that they are **proportional** to each other. In the proportion equation, the ratio on the left side of the equation is equal to the ratio on the right side of the equation.

Consider an example where $A : B$ is $50 : 100$ and $C : D$ is $30 : 60$.

Reducing each ratio to its lowest terms, we obtain the ratio of $A : B$ is $1 : 2$ and the ratio of $C : D$ is $1 : 2$.

Since these ratios are equivalent, they are proportional to each other, and their proportion equation is,

$$A : B = C : D$$

The proportion equation can also be formed by representing the ratios as fractions:

$$\frac{A}{B} = \frac{C}{D}$$

This proportion equation can be simplified by multiplying both sides of the equation by the product of both denominators, BD.

$$\frac{A}{B} = \frac{C}{D}$$ Multiplying both sides by (BD),

$$\frac{A}{B}(BD) = \frac{C}{D}(BD)$$ Simplifying,

$$AD = BC$$

If two sets of fractions are equal, then the product obtained by cross-multiplying the fractions will be equal.

The same result can be obtained by equating the product of the numerator of the 1st ratio and the denominator of the 2nd ratio with the product of the denominator of the 1st ratio and the numerator of the 2nd ratio. This is referred to as cross-multiplication and is shown below:

$$\frac{A}{B} \bowtie \frac{C}{D}$$ Cross-multiplying,

$$AD = BC$$

If $A : B = C : D$

then, $\frac{A}{B} = \frac{C}{D}$ or,

$\frac{A}{C} = \frac{B}{D}$

Notice that the cross-multiplication of $\frac{A}{C} = \frac{B}{D}$ also leads to the same result.

Therefore, $A : B = C : D$ is equivalent to $\frac{A}{B} = \frac{C}{D}$ and is also equivalent to $\frac{A}{C} = \frac{B}{D}$. If any 3 terms of the proportion equation are known, then the 4th term can be calculated.

Proportion Equation With Ratios Having More Than Two Terms

If $A : B : C = D : E : F$, then this ratio can be expressed as,

$$\frac{A}{B} = \frac{D}{E}, \quad \frac{B}{C} = \frac{E}{F}, \quad \text{and} \quad \frac{A}{C} = \frac{D}{F}$$

If $A : B : C = D : E : F$

then,

$\frac{A}{B} = \frac{D}{E}, \frac{B}{C} = \frac{E}{F}, \frac{A}{C} = \frac{D}{F}$

or,

$\frac{A}{D} = \frac{B}{E} = \frac{C}{F}$

Cross multiplying, $\quad AE = BD, \quad BF = CE, \quad \text{and} \quad AF = CD$

The proportion equation, $\quad A : B : C = D : E : F$

can also be illustrated in a table:

1st Term	2nd Term	3rd Term
A	B	C
D	E	F

and expressed as, $A : D = B : E = C : F$

$$A : B : C = D : E : F$$

In fractional form, $\quad \dfrac{A}{D} = \dfrac{B}{E} = \dfrac{C}{F}$

Cross-multiplying gives the same result, $\quad AE = BD, \quad BF = CE, \quad \text{and} \quad AF = CD.$

Example 5.2-a **Solving for the Unknown Quantity in Proportions**

Find the missing term in the following proportions:

(i) $4 : 5 = 8 : x$ (ii) $20 : x = \dfrac{1}{2} : 10$ (iii) $x : 0.9 = 9.88 : 0.45$ (iv) $3 : 3\dfrac{3}{4} = x : 5\dfrac{1}{4}$

Solution

(i) $4 : 5 = 8 : x$

Using fractional notation,	$\dfrac{4}{5} = \dfrac{8}{x}$ **Or** $\dfrac{4}{8} = \dfrac{5}{x}$
Cross-multiplying,	$4x = 40$
Simplifying,	$x = \dfrac{40}{4}$
Therefore,	$x = 10$

	1st Term	2nd Term
1st Ratio	4	5
2nd Ratio	8	x

When working with proportions involving fractions, it is often easier to multiply both sides of the equation by the LCD of all the fractions in the proportion. Recall from Chapter 4 that we can always multiply (or divide) both sides of any equation by the same number (except 0).

Note: don't forget to multiply the unknown (x) term as well!

(ii) $20 : x = \dfrac{1}{2} : 10$

Multiplying both sides by 2,	$40 : 2x = 1 : 20$
Using fractional notation,	$\dfrac{40}{2x} = \dfrac{1}{20}$ **Or** $\dfrac{40}{1} = \dfrac{2x}{20}$
Cross-multiplying,	$800 = 2x$
Simplifying,	$x = \dfrac{800}{2}$
Therefore,	$x = 400$

	1st Term	2nd Term
1st Ratio	40	$2x$
2nd Ratio	1	20

(iii) $x : 0.9 = 9.88 : 0.45$

Using fractional notation,	$\dfrac{x}{0.9} = \dfrac{9.88}{0.45}$ **Or** $\dfrac{x}{9.88} = \dfrac{0.9}{0.45}$
Cross-multiplying,	$0.45x = 8.892$
Simplifying,	$x = \dfrac{8.892}{0.45}$
Therefore,	$x = 19.76$

	1st Term	2nd Term
1st Ratio	x	0.9
2nd Ratio	9.88	0.45

(iv) $3 : 3\dfrac{3}{4} = x : 5\dfrac{1}{4}$

Rewriting as an improper fraction,	$3 : \dfrac{15}{4} = x : \dfrac{21}{4}$
Multiplying both sides by 4,	$12 : 15 = 4x : 21$
Using fractional notation,	$\dfrac{12}{15} = \dfrac{4x}{21}$ **Or** $\dfrac{12}{4x} = \dfrac{15}{21}$
Cross-multiplying,	$252 = 60x$
Simplifying,	$x = \dfrac{252}{60}$
Reducing,	$x = \dfrac{21}{5}$
Rewriting as a mixed number,	$x = 4\dfrac{1}{5}$

	1st Term	2nd Term
1st Ratio	12	15
2nd Ratio	$4x$	21

Solving Application Problems Using Proportions

In many problems, we are asked to determine one value given another value and a fixed ratio or rate that represents the relationship between the two values. We can use proportions to solve for the unknown value, according to the following steps:

Step 1: Establish a variable to represent the unknown value.

Step 2: Identify the known ratio, given as the fixed relationship between the values.

Step 3: Set-up the unknown ratio of the given value to the unknown value, with the units in the same order as the known ratio.

Step 4: Set-up a proportion equation between the known and unknown ratios from Steps 2 and 3.

Step 5: Solve the proportion equation for the unknown variable and write a concluding statement.

Example 5.2-b	Solving Application Problems Using Proportions

A pharmacist can package 900 tablets of aspirin in 2 hours.

(i)   How many tablets can the pharmacist package in $3\frac{1}{2}$ hours?

(ii)   How long would it take the pharmacist to package 3,500 tablets?

Solution

(i)   Let x represent the number of tablets the pharmacist can package in $3\frac{1}{2}$ hours:

Known Ratio: 900 tablets : 2 hours

Unknown Ratio: x tablets: $3\frac{1}{2}$ hours

Writing as a proportion,   tablets : hours = tablets : hours

$$900 : 2 = x : 3\frac{1}{2}$$

Rewriting as an improper fraction, $900 : 2 = x : \dfrac{7}{2}$

Multiplying both sides by 2, $1{,}800 : 4 = 2x : 7$

Using fractional notation, $\dfrac{1{,}800}{4} = \dfrac{2x}{7}$ **Or** $\dfrac{1{,}800}{2x} = \dfrac{4}{7}$

Cross-multiplying, $12{,}600 = 8x$

Simplifying, $x = \dfrac{12{,}600}{8}$

$$x = 1{,}575 \text{ tablets}$$

Therefore, the pharmacist can package 1,575 tablets in $3\frac{1}{2}$ hours.

(ii)   Let y represent the amount of time it would take the pharmacist to package 3,500 tablets:

Known Ratio: 900 tablets : 2 hours

Unknown Ratio: 3,500 tablets : y hours

Writing as a proportion,   tablets : hours = tablets : hours

$$900 : 2 = 3{,}500 : y$$

Using fractional notation, $\dfrac{900}{2} = \dfrac{3{,}500}{y}$ **Or** $\dfrac{900}{3{,}500} = \dfrac{2}{y}$

Cross-multiplying, $900y = 7{,}000$

Simplifying, $y = \dfrac{7{,}000}{900}$

$$y = 7.777777... = 7.78 \text{ h}$$

Therefore, it would take the pharmacist 7.78 hours to package 3,500 tablets.

Example 5.2-c	**Sharing Using Proportions**

Three physicians, A, B, and C, decide to open a private practice together. A invests $31,500, B invests $42,000, and C invests $73,500. The physicians agree to share the profits proportionally to their investments.

(i) What is the ratio of their investments?

(ii) In the first year of running the practice, A's profit was $27,000. What were B's and C's profits?

(iii) In the second year, their total profit was $70,000. How much would each of the physicians receive from this total profit?

Solution

(i) Ratio of their investments:

$$A : B : C$$

$31,500 : 42,000 : 73,500$	Dividing each term by the common factor 100,
$315 : 420 : 735$	Dividing each term by the common factor 5,
$63 : 84 : 147$	Dividing each term by the common factor 7,
$9 : 12 : 21$	Dividing each term by the common factor 3,
$3 : 4 : 7$	

Therefore, the ratio of their investments is $3 : 4 : 7$.

(ii) Physician A's profit was $27,000. Physician B's and Physician C's profits are calculated using one of the two methods, as follows:

Method 1:

$$\text{Ratio of Investment} = \text{Ratio of Profit}$$
$$A : B : C = A : B : C$$

Substituting terms,
$$3 : 4 : 7 = 27,000 : x : y$$

Using fractional notation,
$$\frac{3}{4} = \frac{27,000}{x} \quad \text{and} \quad \frac{3}{7} = \frac{27,000}{y}$$

Cross-multiplying,
$$3x = 108,000 \qquad 3y = 189,000$$

Simplifying,
$$x = \$36,000.00 \qquad y = \$63,000.00$$

Method 2:

$$\text{Ratio of Investment} = \text{Ratio of Profit}$$
$$A : B : C = A : B : C$$

Substituting terms,
$$3 : 4 : 7 = 27,000 : x : y$$

Using fractional notation,
$$\frac{3}{27,000} = \frac{4}{x} = \frac{7}{y}$$

	1st Term	2nd Term	3rd Term
	3	4	7
	27,000	x	y

Hence,
$$\frac{3}{27,000} = \frac{4}{x} \quad \text{and} \quad \frac{3}{27,000} = \frac{7}{y}$$

Cross-multiplying,
$$3x = 108,000 \qquad 3y = 189,000$$

Simplifying,
$$x = \$36,000.00 \qquad y = \$63,000.00$$

Therefore, B's profit was $36,000 and C's profit was $63,000.

(iii)   In the second year, their total profit was $70,000. The profit that each of them would receive is calculated by using one of the methods, as follows:

Method 1:

Since A, B, and C agreed to share profits in the same ratio as their investments, the ratio of their individual investments to their individual profit should be equal to the ratio of the total investment to the total profit.

By adding the simplified terms of their investments (3 + 4 + 7), we know that the total profit of $70,000 should be distributed over 14 units. Therefore, we can set up the following proportion using the total number of units in the ratio:

$$\text{Ratio of Investment} \quad = \quad \text{Ratio of Profit}$$

$$A : B : C : \text{Total} \quad = \quad A : B : C : \text{Total}$$

Substituting terms, $\qquad 3 : 4 : 7 : 14 \quad = \quad A : B : C : 70{,}000$

Using fractional notation, $\qquad \dfrac{3}{14} = \dfrac{A}{70{,}000}, \qquad \dfrac{4}{14} = \dfrac{B}{70{,}000}, \qquad \dfrac{7}{14} = \dfrac{C}{70{,}000}$

Cross-multiplying, $\quad 14A = 210{,}000 \qquad 14B = 280{,}000 \qquad 14C = 490{,}000$

Simplifying, $\qquad A = \$15{,}000.00 \qquad B = \$20{,}000.00 \qquad C = \$35{,}000.00$

Method 2:

$$\text{Ratio of Investment} \quad = \quad \text{Ratio of Profit}$$

$$A : B : C : \text{Total} \quad = \quad A : B : C : \text{Total}$$

Substituting terms, $\qquad 3 : 4 : 7 : 14 \quad = \quad A : B : C : 70{,}000$

Using fractional notation, $\qquad \dfrac{3}{A} = \dfrac{4}{B} = \dfrac{7}{C} = \dfrac{14}{70{,}000}$

	1st Term	2nd Term	3rd Term	4th Term
	3	4	7	14
	A	B	C	70,000

Hence, $\qquad \dfrac{3}{A} = \dfrac{14}{70{,}000} \qquad \dfrac{4}{B} = \dfrac{14}{70{,}000} \qquad \dfrac{7}{C} = \dfrac{14}{70{,}000}$

Cross-multiplying, $\quad 14A = 210{,}000 \qquad 14B = 280{,}000 \qquad 14C = 490{,}000$

Simplifying, $\qquad A = \$15{,}000.00 \qquad B = \$20{,}000.00 \qquad C = \$35{,}000.00$

Method 3:

Sharing Using Ratios:

$$A\text{'s share} = \dfrac{3}{14} \times 70{,}000 = \$15{,}000.00$$

$$B\text{'s share} = \dfrac{4}{14} \times 70{,}000 = \$20{,}000.00$$

$$C\text{'s share} = \dfrac{7}{14} \times 70{,}000 = \$35{,}000.00$$

Therefore, Physician A, Physician B, and Physician C will receive profits of $15,000, $20,000, and $35,000, respectively.

Pro-rations

Pro-ration is defined as sharing or allocating quantities, usually amounts of money, on a proportional basis.

Consider an example where Sarah paid $690 for a biology course, but needed to withdraw from the course after attending half of the classes for medical reasons. As she attended only half the course, the college decided to refund half of her tuition fee, ($\dfrac{\$690}{2} = \$345$). As the college calculated the refund amount proportional to the time she attended the course, we say that the college refunded her tuition fee on a **pro-rata basis**. The amount of money returned is called a **pro-rated amount**.

A few examples where pro-rated calculations are used include:

- When a property is sold, the property tax paid in advance will be refunded on a pro-rata basis.

- When an insurance is cancelled before the end of the period for which the premiums were paid, the amount refunded is calculated on a pro-rata basis.

- Employees' overtime pay, part-time pay, and vacation time are calculated on a pro-rata basis.

Example 5.2-d Calculating the Pro-rated Amount of a Payment

Find the pro-rated health insurance premium for seven months if the annual premium paid for health insurance is $2,250.

Solution

Ratio of the premiums paid:

Premium ($) : Time (months) = Premium ($) : Time (months)

	1st Term	2nd Term
	2,250	12
	x	7

Substituting terms, $2{,}250 : 12 = x : 7$

Using fractional notation, $\dfrac{2{,}250}{12} = \dfrac{x}{7}$ **Or** $\dfrac{2{,}250}{x} = \dfrac{12}{7}$

Cross-multiplying, $15{,}750 = 12x$

Simplifying, $x = \dfrac{15{,}750}{12}$

$$x = \$1{,}312.50$$

Therefore, the pro-rated premium for seven months is $1,312.50.

Example 5.2-e Calculating the Pro-rated Amount of a Refund

Jason paid $350 for a 2-year, weekly subscription of a health journal. After receiving 18 issues of the journal in the second year of his subscription, Jason decided to cancel his subscription. Assuming he is refunded on a pro-rata basis, what should be the amount of his refund? Assume 1 year = 52 weeks.

Solution

Jason paid for 104 issues (2 × 52) and received 70 issues (52 + 18); therefore, he should be refunded for 34 issues (104 − 70).

Issues (#) : Cost ($) = Issues (#) : Cost ($)

	1st Term	2nd Term
	104	350
	34	x

Substituting terms, $104 : 350 = 34 : x$

Using fractional notation, $\dfrac{104}{350} = \dfrac{34}{x}$ **Or** $\dfrac{104}{34} = \dfrac{350}{x}$

Cross-multiplying, $104x = 11{,}900$

Simpifying, $x = \dfrac{11{,}900}{104}$

$$= 114.423076... = \$114.42$$

Therefore, his pro-rated refund should be $114.42.

5.2 | Exercises

Answers to odd-numbered problems are available at the end of the textbook.

1. Determine if the following pairs of ratios are in proportion or not:

   a. $6 : 9$ and $14 : 21$ b. $0.45 : 1$ and $2 : 8$ c. $3 : 0.225$ and $9 : 0.3$ d. $0.5 : 7$ and $2 : 28$

2. Determine if the following pairs of ratios are in proportion or not:

   a. $4 : 16$ and $1 : 4$ b. $0.25 : 1$ and $1 : 4$ c. $2 : 25$ and $8 : 96$ d. $5 : 12$ and $7 : 28$

For Problems 3 to 6, solve the proportions for the unknown value.

3. a. $x : 3.5 = 2.7 : 4$ b. $4 : x = 3 : 1$ c. $5 : 9 = x : 3$ d. $1 : 2 = 0.225 : x$

4. a. $x : 2 = 4 : 0.45$ b. $3 : x = 16 : 24$ c. $15 : 5 = x : 15$ d. $28 : 35 = 4 : x$

5. a. $4.25 : 1.87 = x : 2.2$ b. $2.4 : 1.5 = 5.9 : x$ c. $1 : 4\frac{1}{2} = x : 2\frac{3}{4}$ d. $1\frac{1}{2} : 2\frac{1}{4} = 1\frac{3}{4} : x$

6. a. $5.2 : 6.5 = 1.28 : x$ b. $2.2 : x = 6.8 : 0.45$ c. $x : 18\frac{1}{4} = 8 : 11\frac{3}{4}$ d. $7\frac{1}{5} : x = 5\frac{4}{3} : 3\frac{2}{5}$

7. An ambulance requires 96 litres of gas to cover 800 km. How many litres of gas will it require to cover 1,500 km?

8. Based on Alvin's past experience in the ER, it would take his team three hours to treat 60 patients. How long would his team take to treat 140 patients?

9. On a map, 4.0 cm represents 5.0 km. If the distance between hospital *A* and hospital *B* on the map is 9.3 cm, how many kilometres apart are the hospitals?

10. On a hospital plan, 1.25 cm represents 3 metres. If the actual length of a room is 5.4 m, how many centimetres will be used to represent this length in the plan?

11. The fees for Steve's chemistry, biology, and calculus classes have a ratio of 6 : 5 : 4, respectively. If the fees for his biology class total $4,500, calculate the fees for his chemistry and calculus classes.

12. The ratio of the distance from Ann's house to Hospital *A*, Hospital *B* , and Hospital *C* is 3 : 5 : 2, respectively. If the distance from Ann's house to Hospital *A* is 19.5 km, calculate the distances from Ann's house to Hospital *B* and from Ann's house to Hospital *C*.

13. A patient requires three different intravenously-injected substances - thiamine, folic acid, and magnesium sulfate - in the ratio of 5 : 4 : 3, respectively.

     a. If 25 grams of thiamine was administered, calculate the grams of magnesium sulfate administered.

     b. If 30 grams of magnesium sulfate are given, calculate how many grams of folic acid and thiamine were given.

     c. If the patient received 135 grams of combined medication, what was the dose of each drug?

14. A patient requires 3 different medications - epinephrine, albuterol, and cortisone - in the ratio of 7 : 9 : 5, respectively.

     a. If 35 grams of epinephrine was administered, calculate the grams of cortisone administered.

     b. If 31.5 grams of albuterol are given, calculate how many grams of epinephrine and cortisone were given.

     c. If the patient received 126 grams of combined medication, what was the dose of each drug given?

15. Physicians *A*, *B*, and *C* invested $35,000, $42,000, and $28,000, respectively, to start a walk-in clinic. They realized that they required an additional $45,000 for operating the business. How much additional funding should each of them individually invest to maintain their original investment ratio?

16. Three wealthy surgeons decided to invest $150,000, $375,000, and $225,000, respectively, to purchase a new office for their private practice. They required an additional $90,000 to build an outpatient facility in the clinic. How much additional funding should each of them individually invest to maintain their original investment ratio?

17. Three doctors invested a total of $520,000 in the ratio of 3 : 4 : 6, respectively, to open a private practice. Two months later, each of them invested an additional $25,000 into the business. Calculate their new investment ratio after the additional investments.

18. Three members of a hospital board of directors invested $720,000 for a new hospital wing. The individual investments to the wing were made in the ratio of 5 : 4 : 3, respectively. After the investment, they decided to renovate the hospital building and purchase new hospital beds, so each of the directors invested an additional $60,000. Calculate their new investment ratio after the additional investments.

19. A student pays $620 for a course that has 25 first-aid classes. Calculate the pro-rated refund she would receive if she only attends five classes before withdrawing from the course.

20. Megan joined physiotherapy training sessions that charge $375 for 12 classes. After attending seven classes, she decided that she did not like the classes and wanted to cancel the remaining classes. Calculate the pro-rated refund she should receive.

21. If the annual salary of a registered nurse is $45,000, calculate his bi-weekly salary using pro-ration. Assume that there are 52 weeks in a year (hence, there are 26 bi-weekly payments).

22. Ashley received a job offer at a medical device manufacturing company that would pay her $2,800, bi-weekly. What would her annual salary be, assuming that she would receive 26 bi-weekly payments in a year?

23. Charles set up a new charity fund to support cancer research. For every $10 collected by the charity, the government donated an additional grant of $5 to the charity. At the end of three months, if his charity fund had a total of $135,000, including the government grant money, calculate the total amount of grant money that the charity received from the government.

24. The tax on medical supplies sold in Ontario is such that for every $1.00 worth of materials sold, the buyer has to pay an additional $0.05 in taxes. If $25,000 worth of medical supplies were sold before taxes, calculate the total amount of tax to be paid by the purchasers.

• 25. A first semester organic chemistry class in a college has six more females than males and the ratio of the number of females to males in the class is 8 : 5.

   a. How many students are there in the class?

   b. If four additional female students and two additional male students joined the class, find the new ratio of females to males in the class.

• 26. A medical advisory board has 10 more men than women and the ratio of the number of men to women is 8 : 3.

   a. How many people are there on the board?

   b. If four additional men and four additional women joined the board, calculate the new ratio of men to women.

5.3 | Percents

In Chapter 2, you learned that fractions and decimal numbers are used to represent portions (parts) of a whole number or quantity. In this section, you will learn about percents, another form of representing portions of a whole quantity.

Percent is the number of parts per hundred:

$$C\% = \frac{C}{100} = 0.01C$$

Percent (which literally means "of one hundred") is used to express a quantity out of 100 units and is represented by the symbol '%'.

For example, 5% means 5 **per** hundred, or 5 out of 100, or $\frac{5}{100}$ (5% = 5/100 = 0.05).

- 100% means 100 out of 100 (i.e., the whole quantity)

- 75% means 75 out of 100 (i.e., $\frac{75}{100} = \frac{3}{4}$ or 0.75)

- 50% means 50 out of 100 (i.e., $\frac{50}{100} = \frac{1}{2}$ or 0.50)

- 25% means 25 out of 100 (i.e., $\frac{25}{100} = \frac{1}{4}$ or 0.25)

Note: A percent greater than 100 typically refers to a comparison to the original amount, rather than parts of a whole, which wouldn't be a meaningful number, since the total number of parts cannot exceed the whole.

For example, 200% means 2 times (or double, or twice) the whole quantity; it is not meaningful to express 200% as 200 parts out of 100. Similarly, 350% means $3\frac{1}{2}$ times the whole quantity.

Relationship Between Percents, Fractions, and Decimal Numbers

Fractions and decimal numbers can be converted to percents, and vice-versa. For example, 3 out of 4 equal parts of a quantity can be represented as a fraction, decimal number, or in percent form, as follows:

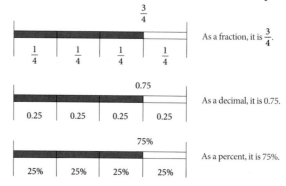

In health applications, percents are used to represent concentrations of dosages of medication, strength of solutions, portions of patients, number of workers in different medical fields, etc. However, when performing calculations, fractions (ratios) or decimal equivalents are used. Therefore, it is necessary to know how to convert from one form to the other.

Converting Percents to Decimal Numbers

If the percent is a whole number or a decimal number, remove the '%' sign and move the decimal point 2 places to the left. This is the same as dividing the number by 100 and dropping the '%' sign.

For example,

- To convert 45% to a decimal number,

$$45\% = 45.0 \qquad \text{Remove the \% sign and move the decimal point 2 places to the left.}$$

$$= 0.45 \qquad \text{This is the same as } \frac{45}{100} = 0.45.$$

Therefore, 45% = 0.45.

- To convert 0.0225% to a decimal number,

$$0.0225\% = 0.0225 \qquad \text{Remove the \% sign and move the decimal point 2 places to the left.}$$

$$= 0.000225 \qquad \text{This is the same as } \frac{0.0225}{100} = 0.000225.$$

Therefore, 0.0225% = 0.000225.

If the percent is a fraction or a mixed number, change it to its decimal equivalent and follow the steps as shown above.

For example, to convert $2\frac{1}{2}\%$ to a decimal number,

$$2\frac{1}{2}\% = 2.5\% \qquad \text{Convert the mixed number to a decimal number.}$$

$$= 2.5 \qquad \text{Remove the \% sign and move the decimal point 2 places to the left.}$$

$$= 0.025 \qquad \text{This is the same as } \frac{2.5}{100} = 0.025.$$

Therefore, $2\frac{1}{2}\% = 0.025$.

Example 5.3-a **Converting Percents to Decimal Numbers**

Convert each percent to its equivalent decimal number.

(i) 85% (ii) $5\frac{1}{4}\%$ (iii) 20.75% (iv) 225% (v) $\frac{2}{3}\%$

Solution

(i) $85\% = 85.0\% = 85.0 = 0.85$ (ii) $5\frac{1}{4}\% = 5.25\% = 5.25 = 0.0525$

(iii) $20.75\% = 20.75 = 0.2075$ (iv) $225\% = 225.0\% = 225.0 = 2.25$

(v) $\frac{2}{3}\% = 0.666666...\% = 0.666666... = 0.006666... = 0.00\overline{6}$

Converting Decimal Numbers to Percents

To convert a decimal number or a whole number to a percent, move the decimal point 2 places to the right and insert the '%' sign. This is the same as multiplying the number by 100 and inserting the '%' sign.

For example,

- To convert 0.35 to a percent,

$$0.35 = 0.35\%$$ Move the decimal point 2 places to the right and insert the % sign.

$$= 35\%$$ This is the same as $0.35 \times 100\% = 35\%$.

Therefore $0.35 = 35\%$.

- To convert 5 to a percent,

$$5 = 5.00\%$$ Move the decimal point 2 places to the right and insert the % sign.

$$= 500\%$$ This is the same as $5 \times 100\% = 500\%$.

Therefore, $5 = 500\%$.

Example 5.3-b **Converting Decimal Numbers to Percents**

Convert each of the following decimal numbers to its equivalent percent.

(i)   0.03   (ii)   0.45   (iii)   5.25   (iv)   0.002   (v) $0.\overline{4}$ (vi) $0.\overline{756}$

Solution

(i) $0.03 = 0.03\% = 3\%$ (ii) $0.45 = 0.45\% = 45\%$

(iii) $5.25 = 5.25\% = 525\%$ (iv) $0.002 = 0.002\% = 0.2\%$

(v) $0.\overline{4} = 0.444444...\% = 44.\overline{4}\%$ (vi) $0.\overline{756} = 0.756756...\% = 75.675675...\% = 75.\overline{675}\%$

Example 5.3-c **Solving Application Problems**

If Alexander earns three times the amount that Emma earns, what percent is Alexander's earnings compared to Emma's earnings?

Solution

Here, 'three times' when converted to a percent $= 3 \times 100\% = 300\%$.

Therefore, Alexander's earnings are 300% of Emma's.

Note: This also means that Alexander earns 200% more than Emma. It is important not to confuse the two statements: if Alexander earns 300% more than Emma, this would actually mean that Alexander's earnings are 400% of Emma's.

Converting Percents to Fractions

If the percent is a whole number, remove the percent sign, express the percent as a fraction over 100, and reduce the fraction to its lowest terms.

For example, to convert 60% to a fraction in its lowest terms:

$$60\% = \frac{60}{100}$$ Reduce the fraction to its lowest terms.

$$= \frac{3}{5}$$

Therefore, $60\% = \frac{3}{5}$.

If the percent includes a decimal number, remove the percent sign, express the percent as a fraction over 100, eliminate the decimal in the numerator by multiplying both the numerator and the denominator by an appropriate power of 10, and reduce the fraction to its lowest terms.

For example, to convert 42.5% to a fraction:

$$42.5\% = \frac{42.5}{100}$$ Eliminate the decimal in the numerator by multiplying both the numerator and the denominator by 10.

$$= \frac{425}{1,000}$$ Reduce the fraction to its lowest terms.

$$= \frac{17}{40}$$

Therefore, $42.5\% = \frac{17}{40}$.

If the percent is a fraction or a mixed number, either convert it to its decimal equivalent (if it can be expressed as a terminating decimal) and follow the steps outlined above, or convert it to an improper fraction, multiply the fraction by $\dfrac{1}{100}$, and reduce the fraction to its lowest terms.

For example, to convert $7\frac{1}{2}\%$ to a fraction:

Method 1: By converting it to its decimal equivalent

$$7\tfrac{1}{2}\% = 7.5\%$$
Convert the mixed number to a decimal number.

$$= \frac{7.5}{100}$$
Eliminate the decimal in the numerator by multiplying both the numerator and denominator by 10.

$$= \frac{75}{1,000}$$
Reduce the fraction to its lowest terms.

$$= \frac{3}{40}$$

Method 2: By converting it to its improper fractional equivalent

$$7\tfrac{1}{2}\% = \frac{15}{2}$$
Convert the mixed number to an improper fraction.

$$= \frac{15}{2} \times \frac{1}{100}$$
Multiply the fraction by $\dfrac{1}{100}$.

$$= \frac{15}{200}$$
Reduce the fraction to its lowest terms.

$$= \frac{3}{40}$$

Therefore, $7\frac{1}{2}\% = \dfrac{3}{40}$.

Example 5.3-d	**Converting Percents to Fractions**

Convert each percent to its equivalent fraction or mixed number and simplify to its lowest terms.

(i) 45% (ii) $8\frac{1}{3}\%$ (iii) 6.25% (iv) 175%

(v) $\frac{1}{5}\%$ (vi) 0.9% (vii) 0.225%

Solution

(i) $45\% = \dfrac{45}{100} = \dfrac{9}{20}$

(ii) $8\frac{1}{3}\% = \dfrac{25}{3}\% = \dfrac{\overset{1}{\cancel{25}}}{3} \times \dfrac{1}{\underset{4}{\cancel{100}}} = \dfrac{1}{12}$

(iii) $6.25\% = \dfrac{6.25}{100} \times \dfrac{100}{100} = \dfrac{625}{10,000} = \dfrac{1}{16}$

(iv) $175\% = \dfrac{175}{100} = \dfrac{7}{4} = 1\frac{3}{4}$

(v) $\dfrac{1}{5}\% = \dfrac{1}{5} \times \dfrac{1}{100} = \dfrac{1}{500}$

(vi) $0.9\% = \dfrac{0.9}{100} \times \dfrac{10}{10} = \dfrac{9}{1,000}$

(vii) $0.225\% = \dfrac{0.225}{100} \times \dfrac{1,000}{1,000} = \dfrac{225}{100,000} = \dfrac{9}{4,000}$

Converting Fractions or Mixed Numbers to Percents

To convert a fraction or a mixed number to a percent, first convert the fraction or mixed number to a decimal number. Then, convert the decimal number to a percent by moving the decimal point 2 places to the right and inserting the % sign. This is the same as multiplying the decimal by 100 and inserting the % sign.

For example,

- To convert $\dfrac{3}{8}$ to a percent:

$$\dfrac{3}{8} = 0.375$$ Convert the fraction to its decimal equivalent.

$$= 0.375\%$$ Convert the decimal to percent, by moving the decimal point 2 places to the right and inserting the % sign.

$$= 37.5\%$$ This is the same as $0.375 \times 100\% = 37.5\%$.

Therefore $\dfrac{3}{8} = 37.5\%$.

- To convert $5\dfrac{1}{2}$ to a percent:

$$5\dfrac{1}{2} = 5.50$$ Convert the mixed number to its decimal equivalent.

$$= 5.50\%$$ Convert the decimal to percent, by moving the decimal point 2 places to the right and inserting the % sign.

$$= 550\%$$ This is the same as $5.50 \times 100\% = 550\%$.

Therefore $5\dfrac{1}{2} = 550\%$.

Example 5.3-e   **Converting Fractions or Mixed Numbers to Percents**

Convert each of the following fractions to its equivalent percent.

(i) $\dfrac{3}{25}$ (ii) $5\dfrac{1}{4}$ (iii) $\dfrac{18}{5}$ (iv) $\dfrac{1}{200}$ (v) $\dfrac{1}{9}$

Solution

(i) $\dfrac{3}{25} = 0.12$

$\quad\quad = 0.12\% = 12\%$

(ii) $5\dfrac{1}{4} = 5.25$

$\quad\quad = 5.25\% = 525\%$

(iii) $\dfrac{18}{5} = 3.60$

$\quad\quad = 3.60\% = 360\%$

(iv) $\dfrac{1}{200} = 0.005$

$\quad\quad = 0.005\% = 0.5\%$

(v) $\dfrac{1}{9} = 0.111111...$

$\quad\quad = 0.111111...\% = 11.111111...\% = 11.\overline{1}\%$

Example 5.3-f   **Solving Application Problems**

Peter and Angela study Pre-health Mathematics, but at different colleges. Peter managed to score 46 out of 60 on his final exam, while Angela scored 63 out of 75 on hers. Who received a better grade on their exam?

Solution

It is not possible to answer the question by simple observation, because Peter's score is expressed out of 60, while Angela's score is out of 75. To compare their scores, we need to convert them to their percent equivalents, as shown below:

Solution
continued

Peter's score: $\dfrac{46}{60} = 0.766666\ldots = 76.\overline{6}\%$

Angela's score: $\dfrac{63}{75} = 0.84 = 84\%$

Therefore, Angela scored better than Peter on the exam.

Solving Percent Problems

Many methods may be used to solve percent problems. Described below are three common methods:

Method 1: Formula Method

Every percent problem will contain three variables: B, P, and R.

Base (B): Whole quantity or value (100%). It usually follows the word 'of', or 'percent of'.

Portion (P): Portion of the whole quantity or value (i.e., part or portion of the base).

Rate (R): Relationship between base and portion, usually expressed as a percent. It usually carries the percent sign (**%**) or the word '**percent**'.

$R\%$ converted to a ratio (or decimal) is $\dfrac{R}{100}$ (or $0.01R$)

Every percent statement can be expressed as: **P is $R\%$ of B.** The value of **R** is used as a decimal or fractional equivalent in calculations.

The relationship between these variables can be expressed as follows:

$$\textit{Portion} = \textit{Rate} \times \textit{Base}$$

As a formula, this is,

Formula 5.3	**Portion, Rate, and Base**
	$$P = R \times B$$

Rearranging, we obtain $R = \dfrac{P}{B}$ and $B = \dfrac{P}{R}$.

Therefore, if any two of these quantities are known, then the third quantity can be calculated.

The **P, R, B Triangle** (shown below) can be used to help in rearranging the formula $P = R \times B$ to find R or B.

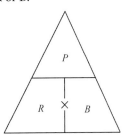

Variables beside each other at the bottom are multiplied ($R \times B$, as shown).

Variable P is divided by the variables at the bottom: R and B.

Cover the variable for which you want to solve to see the new formula.

For example, if you want to solve for R, the formula can be determined by covering R and reading the remaining variables in the triangle to obtain $R = \dfrac{P}{B}$.

Method 2: Ratio-Proportion Method

The whole amount or quantity is represented by 100% and is known as the **base (B)**. The **portion (P)** is a part of the base and it forms a percent, or **rate ($R\%$),** of the base. Thus, in the ratio-proportion method, we first identify the base, portion, and rate in the problem, then we solve for the unknown using the proportion equation.

Portion : Base = Rate % : 100%

$P : B = R\% : 100\%$

$\dfrac{P}{B} = \dfrac{R\%}{100\%}$

$\dfrac{P}{B} = \dfrac{R}{100}$

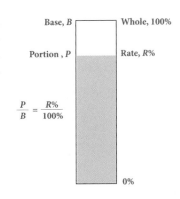

Method 3: Algebraic Method

Solving problems using algebraic methods involves forming an equation for an unknown 'x' and then solving for 'x'. In this method, we assume that the unknown is 'x', and form equation(s) for the given problem (or statement) using key words to represent certain arithmetic operations.

The following are key words and phrases that are commonly used to indicate various arithmetic operations.

Operations	Key Words
Addition (+)	Add, sum, total, and, plus, more than, increased by, appreciate, rise
Subtraction (−)	Subtract, difference, minus, less than, decreased by, depreciate, fall
Multiplication (×), (·)	Multiply, product, times, of
Division (÷), (/)	Divide, ratio, divided by, quotient, per
Equal (=)	Is, was, gives, given by, equals
Unknown value (denoted by a varaible, such as 'x')	What, how much, some amount

For example, we can use these key words to form the algebraic equations for the following:

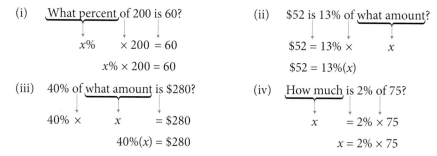

(i)   What percent of 200 is 60?

$$x\% \times 200 = 60$$
$$x\% \times 200 = 60$$

(ii) $52 is 13% of what amount?

$$\$52 = 13\% \times x$$
$$\$52 = 13\%(x)$$

(iii)   40% of what amount is $280?

$$40\% \times x = \$280$$
$$40\%(x) = \$280$$

(iv)   How much is 2% of 75?

$$x = 2\% \times 75$$
$$x = 2\% \times 75$$

Example 5.3-g | **Calculating the Portion of a Whole Quantity**

What is 75% of $250? (Or, 75% of $250 is how much?)

Solution

Method 1: Using the Formula Method

$R\% = 75\%$ (value with % sign); i.e., $R = 0.75$

$B = \$250.00$ (value that follows the word 'of')

$P = ?$ (the other value)

Using Formula 5.3, $P = R \times B$ Substituting values for 'R' and 'B',

$P = 0.75 \times 250.00$ Simplifying,

$= \$187.50$

Therefore, 75% of $250.00 is $187.50.

Method 2: Using the Ratio-Proportion Method

Here, the whole amount of $250 is the base and is represented by 100%. 75% is a portion of the base, as illustrated:

Solution
continued

$$\text{Portion : Base = Rate : 100\%}$$

$$P : B = R\% : 100\%$$

$$P : \$250 = 75\% : 100\%$$

$$\frac{P}{\$250} = \frac{75\%}{100\%}$$

$$\frac{P}{250.00} = \frac{75}{100} \qquad \text{Cross-multiplying,}$$

$$100P = 250.00 \times 75 \qquad \text{Solving for } P,$$

$$P = \frac{250.00 \times 75}{100} \qquad \text{Simplifying,}$$

$$= \$187.50$$

Therefore, 75% of $250.00 is $187.50.

Method 3: Using the Algebraic Method

What is 75% of $250?

$$x = 75\% \times 250.00 \qquad \text{Expressing the percent as a decimal,}$$

$$x = 0.75 \times 250.00$$

$$= \$187.50$$

Therefore, 75% of $250.00 is $187.50.

Note: The following examples use the formula method; however, you can solve them using any of the three methods described earlier.

Example 5.3-h | **Calculating Portion When Rate is More Than 100%**

What is 150% of 200?

Solution

$R\% = 150\%$ (value with % sign)

$\quad = 1.50$

$B = 200$ (value that follows the word 'of')

$P = ?$ (the other value)

Using Formula 5.3, $\quad P = R \times B \qquad$ Substituting values for 'R' and 'B',

$$= 1.50 \times 200 \qquad \text{Simplifying,}$$

$$= 300$$

Therefore, 150% of 200 is 300.

Example 5.3-i	Calculating Portion Using Fractional Rates

Sandra withdraws $25\frac{1}{3}$% of an influenza vaccine from a vial. If the total amount of solution is 300 mL, how many mL did Sandra withdraw?

Solution

Do not round values calculated in intermediary steps. Store these values in your calculator and recall them for subsequent calculations.

$R\% = 25\frac{1}{3}\%$ (value with % sign)

$\quad = 25.333333...\%$

$\quad = 0.253333...$

$B = 300$ mL (whole value)

$P = ?$ (the other value)

Using Formula 5.3, $\quad P = R \times B$ Substituting values for 'R' and 'B',

$\qquad\qquad\qquad = 0.253333... \times 300$ Simplifying,

$\qquad\qquad\qquad = 76$ mL

Alternatively, this can be solved by converting the mixed fraction to an improper fraction:

$R\% = 25\frac{1}{3}\%$ Converting the mixed number to an improper fraction,

$\quad = \dfrac{76}{3}\%$ Expressing the percent as a fraction,

$\quad = \dfrac{76}{3} \times \dfrac{1}{100}$

$\quad = \dfrac{76}{300}$

Using Formula 5.3, $\quad P = R \times B$ Substituting values for 'R' and 'B',

$\qquad\qquad\qquad = \dfrac{76}{300} \times 300$ Simplifying,

$\qquad\qquad\qquad = 76$ mL

Therefore, Sandra withdrew 76 mL of the vaccine.

Example 5.3-j	Calculating Rate When Portion and Base are Known

What percent of $500 is $1,250? (Or, $1,250 is what percent of $500?)

Solution

$B = \$500$ (value that follows the word 'of')

$P = \$1,250$ (the other value)

$R = ?$ (value for the word 'percent')

Using Formula 5.3, $\quad P = R \times B$ Rearranging,

$\qquad\qquad\qquad R = \dfrac{P}{B}$ Substituting values for 'P' and 'B',

$\qquad\qquad\qquad R = \dfrac{1,250.00}{500.00}$ Simplifying,

$\qquad\qquad R\% = \dfrac{1,250.00}{500.00} \times 100\% = 2.5 \times 100\% = 250\%$

Therefore, $1,250 is 250% of $500.

Note: It is tempting to treat $1,250 as the base, since it is the larger number. However, in this question $500 is the base, since it follows the phrase "percent of". This illustrates the importance of reading these types of questions very carefully!

Example 5.3-k	**Calculating Base When Portion and Rate are Known**

50% of what number is 200? (Or, 200 is 50% of what number?)

Solution

$R\% = 50\%$ (value with % sign) $= 0.50$

$P = 200$ (the other value)

$B = ?$ (value that follows the word 'of')

Using Formula 5.3, $\quad P = R \times B \quad$ Rearranging,

$$B = \frac{P}{R} \quad \text{Substituting values for 'P' and 'R',}$$

$$B = \frac{200}{0.50} \quad \text{Simplifying,}$$

$$= 400$$

Therefore, 50% of 400 is 200.

5.3 | Exercises

Answers to odd-numbered problems are available at the end of the textbook.

For the following problems, express the answers rounded to two decimal places, wherever applicable.

Calculate the missing values in Problems 1 to 18.

		Percents	Decimals	Fractions (or mixed numbers) in lowest terms			Percents	Decimals	Fractions (or mixed numbers) in lowest terms
1.	a.	75%	?	?	2.	a.	50%	?	?
	b.	?	0.30	?		b.	?	0.70	?
	c.	?	?	$\frac{1}{4}$		c.	?	?	$\frac{1}{5}$
3.	a.	5%	?	?	4.	a.	2%	?	?
	b.	?	0.2	?		b.	?	0.8	?
	c.	?	?	$\frac{3}{5}$		c.	?	?	$\frac{3}{8}$
5.	a.	150%	?	?	6.	a.	225%	?	?
	b.	?	0.175	?		b.	?	0.225	?
	c.	?	?	$\frac{12}{25}$		c.	?	?	$\frac{7}{20}$
7.	a.	12.5%	?	?	8.	a.	7.5%	?	?
	b.	?	0.45	?		b.	?	0.03	?
	c.	?	?	$4\frac{1}{2}$		c.	?	?	$3\frac{3}{4}$
9.	a.	0.6%	?	?	10.	a.	0.8%	?	?
	b.	?	0.005	?		b.	?	0.003	?
	c.	?	?	$4\frac{3}{5}$		c.	?	?	$1\frac{3}{15}$

		Percents	Decimals	Fractions (or mixed numbers) in lowest terms
11.	a.	0.05%	?	?
	b.	?	0.0025	?
	c.	?	?	$1\frac{1}{8}$
13.	a.	$\frac{2}{5}\%$	?	?
	b.	?	1.08	?
	c.	?	?	$\frac{3}{80}$
15.	a.	$1\frac{1}{4}\%$	?	?
	b.	?	2.025	?
	c.	?	?	$\frac{1}{500}$
17.	a.	$6\frac{2}{3}\%$	?	?
	b.	?	2.5	?
	c.	?	?	$\frac{5}{24}$

		Percents	Decimals	Fractions (or mixed numbers) in lowest terms
12.	a.	0.08%	?	?
	b.	?	0.075	?
	c.	?	?	$2\frac{3}{8}$
14.	a.	$\frac{3}{8}\%$	?	?
	b.	?	2.04	?
	c.	?	?	$\frac{22}{75}$
16.	a.	$2\frac{1}{2}\%$	?	?
	b.	?	1.075	?
	c.	?	?	$\frac{1}{250}$
18.	a.	$4\frac{1}{6}\%$	?	?
	b.	?	7.5	?
	c.	?	?	$\frac{13}{48}$

Calculate the following:

19. a. 20% of 350   b. 12.5% of 800
20. a. 45% of 180   b. 2.5% of 960
21. a. 0.25% of 75   b. $\frac{1}{4}\%$ of 200 km
22. a. 0.755% of 120   b. $\frac{1}{8}\%$ of 450 km
23. a. 130% of 40   b. $5\frac{1}{2}\%$ of $1,100
24. a. 285% of 110   b. $12\frac{3}{4}\%$ of $1,260

25. What is 2.5% of 80?
26. What is 40% of 160?

27. $1\frac{1}{3}\%$ of $300 is how much?
28. $26\frac{2}{3}\%$ of $2,580 is how much?

29. How much is $\frac{1}{4}\%$ of $108?
30. How much is $\frac{3}{4}\%$ of 360 kg?

31. What number is 125% of 6?
32. What number is 250% of 12?

33. 12 is what percent of 30?
34. 18 is what percent of 40?

35. What percent of 4 is 16?
36. What percent of 9 is 45?

37. What percent of 44 is 132?
38. What percent of 22.10 is 110.50?

39. 18 minutes is what percent of an hour?
40. 9 hours is what percent of a day?

41. 400 is 50% of what number?
42. 225 is 25% of what number?

43. 15% of what amount is $27.90?
44. 30% of what amount is 708?

45. 120% of what amount is 156?
46. 215% of what amount is 258?

47. $16.50 is 0.75% of what amount?
48. $16.40 is 0.4% of what amount?

49. How much tax was charged on a defibrillator that costs $2,050, if the tax rate is 12%? How much did the defibrillator cost in total?

50. The monthly gross salary of an optometric technician is $2,390.25. If 20% of the salary was deducted for taxes, how much money was deducted, and what was the technician's net monthly salary (after taxes)?

51. 5% commission on an agent's weekly sales amounted to $1,250. What was the total sales amount for the agent for the week?

52. 3% interest charged on a loan amounted to $210. How much was the loan?

53. In a nutrition survey of 450 people, 117 responded 'yes' to eating 7 servings of fruits or vegetables per day. What percent of the people surveyed responded 'no'?

54. 144 out of 600 students in a health sciences program had previously taken a Mathematics for Pre-Health Sciences course. What percent of these students did not take the course?

55. A company that makes sleeping pills sets sales targets at $225,000 per year for each of its sales people. If Amanda, an excellent salesperson, exceeded her target this year by $66\frac{2}{3}$%, calculate her total sales for the year.

56. The number of medical school applicants in Ontario in 2016 was estimated to be 6,480. If only $16\frac{2}{3}$% of the applicants in Ontario were actually admitted to medical school, calculate the number of applicants in Ontario who were rejected in 2016.

• 57. When there was a boom in the real estate market, Lucy sold her property for $409,500, which was 130% of the amount she had originally paid only a few years earlier. Calculate the amount she originally paid for the property.

• 58. Ronald, an investment banker, sold his shares for $18,900 when there was a boom in the stock market. Calculate the amount he originally paid for the shares if his selling price was 180% of the price he paid.

• 59. Evan, a business development representative of a leading pharmaceutical firm, took his client out for a dinner that cost $180.75 before taxes. If the tax was $23.50, calculate the tax rate.

• 60. A leading information technology company donated $87,790 out of its 2016 fiscal revenue of $17,558,643 towards socially-responsible causes. What percent of their revenue did they contribute towards these causes?

• 61. Neel Plastics Manufacturing Corporation targets to obtain $120,000 of funding from their investors to purchase new machinery. If they were only able to obtain 25.5% of their total target, calculate the amount of money that is yet to be received.

• 62. Pamela and Martha run a business that made a profit of $12,750. As Pamela invested a higher amount in the business, she received 57.5% of the profits and Martha received the remaining profits. Calculate Martha's share of the profit, in dollars.

5.4 | Percent Changes

The percent by which a quantity increases or decreases from its initial (original) value is called **percent change (%C)**. The amount of change (increase or decrease) is calculated as a percent change (%C) of its initial value.

$$Amount\ of\ Change = \%C \times Initial\ Value$$

The amount of change is the difference between the final value (V_f) and the initial value (V_i); i.e., the amount of change can also be calculated by subtracting the initial value from the final value.

V_i → %C → V_f

Amount of change = $V_f - V_i$

$$Amount\ of\ Change = Final\ Value - Initial\ Value$$

Therefore, $$\%C \times Initial\ Value = Final\ Value - Initial\ Value$$

To find a percent increase or decrease, find the amount of increase or decrease and then determine its percent value compared to the initial value.

$$\%C = \frac{(Final\ Value - Initial\ Value)}{Initial\ Value}$$

Percent Change ⟶ $\%C = \frac{(V_f - V_i)}{V_i}$ ⟵ Amount of Change ⟵ Initial Value

Percent change is calculated as a ratio of the amount of change to the initial value. This ratio is converted to its percent equivalent by multiplying it by 100 and inserting a '%' sign, as shown below.

Formula 5.4-a	**Percent Change**

$$\%C = \frac{(V_f - V_i)}{V_i} \times 100\%$$

Percent change is measured either as a percent increase (profit, rise, appreciation, etc.) or as a percent decrease (loss, fall, depreciation, etc.), compared to the initial value.

- If the final value is greater than the initial value, then the percent change is a percent increase, which is a positive value for $\%C$.

- If the final value is smaller than the initial value, then the percent change is a percent decrease, which is a negative value for $\%C$.

Using the amount of change formulas, we can also derive the formula for the final value (V_f), as follows:

$$Amount\ of\ Change = Final\ Value - Initial\ Value$$

Therefore, $\quad Final\ Value = Initial\ Value + (\%C \times Initial\ Value)$

$$V_f = V_i + (\%C \times V_i)$$

Factoring out the common factor V_i, we obtain the following:

$$V_f = V_i (1 + \%C)$$

Formula 5.4-b	**Final Value**

$$V_f = V_i (1 + \%C)$$

Using Formula 5.4-b, the formula to calculate the initial value (V_i) is derived as follows,

$$V_f = V_i (1 + \%C)$$

$$V_i (1 + \%C) = V_f$$

Solving for V_i, $\qquad V_i = \dfrac{V_f}{(1 + \%C)}$

Formula 5.4-c	**Initial Value**

$$V_i = \frac{V_f}{(1 + \%C)}$$

Example 5.4-a — Calculating the Amount of Increase and Final Value

The price of a shipment of syringes that originally sells at $150 is increased by 20%. Calculate the dollar amount of the increase and the price after the increase.

Solution

$$V_i \qquad\qquad V_f$$

$$\boxed{\$150} \xrightarrow{\;\%C = 20\%\text{ (increase)}\;} \boxed{?}$$

Method 1:

$$Amount\ of\ Change = \%C \times Initial\ Value$$
$$= 20\% \times 150.00$$
$$= 0.20 \times 150.00$$
$$= \$30.00\ (increase)$$

$$Final\ Value = Inital\ Value + Amount\ of\ Change$$
$$= 150.00 + 30.00$$
$$= \$180.00$$

Helpful Check:
If the %C is positive (i.e., there is a percent increase), then the final value must be greater than the initial value.

Method 2:

Using Formula 5.4-b,

$$V_f = V_i\,(1 + \%C) \qquad \text{Substituting values,}$$
$$= 150.00(1 + 20\%) \qquad \text{Converting \% to decimal,}$$
$$= 150.00(1 + 0.20) \qquad \text{Solving,}$$
$$= 150.00(1.20)$$
$$= \$180.00$$

$$Amount\ of\ Change = Final\ Value - Initial\ Value$$
$$= 180.00 - 150.00$$
$$= \$30.00\ (increase)$$

Method 3:

Percent (%)	Value ($)
100%	$150.00
120%	x

$$\frac{100\%}{120\%} = \frac{150.00}{x} \qquad \text{Converting \% to decimal,}$$
$$\frac{1}{1.20} = \frac{150.00}{x} \qquad \text{Cross multiplying,}$$
$$x = 1.20(150.00) \qquad \text{Solving,}$$
$$x = \$180.00$$

$$Amount\ of\ Change = Final\ Value - Initial\ Value$$
$$= 180.00 - 150.00$$
$$= \$30.00\ (increase)$$

Therefore, the amount of increase is $30.00 and the price after the increase is $180.00.

Example 5.4-b — Calculating the Amount of Decrease and Final Value

A digital wrist blood pressure monitor that normally sells for $400 is discounted (reduced in price) by 15%. Calculate the dollar amount of discount and the price after the discount.

Solution

$$V_i \qquad\qquad V_f$$

$$\boxed{\$400} \xrightarrow{\;\%C = -15\%\text{ (decrease)}\;} \boxed{?}$$

Method 1:

$$Amount\ of\ Change = \%C \times Initial\ Value$$
$$= -15\% \times 400.00$$
$$= -0.15 \times 400.00$$
$$= -\$60.00\ (decrease)$$

$$Final\ Value = Initial\ Value - Amount\ of\ Change$$
$$= 400.00 - 60.00$$
$$= \$340.00$$

Helpful check:

If the %C is negative (i.e., there is a percent decrease), then the final value must be less than the inital value.

Method 2:

Using Formula 5.4-b,

$$V_f = V_i\,(1 + \%C) \qquad \text{Substituting values,}$$
$$= 400.00(1 - 15\%) \qquad \text{Converting \% to decimal,}$$
$$= 400.00(1 - 0.15) \qquad \text{Solving,}$$
$$= 400.00(0.85)$$
$$= \$340.00$$

$$Amount\ of\ Change = Final\ Value - Initial\ Value$$
$$= 340.00 - 400.00$$
$$= -\$60.00\ (decrease)$$

Solution *continued*

Method 3:

Percent (%)	Value ($)
100%	$400.00
85%	x

$$\frac{100\%}{85\%} = \frac{400.00}{x}$$ Converting % to decimal,

$$\frac{1}{0.85} = \frac{400.00}{x}$$ Cross multiplying,

$$x = 0.85(400.00)$$ Solving,

$$x = \$340.00$$

Amount of Change = Final Value – Initial Value

$$= 340.00 - 400.00$$

$$= -\$60.00 \text{ (decrease)}$$

Therefore, the amount of discount is $60.00 and the price after discount is $340.00.

Example 5.4-c   Calculating Percent Increase

In July, 151,700 people were infected with H1N1, and by August, the number rose to 575,400 people. Calculate the percent change from July to August, rounded to the nearest tenth of a percent.

Solution

Initial Value, $V_i = 151,700$

Final Value, $V_f = 575,400$

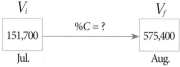

Using Formula 5.4-a, $\%C = \dfrac{(V_f - V_i)}{V_i} \times 100\%$ Substituting values,

$$= \frac{575,400 - 151,700}{151,700} \times 100\% \qquad \text{Solving,}$$

$$= \frac{423,700}{151,700} \times 100\%$$

$$= 2.793012... \times 100\% = 279.3\% \text{ (increase)}$$

Therefore, the percent change in infected people from July to August is an increase of 279.3%.

Example 5.4-d   Calculating Percent Decrease

According to a medical journal, the number of smokers decreased from 5.4 million in 2014 to 4.0 million in 2015. Calculate the percent decrease in the number of smokers, rounded to the nearest tenth of a percent.

Solution

Initial Value, $V_i = 5,400,000$

Final Value, $V_f = 4,000,000$

Using Formula 5.4-a, $\%C = \dfrac{(V_f - V_i)}{V_i} \times 100\%$ Substituting values,

$$= \frac{4,000,000 - 5,400,000}{5,400,000} \times 100\% \qquad \text{Solving,}$$

$$= \frac{-1,400,000}{5,400,000} \times 100\%$$

$$= -0.259259... \times 100\% = -25.9\% \text{ (decrease)}$$

Therefore, the number of smokers from 2014 to 2015 decreased by 25.9%.

Example 5.4-e | **Calculating Percent Change When Initial and Final Values are Given as Percents**

The rate of occurrence in a population of a particular disease increased from 0.5% last year to 0.75% this year. Find the percent increase in the rate of occurrence of the disease.

Solution

Initial Value, V_i = 0.5%
Final Value, V_f = 0.75%

Using Formula 5.4-a, $\quad \%C = \dfrac{(V_f - V_i)}{V_i} \times 100\%$ Substituting the values,

$$= \dfrac{0.75\% - 0.5\%}{0.5\%} \times 100\% \qquad \text{Simplifying,}$$

$$= \dfrac{0.25\%}{0.5\%} \times 100\%$$

$$= \dfrac{0.25}{0.5} \times 100\%$$

$$= 0.50 \times 100\% = 50\% \text{ (increase)}$$

Therefore, the percent increase in the rate of occurrence of the disease is 50%.

Note: It is incorrect to say that the percent increase is 0.75% – 0.5% = 0.25%, because the percent change refers to the change in the rate of occurrence relative to the initial rate of occurrence, not the absolute change in the rate of occurrence. Hence, we should be careful when discussing percent change of percent values, as this can be misleading.

Example 5.4-f | **Understanding Relative Percent Change**

In a diet program, Patient A's weight reduced from 94 kg to 82 kg and Patient B's weight reduced from 74 kg to 64 kg. Who showed a better relative percent decrease in weight?

Solution

First, calculate the amount of change in weight in both patients:

$\quad$ *Amount of Change$_{Patient\ A}$* = 82 – 94 = –12 kg
$\quad$ *Amount of Change$_{Patient\ B}$* = 64 – 74 = –10 kg

By comparing the amounts by which the weights of Patients A and B have changed, it may be tempting to conclude that Patient A has had more success on the diet program than Patient B. However, this comparison is incorrect, because we need to compare the relative change in weight for each patient. This brings us to the understanding of 'percent change'.

To compare the relative change in weights, you have to calculate the 'percent change' in the weights of the two patients.

Using Formula 5.4-a, $\%C = \dfrac{(V_f - V_i)}{V_i} \times 100\%$

Patient A's Percent Change in Weight:

> In health science applications, it is usually more important to calculate percent changes and associated values instead of relying on a mere difference between two values.

$$\%C_{Patient\ A} = \dfrac{(82 - 94)}{94} \times 100\%$$

$$= \dfrac{-12}{94} \times 100\%$$

$$= -0.127659... \times 100\% = -12.8\%$$

Solution
continued

Patient B's Percent Change in Weight:

$$\%C_{Patient\ B} = \frac{(64 - 74)}{74} \times 100\%$$

$$= \frac{-10}{74} \times 100\%$$

$$= -0.135135... \times 100\% = -13.5\%$$

Therefore, even though Patient B had a smaller decrease in weight than Patient A, Patient B had a better relative loss (13.5%) compared to Patient A (12.8%).

Example 5.4-g **Percent Change Comparing Unit Quantities**

A clinic purchased a case of 24 bottles of hand sanitizer that cost $45.00. A month later, it purchased a case of 12 bottles that cost $25.50. By what percent did the unit rate of the hand sanitizer bottles change (rounded to the nearest tenth of a percent)?

Solution

Unit price of the 24 bottles: $\dfrac{45.00}{24} = \$1.875$ per bottle

Unit price of the 12 bottles: $\dfrac{25.50}{12} = \$2.125$ per bottle

There is an increase in the unit price of the hand sanitizer bottles.

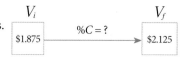

Using Formula 5.4-a, $\%C = \dfrac{(V_f - V_i)}{V_i} \times 100\%$ Substituting values,

$$\%C = \frac{2.125 - 1.875}{1.875} \times 100\%$$ Solving,

$$= \frac{0.25}{1.875} \times 100\%$$

$$= 0.133333... \times 100\% = 13.3\% \text{ (increase)}$$

Therefore, the unit rate of the hand sanitizer bottles increased by 13.3%.

Example 5.4-h **Calculating Initial Value When the Percent Change is Positive**

The value of a pharmaceutical stock increased by 35% since it was purchased. If the stock is now selling at $81, what was its value when it was purchased?

Solution

V_i %C = 35% (increase) V_f

? → $81

Method 1:

Using Formula 5.4-c, $V_i = \dfrac{V_f}{(1 + \%C)}$ Substituting values,

$$= \frac{81.00}{(1 + 35\%)}$$ Converting % to decimal,

$$= \frac{81.00}{(1 + 0.35)}$$ Solving,

$$= \frac{81.00}{1.35}$$

$$= \$60.00$$

Solution
continued

Method 2:

Percent (%)	Value ($)
100%	x
135%	$81.00

$$\frac{100\%}{135\%} = \frac{x}{81.00}$$ Converting % to decimal,

$$\frac{1}{1.35} = \frac{x}{81.00}$$ Cross multiplying,

$$81.00 = 1.35x$$ Solving,

$$x = \$60.00$$

Therefore, the value of the stock when it was purchased was $60.00.

Example 5.4-i   **Calculating Initial Value When the Percent Change is Negative**

After a discount of 25%, each nursing uniform was sold for $155. Calculate the price of a nursing uniform before the discount.

Solution

$$V_i \qquad\qquad\qquad V_f$$

| ? | $\xrightarrow{\%C = -25\% \text{ (decrease)}}$ | $155 |

Method 1:

Using Formula 5.4-c, $V_i = \dfrac{V_f}{(1 + \%C)}$ Substituting values,

$$= \frac{155.00}{(1 - 25\%)}$$ Converting % to decimal,

$$= \frac{155.00}{(1 - 0.25)}$$ Solving,

$$= \frac{155.00}{0.75}$$

$$= 206.666666... = \$206.67$$

Method 2:

Percent (%)	Value ($)
100%	x
75%	$155.00

$$\frac{100\%}{75\%} = \frac{x}{155.00}$$ Converting % to decimal,

$$\frac{1}{0.75} = \frac{x}{155.00}$$ Cross multiplying,

$$155.00 = 0.75x$$ Solving,

$$x = 206.666666\ldots = \$206.67$$

Therefore, the price of the item before the discount was $206.67.

'Reversing' a Percent Increase/Decrease

Common Error: Percent increase cannot be reversed by the same percent decrease.

For example,

$100.00 increased by 10% results in $110.00.

$$V_f = 100.00(1 + 10\%) = \$110.00$$

$$V_i \qquad\qquad\qquad V_f$$

| $100 | $\xrightarrow{\%C = 10\% \text{ (increase)}}$ | **$110** |

However, $110.00 decreased by 10% results in $99.00.

$$V_f = 110.00(1 - 10\%) = \$99.00$$

$$V_f \qquad\qquad\qquad V_i$$

| **$99** | $\xleftarrow{\%C = -10\% \text{ (decrease)}}$ | $110 |

$100.00 increased by 10% = $110.00.

But, $110.00 decreased by 10% ≠ $100.00

Similarly, percent decrease cannot be reversed by the same percent increase.

For example,

$100.00 decreased by 10% results in $90.00.

$$V_f = 100.00(1 - 10\%) = \$90.00$$

However, $90.00 increased by 10% results in $99.00.

$$V_f = 90.00(1 + 10\%) = \$99.00$$

$100.00 decreased by
10% = $90.00.

But, $90.00 increased
by 10% ≠ $100.00

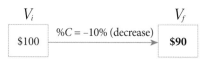

To reverse a percent increase or percent decrease, the proper percent change method should be used, as shown below.

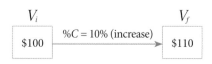

Using Formula 5.4-a

$$\%C = \frac{(V_f - V_i)}{V_i} \times 100\%$$

$$= \frac{100.00 - 110.00}{110.00} \times 100\%$$

$$= -0.090909... \times 100\% = -9.09\% (\text{decrease})$$

Using Formula 5.4-a

$$\%C = \frac{(V_f - V_i)}{V_i} \times 100\%$$

$$= \frac{100.00 - 90.00}{90.00} \times 100\%$$

$$= 0.111111... \times 100\% = 11.11\% \text{ (increase)}$$

Percent Change When the Initial Value (V_i) is Negative

In the equation, $\qquad V_i + Amount\ of\ Change = V_f$

where, $\qquad\qquad Amount\ of\ Change = \%C \times V_i$

- **When the *Amount of Change* is positive (i.e., there is an amount of increase),** regardless of the value or sign for V_i, we add the amount of increase to V_i to determine V_f; i.e., the amount **added** to V_i is **positive**.

$$V_i + Amount\ of\ Increase = V_f$$

- **When the *Amount of Change* is negative (i.e., there is an amount of decrease),** regardless of the value or sign for V_i, we subtract the amount of decrease from V_i to determine V_f; i.e., the amount that is **subtracted** from V_i is **positive**.

$$V_i - Amount\ of\ Decrease = V_f$$

Therefore, the amount that is added (amount of increase) or subtracted (amount of decrease) should always be a positive quantity.

When the original quantity (V_i) is negative, use the absolute sign for V_i to calculate the amount of increase or decrease. This ensures that the amount of increase or decrease will be a positive answer.

Therefore, when V_i is negative,

$$\text{Amount of Increase or Decrease} = \%C \times \text{Absolute value of } V_i$$
$$= \%C \left|V_i\right|$$

The absolute value of a number 'a' written as $|a|$ will always be a positive number (regardless of the sign for 'a').

For example, $|-5| = 5$ and $|5| = 5$.

If the final value is greater than the initial value,	If the final value is less than the initial value,
$\text{Initial Value} + \text{Amount of Increase} = \text{Final Value}$	$\text{Initial Value} - \text{Amount of Decrease} = \text{Final Value}$
$V_i + \%C\left|V_i\right| = V_f$	$V_i - \%C\left|V_i\right| = V_f$
$\%C = \dfrac{(V_f - V_i)}{\left|V_i\right|}$	$\%C = -\dfrac{(V_f - V_i)}{\left|V_i\right|}$
Therefore, the value of $\%C$ will be positive.	Therefore, the value of $\%C$ will be negative.

Example 5.4-j Percent Change When Initial Value is a Negative Value

The temperature of a cryogenic container used for preserving biological specimens was $-129\,°C$. If the temperature was increased by $24\,°C$, calculate the percent change in the new temperature from the previous temperature, rounded to the nearest tenth of a percent.

Solution

Method 1:

Since V_i is negative,

$$\text{Amount of Increase} = \%C\left|V_i\right|$$

$24 = \%C\left|-129\right|$ Substituting values,

$24 = \%C\,(129)$ Taking the absolute value of -129,

$\%C = \dfrac{24}{129}$ Solving,

$= 0.186046... \times 100\% = 18.6\%$ (increase)

Method 2:

Since V_i is negative,

$\%C = \dfrac{(V_f - V_i)}{\left|V_i\right|} \times 100\%$ Substituting values ($V_f - V_i = 24$),

$= \dfrac{24}{\left|-129\right|} \times 100\%$ Taking the absolute value of -129,

$= \dfrac{24}{129} \times 100\%$ Solving,

$= 0.186046... \times 100\% = 18.6\%$ (increase)

Therefore, the new temperature increased by 18.6% from the previous temperature.

5.4 | Exercises

Answers to odd-numbered problems are available at the end of the textbook.

For the following problems, express the answers rounded to two decimal places, wherever applicable.
Calculate the missing values in Problems 1 to 4.

1.

	Initial Value	Percent Increase	Final Value
a.	$270	45%	?
b.	$4,500	137.5%	?
c.	?	50%	$600
d.	?	262.5%	$2,250
e.	$150	?	$225
f.	$3,400	?	$9,200

2.

	Initial Value	Percent Increase	Final Value
a.	$250	35%	?
b.	$3,500	112.5%	?
c.	?	40%	$800
d.	?	187.5%	$6,950
e.	$170	?	$204
f.	$7,500	?	$24,500

3.

	Initial Value	Percent Decrease	Final Value
a.	$145	45%	?
b.	$1,275	112.5%	?
c.	?	25%	$412.5
d.	?	23.75%	$3,400
e.	$740	?	$400
f.	$5,200	?	$1,600

4.

	Initial Value	Percent Decrease	Final Value
a.	$525	35%	?
b.	$6,800	137.5%	?
c.	?	75%	$525
d.	?	18.75%	$4,800
e.	$222	?	$120
f.	$8,125	?	$2,500

5. If Harley's salary as a lab technician of $2,000 per month is increased by 5.5%, what is his new salary?

6. Revenues of a local hospital rose by 280% from last year. If its revenue last year was $860,760, calculate its revenue this year.

7. A solution of 400 L is comprised of half saline and half water. 6% of the saline was removed. Find the new volume of saline in the solution.

8. 4% of the water from a 350 mL solution that is half water was removed. Find the new volume of water in the solution.

9. If blood-glucose meters that sell in stores for $30 each are being offered online for $24 each, calculate the percent discount offered online.

10. If Lilo's student loans for medical school of $12,000 will increase to $12,860 by the end of the year, calculate the percent increase of her debt.

11. Dawson purchased latex gloves that were discounted by 10% from the original price of $50. Calculate the amount he paid.

12. Jamie received an 18% discount on a 1,000-pack of tongue depressors that cost $34.50. How much did the tongue depressors cost Jamie after the discount?

13. A sales tax of 9% increased the cost of a life-saving drug to $178.75. What was the cost of the drug before taxes?

14. After Carla's health insurance decreased the cost of her prescription drugs by 85%, Carla was still required to pay $65.25. Determine the total cost of the prescription drugs before the insurance company made its co-payment.

15. If the temperature of a patient was 37 °C (normal body temperature), and increased by 2 °C, calculate the percent change in the patient's temperature.

16. The average temperature in a viewing room is 4 °C. If the average temperature used to be 5.3 °C, calculate the percent change in temperature.

17. The value of an ambulance depreciated by 18.5% from the purchase price of $36,450 a year ago. What is its current price?

18. A hospital laid off 12% of its 675 employees. How many are still currently employed?

19. The average price for hip replacement surgery is $25,289. This is a decrease of 12% from last year's average price. What was the average price last year?

20. The current price for a medical journal subscription is $129.50. This is 7.5% less than last year's price. What was last year's price?

21. During a sale, an aspirator regulary priced at $999 was sold at $779. What was the percent discount?

22. HIV medication sales dropped from $83,570 to $69,500 over a two-year period. What was the percent decrease in sales during this period?

23. Cough drops regularly priced at $3.50 were sold at a discount of 17.5%. Calculate the discounted price.

24. A town's newborn population increased by 13.5% from 27,000 people. What is the current population of newborns?

25. James' current annual salary as a surgical nurse is $63,536. This is an increase of 4.5% from last year's salary. What was his salary last year?

26. The current enrollment at a college is 22,575, and represents an increase of 7.5% from last year. What was the enrollment last year?

27. If the current mortality rate for laparoscopic surgery of 0.03% drops to 0.01625%, calculate the percent decrease.

28. If the number of miscarriages increased from 0.14% to 0.3%, calculate the percent increase.

29. A pharmacy sold a certain prescription drug for $70. As a result of a decrease in the supply, the price of the drug increased by 20%. To offset this cost, the pharmacy offered a 20% discount on this drug for 3 months to all its patients who had recurring prescriptions. How much will a patient with a recurring prescription have to pay for the drug, after the discount?

30. Harry weighed 90 kg at the start of 2016. At the start of 2017, his body weight was 15% higher than it was at the start of 2016. At the start of 2018, after a year of eating healthier, his body weight was 15% lower than it was at the start of 2017. How much did Harry weigh at the start of 2018?

31. The temperature of an industrial freezer used for laboratory experiments was –112 °C. If the temperature was increased by 9 °C, calculate the percent change in the new temperature from the previous temperature.

32. The temperature of a morgue was –19 °C. If the temperature was decreased by 9 °C, calculate the percent change in the new temperature from the previous temperature.

33. A case of 20 sterilized syringes costs $65.29. The syringes are now sold in cases of 10 that cost $24.50. By what percent did the unit price of syringes change?

34. A new model of a bronchoscope costs $1,800. A hospital had previously purchased four older models, for a total of $4,170. By what percent did the unit price of bronchoscopes change?

35. Last month, a 7.5 metre roll of dry surgical tape was sold for $3.00. However, this month, the manufacturer has launched the same tape in a 6 metre roll, which is being sold at $2.50. By what percent did the unit price change?

36. A 450-count pack of alcohol wipes was sold for $3.50. If the manufacturer reduced the size of the pack to 250 and sold it at a reduced price of $2.00, by what percent did the unit price change?

37. Sandra tried to sell her blood pressure monitor for 50% more than what she had paid for it. Since it did not sell within a month, she decreased the advertised price by 50%, and it sold immediately. By what percent, more or less than her purchase price, did she sell the monitor?

38. If the temperature rose by 12% from the average temperature in a hospital waiting room, then fell by 12% of the higher temperature, by what percent did the final temperature increase or decrease from the average temperature?

• 39. The price of a pharmaceutical share dropped by $2.50 at the end of the first year and dropped by a further $3.45 at the end of the second year. If the price of the share at the end of the second year was $12.55, calculate the percent change in the price of the share at the end of each year from its price at the beginning of each year. What was the percent drop in the price over the entire two-year period?

• 40. A particular model of ultrasound machine sold for $4,000 at the beginning of the year and reduced in price by $80 at the end of the first year. At the end of the second year, the price was increased by $64. Calculate the percent change in the price of this model at the end of each year from its price at the beginning of each year. Calculate the overall percent discount offered over the two-year period from the original price of $4,000.

• 41. The labour cost is 30% of the total cost for manufacturing a $60,000 ambulance. If the cost of labour increased by 5%, by what amount did the cost of the ambulance increase?

• 42. The material cost for manufacturing a $2,000 defibrillator decreased by 10%. If the cost of materials was 40% of the total cost for manufacturing the defibrillator, by what amount did the cost of the defibrillator decrease?

• 43. Tudor and Rani, two sales representatives in a pharmaceutical company, were earning $2,815 per month and $2,875 per month, respectively. After a yearly appraisal, if Tudor's salary increased by 14% and Rani's increased by 11%, who had the higher salary?

• 44. Reggie's annual salary as a radiology technician increased from $42,000 to $46,830 this year and his colleague Gerald's annual salary increased from $39,500 to $44,437.50. Who received a higher rate of increase this year?

5 | Review Exercises   Answers to odd-numbered problems are available at the end of the textbook.

For the following problems, express the answers rounded to two decimal places, wherever applicable.

1. What is the ratio of 6 nickels to 10 dollars, reduced to its lowest terms?

2. What is the ratio of 12 minutes to 2 hours, reduced to its lowest terms?

3. Solve the following proportions for the unknown value:

   a. $4.4 : x = 2.6 : 5$

   b. $8 : 3 = x : 2$

   c. $x : 0.45 = 0.16 : 1.20$

   d. $\dfrac{1}{3} : \dfrac{2}{5} = 3 : x$

4. Solve the following proportions for the unknown value:
   a. $0.75 : x = 4.8 : 5.3$
   b. $1.8 : 0.9 = x : 3.4$
   c. $12.5 : 70 = x : 1.4$
   d. $x : \dfrac{3}{4} = 2 : \dfrac{1}{6}$

5. Determine which of the following ratios are equivalent:
   a. $6 : 8$ and $18 : 24$
   b. $3 : 4.5$ and $21 : 31.5$
   c. $4 : 6$ and $5 : 7$
   d. $0.225 : 1.125$ and $1.5 : 7.5$

6. Determine which of the following ratios are equivalent:
   a. $4.6 : 9.2$ and $3.3 : 6.6$
   b. $4 : 10$ and $10 : 24$
   c. $3.5 : 5$ and $2.1 : 3.6$
   d. $2 : 4$ and $8 : 16$

7. If Christina, a pediatric resident, receives an annual salary of $85,000, calculate her weekly salary using pro-ration. Assume that there are 52 weeks in a year.

8. As the CFO of a bio-technology company, every year Tyler would receive 26 bi-weekly payments of $6,000 each. Calculate his annual salary.

9. The tax on an electron microscope, which costs $350, is $45.50. Using the same tax rate, what will be the tax on an item that costs $1,250?

10. Peter works 5.5 hours per day as an anesthesiologist and his salary per day is $112.75. At this rate, how much will he receive if he works 7.5 hours per day?

11. Which is the better buy based on the unit price: 36 grams of acetaminophen for $2.99 or 48 grams of acetaminophen for $3.75?

12. Which is the better buy based on the unit price: 125 grams of flutamide for $14.75 or 175 grams of flutamide for $18.95?

13. A pack of 10 boxes of blood glucose strips costs $3.30 and each box has 30 strips.
    a. Find the cost per box of blood glucose strips.
    b. Find the cost per blood glucose strip (do not round).

14. A carton of 20 boxes of medical gauze pads costs $90, and each box contains 25 gauze pads.
    a. Find the cost per box of gauze pads.
    b. Find the cost per gauze pad (do not round).

15. Ali can place 6 sutures in 4 minutes.
    a. Calculate his suturing speed in sutures/hour.
    b. At this speed, how many sutures can he place in 1.5 hours ?

16. An ambulance can travel 486 km using 45 litres of gas.
    a. Calculate the fuel efficency of the ambulance in km/litre.
    b. At this rate, how many litres of gas are required for a trip of 810 km?

17. Calculate the unit price for each of the following offers and identify which offer is the best, based on the unit price:
    a. 3 m of dry surgical tape for $4.25
    b. 6 m of dry surgical tape for $5.80
    c. 9 m of dry surgical tape for $11.30

18. Calculate the unit price for each of the following offers and identify which offer is the best, based on the unit price:
    a. 5 boxes of antiseptic wipes for $4.95
    b. 6 boxes of antiseptic wipes for $6.40
    c. 8 boxes of antiseptic wipes for $7.30

19. Jeffrey and Gina were classmates who graduated together from college. Jeffrey found a job as a clinical exercise physiologist that pays him $189 for 9 hours of work every day and Gina found a job as a medical researcher that pays her $174 for 8 hours of work every day. Who is being paid a higher hourly rate and by how much?

20. Gregory travelled 765 km from North York General Hospital to Brockville General Hospital in 8 hours and 20 minutes. Chris travelled 165 km from North York General Hospital to Brantford General Hospital in 2 hours and 10 minutes. Based on this information, whose average speed was greater and by how much (in km/h)?

21. If the ratio of hospital beds to patients is $3 : 5$ and that of patients to nurses is $8 : 6$, calculate the ratio of hospital beds to patients to nurses in the hospital.

22. The ratios of drugs in a certain medication are as follows: acetaminophen to oxacillin is $9 : 2$ and oxacillin to diphenhydramine is $3 : 1$. Calculate the ratio of acetaminophen to oxacillin to diphenhydramine in the medication.

23. Alexander, an immunologist, invests in stocks of biotechnology, government health plans, and stem-cell research in the ratio of $4 : 5 : 3$, respectively. Calculate his investment in government health plan stocks if his investment in biotechnology was $10,900.

24. The ratio of the driving distance from London to Hamilton, Mississauga, and Toronto is $3 : 4 : 5$, respectively. If the distance from London to Hamilton is 125 km, calculate the distance from London to Mississauga and from London to Toronto.

25. Three college classmates, Khan, Thomas, and Lee, decided to start a business and invested $1,200, $2,500, and $3,500, respectively. If Lee decided to leave the business, how much would Khan and Thomas have to pay for Lee's shares if they wanted to maintain their initial investment ratio?

26. Calvin decided to build a rehabilitation office with his two partners, Kevin and Alex. They invested $200,000, $350,000, and $450,000, respectively. After the office was built, Kevin decided to sell his share of the investment to Calvin and Alex. How much would each of them have to pay if they wanted to maintain the same ratio of their investments in the office?

27. The ratio of amoxicillin to ranitidine to erythromycin is 3 : 4 : 5 respectively. The original dosage of ranitidine was 15 mL. After the first treatment, the amount of amoxicillin was increased by 20 mL. Calculate the new medication ratio.

28. The ratio of propranolol to erythromycin to dicyclomine is 5 : 3 : 1, respectively. The original dosage of propranolol was 10.5 mL. After the first treatment, the amount of dicyclomine was increased by 3.5 mL. Calculate the new medication ratio.

29. Anton, Cheryl, and Ellen invested $40,000, $75,000, and $60,000, respectively, to start a walk-in clinic. The clinic did very well in the first year and they wanted to invest an additional $52,500 in total to expand their business. How much would each of them have to individually invest to maintain their original investment ratio?

30. Russel, an anesthesiologist, invested $8,000, $12,000, and $4,000 in medical stocks of three different medical companies. The market showed potential to grow, so he decided to invest an additional $15,000 in total in the stocks of the same companies. How would he invest this amount into stocks of the three respective companies to maintain the original investment ratio?

Calculate the missing values in Problems 31 and 32:

31.

	Percent	Decimal	Fraction in lowest terms
a.	80%	?	?
b.	?	0.48	?
c.	?	?	$\frac{3}{2}$
d.	$16\frac{2}{3}$%	?	?
e.	?	0.0075	?
f.	?	?	$\frac{2}{25}$

32.

	Percent	Decimal	Fraction in lowest terms
a.	0.2%	?	?
b.	?	0.245	?
c.	?	?	$\frac{5}{12}$
d.	$13\frac{1}{3}$%	?	?
e.	?	1.075	?
f.	?	?	$\frac{3}{80}$

33. Answer the following:

   a. 125% of what number is 45?

   b. What percent of $180 is $36?

   c. How much is $\frac{3}{8}$% of $600?

34. Answer the following:

   a. 225% of what number is 180?

   b. What percent of $750 is $300?

   c. How much is $\frac{2}{5}$% of $30?

35. Paul sold an MRI machine for $575,000, which was 125% of the purchased price. Calculate the purchased price.

36. Peter sold his shares for $14,437.50. Calculate the amount he paid for the shares if his selling price was 275% of the amount he paid for the shares.

37. Lian scored 45 out of 60 on a chemistry test. What was his percent grade on the test?

38. There were 48 questions in a test. Ann answered 40 questions correctly. What percent of the questions did she answer correctly?

39. The total budget for the construction of a hospital wing was $1,280,000. If the actual expenses were 111% of the budget, determine the total expenditure for the construction of the hospital.

40. The monthly budget for ER expenses is $14,400. In March, the total expenditures were 112% of the budget, and in April, the total expenditures were 122% of the budget. Determine the total ER expenses for the two-month period.

41. Assume that out of the 350,000 people who immigrated to Canada in 2016, 12.25% were from China, 9.75% were from the Philippines, and the rest were from other countries.

    a. Calculate the number of people who immigrated to Canada from China.

    b. If the combined number of immigrants from China and the Philippines constituted 0.2% of the population of Canada, calculate the population of Canada in 2016. (Round the answer up to the next whole number.)

42. A dinner at a hospital cafeteria costs $27.80 plus 13% sales tax.

    a. What was the value of the tax?

    b. If the tax that you paid was 2% of all the tax money the cafeteria generated that day, calculate the amount of total tax money earned.

43. a. What is 180 increased by 70%?

    b. $90 decreased by 90% is how much?

    c. How much is $4,500 increased by 150%?

    d. What amount increased by $25\frac{3}{4}$% is 855.10 kg?

44. a. What is 2,680 increased by 85%?

    b. $880 decreased by 85% is how much?

    c. How much is $1,850 increased by 300%?

    d. What amount increased by $90\frac{1}{2}$% is 110.49 kg?

45. a. What amount decreased by 10% is $477?

    b. What amount increased by 180% is 20.65?

    c. $1,200 decreased by what percent is $300?

    d. 750 kg is what percent less than 1,000 kg?

46. a. What amount decreased by 28% is $234?

    b. What amount increased by 600% is $25.62?

    c. $800 increased by what percent is $1,800?

    d. 102 km is what percent more than 85 km?

47. 8% of the water from an 800 mL solution that is half water and half saline was removed. Find the new volume of water in the solution.

48. 20% of the water from a 250 mL solution that is half water, half saline was removed. Find the new volume of water in the solution.

49. If plaster and fiberglass materials for fractures are sold in 1 kg bags that sell in stores for $45 each, but $36 each online, calculate the percent discount offered online.

50. A college tuition fee of $4,500 increases to $4,900. Calculate the percent increase in fees.

51. Dry ice used in a lab experiment is kept in a special freezer at a temperature of –85 °C. When it is removed from the freezer, the surface temperature quickly increases to –78 °C. Determine the percent change in the surface temperature of the dry ice.

52. A semen sample is cryopreserved at a temperature of –176 °C. The cryogenic lab changes their storage procedures and decides to store all samples in liquid nitrogen, at a temperature of –196 °C for more optimal storage. Determine the percent change in storage temperature.

53. The selling price of an apartment was $335,000. This is 34% more than the purchase price. Calculate the original purchase price.

54. The selling price of a home was $663,400. This is 24% more than the purchase price. Calculate the original purchase price.

55. An emergency-vehicle manufacturer reduced the price of an ambulance by 8.75%. The current price of the ambulance is $38,325. What was the price of the ambulance before the reduction in price?

56. A property developer reduced the price of building a pediatric ward by 6.25%. The current price of the ward is $703,125. What was the price of the ward before the reduction?

57. A hospital's research department's expenses increased by 30% from last year. If this year's expenses are $234,260, calculate last year's expenses.

58. After paying income taxes of 32%, Sally's annual pay was $35,600. Calculate Sally's income before deducting income taxes.

59. On a mathematics quiz, Chelsea scored 15% more than Zane. By what percent is Zane's score less than Chelsea's?

60. If Sabrina's annual salary as a pediatrician is 10% more than Christina's, by what percent is Christina's annual earnings less than Sabrina's?

• 61. An emergency wing spends $1,200, $1,400, $800, and $1,700 on average on replacing Ambu bags, suture trays, blood pressure monitors, and cardiac monitors, respectively, every month.

    a. What percent of the total expenditures do they spend on suture trays every month?

    b. If they decide to reduce the expenses on both Ambu bags and blood pressure monitors by 50%, what percent of the total reduced expenditures would they now spend on cardiac monitors?

• 62. A surgical wing has 280 nurses, 21 attending physicians, and 28 interns.

    a. What percent of the total employees is now comprised of attending physicians?

    b. If 15% of the nurses quit their jobs, what percent of the total remaining employees is now comprised of attending physicians?

63. Katelyn invested $2,000, $1,800, and $3,100 into a cancer research company, stem-cell research company, and biotechnology company, respectively. Towards the end of 2016, if the value of her shares in the stem-cell research company rose by 20% while those in the cancer research company decreased by 10%, and those in the biotechnology company remained the same, calculate the overall percent change in the value of her total investments.

64. A hospital's board of directors decides to invest their annual savings in different mutual funds. In 2016, they invested $12,500 in high-growth funds, $5,000 in medium-growth funds, and $2,000 in low-growth funds. If the value of their medium-growth funds dropped by 10% this year while the funds in the high-growth funds increased by 25%, and those in the low-growth funds stayed the same, by what percent did the total value of their investments change overall?

5 | Self-Test Exercises

Answers to all problems are available at the end of the textbook.

For the following problems, express the answers rounded to two decimal places, wherever applicable.

1. Which is cheaper: a 240 gram box of cereal for $3.69, or a 360 gram box of cereal for $4.89?

2. A 500 km trip by car took 6 hours and 45 minutes. Calculate the speed of the car in km/h.

3. The average speed of a car is 75 km/h. At this speed, how long (in hours and minutes) will it take to travel 700 km?

4. Solve for the unknown quantity:
   a. $35 : 7 = 60 : x$
   b. $4.5 : 7.6 = x : 3.8$
   c. $x : 8 = 2\frac{1}{4} : 2\frac{1}{2}$

5. The scale on a hospital floor plan is 3 cm = 50 m. Calculate the actual distance between the two rooms that are 2.75 cm apart on a map.

6. The property tax on a clinic assessed at $430,000 is $4,235.50. Calculate the property tax on a another clinic assessed at $612,750. Assume the same tax rate.

7. A piece of medical equipment worth $1,500 depreciates in value at a rate of $300 per year. How many years until the equipment depreciates by $1,400?

8. An emergency vehicle travelled 250 km. If the fuel efficiency of the emergency vehicle is 9 litres per 100 km, calculate the amount of gas used for the trip.

9. Which offer is the best based on the unit price?
   a. 75 grams of oxybutynin for $1.49
   b. 100 grams of oxybutynin for $1.99
   c. 125 grams of oxybutynin for $2.25

10. The ratio of Andrew's billings to Bill's was 3 : 5 and the ratio of Bill's billings to Cathy's was 4 : 6. What was the ratio of the billings of Andrew : Bill : Cathy?

11. For every $25 that a not-for-profit children's charity receives, the government donated $10 towards the same cause. After 2 months of fundraising, the foundation had a total of $9,450, including the government's contribution. Calculate the amount donated by the government.

12. Georgia paid a yearly subscription amount of $250 to receive a health magazine monthly. After receiving two issues, she cancelled her subscription. Calculate the pro-rated refund she should receive from the magazine company.

13. Amir, Brian, and Caterina invested $9,000, $15,000, and $12,000 respectively, to start a small pharmacy. An additional $6,000 is required for operating the pharmacy. How much must each of them invest to maintain their original investment ratio?

14. Nabil and Mohammad invested a total of $100,000 in the ratio of 3 : 5. After one year, both of them withdrew $10,000 from the invesment. Calculate the ratio of their investments after the withdrawal.

15. Patients are distributed to the three doctors at a walk-in clinic, Alice, Bill, and Carol, in the ratio of 3 patients : 4 patients : 7 patients, respectively. If they treated 84 patients altogether, calculate the number of patients treated by each doctor.

16. Calculate the missing values:

	Percent	Decimal	Fraction in lowest terms
a.	$10\frac{5}{6}\%$	?	?
b.	?	2.25	?
c.	?	?	$\frac{1}{150}$
d.	$\frac{1}{2}\%$	?	?
e.	?	0.022	?
f.	?	?	$\frac{97}{365}$

17. Answer the following:

    a. What percent of $30 is $3.75?

    b. 22.5% of $1,500 is how much?

    c. 75 is 15% of what number?

18. Colton's walk-in clinic expenses for the months of July and August were $33,440 and $36,180, which were 110% and 90% of the budgeted expenditure for the months of July and August, respectively. Calculate the total budgeted expenses for the two months.

19. Sandra earns an annual salary of $60,000 as a radiology technician, and every month she spends $1,400 on rent, $600 on car expenses, $200 on loan repayment, $800 on miscellaneous expenses, and saves $2,000.

    a. What percent of her annual salary is accounted for by her annual expenses?

    b. If she invests 25% of the $2,000 savings in a mutual fund every month, what percent of the annual salary is invested in the fund over the entire year?

Calculate the missing values in Problems 20 and 21.

20.

	Initial value	Percent increase	Final value
a.	$80	?	$125
b.	$725	13%	?
c.	?	0.5%	$482.40

21.

	Initial value	Percent decrease	Final value
a.	$60	?	$45
b.	$113	20%	?
c.	?	0.8%	$297.60

22. What amount, when reduced by 13%, results in $696?

23. What amount, when increased by 5%, results in $1,365?

24. Calculate the percent change if an initial value of 20 is:

    a. decreased to 17.

    b. increased to 37.

25. Calculate the original price for latex gloves if Ruby paid $3.50 for a box after receiving a discount of 7%.

26. A plastic surgery clinic is offering a 12% discount on a botox procedure that was priced at $31,800. Calculate the price of the procedure after the discount.

27. In 2016, a cancer drug stock lost 60% of its value. In 2017, the stock's value increased by 80%. Calculate the percent change in the stock's value over the two-year period.

28. The price of a ventilator dropped by 3% from 2015 to 2016, and was worth $225,000 in 2016. If the overall price fell by 5% between 2015 and 2017, calculate its price in 2017.

29. The price of a share of a company that produces Hepatitis vaccines that was purchased for $20 increased by 30% during the first year and decreased by 30% during the second year.

    a. Calculate the value of the share at the end of the two years.

    b. Calculate the percent change in the share price over the two-year period.

30. The value of an experimental drug for multiple sclerosis dropped by $1.25 at the end of the first year, and a further $2.50 at the end of the second year. If the price of the share at the end of the second year was $12.55, calculate the percent change in the price of the share:

    a. For each of the two years.

    b. Over the two-year period.

6 UNITS OF MEASUREMENT

LEARNING OBJECTIVES

- Read, write, and interpret symbols and prefixes used in the metirc and US Customary systems of units.
- Convert within metric units and within US Customary and household units of length, mass, and capacity.
- Convert between metric and US Customary units of length, mass, and capacity.
- Convert units of temperature between the Celsius scale, Fahrenheit scale, and Kelvin scale.
- Read and write Roman Numerals.
- Understand the relationship between Military Time and Standard Time.

CHAPTER OUTLINE

6.1 Metric System of Measurement

6.2 US Customary and Household System of Measurement

6.3 Conversion Between Metric and US Customary Units

6.4 Conversion of Temperature Scales

6.5 Roman Numerals

6.6 Time Conversions

Introduction

In the health sciences, it is very important to accurately express quantities such as lengths, masses, volumes and other measurements. However, there are multiple systems of measurements that could be used to express these values, so any practitioner in the health sciences needs to be aware of the units in the various systems of measurement in use today, and how to convert measurements between these systems. The three main systems of measurement still in use throughout the world are the **metric system**, the **US Customary and Household system**, and the **Imperial system**.

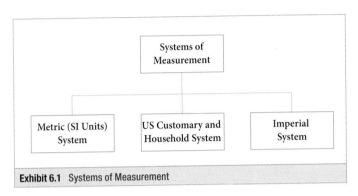

Exhibit 6.1　Systems of Measurement

The **Imperial system** was created in 1824 to replace English units - the previously defined system of measurement used throughout the British Empire. The US Customary system, a United States-based subset of the Imperial system, was created later in the 19th century. The Imperial and US Customary systems share many similarities, such as the names of the units used, but with slightly different measurements. In both systems, fluid and dry substances are measured using different household systems of measurement. In this book, we distinguish this by labeling the US Customary system as the **US Customary and Household system**.

In the United States, US Customary and Household units are primarily used, including in industrial manufacturing, cooking, and cleaning. Imperial units of measurement were historically used in the British Commonwealth countries. However, by the late 20th century, most of these countries adopted the metric system. Today, the Imperial system is seldom used, except for a few common usages that remain in Britain and a few other countries around the world (e.g., a "pint" of beer at a British-style pub still refers to an Imperial pint, which is slightly more volume than a US pint). As such, this book will not examine the Imperial system.

The **metric system** is widely used in the health sciences, most commonly in pharmaceutical math. The metric system was invented during the French Revolution (1789 – 1799) by the *Bureau International des Poids et Mesures* (BIPM). Over the years, it was adapted to the Système International (SI) units, and is now used by 98% of the world. However, the US and two other countries (Liberia and Myanmar) have not fully adapted to the metric system.

The metric system for measurement is simple to use and can be more easily understood than the US Customary and Household system because, in the metric system, all the units are related to one another by powers of ten (i.e., it is a decimal system). Of the seven base SI units used in the metric system, the health sciences sector uses four: the **metre** (length), the **kilogram** (mass), **degrees kelvin** (temperature), and the **second** (time).

In this chapter, you will learn how to convert within and between the metric and US Customary and Household systems.

Converting within Metric Units of Measurement

The metric system uses the metre (m), gram (g), and litre (L) as the base units for the measurements of length, mass, and capacity, respectively.

In this section, you will learn how to convert the commonly-used metric units for length, mass, and capacity:

- **Length:** kilometre (km), metre (m), centimetre (cm), and millimetre (mm)
- **Mass:** kilogram (kg), gram (g), milligram (mg), and microgram (µg or mcg)
- **Capacity:** litre (L) and millilitre (mL)

The conversion factors that relate to the different units in the metric system, including the prefixes used, are shown in Table 6.1.

Table 6.1 — Conversion Factors

The prefix and symbol for units from kilo- to milli- are written in lower case.

Prefix	Symbol	Factor	Factor in Words	Factor as a Power of 10
mega-	M	1,000,000	Million	10^6
kilo-	k	1,000	Thousand	10^3
hecto-	h	100	Hundred	10^2
deca-	da	10	Ten	10^1
Base Unit		1	One	10^0
deci-	d	$\dfrac{1}{10} = 0.1$	One-tenth	10^{-1}
centi-	c	$\dfrac{1}{100} = 0.01$	One-hundredth	10^{-2}
milli-	m	$\dfrac{1}{1,000} = 0.001$	One-thousandth	10^{-3}
micro-	µ or mc	$\dfrac{1}{1,000,000} = 0.000001$	One-millionth	10^{-6}

Base Units

length: metre (m)

mass: gram (g)

capacity: litre (L)

Note:

- *The prefixes hecto-, deca-, and deci- are not commonly used as units of measurement for length, mass, and capacity.*
- *In North America, the prefix centi- is only commonly used in the measurement of length, as in centimetre. However, in Europe, it is also commonly used for measurements of volume, as in centilitre.*
- *The symbol 'mc' is more commonly used than 'µ' to represent the prefix micro- in the health sciences to avoid confusion ('µ' and 'm' can look similar when written).*

Converting units within the metric system involves moving the decimal point to the right or to the left by the appropriate number of places (which is the same as multiplying or dividing by the required powers of 10).

The conversion within the units of measurement can also be shown in a horizontal line diagram, in order from the largest to the smallest.

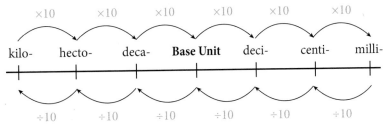

The conversion from a larger unit to a smaller unit represents moving the decimal point to the right or multiplying by powers of 10 as required.

For example, to convert 10.5 kilometres (km) to metres (m), move the decimal point 3 places to the right, or multiply by 10^3 (= 1,000).

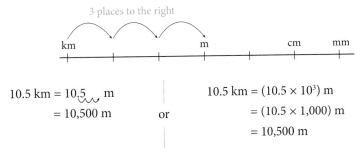

10.5 km = 10.5 m
= 10,500 m

or

10.5 km = (10.5 × 10^3) m
= (10.5 × 1,000) m
= 10,500 m

The conversion from a smaller unit to a larger unit represents moving the decimal point to the left or dividing by powers of 10 as required.

For example, to convert 425 centimetres (cm) to metres (m), move the decimal point 2 places to the left, or divide by 10^2 (= 100).

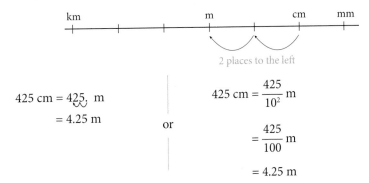

425 cm = 425 m
= 4.25 m

or

$$425 \text{ cm} = \frac{425}{10^2} \text{ m}$$

$$= \frac{425}{100} \text{ m}$$

$$= 4.25 \text{ m}$$

Length

Length is the measure of how tall or long an object is. The SI base unit is the metre, symbolized as "m".

Converting from larger units to smaller units	Converting from smaller units to larger units
1 km = (1 × 1,000) m = 1,000 m	$1 \text{ m} = \left(\dfrac{1}{1,000}\right) \text{ km} = 0.001 \text{ km}$
1 m = (1 × 100) cm = 100 cm	$1 \text{ cm} = \left(\dfrac{1}{100}\right) \text{ m} = 0.01 \text{ m}$
1 cm = (1 × 10) mm = 10 mm	$1 \text{ mm} = \left(\dfrac{1}{10}\right) \text{ cm} = 0.1 \text{ cm}$

Mass

Mass is the constant amount of material that makes up an object. Surprisingly, the SI base unit of mass is not the gram, but the kilogram, symbolized as "kg". This is because the gram is a very small measure of mass, and so the kilogram is considered to be a more useful base unit in SI.

Converting from larger units to smaller units	Converting from smaller units to larger units
1 kg = (1 × 1,000) g = 1,000 g	$1 \text{ g} = \left(\dfrac{1}{1,000}\right) \text{kg} = 0.001 \text{ kg}$
1 g = (1 × 1,000) mg = 1,000 mg	$1 \text{ mg} = \left(\dfrac{1}{1,000}\right) \text{g} = 0.001 \text{ g}$
1 mg = (1 × 1,000) mcg = 1,000 mcg	$1 \text{ mcg} = \left(\dfrac{1}{1,000}\right) \text{mg} = 0.001 \text{ mg}$

1 metric ton or "tonne" (t) = 1,000 kg

Note: Do not confuse mass with weight; weight is the measure of the object's heaviness dependent on the gravitational force acting upon the object, whereas mass refers to the amount of matter in the object. Hence, you could lose weight by going into outer space, but losing mass requires a controlled diet and exercise! However, since mass and weight are directly related on earth, where the gravitational force is constant, kilograms are often used as a measure of "weight" (e.g., Example 6.1-c).

Volume

Volume is the three-dimensional space an object occupies.

The capitalized 'L' is used to represent litre in order to avoid confusion with the number 1.

Converting from larger units to smaller units	Converting from smaller units to larger units
1 L = (1 × 1,000) mL = 1,000 mL	$1 \text{ mL} = \left(\dfrac{1}{1,000}\right) \text{L} = 0.001 \text{ L}$

Note: The litre is not considered to be a base unit of measurement in SI, because it can be derived from the cubic units of length: 1 cubic decimetre (dm³) = 1 L

Example 6.1-a   **Converting Measurements**

Convert the following measurements:

  (i)   7.5 cm to millimetres
  (ii)   1,120 cm to metres
  (iii)   2.56 kg to grams
  (iv)   21,750 mL to litres

Solution

  (i)   7.5 cm to millimetres:

       7.5 cm = (7.5 × 10 mm) = 75 mm

       (same as 7.5 = 75 mm)

  (ii)   1,120 cm to metres:

       $1,120 \text{ cm} = \dfrac{1,120}{100} \text{ m} = 11.2 \text{ m}$

       (same as 1120. = 11.2 m)

  (iii)   2.56 kg to grams:

       2.56 kg = (2.56 × 1,000) g = 2,560 g

       (same as 2.56 = 2,560 g)

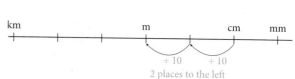

  (iv)   21,750 mL to litres:

       $21,750 \text{ mL} = \dfrac{21,750}{1,000} \text{ L} = 21.75 \text{ L}$

       (same as 21750. = 21.75 L)

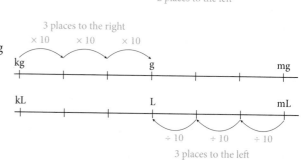

Example 6.1-b

Converting Measurements Involving Two Steps

Convert the following measurements:

(i)   5.02 km to centimetres

(ii)   3,125,000 mg to kilograms

Solution

(i)   5.02 km to centimetres:

Method 1:

Step 1: Convert 5.02 km to metres

$$5.02 \text{ km} = (5.02 \times 1,000) \text{ m}$$
$$= 5,020 \text{ m}$$

Step 2: Convert 5,020 m to centimetres

$$5,020 \text{ m} = (5,020 \times 100) \text{ cm}$$
$$= 502,000 \text{ cm}$$

Method 2:

$$5.02 \text{ km} = (5.02 \times 10^5) \text{ cm}$$
$$= (5.02 \times 100,000) \text{ cm}$$
$$= 502,000 \text{ cm}$$

Therefore, 5.02 km is equal to 502,000 cm.

(ii)   3,125,000 mg to kilograms:

Method 1:

Step 1: Convert 3,125,000 mg to grams

$$3,125,000 \text{ mg} = \left(\frac{3,125,000}{1,000}\right) \text{ g}$$
$$= 3,125 \text{ g}$$

Step 2: Convert 3,125 g to kilograms

$$3,125 \text{ g} = \left(\frac{3,125}{1,000}\right) \text{ kg}$$
$$= 3.125 \text{ kg}$$

Method 2:

$$3,125,000 \text{ mg} = \left(\frac{3,125,000}{10^6}\right) \text{ kg}$$
$$= \left(\frac{3,125,000}{1,000,000}\right) \text{ kg}$$
$$= 3.125 \text{ kg}$$

Therefore, 3,125,000 mg is equal to 3.125 kg.

Example 6.1-c   **Word Problem Involving Conversion of Measurements**

Megan's baby weighed 4 kg at birth. In two months, her baby lost 350 g. Calculate her baby's new weight, in grams.

Solution

Since the answer needs to be expressed in grams, first convert all measurements into grams.

$$4 \text{ kg} = (4 \times 1,000) \text{ g} \qquad \text{[using 1 kg = 1,000 g]}$$
$$= 4,000 \text{ g}$$

As the baby lost 350 g, this needs to be subtracted from the total.

$$\text{New weight} = (4,000 - 350) \text{ g}$$
$$= 3,650 \text{ g}$$

Therefore, the baby's new weight is 3,650 g.

Area Units

To find the area of an object, multiply length × width. The answer will be expressed in units squared (units²). When converting between square units, the number must be multiplied or divided two times.

For example, 1 cm² = 10 mm × 10 mm = 100 mm².

Converting from larger units to smaller units	Converting from smaller units to larger units
1 km² = (1 × 1,000²) m² = 1,000,000 m²	$1\ m^2 = \left(\dfrac{1}{1{,}000^2}\right) km^2 = 0.000001\ km^2$
1 m² = (1 × 100²) cm² = 10,000 cm²	$1\ cm^2 = \left(\dfrac{1}{100^2}\right) m^2 = 0.0001\ m^2$
1 cm² = (1 × 10²) mm² = 100 mm²	$1\ mm^2 = \left(\dfrac{1}{10^2}\right) cm^2 = 0.01\ cm^2$

Cubic Units

To find the volume of a container, multiply length × width × height. The answer will be expressed in units cubed (units³). When converting between cubed units, the number must be multiplied or divided three times.

For example, 1 cm³ = 10 mm × 10 mm × 10 mm = 1,000 mm³.

The cubic centimetre, **cm³**, can also be expressed as **cc**.

Converting from larger units to smaller units	Converting from smaller units to larger units
1 km³ = (1 × 1,000³) m³ = 1,000,000,000 m³	$1\ m^3 = \left(\dfrac{1}{1{,}000^3}\right) km^3 = 0.000000001\ km^3$
1 m³ = (1 × 100³) cm³ = 1,000,000 cm³	$1\ cm^3 = \left(\dfrac{1}{100^3}\right) m^3 = 0.000001\ m^3$
1 cm³ = (1 × 10³) mm³ = 1,000 mm³	$1\ mm^3 = \left(\dfrac{1}{10^3}\right) cm^3 = 0.001\ cm^3$

Example 6.1-d **Converting Measurements Using Area and Cubic Units**

Convert the following units:

(i)   0.006 km² to m²   (ii)   4,000 cm² to m²   (iii)   65 m³ to cm³   (iv)   138 m³ to km³

Solution

(i)   0.006 km²
= (0.006 × 1,000²) m²
= 6,000 m²

(ii)   4,000 cm²
$= \left(\dfrac{4{,}000}{100^2}\right) m^2$
= 0.4 m²

(iii)   65 m³
= (65 × 100³) cm³
= 65,000,000 cm³

(iv)   138 m³
$= \left(\dfrac{138}{1{,}000^3}\right) km^3$
= 0.000000138 km³

Conversion Between Cubic Units and Capacity

When converting cubic units to their capacity equivalents, it is important to remember the base conversion: 1 dm³ = 1 L.

We can visualize this conversion using shapes:

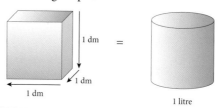

We can convert any measure of cubic units to its capacity equivalent, and vice versa, using the "bridge" method. Knowing that 1 dm³ = 1 L, we can convert a given cubic unit to its equivalent capacity in L, or given capacity to its equivalent cubic unit in dm³; we can then further convert the value to the desired unit.

As previously learned, cubic units are multiplied or divided by a factor of 1,000 or 10^3. Capacity units are multiplied and divided by a factor of 10 or 10^1.

km³	hm³	dam³	m³	dm³	cm³ (or cc)	mm³
kL	hL	daL	L	dL	cL	mL

Example 6.1-e   **Converting Between Cubic Units and Capacity**

Convert between the following cubic units and capacity units:

(i)   0.17 m³ to cL   (ii)   5 cm³ to mL   (iii)   24.5 mL to cm³   (iv)   4.8 kL to m³

Solution

(i)   0.17 m³ to cL

km³	hm³	dam³	m³	dm³	cm³ (or cc)	mm³
kL	hL	daL	L	dL	cL	mL

0.17 m³ × 1,000 = 170 dm³   Convert m³ to the base unit, dm³.

170 dm³ = 170 L   Using the bridge, convert cubic unit dm³ to capacity unit L.

170 L × 100 = 17,000 cL   Convert L to cL.

Therefore, 0.17 m³ is equal to 17,000 cL.

(ii)   5 cm³ to mL

km³	hm³	dam³	m³	dm³	cm³ (or cc)	mm³
kL	hL	daL	L	dL	cL	mL

5 cm³ ÷ 1,000 = 0.005 dm³   Convert cm³ to the base unit, dm³.

0.005 dm³ = 0.005 L   Using the bridge, convert cubic unit dm³ to capacity unit L.

0.005 L × 1,000 = 5 mL   Convert L to mL.

Therefore, 5 cm³ is equal to 5 mL.

Therefore, you found another bridge, which is 1 cm³ = 1 mL! This makes sense, since 1 L = 1,000 mL, 1 dm³ = 10^3 or 1,000 cm³, and 1 L = 1 dm³.

(iii)   24.5 mL to cm³

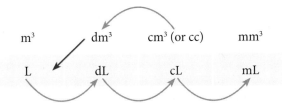

km³	hm³	dam³	m³	dm³	cm³ (or cc)	mm³
kL	hL	daL	L	dL	cL	mL

24.5 mL = 24.5 cm³   Using the bridge you found in (ii), convert capacity unit mL to cubic unit cm³.

Therefore, 24.5 mL is equal to 24.5 cm³.

(iv)   4.8 kL to m³

| km³ | hm³ | dam³ | m³ | dm³ | cm³ (or cc) | mm³ |
| kL | hL | daL | L | dL | cL | mL |

4.8 kL × 1,000 = 4,800 L   Convert kL to the base unit, L.

4,800 L = 4,800 dm³   Using the bridge, convert capacity unit L to cubic unit dm³.

4,800 dm³ ÷ 1,000 = 4.8 m³   Convert dm³ to m³.

Therefore, 4.8 kL = 4.8 m³

And we've found one final bridge: 1 kL = 1 m³.

6.1 | Exercises

Answers to odd-numbered problems are available at the end of the textbook.

Calculate the missing values in Problems 1 to 8.

1.

	metres (m)	centimetres (cm)	millimetres (mm)
a.	2.40	?	?
b.	?	860	?
c.	?	?	34,420

2.

	metres (m)	centimetres (cm)	millimetres (mm)
a.	1.20	?	?
b.	?	975	?
c.	?	?	23,170

3.

	metres (m)	centimetres (cm)	millimetres (mm)
a.	0.25	?	?
b.	?	58	?
c.	?	?	8,470

4.

	metres (m)	centimetres (cm)	millimetres (mm)
a.	0.67	?	?
b.	?	95	?
c.	?	?	5,200

5.

	kilometres (km)	metres (m)	centimetres (cm)
a.	1.62	?	?
b.	?	2,390	?
c.	?	?	2,320

6.

	kilometres (km)	metres (m)	centimetres (cm)
a.	1.25	?	?
b.	?	1,454	?
c.	?	?	1,190

7.

	kilometres (km)	metres (m)	centimetres (cm)
a.	0.65	?	?
b.	?	154	?
c.	?	?	1,770

8.

	kilometres (km)	metres (m)	centimetres (cm)
a.	0.17	?	?
b.	?	230	?
c.	?	?	9,400

For Problems 9 to 12, convert the measurements to the units indicated.

9. a. 23 m = ____ cm   b. 16.5 cm = ____ mm   c. 5 km = ____ m

10. a. 7 m = ____ cm   b. 45 cm = ____ mm   c. 2.07 km = ____ m

11. a. 335 cm = ____ m   b. 603 mm = ____ cm   c. 1,487 m = ____ km

12. a. 793.12 cm = ____ m   b. 379 mm = ____ cm   c. 6,745 m = ____ km

13. Arrange the following measurements in order from smallest to largest:

0.15 km, 150,800 mm, 155 m, 15,200 cm

14. Arrange the following measurements in order from largest to smallest:

19,750 cm, 1.97 km, 1,950 m, 195,700 mm

15. The distance between two hospitals in an urban center is 5.7 km. An ambulance is dispatched from one hospital to the other with a patient in serious condition. After the ambulance had travelled 925 m, the patient suddenly goes into critical condition, and the ambulance has to turn on its sirens and emergency lights. How many metres away from the second hospital is the ambulance?

16. A serious car accident occurs 2.5 km away from a hospital. The driver of one of the vehicles is in critical condition, and a nearby ambulance is dispatched to bring the driver to the hospital immediately. If the ambulance is 875 m away from the scene of the accident, how far will the ambulance have to travel, in total, to the scene of the accident and back to the hospital?

17. Ali is 1.75 m tall. Eric is 30 mm taller than Ali. Calculate Eric's height, in centimetres.

18. Five-year-old Aran's height is 1.2 m. His sister Girija is 140 mm taller than him. Calculate Girija's height, in centimetres.

For Problems 19 and 20, convert the measurements to the units indicated. [1 mm = 1,000 μm]

19. a. 4.5 mm = ___ μm   b. 0.03 mm = ___ μm   c. 0.6 cm = ___ μm   d. 450 μm = ___ mm

20. a. 2.8 mm = ___ μm   b. 0.005 mm = ___ μm   c. 0.21 cm = ___ μm   d. 30 μm = ___ mm

To obtain the diameter of your field of vision under a microscope, you have to divide the diameter of the eyepiece lens (usually measured in mm) by the objective magnification. The resulting length is very small, and therefore is usually expressed in micrometres (μm).

21. What is the diameter of your field of vision under a microscope with an eyepiece diameter of 22 mm and an objective magnification of 40? Express your answer in micrometres.

22. What is the diameter of your field of vision under a microscope with an eyepiece diameter of 18 mm and an objective magnification of 60? Express your answer in micrometres.

Calculate the missing values in Problems 23 to 30.

23.
	kilograms (kg)	grams (g)
a.	2.62	?
b.	?	6,750

24.
	kilograms (kg)	grams (g)
a.	3.79	?
b.	?	8,620

25.
	milligrams (mg)	micrograms (mcg)
a.	0.84	?
b.	?	580

26.
	milligrams (mg)	micrograms (mcg)
a.	0.32	?
b.	?	930

27.
	kilograms (kg)	grams (g)	milligrams (mg)
a.	1.65	?	?
b.	?	4,950	?
c.	?	?	6,440

28.
	kilograms (kg)	grams (g)	milligrams (mg)
a.	2.45	?	?
b.	?	8,700	?
c.	?	?	3,890

29.
	kilograms (kg)	grams (g)	milligrams (mg)
a.	0.76	?	?
b.	?	35,760	?
c.	?	?	50,300

30.
	kilograms (kg)	grams (g)	milligrams (mg)
a.	0.45	?	?
b.	?	25,090	?
c.	?	?	20,080

For Problems 31 to 34, convert the measurements to the units indicated.

31. a. 18 kg = ___ g   b. 2 kg = ___ mg   c. 3 t = ___ kg   d. 560 mg = ___ mcg

32. a. 7 kg = ___ g   b. 14 kg = ___ mg   c. 15 t = ___ kg   d. 0.05 mg = ___ mcg

33. a. 5,903 g = ___ kg   b. 2,884 mg = ___ g   c. 9,704 kg = ___ t   d. 480 mcg = ___ mg

34. a. 5,014 g = ___ kg   b. 6,629 mg = ___ g   c. 3,075 kg = ___ t   d. 25 mcg = ___ mg

35. Arrange the following measurements in order from smallest to largest:

    0.075 mcg, 123,200 g, 850,250 mg, 125 kg

36. Arrange the following measurements in order from largest to smallest:

    0.025 mcg, 50,750 mg, 125,700 g, 27 kg

37. If one tablespoon of cough syrup weighs 20 g, how many tablespoons of cough syrup are there in a bottle containing 1.1 kg of cough syrup?

38. If a bowl has a 40 g capacity, how many bowls are required to hold 1.35 kg?

39. Linda bought 0.75 kg of insulin and used 575 g of it. Calculate the quantity of insulin left, in grams.

40. Ben bought 35 grams of Advil and took 400 milligrams of it. Calculate the quantity of Advil left, in grams.

41. 450 g of hand sanitizer cost $3.25. At this price, how much will it cost to buy 2.25 kg of hand sanitizer?

42. 250 g of dry surgical tape cost $2.75. At this price, how much will it cost to buy 2 kg of dry surgical tape?

Calculate the missing values in Problems 43 to 46.

43.

	litre (L)	millilitre (mL)
a.	3.25	?
b.	?	5,060

44.

	litre (L)	millilitre (mL)
a.	1.75	?
b.	?	1,975

45.

	litre (L)	millilitre (mL)
a.	0.045	?
b.	?	220

46.

	litre (L)	millilitre (mL)
a.	0.015	?
b.	?	5,730

For Problems 47 to 50, convert the measurements to the units indicated.

47. a. 205 mL = ____ L   b. 5.05 L = ____ mL   c. 58.5 L = ____ kL

48. a. 370 mL = ____ L   b. 9.25 L = ____ mL   c. 125 L = ____ kL

49. a. 2,708 dL = ____ L   b. 4.68 L = ____ dL   c. 3.65 hL = ____ cL

50. a. 6,503 dL = ____ L   b. 0.06 L = ____ dL   c. 402 cL = ____ hL

51. A bottle can hold 900 mL of baby formula. Calculate the total volume of baby formula in five bottles. Express the answer in litres.

52. Andy drinks 250 mL of milk every day. Calculate the quantity of milk he will require for 7 days. Express the answer in litres.

53. A milk carton contains 1.75 L of milk. If three glasses with a volume of 320 mL each are filled with milk from the carton, how much milk will be left in the carton? Express the answer in millilitres.

54. A bag can hold 1.5 L of 0.9% sodium chloride solution. If four patients are given 280 mL each of the solution, how much is left in the original bag? Express the answer in millilitres.

For Problems 55 to 60, convert the measurements to the units indicated.

55. a. 4,280,000 cm^2 = ____ m^2 b. 0.0543 dm^3 = ____ mm^3 c. 6,000,000 mm^3 = ____ cm^3

56. a. 6.8 dm^2 = ____ mm^2 b. 8 m^3 = ____ mm^3 c. 52,000 cm^3 = ____ m^3

57. a. 2,653 cm^3 = ____ L   b. 0.027 m^3 = ____ daL   c. 2.9 cm^3 = ____ mL

58. a. 482 m^3 = ____ kL   b. 2.83 dam^3 = ____ L   c. 26,513 cm^3 = ____ dL

59. a. 890 mL = ____ cm^3 b. 1.532 daL = ____ m^3 c. 45,000 mL = ____ hm^3

60. a. 85 L = ____ m^3 b. 55.5 mL = ____ dm^3 c. 70 mL = ____ cm^3

61. A water tank that measures 2.2 m^3 is $\frac{1}{4}$ full. How many additional litres of water are required to fill the tank?

62. The volume of a petri dish is 95,000 mm^3. How many millilitres of liquid can it hold?

63. A syringe can hold 3 mL of liquid. What is the volume of the syringe, measured in cm^3?

64. An IV bag can hold 1 L of liquid. What is the volume of the IV bag, measured in cm^3?

- 65. A local city council sets the price of tap-water for local residents at $2.15/m³. In contrast, a 750 mL bottle of water is sold from a local convenience store for $1.89.

  a. Compare the price per litre for each type of water.

  b. How many 750 mL bottles of water would you be able to fill from the tap for the same price as the convenience store is charging?

  c. If a good-quality, hard-plastic 750 mL water bottle costs $26, how many times will you have to fill the bottle from the tap to recuperate the cost of the water bottle in savings on the price of water?

- 66. A homeowner is analyzing the costs for reverse osmosis (r.o.) water. One option is to purchase a water cooler and fill jugs at a u-fill water store that charges $2.65 for an 18.9 L jug of r.o. water. The other option is to install an r.o. system and pay the tap-water rate of $3.62/m³.

  a. Compare the price per litre for each type of r.o. water.

  b. If the homeowner figures he'll use 250 L every month, how much will he save in monthly water costs to install the r.o. system instead of filling the jugs at the u-fill store?

  c. If the r.o. system costs $500 more to install than the water cooler, how many months will it take for the owner to recuperate his costs in savings on the price of water?

6.2 | US Customary and Household System of Measurement

As mentioned in the introduction of this chapter, while the Imperial and US Customary systems are similar, they are not identical. There are a number of differences between them, specifically in volume measurements.

For example,

- 1 US fluid ounce is approximately 1.041 Imperial fluid ounces
- 1 US gallon is approximately 0.833 Imperial gallons

The rest of this section will focus on the US Customary system of measurement, which uses the yard (yd), the pound (lb), and the gallon (gal) as the base units for the measurements of length, mass, and capacity, respectively. The household system uses the teaspoon (tsp), tablespoon (tbsp), cup (c), and quart (qt) as the base units for measurements of volume. Together, these two systems form the US Customary and Household system.

In the United States, many items are measured using US Customary and Household units. For example, road distance is measured in miles, butter is measured in pounds, and gasoline is measured in gallons.

In this section, you will learn how to convert within the commonly used units for length, mass, and capacity within the following US Customary and Household units:

The **base unit** is yard (for length), pound (for mass), and gallon (for capacity).

- **Length:** mile (mi), yard (yd), foot (ft), and inch (in.)
- **Mass:** ton (ton), pound (lb), and ounce (oz)
- **Capacity:** gallon (gal), quart (qt), pint (pt), cup (c), fluid ounce (fl oz), tablespoon (tbsp), and teaspoon (tsp).

Converting within US Customary and Household Units of Measurement

Length

- 1 mile is 1,760 yards, or 5,280 feet
- 1 yard is 3 feet
- 1 foot is 12 inches

1 mi = 1,760 yd = 5,280 ft

1 yd = 3 ft

1 ft = 12 in

Mass

- 1 ton is 2,000 pounds   1 ton = 2,000 lb
- 1 pound is 16 ounces   1 lb = 16 oz

Note: The US Customary unit for ton is called 'short ton' and is represented by the word 'ton'. This is to distinguish it from the metric ton that has the symbol 't', where 1 t = 1,000 kg.

Volume

- 1 gallon is 4 quarts   1 gal = 4 qt
- 1 quart is 2 pints   1 qt = 2 pt
- 1 pint is 2 cups   1 pt = 2 c
- 1 cup is 8 fluid ounces   1 c = 8 fl oz
- 1 fluid ounce is 2 tablespoons   1 fl oz = 2 tbsp
- 1 tablespoon is 3 teaspoons   1 tbsp = 3 tsp

There are a number of methods for converting measurements from one unit to another. In Section 6.1, to convert within the metric system, we multiplied or divided by powers of 10 because the units are related by factors of 10, 100, 1,000, $\frac{1}{10}$, $\frac{1}{100}$, $\frac{1}{1,000}$, etc. Conversions within the US Customary and Household system can also be performed by using direct multiplication or division, using the conversion factors as shown in the diagram below.

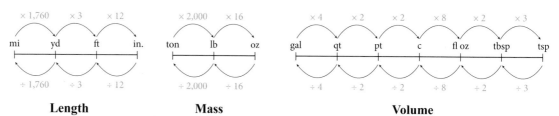

Length	**Mass**	**Volume**

For example, since 1 yd = 3 ft and 1 ft = 12 in, in order to convert 5 yards to inches, multiply by first converting yards to feet and then feet to inches.

$$\text{i.e., } 5 \text{ yd} = (5 \times 3) \text{ ft} = 15 \text{ ft}$$
$$= (15 \times 12) \text{ in} = 180 \text{ in}$$

Example 6.2-a | **Converting a Measurement Using Direct Multiplication**

Convert the following measurements:

(i)   2.25 ft to inches   (ii)   5.5625 lb to ounces   (iii)   2.75 gal to pints

Solution

(i)   2.25 ft in to inches:

$$2.25 \text{ ft} = (2.25 \times 12) \text{ in} \qquad [\text{using } 1 \text{ ft} = 12 \text{ in}]$$
$$= 27 \text{ in}$$

Therefore, 2.25 ft is equal to 27 in.

(ii)   5.5625 lb to ounces:

$$5.5625 \text{ lb} = (5.5625 \times 16) \text{ oz} \qquad [\text{using } 1 \text{ lb} = 16 \text{ oz}]$$
$$= 89 \text{ oz}$$

Therefore, 5.5625 lb is equal to 89 oz.

(iii)   2.75 gal to pints:

$$2.75 \text{ gal} = (2.75 \times 4) \text{ qt} \qquad [\text{using 1 gal = 4 qt}]$$

$$= 11 \text{ qt}$$

$$= (11 \times 2) \text{ pt} \qquad [\text{using 1 qt = 2 pt}]$$

$$= 22 \text{ pt}$$

Therefore, 2.75 gal is equal to 22 pt.

Example 6.2-b   **Converting a Measurement Using Direct Division**

Convert the following measurements:

(i)   9,900 ft to miles   (ii)   73 oz to pounds   (iii)   95 qt to gallons

Solution

(i)   9,900 ft to miles:

$$9,900 \text{ ft} = \frac{9,900}{3} \text{ yd} \qquad\qquad [\text{using 1 yd = 3 ft}]$$

$$= 3,300 \text{ yd}$$

$$= \frac{3,300}{1,760} \text{ mi} \qquad\qquad [\text{using 1 mi = 1,760 yd}]$$

$$= 1.875 \text{ mi}$$

Therefore, 9,900 ft is equal to 1.875 mi.

(ii)   73 oz to pounds:

$$73 \text{ oz} = \frac{73}{16} \text{ lb} \qquad\qquad [\text{using 1 lb = 16 oz}]$$

$$= 4.5625 \text{ lb}$$

Therefore, 73 oz is equal to 4.5625 lb.

(iii)   95 qt to gallons:

$$95 \text{ qt} = \frac{95}{4} \text{ gal} \qquad\qquad [\text{using 1 gal = 4 qt}]$$

$$= 23.75 \text{ gal}$$

Therefore, 95 qt is equal to 23.75 gal.

Example 6.2-c   **Performing Conversions With Multiple Units**

Convert the following measurements:

(i)   12 ft 10 in (denoted 12'10") to inches   (ii)   58 inches to ft and in

(iii)   5 lb 11 oz to ounces   (iv)   183 ounces to lb and oz

Solution

(i)   12 ft = (12 × 12) in = 144 in   (ii) $58 \text{ in} = \frac{58}{12} \text{ ft} = 4\frac{10}{12} \text{ ft} = 4'12"$

12'10" = 144 in + 10 in = 154 in

(iii)   5 lb = (5 × 16) oz = 80 oz   (iv) $183 \text{ oz} = \frac{183}{16} \text{ lb} = 11\frac{7}{16} \text{ lb} = 11 \text{ lb } 7 \text{ oz}$

5 lb 11 oz = 80 oz + 11 oz = 91 oz

When converting between units, especially when multiple conversions are necessary, it can be helpful to apply a more formally-defined method than directly multiplying or dividing. In this section, you will learn about two commonly used methods used to perform conversions of units within the US Customary and Household system:

(i)   the conversion factor (ratio) method (also known as dimensional analysis), and

(ii)   the proportion method.

Conversion Factor (Ratio) Method

For any known relationship between two units, we can find two conversion factors to use in converting units.

For example, consider the relationship 1 foot = 12 inches.

Dividing both sides of the equation by 1 foot,

$$\frac{1\ \cancel{foot}}{1\ \cancel{foot}} = \frac{12\ inches}{1\ foot}$$

$$1 = \frac{12\ inches}{1\ foot}$$

Dividing both sides of the equation by 12 inches,

$$\frac{1\ foot}{12\ inches} = \frac{12\ \cancel{inches}}{12\ \cancel{inches}}$$

$$\frac{1\ foot}{12\ inches} = 1$$

Therefore, the relationship between two units can be written as two conversion factors (or ratios):

$$\frac{12\ inches}{1\ foot} \quad or \quad \frac{1\ foot}{12\ inches}$$

Since the conversion factors are equal to 1, they can be used to multiply the given measurement to convert it from one unit to another. The following examples will illustrate how to use them in conversions.

Example 6.2-d	Finding Conversion Factors for a Given Relationship

Find the two conversion factors for the following known relationship: 1 yard = 3 feet.

Solution

1 yard = 3 feet

Dividing both sides of the equation by 1 yard: $1 = \dfrac{3\ feet}{1\ yard}$

Dividing both sides of the equation by 3 feet: $\dfrac{1\ yard}{3\ feet} = 1$

Therefore, the two conversion factors are $\dfrac{3\ feet}{1\ yard}$ and $\dfrac{1\ yard}{3\ feet}$.

Example 6.2-e	Using a Conversion Factor to Convert Units of Measurements

Convert 90 in. to feet. Use the relationship 1 foot = 12 inches.

Solution

90 in. to feet:

Step 1: Write the two conversion factors: $\dfrac{1\ foot}{12\ inches}$ and $\dfrac{12\ inches}{1\ foot}$

Step 2: Write the measurement to be converted: 90 inches

Step 3: Identify the correct conversion factor that will cancel the unit to be converted (in this case, the conversion factor that has the unit 'inches' in its denominator): $\dfrac{1\ foot}{12\ inches}$

Step 4: Multiply the measurement to be converted by this conversion factor:

$$90\ inches \times \frac{1\ foot}{12\ inches}$$

Step 5: Cross-cancel the units that appear in both the numerator and denominator and simplify the resulting fraction to get the answer:

$$90\ inches = 90\ \cancel{inches} \times \frac{1\ foot}{12\ \cancel{inches}}$$

$$= \left(\frac{90}{12}\right)\ feet$$

$$= 7.5\ feet$$

Therefore, 90 inches is equal to 7.5 feet.

The conversion factor method can be expanded to perform conversions in a single step. This is known as **dimensional analysis**.

For example, knowing that 1 foot = 12 inches and 1 yard = 3 feet, the conversion factor can be expanded as follows:

$$\frac{1 \text{ foot}}{12 \text{ inches}} \times \frac{1 \text{ yard}}{3 \text{ feet}}$$

When simplified, $\quad \dfrac{1 \text{ foot}}{12 \text{ inches}} \times \dfrac{1 \text{ yard}}{3 \text{ feet}} = \dfrac{1 \text{ yard}}{36 \text{ inches}}$

Therefore, this results in a new conversion factor of $\dfrac{1 \text{ yard}}{36 \text{ inches}}$; i.e., 1 yard = 36 inches.

Similarly, knowing that 1 tbsp = 3 tsp, 1 fl oz = 2 tbsp, and 1 cup = 8 fl oz, the conversion factor can be expanded as follows:

$$\frac{1 \text{ tbsp}}{3 \text{ tsp}} \times \frac{1 \text{ fl oz}}{2 \text{ tbsp}} \times \frac{1 \text{ cup}}{8 \text{ fl oz}}$$

When simplified,

$$\frac{1 \text{ tbsp}}{3 \text{ tsp}} \times \frac{1 \text{ fl oz}}{2 \text{ tbsp}} \times \frac{1 \text{ cup}}{8 \text{ fl oz}} = \frac{1 \text{ cup}}{48 \text{ tsp}}$$

Therefore, this results in a new conversion factor of $\dfrac{1 \text{ cup}}{48 \text{ tsp}}$; i.e., 1 cup = 48 tsp.

Example 6.2-f	Using Dimensional Analysis to Convert Units of Measurements

Convert the following measurements:

(i) 5.9 yd to inches (ii) 72 c to gallons (iii) 0.06 US ton to ounces

Solution

(i) 5.9 yd to inches:

Multiply with the conversion factors $\left(\dfrac{3 \text{ feet}}{1 \text{ yard}}\right)$ and $\left(\dfrac{12 \text{ inches}}{1 \text{ foot}}\right)$ to cross-cancel the units 'yd' and 'ft'.

$$5.9 \text{ yd} = 5.9 \text{ yards} \times \left(\frac{3 \text{ feet}}{1 \text{ yard}}\right) \times \left(\frac{12 \text{ inches}}{1 \text{ foot}}\right)$$

$$= 5.9 \times 3 \times 12 \text{ inches}$$

$$= 212.4 \text{ in}$$

Therefore, 5.9 yd is equal to 212.4 in.

(ii) 72 c to gallons:

Multiply with the conversion factors $\left(\dfrac{1 \text{ pint}}{2 \text{ cups}}\right)$, $\left(\dfrac{1 \text{ quart}}{2 \text{ pints}}\right)$, and $\left(\dfrac{1 \text{ gallon}}{4 \text{ quarts}}\right)$ to cross-cancel the units 'c', 'pt', and 'qt'.

$$72 \text{ c} = 72 \text{ cups} \times \left(\frac{1 \text{ pint}}{2 \text{ cups}}\right) \times \left(\frac{1 \text{ quart}}{2 \text{ pints}}\right) \times \left(\frac{1 \text{ gallon}}{4 \text{ quarts}}\right)$$

$$= \frac{72}{2 \times 2 \times 4} \text{ gallons}$$

$$= \frac{72}{16} \text{ gallons}$$

$$= 4.5 \text{ gal}$$

Therefore, 72 c is equal to 4.5 gal

(iii) 0.06 US ton to ounces:

Multiply with the conversion factors $\left(\dfrac{2{,}000 \text{ pounds}}{1 \text{ US ton}}\right)$ and $\left(\dfrac{16 \text{ ounces}}{1 \text{ pound}}\right)$ to cross-cancel the units 'US ton' and 'lb'.

$$0.06 \text{ US ton} = 0.06 \text{ US ton} \times \left(\frac{2{,}000 \text{ pounds}}{1 \text{ US ton}}\right) \times \left(\frac{16 \text{ ounces}}{1 \text{ pound}}\right)$$

$$= 0.06 \times 2{,}000 \times 16 \text{ ounces}$$

$$= 1{,}920 \text{ oz}$$

Therefore, 0.06 US ton is equal to 1,920 oz.

Proportion Method

When forming the proportion equation, the order in which the units of the terms in the ratio are written should be consistent on either side of the equation;

i.e., km : m = km : m

This is similar to the method learned in Chapter 5 (Ratios, Proportions, Percents, and Percent Changes). In this method, we equate two sets of ratios, where one of the ratios is formed from a given or known relationship. The second ratio is formed from the question asked, using the value for the unit to be converted and the unit required. These two ratios are equated to form the proportion equation, and the unknown unit is solved for by using cross-multiplication and simplification.

| Example 6.2-g | Using the Proportion Method to Convert Units of Measurements |

Convert the following measurements:

(i)   8.5 mi to feet (ii)   25 pt to gallons (iii)   0.9 US ton to pounds

Solution

(i)   8.5 mi to feet:

$$\text{mi} : \text{ft} = \text{mi} : \text{ft}$$

$$8.5 : x = 1 : 5{,}280 \qquad [\text{Using } 1 \text{ mi} = 5{,}280 \text{ ft}]$$

In fractional form, $\dfrac{8.5}{x} = \dfrac{1}{5{,}280}$

Cross-multiplying, $\quad x = 8.5 \times 5{,}280 = 44{,}880 \text{ ft}$

Therefore, 8.5 mi is equal to 44,880 ft.

(ii)   25 pt to gallons:

First, converting from pints to quarts,

$$\text{qt} : \text{pt} = \text{qt} : \text{pt}$$

$$x : 25 = 1 : 2 \qquad [\text{Using } 1 \text{ qt} = 2 \text{ pt}]$$

In fractional form, $\dfrac{x}{25} = \dfrac{1}{2}$

Cross-multiplying, $\quad 2x = 25$

$$x = \frac{25}{2} = 12.5 \text{ qt}$$

Therefore, 25 pt is equal to 12.5 qt.

Converting from quarts to gallons,

$$\text{gal} : \text{qt} = \text{gal} : \text{qt}$$

$$x : 12.5 = 1 : 4 \qquad [\text{Using } 1 \text{ gal} = 4 \text{ qt}]$$

In fractional form, $\dfrac{x}{12.5} = \dfrac{1}{4}$

Cross-multiplying, $\quad 4x = 12.5$

$$x = \frac{12.5}{4} = 3.125 \text{ gal}$$

Therefore, 25 pt is equal to 3.125 gal (25 pt = 12.5 qt = 3.125 gal).

(iii) 0.9 US ton to pounds:

$$\text{US ton} : \text{lb} = \text{US ton} : \text{lb}$$

$$0.9 : x = 1 : 2,000 \qquad [\text{Using 1 US ton} = 2,000 \text{ lb}]$$

In fractional form, $\dfrac{0.9}{x} = \dfrac{1}{2,000}$

Cross-multiplying, $\quad x = 0.9 \times 2,000 = 1,800 \text{ lb}$

Therefore, 0.9 US ton is equal to 1,800 lb.

Note: The Conversion Factor method (or dimensional analysis) is preferable over the Proportion method when two or more steps are involved in the conversion.

For example, converting 25 pt to gallons, as in Example 6.2-g (ii), can be more simply performed using dimensional analysis, as follows:

1st conversion factor from 1 qt = 2 pt

2nd conversion factor from 1 gal = 4 qt

$$25 \text{ pt} = 25 \text{ pt} \times \left(\frac{1 \text{ qt}}{2 \text{ pt}}\right) \times \left(\frac{1 \text{ gal}}{4 \text{ qt}}\right)$$

$$= \frac{25}{2 \times 4} \text{ gal} = 3.125 \text{ gal}$$

Example 6.2-h | **Converting Measurements in Word Problems**

(i) A PVC tube of length 10.5 yd is cut into seven equal pieces. Calculate the length of each piece, in feet and inches.

(ii) A mother gives birth to quadruplets, weighing 3 lb 4 oz, 3 lb 2 oz, 3 lb 5 oz, and 2 lb 15 oz, respectively. What is the total birth weight of the four babies?

Solution

(i) Since the answer needs to be measured in feet, convert all measurements into feet before doing any calculations.

$$\text{yd} : \text{ft} = \text{yd} : \text{ft}$$

$$10.5 : x = 1 : 3 \qquad [\text{Using 1 yd} = 3 \text{ ft}]$$

$$\frac{10.5}{x} = \frac{1}{3}$$

$$x = 10.5 \times 3 = 31.5 \text{ ft}$$

If the tube is cut into seven equal pieces, then the total length needs to be divided by seven.

$$\frac{31.5 \text{ ft}}{7} = 4.5 \text{ ft}$$

Now convert the decimal portion into inches:

$$4.5 \text{ ft} = 4 \text{ ft} + (0.5 \times 12) \text{ in} = 4 \text{ ft } 6 \text{ in}$$

Therefore, the length of each piece is 4 ft 6 in, or 4'6".

Note: It is also correct to divide the tube into seven pieces first, and then convert that length from yards to feet.

(ii) First add all the pounds and all the ounces individually:

$$3 \text{ lb} + 3 \text{ lb} + 3 \text{ lb} + 2 \text{ lb} = 11 \text{ lb}$$

$$4 \text{ oz} + 2 \text{ oz} + 5 \text{ oz} + 15 \text{ oz} = 26 \text{ oz}$$

Now convert 26 oz to lb and oz:

$$26 \text{ oz} = \frac{26}{16} \text{ lb} = 1\frac{10}{16} \text{ lb} = 1 \text{ lb } 10 \text{ oz}$$

Now add the two values together to get the total birth weight:

$$11 \text{ lb} + 1 \text{ lb } 10 \text{ oz} = 12 \text{ lb } 10 \text{ oz}$$

Therefore, the total weight of the four babies is 12 lb 10 oz.

6.2 | Exercises

Answers to odd-numbered problems are available at the end of the textbook.

Calculate the missing values in Problems 1 to 8.

1.

	yards (yd)	feet (ft)	inches (in.)
a.	42	?	?
b.	?	48	?
c.	?	?	648

2.

	yards (yd)	feet (ft)	inches (in.)
a.	84	?	?
b.	?	72	?
c.	?	?	540

3.

	yards (yd)	feet (ft)	inches (in.)
a.	46.5	?	?
b.	?	22.5	?
c.	?	?	2,880

4.

	yards (yd)	feet (ft)	inches (in.)
a.	67.5	?	?
b.	?	37.5	?
c.	?	?	3,960

5.

	miles (mi)	yards (yd)	feet (ft)
a.	3	?	?
b.	?	6,160	?
c.	?	?	10,560

6.

	miles (mi)	yards (yd)	feet (ft)
a.	2	?	?
b.	?	9,680	?
c.	?	?	18,480

7.

	miles (mi)	yards (yd)	feet (ft)
a.	2.25	?	?
b.	?	2,200	?
c.	?	?	6,192

8.

	miles (mi)	yards (yd)	feet (ft)
a.	42.5	?	?
b.	?	3,080	?
c.	?	?	25,080

In Problems 9 to 12, convert the measurements to the units indicated.

9. a. 12.5 yd = ___ ft   b. 11.83 ft = ___ in.   c. 1.07 mi = ___ yd

10. a. 17.5 yd = ___ ft   b. 12.92 ft = ___ in.   c. 2.03 mi = ___ yd

11. a. 78 ft = ___ yd   b. 570 in. = ___ ft   c. 5,705 yd = ___ mi

12. a. 56 ft = ___ yd   b. 420 in. = ___ ft   c. 7,350 yd = ___ mi

13. A child was 3 ft 8 in. tall in the beginning of the year, and by the end of the year had grown by another 7 in. Calculate the child's new height, in inches.

14. Suture thread comes in a roll that is 7 ft long. One piece measuring 2 ft 3 in. is cut from it. Calculate the length of the remaining portion of the thread, in inches.

15. A hospital bed frame requires 13.5 yd of steel cut into 9 equal pieces. Calculate the length of each piece, in feet.

16. A hospital driveway is 32 yd in length and has 12 equally spaced road markings. Calculate the length of each space, in feet.

17. The length of a river is 39,600 ft. Calculate the length of the river, in miles.

18. The height of a mountain is 81,840 ft. Calculate the height of the mountain, in miles.

Calculate the missing values in Problems 19 to 26.

19.

	pound (lb)	ounce (oz)
a.	?	288
b.	8	?

20.

	pound (lb)	ounce (oz)
a.	?	384
b.	12	?

21.

	pound (lb)	ounce (oz)
a.	?	232
b.	25.25	?

22.

	pound (lb)	ounce (oz)
a.	?	296
b.	19.75	?

23.

	US ton (ton)	pound (lb)
a.	35	?
b.	?	14,500

24.

	US ton (ton)	pound (lb)
a.	37	?
b.	?	23,500

25.

	US ton (ton)	pound (lb)
a.	12.75	?
b.	?	65,000

26.

	US ton (ton)	pound (lb)
a.	17.25	?
b.	?	47,000

In Problems 27 to 32, convert the measurements to the units indicated.

27. a. 11.625 lb = ____ oz   b. 2.625 ton = ____ lb

28. a. 9.187 lb = ____ oz   b. 5.5875 ton = ____ lb

29. a. 7 lb 9 oz = ____ oz   b. 142 oz = _____ lb _____ oz

30. a. 9 lb 11 oz = ____ oz   b. 121 oz = ____ lb ____ oz

31. a. 55,825 lb = ____ ton   b. 150 oz = ____ lb

32. a. 79,125 lb = ____ ton   b. 200 oz = ____ lb

33. Arrange the following measurements in order from largest to smallest:

   34,400 oz, 1.2 ton, 2,250 lb

34. Arrange the following measurements in order from smallest to largest:

   0.95 ton, 1,920 lb, 29,760 oz

35. A PVC tube weighing 2 lb 8 oz is cut into 8 equal portions. Calculate the mass of each piece, in ounces.

36. The mass of 12 cans of soft drink is 5 lb 4 oz. Calculate the mass of each can of soft drink, in ounces.

37. A mother gives birth to triplets, weighing 3 lb 11 oz, 3 lb 15 oz, and 3 lb 10 oz, respectively. Calculate their total combined birth weight and their average birth weight in pounds and ounces.

38. The average birth weight for a set of quadruplets was 2 lb 14 oz. If the first three babies delivered weighed 3 lb 1 oz, 2 lb 15 oz, and 2 lb 11 oz, respectively, determine the birth weight of the fourth baby that is delivered in pounds and ounces.

39. A hospital bought 1.25 tons of hand sanitizer over the course of a year. If it is ordered in bottles weighing 2.5 pounds each, calculate the number of bottles that the hospital purchased in the year.

40. A bookstore received a shipment of 1,600 chemistry textbooks. The total mass of the shipment is 2.2 tons. Calculate the weight of each book, in pounds.

Calculate the missing values in Problems 41 to 48.

41.

	quart (qt)	pint (pt)	cup (c)
a.	22	?	?
b.	?	38	?
c.	?	?	68

42.

	quart (qt)	pint (pt)	cup (c)
a.	28	?	?
b.	?	26	?
c.	?	?	74

43.	quart (qt)	pint (pt)	cup (c)
a.	32.5	?	?
b.	?	45	?
c.	?	?	94

44.	quart (qt)	pint (pt)	cup (c)
a.	47.5	?	?
b.	?	51	?
c.	?	?	102

45.	gallon (gal)	quart (qt)	pint (pt)
a.	12	?	?
b.	?	18	?
c.	?	?	56

46.	gallon (gal)	quart (qt)	pint (pt)
a.	15	?	?
b.	?	24	?
c.	?	?	64

47.	gallon (gal)	quart (qt)	pint (pt)
a.	7.5	?	?
b.	?	14	?
c.	?	?	50

48.	gallon (gal)	quart (qt)	pint (pt)
a.	9.5	?	?
b.	?	22	?
c.	?	?	30

In Problems 49 to 52, convert the measurements to the units indicated.

49. a. 9.5 qt = ___ pt   b. 16.5 qt = ___ c   c. 12.25 gal = ___ qt   d. 6 fl oz = ___ c

50. a. 14.5 qt = ___ pt   b. 27.5 pt = ___ c   c. 17.25 gal = ___ qt   d. 8 tbsp = ___ c

51. a. 19 pt = ___ qt   b. 39 c = ___ pt   c. 6 tbsp = ___ tsp   d. 90 tbsp ___ fl oz

52. a. 23 pt = ___ qt   b. 55 c = ___ pt   c. 89 tsp = ___ tbsp   d. 7 fl oz = ___ tsp

53. Arrange the following measurements in order from smallest to largest:
    29 c, 6 qt, 14 pt, 2 gal

54. Arrange the following measurements in order from largest to smallest:
    45 c, 23 pt, 10 qt, 3 gal

55. Mythili drinks 2 cups of milk every day. How many gallons of milk will she require for a month of 30 days?

56. If a baby requires 24 fl oz of milk on average everyday, how many cups of milk will be required for a week?

57. An IV solution container had 6 qt of solution. If 15 cups of IV solution was used from the container, how many cups of IV solution is left in the container?

58. A water jug contained 18 qt of spring water. If 25 pints of water was used from the jug, how many pints of water remain in the jug?

6.3 | Conversion Between Metric and US Customary Units

Conversion of units between the metric and US Customary systems is achieved by using conversion tables and either the conversion factor method (i.e., dimensional analysis) or the proportion method discussed in Section 6.2. For the examples in this section, the conversion factor approach will be used.

Conversion tables between the commonly used metric and US Customary and Household units of measurement are provided below (all the conversions provided are from US to metric, as metric is the preferred system of measurement in Canada - there is a quick metric to US conversion table provided on page 239).

Length

- **Metric units:** kilometre (km), metre (m), centimetre (cm), and millimetre (mm)
- **US Customary units:** mile (mi), yard (yd), foot (ft), and inch (in.)

Conversion Table

US Customary Units	Metric Units
1 mi	1.609 km
1 yd	0.9144 m
1 ft	30.48 cm
1 in.	**2.54 cm**

1 in. = 2.54 cm is an exact conversion. All other conversions in the table are based on this.

Example 6.3-a | **Converting Metric Units of Length to US Customary Units**

Convert the following measurements (round your answers to the nearest hundredth, as appropriate):

(i)   250 cm to inches   (ii)   45 m to feet

Solution

(i)   250 cm to inches:

Use $\left(\dfrac{1 \text{ in}}{2.54 \text{ cm}}\right)$ as the conversion factor to cross-cancel the unit 'cm'.

$$250 \text{ cm} = 250 \text{ cm} \times \left(\frac{1 \text{ in}}{2.54 \text{ cm}}\right)$$

$$= \frac{250}{2.54} \text{ in}$$

$$= 98.425196\ldots = 98.43 \text{ in}$$

Therefore, 250 cm is equal to 98.43 in.

(ii)   45 m to feet:

Use $\left(\dfrac{100 \text{ cm}}{1 \text{ m}}\right)$ as the first conversion factor to cross-cancel the unit 'm' and $\left(\dfrac{1 \text{ ft}}{30.48 \text{ cm}}\right)$ as the second conversion factor to cross-cancel the unit 'cm'.

$$45 \text{ m} = 45 \text{ m} \times \left(\frac{100 \text{ cm}}{1 \text{ m}}\right) \times \left(\frac{1 \text{ ft}}{30.48 \text{ cm}}\right)$$

$$= \frac{45 \times 100}{30.48} \text{ ft}$$

$$= 147.637795\ldots = 147.64 \text{ ft}$$

Therefore, 45 m is equal to 147.64 ft.

Example 6.3-b | **Converting US Customary Units of Length to Metric Units**

Convert the following measurements:

(i)   2.5 in. to centimetres   (ii)   8.75 yd to centimetres

Solution

(i)   2.5 in. to centimetres:

Use $\left(\dfrac{2.54 \text{ cm}}{1 \text{ in}}\right)$ as the conversion factor to cross-cancel the unit 'in.'

$$2.5 \text{ in} = 2.5 \text{ in} \times \left(\frac{2.54 \text{ cm}}{1 \text{ in}}\right)$$

$$= 2.5 \times 2.54 \text{ cm}$$

$$= 6.35 \text{ cm}$$

Therefore, 2.5 in. is equal to 6.35 cm.

(ii) 8.75 yd to centimetres:

Use $\left(\dfrac{0.9144 \text{ m}}{1 \text{ yd}}\right)$ as the first conversion factor to cross-cancel the unit 'yd' and $\left(\dfrac{100 \text{ cm}}{1 \text{ m}}\right)$ as the second conversion factor to cross-cancel the unit 'm'.

$$8.75 \text{ yd} = 8.75 \cancel{\text{ yd}} \times \left(\dfrac{0.9144 \cancel{\text{ m}}}{1 \cancel{\text{ yd}}}\right) \times \left(\dfrac{100 \text{ cm}}{1 \cancel{\text{ m}}}\right)$$

$$= 8.75 \times 0.9144 \times 100 \text{ cm}$$

$$= 800.1 \text{ cm}$$

Therefore, 8.75 yd is equal to 800.1 cm.

Mass

- **Metric units:** kilogram (kg), gram (g), and milligram (mg)
- **US Customary units:** US ton (ton), pound (lb), and ounce (oz)

Conversion Table

The approximate conversion 1 kg = 2.2 lb is commonly used for quick calculations.

US Customary Units	Metric Units
1 ton	907.2 kg
1 lb	0.4536 kg
1 oz	28.35 g

Example 6.3-c	Converting Metric Units of Mass to US Customary Units

Convert the following measurements (round your answers to the nearest hundredth, as appropriate):

(i)   2.5 kg to pounds   (ii)   400 g to ounces

Solution

(i)   2.5 kg to pounds:

Use $\left(\dfrac{1 \text{ lb}}{0.4536 \text{ kg}}\right)$ as the conversion factor to cross-cancel the unit 'kg'.

$$2.5 \text{ kg} = 2.5 \cancel{\text{ kg}} \times \left(\dfrac{1 \text{ lb}}{0.4536 \cancel{\text{ kg}}}\right)$$

$$= \dfrac{2.5}{0.4536} \text{ lb}$$

$$= 5.511463\ldots = 5.51 \text{ lb}$$

Therefore, 2.5 kg is equal to 5.51 lb.

(ii)   400 g to ounces:

Use $\left(\dfrac{1 \text{ oz}}{28.35 \text{ g}}\right)$ as the conversion factor to cross-cancel the unit 'g'.

$$400 \text{ g} = 400 \cancel{\text{ g}} \times \left(\dfrac{1 \text{ oz}}{28.35 \cancel{\text{ g}}}\right)$$

$$= \dfrac{400}{28.35} \text{ oz}$$

$$= 14.109347\ldots = 14.11 \text{ oz}$$

Therefore, 400 g is equal to 14.11 oz.

Example 6.3-d   **Converting US Customary Units of Mass to Metric Units**

Convert the following measurements (round your answers to the nearest hundredth, as appropriate):

(i)   1.75 lb to grams   (ii)   225 oz to kilograms

Solution

(i)   1.75 lb to grams:

Use $\left(\dfrac{0.4536\ \text{kg}}{1\ \text{lb}}\right)$ as the first conversion factor to cross-cancel the unit 'lb' and $\left(\dfrac{1{,}000\ \text{g}}{1\ \text{kg}}\right)$ as the second conversion factor to cross-cancel the unit 'kg'.

$$1.75\ \text{lb} = 1.75\ \cancel{\text{lb}} \times \left(\frac{0.4536\ \cancel{\text{kg}}}{1\ \cancel{\text{lb}}}\right) \times \left(\frac{1{,}000\ \text{g}}{1\ \cancel{\text{kg}}}\right)$$

$$= 1.75 \times 0.4536 \times 1{,}000\ \text{g}$$

$$= 793.8\ \text{g}$$

Therefore, 1.75 lb is equal to 793.8 g.

(ii)   225 oz to kilograms:

Use $\left(\dfrac{28.35\ \text{g}}{1\ \text{oz}}\right)$ as the first conversion factor to cross-cancel the unit 'oz' and $\left(\dfrac{1\ \text{kg}}{1{,}000\ \text{g}}\right)$ as the second conversion factor to cross-cancel the unit 'g'.

$$225\ \text{oz} = 225\ \cancel{\text{oz}} \times \left(\frac{28.35\ \cancel{\text{g}}}{1\ \cancel{\text{oz}}}\right) \times \left(\frac{1\ \text{kg}}{1{,}000\ \cancel{\text{g}}}\right)$$

$$= \frac{225 \times 28.35}{1{,}000}\ \text{kg}$$

$$= 6.37875 = 6.38\ \text{kg}$$

Therefore, 225 oz is equal to 6.38 kg.

Capacity

- **Metric units:** litre (L), and millilitre (mL)

- **US Customary units:** gallon (gal), quart (qt), pint (pt), cup (c), and fluid ounce (fl oz)

Conversion Table

Approximate household unit conversions for quick calculations:

1 tbsp = 15 mL

1 tsp = 5 mL

US Customary Units	Metric Units
1 gal	3.785 L
1 qt	0.9464 L
1 pt	473.2 mL
1 c	236.6 mL
1 fl oz	29.57 mL

Example 6.3-e **Converting Metric Units of Capacity to US Customary Units**

Convert the following measurements (round your answers to the nearest hundredth, as appropriate):

(i)   60 L to gallons

(ii)   425 mL to fluid ounces

Solution

(i)   60 L to gallons:

Use $\left(\dfrac{1 \text{ gal}}{3.785 \text{ L}}\right)$ as the conversion factor to cross-cancel the unit 'L'.

$$60 \text{ L} = 60 \text{ L} \times \left(\frac{1 \text{ gal}}{3.785 \text{ L}}\right)$$

$$= \frac{60}{3.785} \text{ gal}$$

$$= 15.852047... = 15.85 \text{ gal}$$

Therefore, 60 L is equal to 15.85 gal.

(ii)   425 mL to fluid ounces:

Use $\left(\dfrac{1 \text{ fl oz}}{29.57 \text{ mL}}\right)$ as the conversion factor to cross-cancel the unit 'mL'.

$$425 \text{ mL} = 425 \text{ mL} \times \left(\frac{1 \text{ fl oz}}{29.57 \text{ mL}}\right)$$

$$= \frac{425}{29.57} \text{ fl oz}$$

$$= 14.372675... \ 14.37 \text{ fl oz}$$

Therefore, 425 mL is equal to 14.37 fl oz.

Example 6.3-f **Converting US Customary Units of Capacity to Metric Units**

Convert the following measurements (round your answers to the nearest hundredth, as appropriate):

(i)   2.5 gal to litres

(ii)   30 fl oz to millilitres

Solution

(i)   2.5 gal to litres:

Use $\left(\dfrac{3.785 \text{ L}}{1 \text{ gal}}\right)$ as the conversion factor to cross-cancel the unit 'gal'.

$$2.5 \text{ gal} = 2.5 \text{ gal} \times \left(\frac{3.785 \text{ L}}{1 \text{ gal}}\right)$$

$$= 2.5 \times 3.785 \text{ L}$$

$$= 9.4625 = 9.46 \text{ L}$$

Therefore, 2.5 gal is equal to 9.46 L.

(ii)   30 fl oz to millilitres:

Use $\left(\dfrac{29.57 \text{ mL}}{1 \text{ fl oz}}\right)$ as the conversion factor to cross-cancel the unit 'fl oz'.

$$30 \text{ fl oz} = 30 \text{ fl oz} \times \left(\frac{29.57 \text{ mL}}{1 \text{ fl oz}}\right)$$

$$= 30 \times 29.57 \text{ mL}$$

$$= 887.1 \text{ mL}$$

Therefore, 30 fl oz is equal to 887.1 mL.

Quick Metric to US Customary Conversions

The following approximate conversions from metric units to US Customary units are useful to conceptualize the magnitude of the US Customary units.

- 1 km is a little more than half a mile (1 km ≈ 0.6 mi).

- 1 m is a little more than a yard, or 3 feet (1 m ≈ 1.1 yd, or 3.3 ft).

- 1 cm is a little less than half an inch (1 cm ≈ 0.4 in.).

- 1 kg is a little more than 2 pounds (1 kg ≈ 2.2 lb).

- 1 L is a little more than a quart (1 L ≈ 1.1 qt).

Note: Do **not** use these approximate conversions in the Exercise Problems in this chapter. Use the exact conversions as given in the length, mass, and capacity Conversion Tables in this section.

6.3 | Exercises

Answers to odd-numbered problems are available at the end of the textbook.

For the following problems, express the answers rounded to two decimal places, wherever applicable.

Calculate the missing values in Problems 1 to 12.

1.

	Metric Units	US Customary Units
a.	250 km	? mi
b.	? km	120 mi

2.

	Metric Units	US Customary Units
a.	175 km	? mi
b.	? km	80 mi

3.

	Metric Units	US Customary Units
a.	17.5 m	? yd
b.	? m	22 yd

4.

	Metric Units	US Customary Units
a.	11 m	? yd
b.	? m	12.5 yd

5.

	Metric Units	US Customary Units
a.	250 m	? ft
b.	? m	75 ft

6.

	Metric Units	US Customary Units
a.	12 m	? ft
b.	? m	45.5 ft

7.

	Metric Units	US Customary Units
a.	100 cm	? in.
b.	? cm	3.5 in.

8.

	Metric Units	US Customary Units
a.	80 cm	? in.
b.	? cm	7.5 in.

9.

	Metric Units	US Customary Units
a.	250 cm	? ft
b.	? cm	120 ft

10.

	Metric Units	US Customary Units
a.	175 cm	? ft
b.	? cm	80 ft

11.

	Metric Units	US Customary Units
a.	175 mm	? in
b.	? mm	5.25 in

12.

	Metric Units	US Customary Units
a.	110 mm	? in
b.	? mm	12.5 in

13. Arrange the following measurements in order from largest to smallest:

    82.5 ft, 900 in., 4,250 cm, 28 yd, 24 m

14. Arrange the following measurements in order from smallest to largest:

    1,280 cm, 44 ft, 15 yd, 450 in., 12 m

15. June bought 5.5 metres of elastic bandage wrap and used 10 feet of it. Calculate the remaining quantity of bandage wrap, in metres.

16. A gel electrophoresis machine is 10 inches long. It is divided into 5 lanes of equal length. Calculate the length of each lane, in centimetres.

17. The distance from Toronto to Gatineau, Quebec is 320 km. After driving 100 miles from Toronto, calculate the distance left to reach Gatineau, in kilometres, rounded to the nearest whole kilometre.

18. The distance from Niagara Falls to New York is 410 miles. After driving 550 kilometres from Niagara Falls, what is the distance to be travelled, in kilometres, to reach New York (rounded to the nearest whole kilometre)?

Calculate the missing values in Problems 19 to 26.

19.

	Metric Units	US Customary Units
a.	3,500 kg	? tons
b.	? kg	2.5 tons

20.

	Metric Units	US Customary Units
a.	4,250 kg	? tons
b.	? kg	4 tons

21.

	Metric Units	US Customary Units
a.	15.5 kg	? lb
b.	? kg	45 lb

22.

	Metric Units	US Customary Units
a.	70 kg	? lb
b.	? kg	135.5 lb

23.

	Metric Units	US Customary Units
a.	1,200 g	? lb
b.	? g	6.5 lb

24.

	Metric Units	US Customary Units
a.	750 g	? lb
b.	? g	4.5 lb

25.

	Metric Units	US Customary Units
a.	200 g	? oz
b.	? g	4 oz

26.

	Metric Units	US Customary Units
a.	175 g	? oz
b.	? g	2.5 oz

27. Arrange the following measurements in order from largest to smallest:
2.5 kg, 2,450 g, 5.7 lb, 80 oz

28. Arrange the following measurements in order from smallest to largest:
4.5 kg, 4,560 g, 9.5 lb, 155 oz

29. A hospital supplier purchased 2 pounds of ziprasidone, which comes in 40 mg tablets. If 7,500 tablets are dispensed over the course of the month, how many grams of the medication remain?

30. A patient requires 0.25 mg of alprazolam 3 times a day. There are 160 patients in the hospital who require alprazolam, and the hospital pharmacy has a supply of 0.5 oz of the medication. How many grams of the supply will remain after 30 days?

31. William weighs 80 kg. His brother, Klaas, weighs 25 pounds less than him. Calculate Klaas' weight, in kg.

32. A medical equipment bag weighs 2.25 kg. The total weight of the bag with its contents is 50 pounds. Calculate the weight of the contents in the bag, in kg.

33. A baby weighs 8 lb 12 oz at birth. Calculate the baby's weight in kilograms.

34. A baby weighs 5.5 kg at birth. Calculate the baby's weight in pounds and ounces.

Calculate the missing values in Problems 35 to 46.

35.

	Metric Units	US Customary Units
a.	50 L	? gal
b.	? L	10.5 gal

36.

	Metric Units	US Customary Units
a.	25.5 L	? gal
b.	? L	30 gal

37.

	Metric Units	US Customary Units
a.	15 L	? qt
b.	? L	14 qt

38.

	Metric Units	US Customary Units
a.	22 L	? qt
b.	? L	12 qt

39.

	Metric Units	US Customary Units
a.	7.5 L	? pt
b.	? L	14 pt

40.

	Metric Units	US Customary Units
a.	6 L	? pt
b.	? L	10.5 pt

41.

	Metric Units	US Customary Units
a.	4.5 L	? c
b.	? L	14 c

42.

	Metric Units	US Customary Units
a.	5 L	? c
b.	? L	18 c

43.	Metric Units	US Customary Units
a.	8 mL	? fl oz
b.	? mL	20.5 fl oz

44.	Metric Units	US Customary Units
a.	3.5 mL	? fl oz
b.	? mL	15 fl oz

45.	Metric Units	US Customary Units
a.	500 mL	? c
b.	? mL	3.5 c

46.	Metric Units	US Customary Units
a.	150 mL	? c
b.	? mL	0.25 c

47. Arrange the following measurements in order from largest to smallest:
3.5 L, 4.8 qt, 10.5 pt, 1 gal

48. Arrange the following measurements in order from smallest to largest.
7.5 L, 8.5 qt, 15 pt, 1.7 gal

49. A recipe calls for 2.5 tbsp of olive oil. If the bottle contains 250 mL of olive oil, how many mL of oil remain if the recipe is tripled?

50. The fuel tank of a rapid response vehicle can hold 18 gallons. It is 2/3 empty. Calculate the volume of the fuel in the tank, in litres.

51. There are ten bags of blood with each storing 3.5 fl oz. If 1 L of blood is used, calculate the remaining amount of blood, in fl oz.

52. A bottle of cough syrup has a capacity of 250 mL. If you take 3 tsp two times a day for 3 days, how much cough syrup is left in mL?

6.4 | Conversion of Temperature Scales

Temperature is a system of measurement that allows us to express how hot or cold an object or environment is. It is most useful as a relative scale, which allows us to make comparisons between two different temperature values using convenient numbers, but that cannot be compared with ratios. As such, temperature is typically measured in **degrees**, which refers to a relative scale as opposed to an absolute scale. There are three common scales when measuring temperature:

(1) °C, the Celsius scale

(2) °F, the Fahrenheit scale

(3) K, the Kelvin scale

The first two, Celsius and Fahrenheit, are relative (i.e., degree) scales that are used for common purposes, while the third scale, Kelvin, is an absolute (i.e., true) scale that is used for scientific purposes, and is part of the SI units of measurement.

Celsius and Fahrenheit Scales

The Celsius scale (°C) is the temperature scale used within the metric system, and is the standard used by most countries, including Canada. This scale, named for Swedish astronomer Anders Celsius, is derived from the basis that pure water, at sea level pressure, freezes at 0 °C and boils at 100 °C; it is for this reason that it was originally called the "centigrade" (meaning "hundred steps") scale. Hence, each °C is exactly one hundredth of the thermodynamic change between the freezing point and the boiling point of pure water at sea level pressure.

The Fahrenheit scale (°F), on the other hand, is primarily used in the U.S. It is named for the German physicist Daniel Gabriel Fahrenheit, and is derived from the basis that pure water, at sea level pressure, freezes at 32 °F and boils at 212 °F.

Therefore, the difference between the freezing and boiling points of water is 100 °C (100 °C − 0 °C) and 180 °F (212 °F − 32 °F).

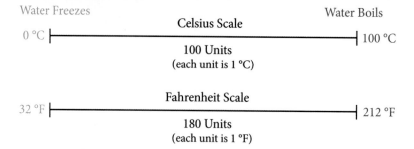

Water Freezes   Celsius Scale   Water Boils

0 °C ⊢————————————————————⊣ 100 °C

100 Units
(each unit is 1 °C)

Fahrenheit Scale

32 °F ⊢————————————————————⊣ 212 °F

180 Units
(each unit is 1 °F)

100 units in the Celsius scale, starting from 0 °C, is equivalent to 180 units in the Fahrenheit scale, starting from 32 °F.

Therefore, to convert from °C to °F, multiply °C by a factor of $\dfrac{180}{100} = \dfrac{9}{5} = 1.8$ and add 32 °F.

$$°F = 1.8(°C) + 32 \quad \text{or} \quad °F = \dfrac{9}{5}(°C) + 32$$

Similarly, to convert from °F to °C, subtract 32 °F and divide by 1.8 (or multiply by $\dfrac{5}{9}$).

$$°C = \dfrac{(°F - 32)}{1.8} \quad \text{or} \quad °C = \dfrac{5}{9}(°F - 32)$$

Conversion Table

Normal body temperature is about 37 °C or 98.6 °F.

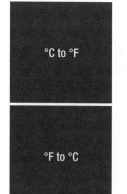

| °C to °F | $°F = 1.8(°C) + 32$ **or** $°F = \dfrac{9}{5}(°C) + 32$ |
| °F to °C | $°C = \dfrac{(°F - 32)}{1.8}$ **or** $°C = \dfrac{5}{9}(°F - 32)$ |

Example 6.4-a   **Converting Between the Celsius (°C) Scale and Fahrenheit (°F) Scale**

Convert the following (round to the nearest hundredth, as needed):

(i)   25 °C to Fahrenheit   (ii)   90 °F to Celsius

Solution

(i)   25 °C to Fahrenheit:

$$°F = 1.8(°C) + 32$$
$$= 1.8(25) + 32$$
$$= 77 \text{ °F}$$

Therefore, 25 °C is equal to 77 °F.

(ii)   90 °F to Celsius:

$$°C = \dfrac{(°F - 32)}{1.8}$$
$$= \dfrac{(90 - 32)}{1.8}$$
$$= 32.222222... = 32.22 \text{ °C}$$

Therefore, 90 °F is equal to 32.22 °C.

Example 6.4-b | **Comparing Temperatures Measured Using Different Scales**

Which is the higher temperature: 80 °C or 175 °F?

Solution

Convert 80 °C to °F and compare with 175 °F.

$$°F = 1.8(°C) + 32$$
$$= 1.8(80) + 32$$
$$= 176 °F$$

i.e., 80 °C = 176 °F > 175 °F

i.e., 80 °C > 175 °F

or

Convert 175 °F to °C and compare with 80 °C.

$$°C = \frac{(°F - 32)}{1.8} = \frac{(175 - 32)}{1.8}$$
$$= 79.444444... = 79.44 °C$$

i.e., 175 °F = 79.44 °C < 80 °C

i.e., 80 °C > 175 °F

Therefore, 80 °C is a (slightly) higher temperature than 175 °F.

Kelvin Scale

Another unit of measure for temperature is the **Kelvin scale**, which is an absolute temperature scale, meaning that its zero point is "absolute zero", at which point there is a complete absence of heat energy and all molecules cease to move. It is named for the U.K. engineer and physicist William Thomson, 1st Baron Kelvin. The Kelvin scale is frequently used in physics and chemistry, because, since it's an absolute scale, the values represent temperatures that can be compared using ratios, and there will never be negative numbers. Its unit is the **Kelvin**, symbolized using K (not °K), which is the base unit of temperature in the S.I. units of measurement, and is equal in magnitude to 1 °C.

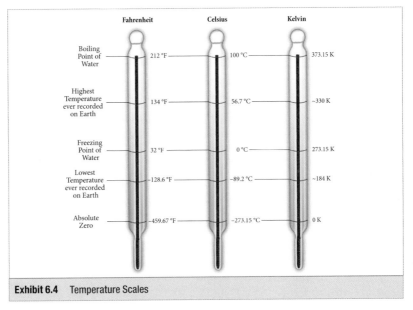

Exhibit 6.4 **Temperature Scales**

To convert between Celsius (°C) and Kelvin (K) measurements and to convert between Fahrenheit (°F) and Kelvin (K), use the conversion tables below.

Conversion Table

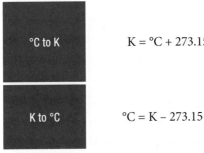

°C to K	K = °C + 273.15
K to °C	°C = K − 273.15

°F to K
$$K = \frac{(°F - 32)}{1.8} + 273.15 \quad \textbf{or}$$
$$K = \frac{5}{9}(°F - 32) + 273.15$$

K to °F
$$°F = 1.8(K - 273.15) + 32 \quad \textbf{or}$$
$$°F = \frac{9}{5}(K - 273.15) + 32$$

Example 6.4-c **Converting Between the Celsius (°C) , Fahrenheit (°F), and Kelvin (K) Scales**

Convert the following (round to the nearest hundredth, as needed):

(i)   25 °C to Kelvin   (ii)   300 K to Celsius   (iii)   75 °F to Kelvin   (iv)   350 K to Fahrenheit

Solution

(i)   25 °C to Kelvin:

$$K = °C + 273.15$$
$$= 25 + 273.15$$
$$= 298.15 \text{ K}$$

Therefore, 25 °C is equal to 298.15 K.

(ii)   300 K to Celsius:

$$°C = K - 273.15$$
$$= 300 - 273.15$$
$$= 26.85 \text{ °C}$$

Therefore, 300 K is equal to 26.85 °C.

(iii)   75 °F to Kelvin:

$$K = \frac{(°F - 32)}{1.8} + 273.15$$
$$= \frac{(75 - 32)}{1.8} + 273.15$$
$$= \frac{43}{1.8} + 273.15$$
$$= 297.038888... = 297.04 \text{ K}$$

Therefore, 75 °F is equal to 297.04 K.

(iv)   350 K to Fahrenheit:

$$°F = 1.8(K - 273.15) + 32$$
$$= 1.8(350 - 273.15) + 32$$
$$= 1.8(76.85) + 32$$
$$= 170.33 \text{ °F}$$

Therefore, 350 K is equal to 170.33 °F.

Comparison Among Temperature Scales

The following table provides a comparison among the temperature scales.

Table 6.4   **Comparison Among Temperature Scales**

Temperature Scales			Description
Fahrenheit	Celsius	Kelvin	
212 °F	100 °C	373.15 K	Boiling point of water at sea level
134 °F	56.7 °C	329.85 K	Highest recorded temperature on Earth: Death Valley, USA in 1913
113 °F	45 °C	318.15 K	Highest recorded temperature in Canada: Yellow Grass, SK in 1937
98.6 °F	37 °C	310.15 K	Average human body temperature
86 °F	30 °C	303.15 K	Hot summer day in Canada
73.4 °F	23 °C	296.15 K	Average room temperature
59 °F	15 °C	288.15 K	Mild spring day in Canada
32 °F	0 °C	273.15 K	Freezing point of water at sea level
14 °F	−10 °C	263.15 K	Cold winter day in Canada
−4 °F	−20 °C	253.15 K	Extreme cold advisory
− 81.4 °F	− 63 °C	210.15 K	Lowest recorded temperature in Canada: Snag, Yukon in 1947
− 128.6 °F	− 89.2 °C	183.95 K	Lowest recorded temperature on Earth: Vostok, Antarctica in 1983
− 459.67 °F	− 273.15 °C	0 K	Absolute zero

For the following problems, express the answers rounded to two decimal places, wherever applicable.

In Problems 1 to 24, convert the temperatures.

1. 21 °C = ___ °F
2. 10 °C = ___ °F
3. 98.6 °F = ___ °C
4. 85 °F = ___ °C
5. 140 °C = ___ °F
6. 180 °C = ___ °F
7. −15 °F = ___ °C
8. −40 °F = ___ °C
9. 280 K = ___ °C
10. 260 K = ___ °C
11. 19 °C = ___ K
12. −10 °C = ___ K
13. 300 K = ___ °C
14. 250 K = ___ °C
15. −20 °C = ___ K
16. 35 °C = ___ K
17. 50 °F = ___ K
18. 100 °F = ___ K
19. 600 K = ___ °F
20. 350 K = ___ °F
21. −80 °F = ___ K
22. 25 K = ___ °F
23. −22 °F = ___ K
24. −40 °F = ___ K

25. Arrange the following temperatures in order from highest to lowest:

    56 °F, 24 °C, 300 K

26. Arrange the following temperatures in order from highest to lowest:

    232 K, −34 °F, −40 °C,

27. Arrange the following temperatures in order from highest to lowest:

    78 °C, 345 K, 110 °F

28. Arrange the following temperatures in order from highest to lowest:

    −5 °C, −2 °F, 11 K

29. Arrange the following temperatures in order from highest to lowest:

    −49 °F, 229 K, −46 °C

30. Arrange the following temperatures in order from highest to lowest:

    173 °F, 90°C, 350 K

31. The average temperature of a morgue is 3 °C. Calculate the temperature, in °F.

32. Sarah is conducting an experiment. Her instructions say to set the burner to 45 °F, but her hot plate is measured in °C. Calculate the temperature in °C.

33. A medical container is kept at a temperature of 144 K. Calculate the temperature in °C.

34. In a research facility, bacteria is killed at a temperature of 80 °C. Calculate this temperature in K.

35. A child comes to the hospital with a fever of 38 °C. Another patient has a fever of 103 °F. Which patient has the higher fever?

36. One mortuary cold chamber has a temperature of 32 °F, while another chamber has a temperature of −4 °C. Which chamber is colder?

37. Dry ice is formed at −78.5 °C. Convert the temperature into Kelvin.

38. Bacteria is heated to 200 °F. Convert the temperature into °Celsius.

39. A fatal body temperature for a human is 108 °F. A patient's temperature is 40 °C. Is she close to the danger point?

40. If a certain type of protein denatures at 41 °C, and a solution containing some of these proteins is heated to 115 °F, is the solution denatured?

6.5 | Roman Numerals

Roman numerals were used in Ancient Rome to depict numbers. The system was used for several centuries after the Roman Empire declined. In our daily lives, we use decimal numbers comprised of the digits 0 to 9 to do most of our mathematical activities. However, there are still many applications of Roman numerals in today's society. A few examples of this include on faces of analog clocks, names of monarchs and popes (e.g., Queen Elizabeth II, Pope Benedict XVI), and names of large sporting events (e.g., the XXI Olympic Winter Games in Vancouver, Super Bowl LI).

Face on an analog clock	Queen Elizabeth II	Superbowl LI (51)

Exhibit 6.5   Examples of Roman Numerals in Today's Society

In the health care field, Roman numerals are often found in prescriptions for drug dosages and medical records and charts.

The Roman numeral system is based on seven symbols: I, V, X, L, C, D, and M. Numbers under 30 are usually expressed in lowercase form and numbers 30 and above are usually written in uppercase form.

How can you remember the Roman numerals, in descending order? Think...

MeDiCaL XaVIer

Roman Numeral	M	D	C	L	X	V	I	ss
Decimal Number	1,000	500	100	50	10	5	1	0.5

	Count by Ones		Count by Tens		Count by Hundreds
1	I	10	X	100	C
2	II	20	XX	200	CC
3	III	30	XXX	300	CCC
4	IV (not IIII)	40	XL (not XXXX)	400	CD (not CCCC)
5	V	50	L	500	D
6	VI	60	LX	600	DC
7	VII	70	LXX	700	DCC
8	VIII	80	LXXX	800	DCCC
9	IX (not VIIII)	90	XC (not LXXXX)	900	CM (not DCCCC)
10	X	100	C	1,000	M

Converting from Decimal Numbers to Roman Numerals

To write a decimal number using Roman numerals, first write the number in its expanded form and convert the digit in each place value, one at a time, starting with the highest place value, according to the following guidelines:

- The numerals representing the "ones" (i.e., I (i), X (x), C, and M) can be written sequentially up to a maximum of three times, either by themselves to represent the digits 1, 2, or 3 (e.g., 3 = iii, 20 = xx, 300 = CCC), or following a "five" to represent the digits 6, 7, or 8 (e.g., 6 = 5 + 1 = vi, 80 = 50 + 30 = LXXX, 700 = 500 + 200 = DCC).
- The numerals representing the "fives" (i.e., V (v), L, and D) cannot be used more than once (e.g., 15 = xv, not vvv).
- To build "fours", instead of writing a sequence of four numerals, write one of those numerals in front of the corresponding "five" of that numeral, which indicates that it's being subtracted (e.g., 4 = 5 – 1 = iv, 40 = 50 – 10 = XL, 400 = 500 – 100 = CD, etc.).
- Similarly, to build "nines", write one of the numerals in front of the corresponding "ten" of that numeral, (e.g., 9 = 10 – 1 = ix, 90 = 100 – 10 = XC, 900 = 1,000 – 100 = CM, etc.).

'I' can only precede 'V' and 'X';

'X' can only precede 'L' and 'C';

'C' can only precede 'D' and 'M';

'V', 'L', 'D' can never precede a larger numeral;

e.g., 99 = XCIX (90 + 9), not IC.

Note: *Anytime a smaller numeral precedes a larger numeral, it **always** indicates that it is being subtracted.*

For larger values, a bar over the Roman numeral represents the value multiplied by 1,000:

4,000 is represented as $\overline{IV}$ (not MMMM);

6,000 is represented as $\overline{VI}$.

- $\overline{V} = 5 \times 1,000 = 5,000$
- $\overline{X} = 10 \times 1,000 = 10,000$
- $\overline{L} = 50 \times 1,000 = 50,000$

- $\overline{C} = 100 \times 1,000 = 100,000$
- $\overline{D} = 500 \times 1,000 = 500,000$
- $\overline{M} = 1,000 \times 1,000 = 1,000,000$

For example,

$$1,437 = \quad 1,000 \quad + \quad (500 - 100) \quad + \quad 30 \quad + \quad (5 + 2)$$
$$\downarrow \qquad\qquad \downarrow \qquad\qquad \downarrow \qquad\quad \downarrow$$
$$M \quad + \quad CD \quad + \quad XXX \quad + \quad VII \quad = \quad MCDXXXVII$$

Example 6.5-a	Converting Decimal Numbers to Roman Numerals

Convert the following decimal numbers into their equivalent Roman numerals.

(i) 67   (ii) 256   (iii) 1,874   (iv) 65,100   (v) 9.5

Solution

(i) $67 = \quad (50 + 10) \quad + \quad (5 + 2)$

Numbers greater than 30 are written in uppercase Roman numerals.

$$\downarrow \qquad\qquad \downarrow$$
$$LX \quad + \quad VII \quad = \quad LXVII$$

Therefore, 67 is equal to LXVII.

(ii) $256 = \quad 200 \quad + \quad 50 \quad + (5 + 1)$

$$\downarrow \qquad\quad \downarrow \qquad\quad \downarrow$$
$$CC \quad + \quad L \quad + \quad VI \quad = \quad CCLVI$$

Therefore, 256 is equal to CCLVI.

(iii)   1,874 =   1,000   +   (500 + 300)   +   (50 + 20)   +   (5 – 1)

                          M   +   DCCC   +   LXX   +   IV   =   MDCCCLXXIV

Therefore, 1,874 is equal to MDCCCLXXIV.

(iv)   65,100 =   (50,000 + 10,000)   +   5,000   +   100

                          $\overline{\text{LX}}$ + $\overline{\text{V}}$ +   C   = $\overline{\text{LXV}}$C

Therefore, 65,100 is equal to $\overline{\text{LXV}}$C.

(v)   9.5 =   (10 – 1)   +   0.5

Numbers 30 and
under are written
in lowercase
Roman numerals.

                          ix   +   ss   =   ixss

Therefore, 9.5 is equal to ixss.

Converting from Roman Numerals to Decimal Numbers

Though slightly more challenging, a number expressed in Roman numerals can still be broken into "place values" (i.e., 1,000's, 100's, 10's, 1's), and then converted to decimal numbers using the rules we established previously.

For example,

MMDCLXXXIX =   MM   DC   LXXX   IX

                  2,000   +   (500 + 100)   +   (50 + 30)   +   (10 – 1)   = = 2,689

Example 6.5-b	Converting Roman Numerals to Decimal Numbers

Convert the following Roman numerals to their equivalent decimal numbers.

(i)   MMDC   (ii)   MCLVIIss   (iii)   CCLX   (iv)   CCXL   (v)   MCMXCIX

Solution

(i)   MMDC =   MM   DC

                2,000   +   (500 + 100)   =   2,600

Therefore, MMDC is equal to 2,600.

(ii)   MCLVIIss =   M   C   L   VII   ss

                    1,000   +   100   +   50   +   (5 + 2)   +   0.5   =   1,157.5

Therefore, MCLVIIss is equal to 1,157.5

(iii)   CCLX =   CC   LX

200   +   (50 + 10)   = 260

Therefore, CCLX is equal to 260.

(iv)   CCXL =   CC   XL

200   +   (50 − 10)   = 240

Therefore, CCXL is equal to 240.

(v)   MCMXCIX =   M   CM   XC   IX

1,000   +   (1,000 − 100)   +   (100 − 10)   +   (10 − 1)   =   1,999

Therefore, MCMXCIX is equal to 1,999.

6.5 | Exercises

Answers to odd-numbered problems are available at the end of the textbook.

For Problems 1 to 20, convert the Roman numerals to decimal numbers.

1. a. x	b. ii	2. a. LXIX	b. XCIIss
3. a. XL	b. LVIII	4. a. DVI	b. DCXCIII
5. a. xxiv	b. CDLXX	6. a. XLIVss	b. CDLIV
7. a. DCLXIX	b. CMLVI	8. a. xxi	b. CDLXXIII
9. a. CXss	b. DCCXCV	10. a. XCIV	b. CMXIX
11. a. xiii	b. CDXLVII	12. a. xx	b. DLXXXVIII
13. a. XXXIVss	b. CXVII	14. a. XLII	b. xv
15. a. DCCLIX	b. CCLI	16. a. LXXX	b. DII
17. a. DVII	b. Css	18. a. ix	b. CLXXXIV
19. a. DCCXXIX	b. xi	20. a. XLVI	b. LXV

For Problems 21 to 40, convert the decimal numbers to Roman numerals.

21. a. 49	b. 6	22. a. 8.5	b. 12
23. a. 67	b. 90	24. a. 108	b. 8,956
25. a. 2	b. 7,800	26. a. 5.5	b. 1,444
27. a. 75	b. 43	28. a. 5,489	b. 10
29. a. 39	b. 5,764	30. a. 40,700	b. 600,000
31. a. 28	b. 900.5	32. a. 7,623	b. 694
33. a. 38	b. 506	34. a. 7,000,100	b. 68
35. a. 7,545	b. 1,389	36. a. 11	b. 60,008
37. a. 8,555	b. 15	38. a. 50,900	b. 6,783
39. a. 31	b. 300	40. a. 88	b. 9.5

There are two ways of expressing time: standard time and military time. Standard time is expressed in 12-hour formats, and uses AM and PM to distinguish between daytime and nighttime. Military time, or 24-hour time, assigns each hour a different value from 0 to 24. In the healthcare field, military time is used to eliminate time ambiguities in a patient's medical records. Below is a chart comparing standard time to military time.

Standard	Military	Standard	Military
12:00 AM	0000 h	12:00 PM	1200 h
1:00 AM	0100 h	1:00 PM	1300 h
2:00 AM	0200 h	2:00 PM	1400 h
3:00 AM	0300 h	3:00 PM	1500 h
4:00 AM	0400 h	4:00 PM	1600 h
5:00 AM	0500 h	5:00 PM	1700 h
6:00 AM	0600 h	6:00 PM	1800 h
7:00 AM	0700 h	7:00 PM	1900 h
8:00 AM	0800 h	8:00 PM	2000 h
9:00 AM	0900 h	9:00 PM	2100 h
10:00 AM	1000 h	10:00 PM	2200 h
11:00 AM	1100 h	11:00 PM	2300 h

Standard Time to Military Time

To convert from standard time to military time,

- If the time is between 12:00 AM and 12:59 AM (inclusive), write the time as '00' for the two-digit hour, followed by numbers for the two-digit minutes, without a colon between the hours and minutes. Add 'h' to the end of the time.

- If the time is between 1:00 AM and 12:59 PM (inclusive), rewrite the digits in four-digit format, without a colon. If the time is earlier than 10:00 AM, you will need to add a '0' in front of the hour to fill all four digits. Add 'h' to the end of the time.

- If the time is between 1:00 PM and 11:59 PM (inclusive), add 12 to the number of hours, and then rewrite the digits in four-digit format, without a colon. Add 'h' to the end of the time.

Example 6.6-a	Converting Standard Time to Military Time

Convert the following standard times to military times:

(i) 12:12 AM   (ii) 8:30 AM   (iii) 11:59 PM

Solution

(i) 12:12 AM

The time is between 12:00 AM and 12:59 AM.

Writing '00' as the two-digit hour, followed by the two-digit minutes, we obtain that 12:12 AM is equal to 0012 h.

(ii) 8:30 AM

The time is between 1:00 AM and 12:59 PM.

Rewriting the digits in four-digit format, we obtain that 8:30 AM is equal to 0830 h.

(iii) 11:59 PM

The time is between 1:00 PM and 11:59 PM, so we need to add 12 to the number of hours.

Number of hours: 11 + 12 = 23

Rewriting the digits in four-digit format, we obtain that 11:59 PM is equal to 2359 h.

Military Time to Standard Time

To convert from military time to standard time,

- If the time is between 0000 h and 0059 h (inclusive), add 12 to the hours, add a colon before the second-last digit, and add 'AM' to the end of the time.

- If the time is between 0100 h and 1159 h (inclusive), add a colon before the second-last digit, and add 'AM' to the end of the time.

- If the time is between 1200 h and 1259 h (inclusive), add a colon before the second-last digit, and add 'PM' to the end of the time.

- If the time is between 1300 h and 2359 h (inclusive), subtract 12 from the number of hours (the first two digits). Then, add a colon before the second-last digit, and add 'PM' to the end of the time.

| Example 6.6-b | Converting Military Time to Standard Time |

Convert the following military times to standard times:

(i)   0059 h   (ii)   0924 h   (iii)   1242 h   (iv)   2036 h

Solution

(i) 0059 h

The time is between 0000 h and 0059 h, so 12 is added to the number of hours and the 'AM' ending is added.

Number of hours: 0 + 12 = 12

Therefore, 0059 h is equal to 12:59 AM.

(ii) 0924 h

The time is between 0100 h and 1159 h, so the 'AM' ending is added.

Therefore, 0924 h is equal to 9:24 AM.

(iii) 1242 h

The time is between 1200 h and 1259 h, so the 'PM' ending is added.

Therefore, 1242 h is equal to 12:42 PM.

(iv) 2036 h

The time is between 1300 h and 2359 h, so 12 is subtracted from the number of hours and the 'PM' ending is added.

Number of hours: 20 – 12 = 8

Therefore, 2036 h is equal to 8:36 PM.

For Problems 1 to 20, convert the standard time to military time.

1.	11:12 AM	2.	6:04 AM	3.	10:45 PM	4.	1:35 PM
5.	3:19 AM	6.	9:15 AM	7.	2:29 PM	8.	7:40 PM
9.	10:10 AM	10.	8:47 AM	11.	8:47 PM	12.	4:31 PM
13.	7:35 AM	14.	1:55 AM	15.	12:50 PM	16.	5:33 PM
17.	12:15 AM	18.	12:00 AM	19.	6:25 PM	20.	11:59 PM

For Problems 21 to 40, convert the military time to standard time.

21.	1205 h	22.	1734 h	23.	0458 h	24.	1619 h
25.	0820 h	26.	2025 h	27.	2138 h	28.	0222 h
29.	0945 h	30.	1830 h	31.	1417 h	32.	0113 h
33.	2349 h	34.	1525 h	35.	0007 h	36.	0020 h
37.	1123 h	38.	1938 h	39.	0657 h	40.	0335 h

6 | Review Exercises

For the following problems, express your answers rounded to two decimal places, wherever applicable.

1.
   a. 7.05 m = ___ cm
   b. 15.05 km = ___ m
   c. 75 mm = ___ cm
   d. 905 cm = ___ m

2.
   a. 37.02 m = ___ cm
   b. 6.059 km = ___ m
   c. 1,026 mm = ___ cm
   d. 405 cm = ___ m

3.
   a. 39.33 yd = ___ ft
   b. 4.58 ft = ___ in.
   c. 115 in. = ___ ft
   d. 5,290 yd = ___ mi

4.
   a. 43.67 yd = ___ ft
   b. 15.083 ft = ___ in.
   c. 102 in. = ___ ft
   d. 3,085 yd = ___ mi

5.
   a. 10.032 kg = ___ g
   b. 45.052 g = ___ mg
   c. 362 g = ___ kg
   d. 42,070 mg = ___ g

6.
   a. 3.753 kg = ___ g
   b. 7.087 g = ___ mg
   c. 780 g = ___ kg
   d. 29,050 mg = ___ g

7.
   a. 6.44 lb = ___ oz
   b. 4.9105 ton = ___ lb
   c. 32,000 lb = ___ ton
   d. 120 oz = ___ lb

8.
   a. 26.125 lb = ___ oz
   b. 1.1245 ton = ___ lb
   c. 23,000 lb = ___ ton
   d. 245 oz = ___ lb

9.
   a. 6.049 L = ___ mL
   b. 9,006 mL = ___ L
   c. 9.5 gal = ___ qt
   d. 75 pt = ___ qt

10.
   a. 86.63 L = ___ mL
   b. 2,092 mL = ___ L
   c. 15.75 gal = ___ qt
   d. 32 pt = ___ qt

11. a. 140 m² = ____ km²

    b. 4 m³ = ____ cm³

    c. 5 mL = ____ dm³

    d. 2.4 m³ = ____ L

12. a. a. 0.68 m² = ____ mm²

    b. 130,000 cm³ = ____ m³

    c. 0.08 kL = ____ dm³

    d. 35 cm³ = ____ mL

Perform the conversions in Problems 13 to 18.

13. a. 65 km to miles

    b. 9 m to feet

    c. 2.5 yd to centimetres

    d. 3.2 mi to metres

14. a. 89 km to miles

    b. 4 m to feet

    c. 6.5 yd to centimetres

    d. 0.5 mi to metres

15. a. 5 kg to pounds

    b. 1,250 g to ounces

    c. 0.25 lb to grams

    d. 320 oz to kilograms

16. a. 4.4 kg to pounds

    b. 750 g to ounces

    c. 1.25 lb to grams

    d. 150 oz to kilograms

17. a. 35 L to gallons

    b. 26 mL to fluid ounces

    c. 17 gal to litres

    d. 42 fl oz to litres

18. a. 115 L to gallons

    b. 12 mL to fluid ounces

    c. 45 gal to litres

    d. 75 fl oz to litres

19. a. 410 °F = ____ °C

    b. 80 °C = ____ °F

    c. 15 °F = ____ °C

    d. −30 °C = ____ °F

20. a. 8 °F = ____ °C

    b. 25 °C = ____ °F

    c. 300 °F = ____ °C

    d. −5 °C = ____ °F

21. a. 240 K = ____ °C

    b. 21 °C = ____ K

    c. 42 °F = ____ K

    d. 300 K = ____ °F

22. a. 212 K = ____ °C

    b. 27 °C = ____ K

    c. 75 °F = ____ K

    d. 200 K = ____ °F

For Problems 23 to 26, convert the standard times to military times.

23. a. 2:00 PM

    b. 4:20 AM

    c. 12:18 PM

    d. 5:45 AM

24. a. 7:58 AM

    b. 9:00 PM

    c. 11:40 AM

    d. 10:08 PM

25. a. 8:20 AM

    b. 5:09 PM

    c. 9:00 PM

    d. 7:15 AM

26. a. 6:34 AM

    b. 3:00 PM

    c. 1:46 PM

    d. 12:25 AM

For Problems 27 to 30, convert the military times to standard times.

27. a. 0924 h

    b. 1120 h

    c. 2346 h

    d. 1612 h

28. a. 0345 h

    b. 0950 h

    c. 2230 h

    d. 1805 h

29. a. 0538 h

    b. 1200 h

    c. 2254 h

    d. 0030 h

30. a. 0000 h

    b. 1739 h

    c. 1100 h

    d. 1537 h

31. Arrange the following measurements in order from largest to smallest:

   7.5 km, 9,200 yd, 5.25 mi

32. Arrange the following measurements in order from smallest to largest:

   3.75 mi, 7,000 yd, 6 km

33. Arrange the following measurements in order from largest to smallest:

   7 lb, 3 kg, 115 oz

34. Arrange the following measurements in order from smallest to largest:

   4.5 kg, 9 lb, 150 oz

35. Arrange the following measurements in order from largest to smallest:

   70 L, 18 gal, 75 qt

36. Arrange the following measurements in order from smallest to largest:

   11 gal, 40 L, 45 qt

For Problems 37 to 40, convert the Roman numerals to decimal numbers.

37. a. CD
    b. CLIX
    c. xv
    d. iiss

38. a. DXC
    b. xi
    c. MMCM
    d. viiss

39. a. xxx
    b. xiv
    c. CCXXIX
    d. CML

40. a. LIX
    b. MCDXX
    c. xxviii
    d. MDCXLVI

For Problems 41 to 44, convert the decimal numbers to Roman numerals.

41. a. 23,749
    b. 62
    c. 456
    d. 9

42. a. 13,980
    b. 54
    c. 320
    d. 43

43. a. 567.5
    b. 461
    c. 15
    d. 14,960

44. a. 1,429
    b. 9,090
    c. 14.5
    d. 647

45. An ambulance travelled 23 km to North York General Hospital. From there, it travelled another 125 mi to another hospital. Calculate the total distance travelled, in (a) kilometres and (b) miles.

46. A tumor has a diameter 3.7 inches. After a few months of radiation therapy, it has shrunk by 4 cm. What is the tumor's new diameter, in (a) inches and (b) centimetres?

47. Diana went on a diet and lost 26 pounds. Her weight at the end of the dieting period was 79 kg. What was her original weight, in (a) pounds and (b) kilograms?

48. The maximum weight a hospital elevator can carry is 540 kg. Three people with an average weight of 65 kg and four people with an average weight of 155 pounds are waiting to get into the elevator. Determine if the elevator will be able to carry all seven of them at the same time.

49. An emergency vehicle has a full tank, and then uses 8.5 gallons of fuel. If the total capacity of the fuel tank is 42.5 L, how much fuel is left in the tank, in (a) gallons and (b) litres?

50. An OR nurse ordered 31 gal of IV fluids. At the end of the night, 32 L of the solution are remaining. Calculate the quantity of IV fluid used, in (a) gallons and (b) litres.

51. A patient suffering from hypothermia has her temperature go up by 3 °C every 15 minutes with a heat blanket. If her current temperature is 89.5 °F, how long will it take for her temperature to reach 37 °C?

52. The temperature of a sterile container used for organ transportation is –129 °C. The temperature of another container is –130 °F. What is the difference in temperature between the containers, in (a) °C and (b) °F?

For the following problems, round your answers to two decimal places, wherever applicable.

1. a. 27.3 cm = ___ mm
   b. 12.5 m = ___ cm
   c. 8,105 m = ___ km
   d. 1,065 mm = ___ cm

2. a. 15.67 yd = ___ ft
   b. 5.167 ft = ___ in.
   c. 430 in. = ___ ft
   d. 5,700 yd = ___ mi

3. a. 53.107 kg = ___ g
   b. 6.223 g = ___ mg
   c. 5,519 mg = ___ g
   d. 84,176 g = ___ kg

4. a. 7.9375 lbs = ___ oz
   b. 4.015 ton = ___ lb
   c. 40,000 lb = ___ ton
   d. 149 oz = ___ lb

5. a. 5.7 L = ___ mL
   b. 9,060 mL = ___ L
   c. 6.25 gal = ___ pt
   d. 83 c = ___ qt

6. a. 150 °F = ___ °C
   b. –10 °C = ___ °F
   c. 350 K = ___ °C
   d. 22 °F = ___ K

For Problems 7 to 10, convert the Roman numerals to decimal numbers.

7. a. XL
   b. xiss
   c. LIV
   d. MCDL

8. a. xxiv
   b. xxvi
   c. CLIX
   d. MMCMXXIV

9. a. LXIX
   b. iiss
   c. CMXLVI
   d. xix

10. a. MDCXX
    b. CCIX
    c. xxiss
    d. MDXCIV

For Problems 11 to 14, convert the decimal numbers to Roman numerals.

11. a. 19
    b. 5,600
    c. 412
    d. 3.5

12. a. 1,783
    b. 112.5
    c. 900
    d. 679

13. a. 6,895
    b. 474
    c. 18.5
    d. 49

14. a. 62
    b. 59,000
    c. 45,385
    d. 591

For Problems 15 to 18, convert the standard times to military times.

15. a. 12:00 AM
    b. 6:30 PM
    c. 7:15 PM
    d. 8:24 AM

16. a. 4:38 PM
    b. 12:15 PM
    c. 7:14 PM
    d. 5:00 PM

17. a. 3:21 AM
    b. 7:50 PM
    c. 1:00 AM
    d. 11:45 PM

18. a. 8:56 AM
    b. 9:00 PM
    c. 10:27 AM
    d. 6:45 PM

For Problems 19 to 22, convert the military times to standard times.

19. a. 1700 h

    b. 0125 h

    c. 1934 h

    d. 1636 h

20. a. 0715 h

    b. 0310 h

    c. 2030 h

    d. 0845 h

21. a. 1925 h

    b. 1550 h

    c. 0627 h

    d. 1329 h

22. a. 1452 h

    b. 2144 h

    c. 2300 h

    d. 0645 h

Perform the conversions in Problems 23 to 28.

23. a. 250 km to miles

    b. 45 m to feet

    c. 8.75 yd to centimetres

    d. 2.5 mi to metres

24. a. 2.5 kg to pounds

    b. 400 g to ounces

    c. 1.75 lb to grams

    d. 225 oz to kilograms

25. a. 60 L to gallons

    b. 425 mL to fluid ounces

    c. 2.5 gal to litres

    d. 30 fl oz to litres

26. a. 0.025 hm^2 to dm^2

    b. 105 m^2 to hm^2

    c. 4 cm^2 to dm^2

    d. 700 dam^2 to km^2

27. a. 450 cm^3 to mm^3

    b. $60,000 \text{ mm}^3$ to m^3

    c. 4 cm^3 to dm^3

    d. 700 dam^3 to km^3

28. a. 12.5 m^3 to L

    b. 600 cL to cm^3

    c. 0.05 m^3 to daL

    d. 100 cm^3 to L

29. Arrange the following measurements in order from largest to smallest:

    65 m, 215 ft, 2,500 in.

30. Arrange the following measurements in order from smallest to largest:

    2.5 lb, 1,200 g, 45 oz

31. Arrange the following measurements in order from largest to smallest:

    84 L, 22 gal, 175 pt

32. An emergency medical helicopter is flying at an altitude of 8,250 ft above ground and a news helicopter is at 2,208 m above ground. What is the difference in altitude between the two helicopters, in (a) feet and (b) metres?

33. A baby weighed 7.3 pounds at birth and another baby weighed 2.8 kg. Calculate the difference in weight of the two babies, in (a) ounces and (b) grams.

34. There are five patients in a hospital, each needing 7.5 mL of Norvir administered twice a day. If the pharmacy has 2.4 L of medication, how many days will this supply last?

35. Roger is conducting a chemistry experiment, where the solution needs to be heated to exactly 100 °C, but the burner is set in Fahrenheit. His lab partner sets the burner at 176 °F, but Roger does not think that this is right. By how many degrees should Roger increase or decrease the temperature setting on the burner, in °F?

36. The temperature of sterilized instruments is 450 K. What is this temperature in degrees Celsius?

37. One common usage of Roman numerals in the medical field is in using the old apothecaries system of measurement for pharmaceuticals. A "dram" is approximately 1.7 g. If a pharmacist orders a large bottle of prescription medication labelled XLV drams, and the medication comes in 50 mg tablets, how many tablets are contained in the bottle?

38. A patient's IV line starts running at 1945 h on Monday and will take 7.5 hours to complete. When will the IV line be finished, in standard time?

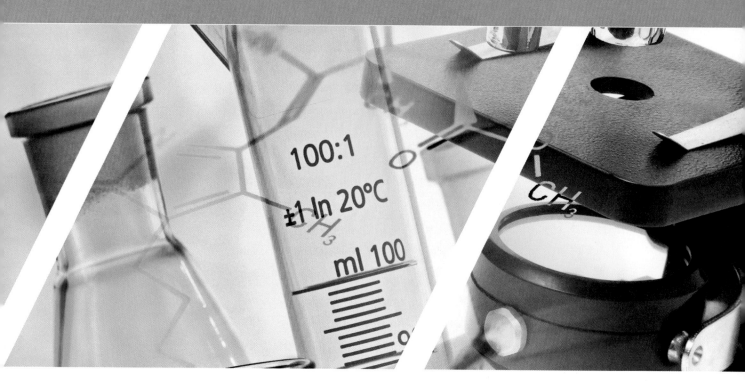

7 BASIC GEOMETRY

LEARNING OBJECTIVES

- Recognize and use various notations to represent points, lines, line segments, rays, and angles.
- Classify angles and determine the angle relationships between parallel lines and transversals.
- Classify triangles, quadrilaterals, and polygons based on properties of their sides and angles.
- Apply properties of similar and congruent triangles in solving problems involving triangles.
- Compute the perimeter and area of plane figures, such as triangles, quadrilaterals, and circles.
- Compute the surface area and volume of common three-dimensional solid objects.
- Determine the unknown length of one side of a right triangle, using the Pythagorean Theorem.

CHAPTER OUTLINE

7.1 Lines and Angles

7.2 Classification and Properties of Plane Figures

7.3 Perimeters and Areas of Plane Geometric Figures

7.4 Surface Areas and Volumes of Common Solid Objects

7.5 Pythagorean Theorem

Introduction

Geometry is a branch of mathematics that is concerned with the properties, measurements, and relationships of 2-dimensional plane figures and 3-dimensional solid objects, as well as the study of their sizes, shapes, and positions. Geometry (which translates to "Earth Measurement" from Greek) is linked to many other topics in mathematics, and is applied everywhere by people in the fields of art, architecture, engineering, land surveying, astronomy, nature, sports, machinery, and more.

Geometry has many practical uses in health sciences. For example, geometry can be used to determine the quantity of liquid a medicine jar can hold, the amount of skin that needs to be grafted, the distance between hospitals, etc. In this chapter, you will learn the most basic form of geometry, called Euclidean Geometry (named for Euclid of Alexandria), dating back to the 3rd century BCE in Ancient Greece. It is the study of relative positions, properties and measurements of geometric objects, such as points, lines, angles, shapes, surfaces and solids.

7.1 | Lines and Angles

Euclidean Geometry begins with the notion of a point. A **point** represents a **location** and it has no dimensions; that is, it has no length, width, or height. From there, we can build up the notion of 1-dimensional objects, such as lines, line segments, and rays, by connecting two points together, and subsequently angles, which are formed by the intersection of two or more lines, line segments, or rays. Lines and angles are crucial concepts in order to determine measurements of length and area that we will examine later in this chapter.

Lines, Line Segments, and Rays

A **line** is an object that has only one dimension: length. A line is created by joining two points. It includes all the points that fall directly between them, and extends indefinitely in opposite directions. It is denoted with the names of the two points over-lined with a double-arrowhead. It has no end-points.

Line A B **Line $\overleftrightarrow{AB}$ (or $\overleftrightarrow{BA}$)**

A **line segment** is the portion of a line bounded between two points. A line segment is created by joining two points, and includes all the points that fall directly between them. It is denoted with the names of the two points, over-lined with a straight line. It has two end-points.

Line Segment A B **Line Segment $\overline{AB}$ (or $\overline{BA}$)**

From these points, we can construct rays with a common vertex, and find the angle measure between the two rays. An angle is the space between two intersecting points, and is usually measured in degrees (°) and denoted by the Greek letter theta (θ).

A **ray** is the portion of a line bounded in one direction by a point. A ray is created by joining two points. It includes all the points that fall directly between them, and extends indefinitely in one direction only. It is denoted with the names of the two points, over-lined with a single arrowhead. It has only one end-point.

Ray A B **Ray $\overrightarrow{AB}$**

A B **Ray $\overrightarrow{BA}$**

Note: When labeling a ray, the order of the letters matters. For example, ray $\overrightarrow{AB}$ originates at point A and extends indefinitely in the direction of point B, while ray $\overrightarrow{BA}$ originates at point B and extends indefinitely in the direction of point A.

Example 7.1-a   **Identifying Lines, Line Segments, and Rays**

Identify and label the following geometric objects:

(i)   (ii)   (iii)   (iv)

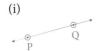

Solution

(i) Line $\overleftrightarrow{PQ}$ or $\overleftrightarrow{QP}$ (ii) Ray $\overrightarrow{NM}$ (iii) Line segment $\overline{CD}$ or $\overline{DC}$ (iv) Ray $\overrightarrow{YX}$

Angle Measures in Degrees

An angle is formed when two rays intersect at their endpoints. The point of intersection is called the **vertex** of the angle and the two rays are called the sides of the angle. The angle is identified by the symbol $\angle$, followed by the letters of the three points of the two rays, with the vertex in the middle.

For example, rays $\overrightarrow{BA}$ and $\overrightarrow{BC}$ form the angle $\angle ABC$ or $\angle CBA$. When the context is clear, we may simply refer to this angle as $\angle B$.

When naming an angle, the vertex is always written in the middle.

$\angle ABC$ (or $\angle CBA$) $= \theta$

Or simply, $\angle B = \theta$

The size of the angle is measured in degrees (denoted with the symbol "°"), where one revolution of a circle is 360°. One degree is a $\frac{1}{360}$ slice of one revolution of a circle. Imagine a circle centred at point B, divided into 360 equal sectors through B. The degree measure of $\angle ABC$ is the number of sectors that can fit in the wedge formed between rays $\overrightarrow{BA}$ and $\overrightarrow{BC}$. Exhibit 7.1 shows a circle divided into 36 sectors, where each sector represents 10°, and the angle $\angle ABC = 60°$

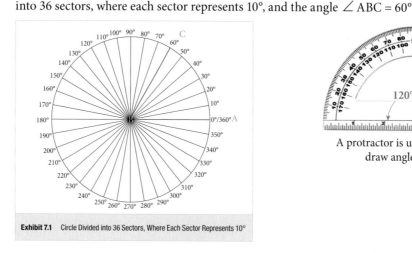

A protractor is used to measure and draw angles in degrees.

Exhibit 7.1   Circle Divided into 36 Sectors, Where Each Sector Represents 10°

Two rays from the centre of a circle extending in opposite directions create a line which divides the circle into two equal halves, thus the angle between two opposite rays has an angle measure equal to $\frac{1}{2}$ a revolution or $\frac{360°}{2} = 180°$.

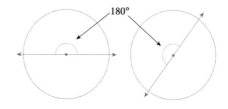

Two perpendicular lines through the centre of a circle cut the circle into four equal quadrants, thus the angle between two perpendicular rays has an angle measure equal to $\frac{1}{4}$ a revolution or $\frac{360°}{4} = 90°$.

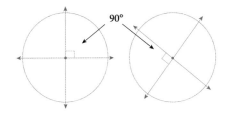

Classification of Angles

Angles are classified according to their size in degrees.

Right angles $(\theta = 90°)$	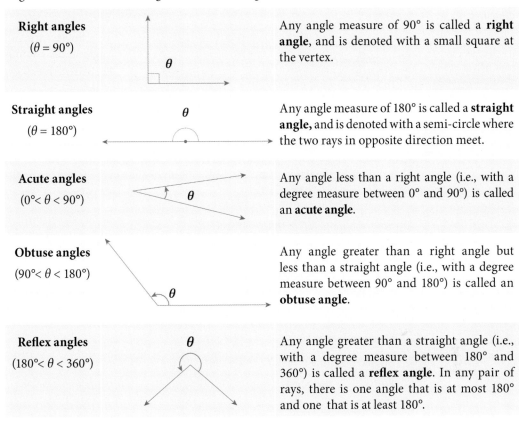	Any angle measure of 90° is called a **right angle**, and is denoted with a small square at the vertex.
Straight angles $(\theta = 180°)$		Any angle measure of 180° is called a **straight angle,** and is denoted with a semi-circle where the two rays in opposite direction meet.
Acute angles $(0° < \theta < 90°)$		Any angle less than a right angle (i.e., with a degree measure between 0° and 90°) is called an **acute angle**.
Obtuse angles $(90° < \theta < 180°)$		Any angle greater than a right angle but less than a straight angle (i.e., with a degree measure between 90° and 180°) is called an **obtuse angle**.
Reflex angles $(180° < \theta < 360°)$		Any angle greater than a straight angle (i.e., with a degree measure between 180° and 360°) is called a **reflex angle**. In any pair of rays, there is one angle that is at most 180° and one that is at least 180°.

Example 7.1-b | **Classifying Angles**

Identify the following angles as acute, right, obtuse, straight, or reflex:

(i)   (ii)   (iii)   (iv)   (v)

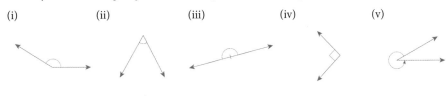

Solution

(i) Obtuse   (ii) Acute   (iii) Straight   (iv) Right   (v) Reflex

Supplementary and Complementary Angles

Angle pairs with measures that sum to a right angle (90°) or a straight angle (180°) are given special names:

Supplementary angles

$(\theta + \phi = 180°)$

Two angles are called **supplementary angles** if their sum is 180°.
Each angle is called a supplement of the other.

Since the sum of complementary angles is 90°, each angle must be acute (i.e., less than 90°). As a result, only acute angles have complements.

Complementary angles

$(\theta + \phi = 90°)$

Two angles are called **complementary angles** if their sum is 90°.
Each angle is called a complement of the other.

| Example 7.1-c | Complementary and Supplementary Angles |

Determine the supplement and complement (if possible) of the following angles:

(i) 30°   (ii) 45°   (iii) 72°   (iv) 90°   (v) 126°

Solution

(i) Supplement of 30° = 180° − 30° = 150°

   Complement of 30° = 90° − 30° = 60°

(ii) Supplement of 45° = 180° − 45° = 135°

   Complement of 45° = 90° − 45° = 45°

> A 45° angle is self-complementary.

(iii) Supplement of 72° = 180° − 72° = 108°

   Complement of 72° = 90° − 72° = 18°

(iv) Supplement of 90° = 180° − 90° = 90°

   Since 90° is not acute, it does not have a complementary angle.

> A 90° (right) angle is self-supplementary.

(v) Supplement of 126° = 180° − 126° = 54°

   Since 126° is not acute, it does not have a complementary angle.

Opposite and Adjacent Angles

When two lines intersect at a point P, they create four angles. Every pair of consecutive angles, called **adjacent angles**, is supplementary, since each line forms a straight angle (180°) at point P and the other line cuts it into two angles, which have a sum of 180°. As a result, the angles opposite to each other, called **opposite angles**, are always equal (or congruent).

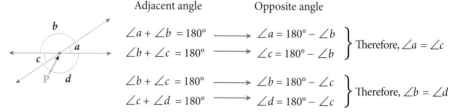

Note: When two lines intersect, the adjacent angles are supplementary (sum of 180°) and opposite angles are congruent (equal).

Example 7.1-d **Opposite and Adjacent Angles**

Determine the measures of the three unknown angles in the following diagram:

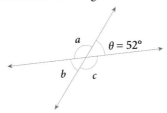

Solution

(i) Since angle a is adjacent to angle θ, it is supplementary to angle θ.
Therefore, $\angle a = 180° - 52° = 128°$.

(ii) Since angle b is opposite to angle θ, it is congruent to angle θ.
Therefore, $\angle b = 52°$.

(iii) Since angle c is adjacent to angle θ, it is supplementary to angle θ.
Therefore, $\angle c = 180° - 52° = 128°$.

Note: Angle c is also opposite to angle a, so ∠c = ∠a = 128°.

Parallel Lines and Transversal Angles

Parallel lines are lines in a plane which do not meet (or intersect) even when extended. To demonstrate that the lines are parallel, small arrowheads are drawn.

Also, the symbol "$//$" is used to indicate that the lines are parallel; e.g., $\overline{AB} // \overline{CD}$

A **transversal** is a line that intersects two distinct parallel lines, and the angles it forms with each of the two parallel lines are congruent.

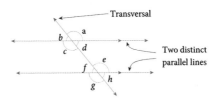

Parallel lines never intersect even when extended. They are identified by arrowheads marked on the pair of lines.

The four angles, a, b, c, and d, are congruent to the four angles, e, f, g, and h, respectively; i.e.,
$\angle a = \angle e$, $\angle b = \angle f$, $\angle c = \angle g$, and $\angle d = \angle h$

This means that there are special relationships with special names between the angles formed by the transversal and each of the parallel lines, as classified below:

Corresponding angles have a pattern that looks like the letter F:

Corresponding angles (e.g., $\angle d = \angle h$)	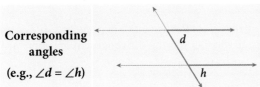	The angles formed on the same corner of the intersection between the transversal and each of the parallel lines are called **corresponding angles**, and they are *congruent*.

Co-interior angles have a pattern that looks like the letter C:	**Co-interior angles** (e.g., $\angle d + \angle e = 180°$)	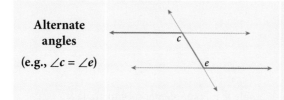	The angles formed on the same side of the transversal and on the interior of the parallel lines are called **co-interior angles**, and they are *supplementary*.
Alternate angles have a pattern that looks like the letter Z:	**Alternate angles** (e.g., $\angle c = \angle e$)	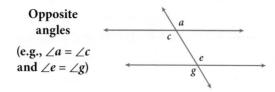	The angles formed on opposite sides of the transversal and on the interior of the parallel lines are called **alternate angles**, and they are *congruent*.
Opposite angles have a pattern that looks like the letter X:	**Opposite angles** (e.g., $\angle a = \angle c$ and $\angle e = \angle g$)	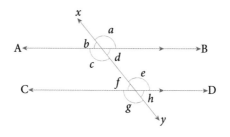	The angles formed by any intersecting lines that are opposite to the same vertex are called **opposite angles**, and they are *congruent*.

To summarize, consider the angles formed by two distinct parallel lines (AB//CD) and a transversal *xy*.

Corresponding angles are equal	**Co-interior angles are supplementary**
$\angle a = \angle e$	
$\angle b = \angle f$	$\angle d + \angle e = 180°$
$\angle c = \angle g$	$\angle c + \angle f = 180°$
$\angle d = \angle h$	
Alternate angles are equal	**Opposite angles are equal**
	$\angle a = \angle c$
$\angle d = \angle f$	$\angle b = \angle d$
$\angle c = \angle e$	$\angle e = \angle g$
	$\angle f = \angle h$

| Example 7.1-e | Identifying Relationships Between Angles |

State the relationship to angle θ of each of the five unknown angles a, b, c, d, and e identified in the following diagram, and also state whether the angle is congruent or supplementary to θ:

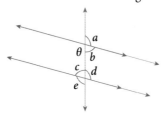

Solution

(i)   Angle a is opposite angle θ, hence it is congruent to θ.

(ii) Angle b is adjacent to angle θ, hence it is supplementary to θ.

(iii) Angle c is co-interior to angle θ, hence it is supplementary to θ.

(iv) Angle d is alternate to angle θ, hence it is congruent to θ.

(v)   Angle e is corresponding to angle θ, hence it is congruent to θ.

Example 7.1-f   **Calculating Measure of Transversal Angles**

Calculate the angle measure of the five unknown angles identified in Example 7.1-e, given that angle $\theta = 105°$.

Solution

(i)   Since angle a is congruent to θ, $a = \theta = 105°$.

(ii) Since angle b is supplementary to θ, $b = 180 - \theta = 180 - 105 = 75°$.

(iii) Since angle c is supplementary to θ, $c = 180 - \theta = 180 - 105 = 75°$.

(iv) Since angle d is congruent to θ, $d = \theta = 105°$.

(v)   Since angle e is congruent to θ, $e = \theta = 105°$.

Example 7.1-g   **An Application of Transversal Angles - Intersections of Roads**

Alder Road, Birch Street, and Cedar Avenue are all straight roads that run in different directions, and their intersections form a triangle. Alder Road intersects Birch Street at an angle of 72° and Cedar Avenue at an internal angle of 47°, both as measured from within the triangle. Using the angle relationships learned in this section, find the angle of intersection between Birch Street and Cedar Avenue, where a hospital is located.

Solution

Step 1:   Draw a diagram representing the intersection of roads and mark the known angles. Name the triangle as XYZ and let θ be the angle of intersection between Birch Street and Cedar Avenue.

Step 2:   To make use of the angle relationships that we learned in this section, draw an imaginary road, parallel to Alder Road, that runs through X, the intersection of Birch Street and Cedar Avenue.

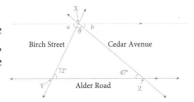

Step 3:   Calculate the alternate transversal angles that are formed and use those to calculate the angle of intersection between Birch Street and Cedar Avenue.

$$\angle a = 72° \text{ (Alternate Angle)}$$
$$\angle b = 47° \text{ (Alternate Angle)}$$

Step 4:   The three angles a, θ, and b at the vertex X of the triangle XYZ must be equal to 180° (angles in a straight line).

$$\angle a + \theta + \angle b = 180°$$
$$\theta = 180° - \angle a - \angle b$$
$$= 180° - 72° - 47°$$
$$\theta = 61°$$

Given interior angles a, b, and c in a triangle:

$$\angle a + \angle b + \angle c = 180°$$

Therefore, the angle of intersection between Birch Street and Cedar Avenue is 61°.

The above example demonstrates that the three internal angles of a triangle must add up to 180°. We will examine this further now as we begin to analyze plane figures in the next section.

7.1 | Exercises

1. Draw and label the following geometric objects:
   a. Line $\overleftrightarrow{EF}$ b. Line segment $\overline{GH}$ c. Ray $\overrightarrow{JK}$

2. Draw and label the following geometric objects:
   a. Line $\overleftrightarrow{ST}$ b. Line segment $\overline{UV}$ c. Ray $\overrightarrow{XW}$

3. Identify and name the following geometric objects:

   a.

   b.

   c.

4. Identify and name the following geometric objects:

   a.

   b.

   c.

For the figures shown in Problems 5 to 8, answer the following questions:

(i) Name the angle using the three-letter naming convention (e.g. $\angle ABC$).

(ii) Classify the angle as acute, right, or obtuse.

(iii) Determine the approximate angle measure using a protractor.

(iv) Calculate the supplement and complement (if applicable) of the angle.

5. a. 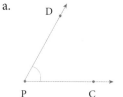   b.

6. a. 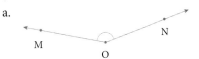   b.

7. a. 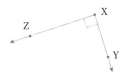   b.

8. a.    b.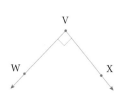

9. Determine the measure of the angle that is complementary to: a. 32.5°   b. 18°

10. Determine the measure of the angle that is complementary to: a. 83.1°   b. 5°

11. Determine the measure of the angle that is supplementary to: a. 123.4°   b. 89°

12. Determine the measure of the angle that is supplementary to: a. 7.8°   b. 92°

For the figures shown in Problems 13 to 16, determine the congruent pairs of angles:

13. a.
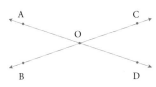

b.
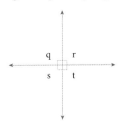

14. a.
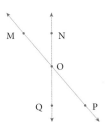

b.
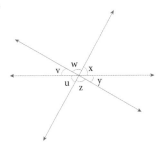

15.
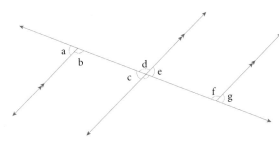

16.
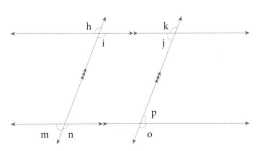

For the figures shown in Problems 17 to 20, determine the value of the unknown angles.

17. a.

b.
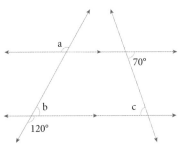

18. a.
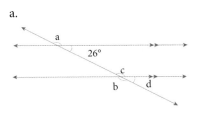

b.
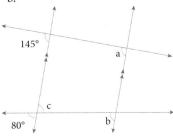

19.   a.

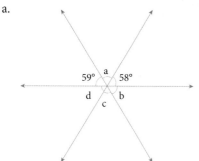

b.

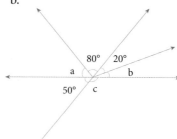

20.   a.

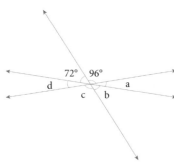

b.

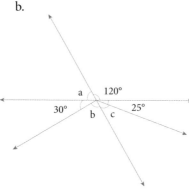

21.   A small island is situated at the south of Lois Lake, separated from the mainland by two tributaries of Lois Lake: Crag Creek to the West and Slip Stream to the East. A straight highway called River Road connects the island to the mainland, where an emergency clinic is located in either direction. The River Road bridge over Crag Creek forms an angle of 77° with the creek, and the bridge over Slip Stream forms an angle of 71° with the stream, both on the island's side. Assuming that both Crag Creek and Slip Stream are fairly straight, determine the angle that they form with each other when they branch off Lois Lake.

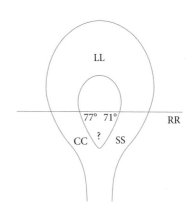

22.   The South-West corner of the intersection of Main Street and Queen Street forms an angle of 104°. Further north on Main Street, the South-West corner of the intersection of Main and King Street forms an angle of 63°. Determine the acute angle formed by the intersection of Queen and King, assuming that all three roads are perfectly straight.

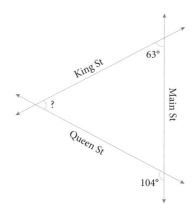

For the figures shown in Problems 23 and 24, use transversal angles and the fact that the sum of the three internal angles of a triangle always equals 180°.

23. a. Calculate the value of θ.

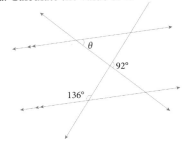

b. Calculate the value of a, b, and c.

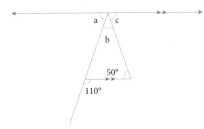

24. a. Calculate the value of θ.

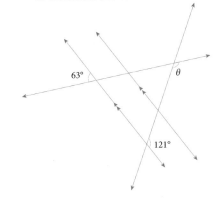

b. Calculate the value of a, b, and c.

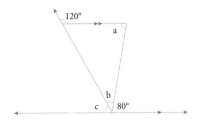

7.2 | Classification and Properties of Plane Figures

The study of geometry that deals with the objects or figures that are flat (i.e., 2-dimensional) is known as **plane geometry**. In plane geometry, we study the properties and relations of plane figures such as triangles, quadrilaterals, polygons, and circles. A plane figure is continuous and closed, meaning that it can be drawn without lifting the pencil from the page and that the start-point is the same as the end-point of the object.

Some examples of plane figures are shown below:

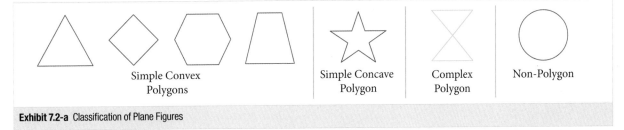

Exhibit 7.2-a Classification of Plane Figures

Polygons

A polygon is a plane figure that is created by joining a finite number of line segments together at their vertices; i.e., a polygon is a plane figure that is bound by three or more straight edges, known as sides. The first six shapes in Exhibit 7.2-a are polygons. The circle (i.e., the 7th shape) in Exhibit 7.2-a is not a polygon, as it is not formed by joining a finite number of line segments together. However, the circle is a special shape and you will learn of its properties later in the chapter.

A **simple polygon** is a polygon which does not intersect itself. The first five shapes in Exhibit 7.2-a are simple polygons. A polygon that is not simple (i.e., it intersects itself) is called a **complex polygon**. The hourglass shape (i.e. the 6th shape) in Exhibit 7.2-a is an example of a complex polygon.

A **convex polygon** is a simple polygon whose internal angles are all less than 180°. The first four shapes in Exhibit 7.2-a are convex polygons. Every simple polygon that is not convex (i.e., it contains an internal angle greater than 180°) is called a **concave polygon**. The star shape (i.e., the 5th shape) in Exhibit 7.2-a is an example of a concave polygon.

A **regular convex polygon** is a convex polygon whose sides are all the same length and whose internal angles have the same measure. The first three shapes in Exhibit 7.2-a are regular convex polygons.

Polygons are named according to the number of sides that they have. The first eight regular convex polygons are shown below:

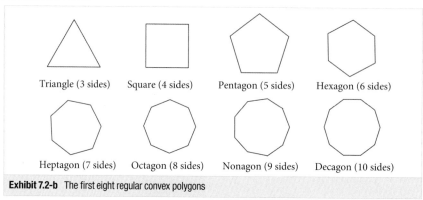

Triangle (3 sides)   Square (4 sides)   Pentagon (5 sides)   Hexagon (6 sides)

Heptagon (7 sides)   Octagon (8 sides)   Nonagon (9 sides)   Decagon (10 sides)

Exhibit 7.2-b   The first eight regular convex polygons

Classification and Properties of Triangles

We will now examine one type of convex polygon: triangles. A **triangle** (literally meaning "three-angles") is any polygon with three sides and three internal angles. We will now look at the different sub-categories and classifications of triangles and the various properties of the figures.

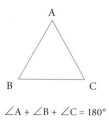

As we learned in the previous section, the sum of the three internal angles of a triangle equals 180°. Therefore, since the sum of the internal angles equals 180°, each internal angle must be less than 180°, which means every triangle is a convex polygon.

$$\angle A + \angle B + \angle C = 180°$$

Every triangle can be classified in two ways: by angle measure **and** by side length.

Classification of Triangles by Angle Measures

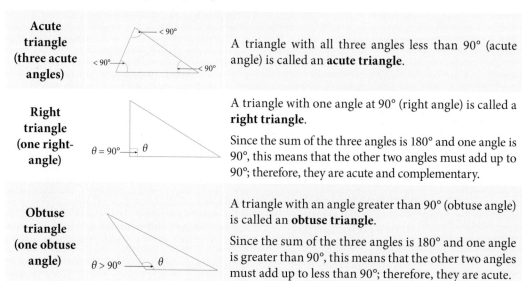

Acute triangle (three acute angles)	*(diagram, all angles < 90°)*	A triangle with all three angles less than 90° (acute angle) is called an **acute triangle**.
Right triangle (one right-angle)	*(diagram, θ = 90°)*	A triangle with one angle at 90° (right angle) is called a **right triangle**. Since the sum of the three angles is 180° and one angle is 90°, this means that the other two angles must add up to 90°; therefore, they are acute and complementary.
Obtuse triangle (one obtuse angle)	*(diagram, θ > 90°)*	A triangle with an angle greater than 90° (obtuse angle) is called an **obtuse triangle**. Since the sum of the three angles is 180° and one angle is greater than 90°, this means that the other two angles must add up to less than 90°; therefore, they are acute.

Classification of Triangles by Side Measures

Equilateral triangle (three equal sides)

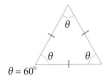

$\theta = 60°$

A triangle that has sides of equal lengths is called an **equilateral triangle**.

Each angle of an equilateral triangle is 60°. Therefore, every equilateral triangle is also an acute triangle.

Isosceles triangle (two equal sides)

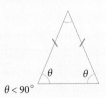

$\theta < 90°$

A triangle that has two sides of equal lengths is called an **isosceles triangle**.

The angles opposite to the equal sides of an isosceles triangle will have equal measure.

An isosceles triangle may be acute, right, or obtuse (but the equal angles will be acute).

Scalene triangle (no equal sides)

A triangle with sides of different lengths is called a **scalene triangle**.

The angles of a scalene triangle will all be different.

A scalene triangle may be acute, right, or obtuse.

Every equilateral triangle is an acute triangle since all three angles are equal to 60°.

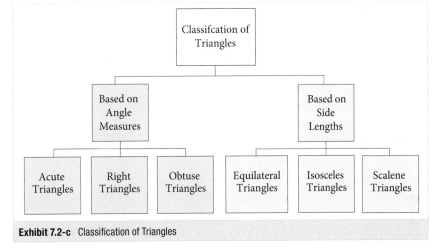

Exhibit 7.2-c Classification of Triangles

Note: It is common for the vertices to be labelled using capital letters, and the sides to be labelled using lower case that correspond to their respective opposite angles, as shown in the diagram.

Example 7.2-a | **Classifying Triangles**

Classify the following triangles by angle measure and by side length:

(i)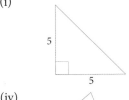

(ii)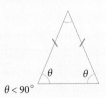

(iii)

(iv)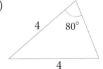

(v)

(vi)

Solution

(i) Right and Isosceles triangle (ii) Acute and Equilateral triangle (iii) Obtuse and Scalene triangle

(iv) Acute and Isosceles triangle (v) Obtuse and Isosceles triangle (vi) Right and Scalene triangle

---

| **Example 7.2-b** | **Calculating Unknown Angles in a Triangle** |

Calculate the measure of the unknown angle in each of the following triangles. Then, classify the triangle by angle measure and by side length.

(i) $\triangle XYZ$, $\angle X = 30°$, $\angle Y = 120°$

(ii) $\triangle ABC$, $\angle A = 35°$, $\angle C = 55°$

(iii) $\triangle RST$, $\angle S = 60°$, $\angle T = 60°$

Solution

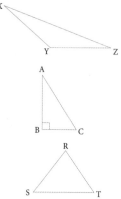

(i) $\angle Z = 180° - (30° + 120°) = 30°$

Since $\angle Y > 90°$, $\triangle XYZ$ is an **Obtuse triangle**.

Since $\angle X = \angle Z$, $\triangle XYZ$ is an **Isosceles triangle**.

(ii) $\angle B = 180° - (35° + 55°) = 90°$

Since $\angle B = 90°$, $\triangle ABC$ is a **Right triangle.**

Since no angles are equal, $\triangle ABC$ is a **Scalene triangle**.

(iii) $\angle R = 180° - (60° + 60°) = 60°$

Since all angles are less than 90°, $\triangle RST$ is an **Acute triangle.**

Since all angles are equal, $\triangle RST$ is an **Equilateral triangle.**

| **Example 7.2-c** | **Constructing Triangles** |

Given that $\angle BAC = 37°$, a = 5 cm, and b = 8 cm, draw two different triangles, $\triangle ABC$, such that:

(i) $\triangle ABC$ is an obtuse, isosceles triangle.   (ii) $\triangle ABC$ is an acute, scalene triangle.

Solution   (i)

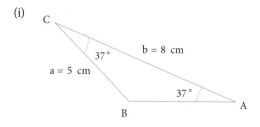

(ii)

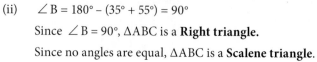

| **Example 7.2-d** | **Application of Triangles – Distances Between Cities** |

An emergency medical-services helicopter finds that the flying distance from hospital A to hospital B is the same as that of hospital A to hospital C, which is approximately 345 km. The angle from hospital A between hospital B and hospital C is 76°. What kind of triangle is created between the three hospitals?

Solution

Since the distance between hospital A and hospital B is equal to the distance between hospital A to hospital C, the angles opposite to these sides are equal.

Let the equal angles be θ.

$$\theta + \theta + 76° = 180°$$
$$2\theta = 180° - 76° = 104°$$
$$\theta = \frac{104°}{2} = 52°$$

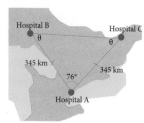

The angles are 52°, 52°, and 76°.

The two sides are equal and all three angles are less than 90°.

Therefore, the triangle created is an acute, isosceles triangle.

Classification and Properties of Quadrilaterals

We will now examine another class of convex polygons and their properties: **convex quadrilaterals**.

A **quadrilateral** (literally meaning "four-sided") is any polygon with 4 sides and 4 internal angles. The sum of a quadrilateral's four interior angles is 360°. In this section, we will examine **convex quadrilaterals** only, in which each of the internal angles is less than 180°.

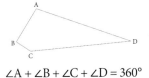

$$\angle A + \angle B + \angle C + \angle D = 360°$$

There are two main classes of quadrilaterals: parallelograms, which have special properties, and non-parallelograms.

A **parallelogram** is a quadrilateral with opposite sides that are parallel. As a result, in a parallelogram, the opposite sides are equal, the opposite angles are equal, and the adjacent angles are supplementary ($\theta + \phi = 180°$). A **non-parallelogram** is a shape in which at least one set of sides is not parallel. In this book, non-parallelograms are grouped into two categories: trapezoids and kites.

Classification of Quadrilaterals that are Parallelograms

Within the class of parallelograms, there are three sub-classes:

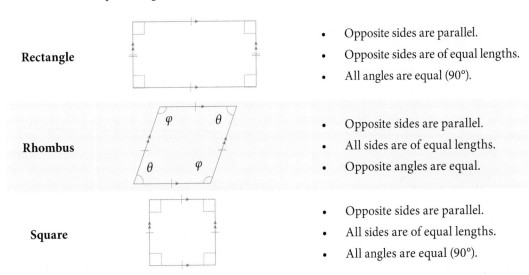

Rectangle	• Opposite sides are parallel. • Opposite sides are of equal lengths. • All angles are equal (90°).
Rhombus	• Opposite sides are parallel. • All sides are of equal lengths. • Opposite angles are equal.
Square	• Opposite sides are parallel. • All sides are of equal lengths. • All angles are equal (90°).

Note: A parallelogram that is neither a rectangle, nor a square, nor a rhombus is known simply as a parallelogram.

Classification of Quadrilaterals that are Non-Parallelograms

Within the class of non-parallelograms, there are two sub-classes:

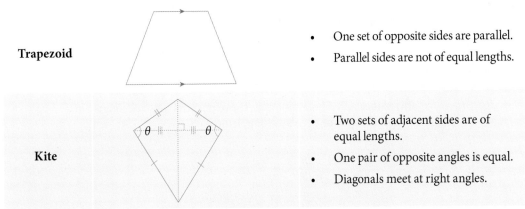

| Trapezoid | • One set of opposite sides are parallel.
• Parallel sides are not of equal lengths. |
| Kite | • Two sets of adjacent sides are of equal lengths.
• One pair of opposite angles is equal.
• Diagonals meet at right angles. |

Note: A quadrilateral that is a non-parallelogram, which is neither a trapezoid nor a kite, is known as a general quadrilateral. In this textbook, we will be focusing on parallelograms.

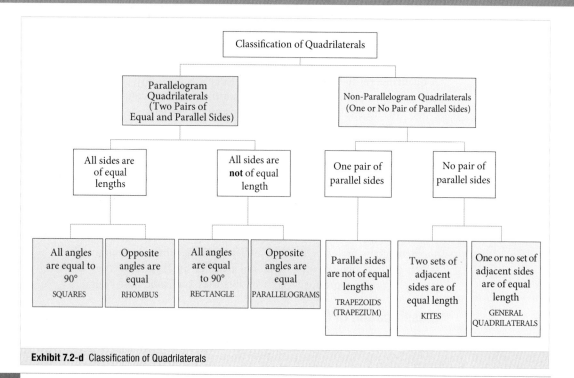

Exhibit 7.2-d Classification of Quadrilaterals

Example 7.2-e | **Classifying Quadrilaterals**

Classify the following quadrilaterals:

(i)

(ii)

(iii)

Solution

(i)   One pair of opposite sides is parallel - Trapezoid

(ii) All sides are of equal lengths and all angles are equal (90°) - Square

(iii) Opposite sides are parallel - Parallelogram

Example 7.2-f | **Calculating Unknown Angles in a Quadrilateral**

Using the properties of various quadrilaterals, calculate the measure of the unknown angle(s) in each of the following:

(i)   WXYZ is a rectangle.

(ii) ABCD is a rhombus and $\angle D = 25°$.

Solution

(i)   Since WXYZ is a rectangle, the four angles are all equal to 90°.

$\angle W = \angle X = \angle Y = \angle Z = 90°$

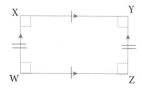

(ii) Since ABCD is a rhombus, the opposite angles are congruent and adjacent angles are supplementary.
Therefore,

$\angle B = \angle D = 25°$

$\angle A = \angle C = 180° - 25° = 155°$

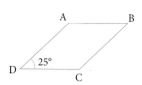

Example 7.2-g | Identifying Quadrilaterals Based on Angle Measures

For the following quadrilaterals, find the missing angle measure, then classify the type of quadrilateral:

(i) MNOP, given that $\angle M = 112°$, $\angle N = 68°$, and $\angle O = 112°$, and the shape has congruent sides.

(ii) STUV, given that $\angle S = 45°$, $\angle U = 45°$, and $\angle V = 135°$

Solution

(i) $\angle M + \angle N + \angle O + \angle P = 360°$ Substituting the known values and solving for $\angle P$,

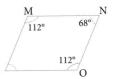

$\angle P = 360° - (112° + 68° + 112°) = 68°$

Since the opposite angles are equal and not equal to 90°, and since all 4 sides are congruent (i.e., of equal length), we know that MNOP is a rhombus.

(ii) $\angle S + \angle T + \angle U + \angle V = 360°$ Substituting the known values and solving for $\angle T$,

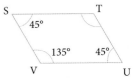

$\angle T = 360° - (45° + 45° + 135°) = 135°$

Since the opposite angles are equal and not equal to 90°, STUV is either a parallelogram or a rhombus (we cannot tell which without knowing the side lengths).

Example 7.2-h | Constructing Quadrilaterals

Jeremy labels a point A on his paper and draws a straight line 20 cm long to another point B. From there, he uses a compass to measure a 90° angle from $\overline{AB}$ and draws a line from point B to a third point C, that is perpendicular to $\overline{AB}$ and is 15 cm long. How many different types of quadrilaterals can Jeremy create by plotting a fourth point D and then connecting the line segments $\overline{CD}$ and $\overline{DA}$?

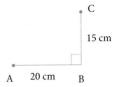

Solution

Since the lengths of two sides are different, Jeremy cannot create a square or a rhombus. However, he can create 4 other kinds of quadrilaterals:

Option A: Jeremy can create a **rectangle** by measuring out another right angle from point C and drawing a line segment $\overline{CD}$ parallel to $\overline{AB}$ and 20 cm long.

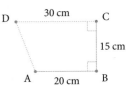

Option B: Jeremy can create a **trapezoid** by measuring out another right angle from point C and drawing a line segment $\overline{CD}$ parallel to $\overline{AB}$ but of a length other than 20 cm.

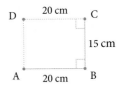

Option C: Jeremy can create a **kite** by drawing a dashed line from point A to point C, then drawing a line segment from point B to a fourth point D that is perpendicular to $\overline{AC}$ and twice the length from B to $\overline{AC}$.

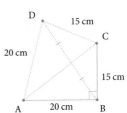

Option D: Jeremy can create a **general quadrilateral** by placing point D in any location that is any distance, other than 15 cm, away from C and not parallel to $\overline{AB}$.

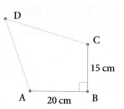

7.2 | Exercises

Answers to odd-numbered problems are available at the end of the textbook.

Classify the triangles shown in Problems 1 and 2 by side length and angle measure:

1. a. 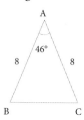   b. 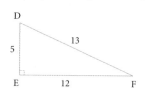   c.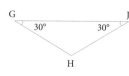

2. a. 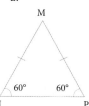   b. 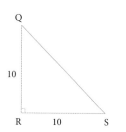   c.

Classify the quadrilaterals shown in Problems 3 and 4:

3. a. 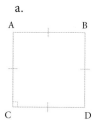   b. 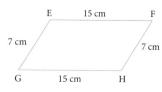   c.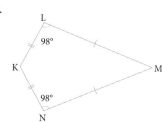

4. a. 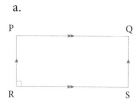   b. 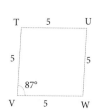   c.

In Problems 5 to 8, determine the unknown angle(s) for each quadrilateral ABCD:

5. ABCD is a square

6. ABCD is a parallelogram, with $\angle A = 77°$

7. ABCD is a kite, with $\overline{AB} = \overline{BC}$, $\overline{AD} = \overline{DC}$, $\angle A = 105°$, and $\angle D = 52°$

8. ABCD is a trapezoid, with $\overline{AB}$ parallel to $\overline{CD}$, $\angle A = 93°$, and $\angle B = 116°$

In Problems 9 to 12, classify the quadrilateral ABCD based on the properties given:

9. $\overline{AB} = \overline{BC} = \overline{CD} = \overline{DA}$ and $\angle A = 105°$

10. $\overline{AB} = \overline{CD}$, $\overline{BC} = \overline{DA}$, and $\angle A = \angle B$

11. $\overline{AB} = \overline{BC} = \overline{CD} = 15$ cm, $\overline{DA} = 27$ cm, and $\overline{BC}$ is parallel to $\overline{DA}$

12. $\overline{AB} = \overline{BC} = 20$ cm, $\overline{AD} = \overline{DC} = 30$ cm, and $\angle A = \angle C$

In Problems 13 to 16, state the names of all the possible quadrilaterals based on the given property:

13. a. 4 equal angles b. 4 equal sides

14. a. 4 right angles b. No equal sides

15. a. 2 pairs of parallel sides b. 2 pairs of equal angles

16. a. At least 1 pair of parallel sides b. At least 1 pair of equal angles

7.3 | Perimeters and Areas of Plane Geometric Figures

In Section 7.2, we introduced the concept of **plane figures**; i.e., geometric objects that can be drawn in 2-dimensions. In this section, we will introduce two important measurements of those figures, specifically for certain convex polygons and circles: perimeter and area.

The **perimeter** (P) of a plane figure is the total length of the boundary of the plane figure. In a polygon, the perimeter is the sum of the lengths of the line segments (sides) that form the boundary of the polygon. Perimeter is measured in units of length - e.g., centimetre (cm), metre (m), inch (in), foot (ft), etc.

The **area** (A) of a plane figure is the amount of 2-dimensional surface that is enclosed within the figure. Area is measured using square units - e.g., square centimetre (cm^2), square metre (m^2), square inch (in^2), square foot (ft^2), etc. - all of which represent the amount of surface occupied by squares with the respective side lengths.

Squares and Rectangles

A **square** is a quadrilateral whose sides are all equal in length and angles are all right angles - this makes it a regular polygon. We denote the length of each **side** by the letter s.

A **rectangle** is a quadrilateral whose angles are all right angles and opposite sides are equal in length – it is differentiated from a square by the property that the sides need not all be of the same length. We denote the longer side by the letter l (for **length**), and the shorter side by the letter w (for **width**).

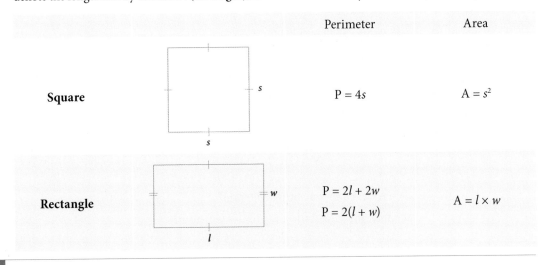

		Perimeter	Area
Square	s ... s	$P = 4s$	$A = s^2$
Rectangle	w ... l	$P = 2l + 2w$ $P = 2(l + w)$	$A = l \times w$

Example 7.3-a	**Calculating the Perimeter and Area of Squares and Rectangles**

Find the perimeter and area of the following figures:

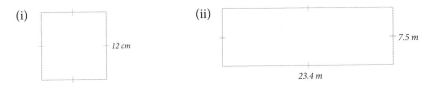

(i) 12 cm

(ii) 7.5 m   23.4 m

Solution

(i)   The figure is a square.

Using P = 4s,

$$P = 4(12 \text{ cm}) = 48 \text{ cm}$$

Using A = s²,

$$A = (12 \text{ cm})^2 = 144 \text{ cm}^2$$

Therefore, the perimeter is 48 cm and the area is 144 cm².

(ii) The figure is a rectangle.

Using P = 2l + 2w,

$$P = 2(23.4 \text{ m}) + 2(7.5 \text{ m}) = 61.8 \text{ m}$$

Using A = l × w,

$$A = (23.4 \text{ m})(7.5 \text{ m}) = 175.5 \text{ m}^2$$

Therefore, the perimeter is 61.8 m and the area is 175.5 m².

Example 7.3-b   **Determining the Cost to Lay a Rectangular Garden**

A rectangular garden for a local nursing home is being built to be 6.5 m long and 3.2 m wide. The fencing for the garden costs $2.95/m and the soil costs $6.25/m². Calculate the cost to lay the garden.

Solution

Using P = 2l + 2w,

$$P = 2(6.5 \text{ m}) + 2(3.2 \text{ m}) = 19.4 \text{ m}$$

$$\text{Fencing cost} = \frac{\$2.95}{1 \text{ m}} \times 19.4 \text{ m} = \$57.23$$

Using A = l × w,

$$A = (6.5 \text{ m})(3.2 \text{ m}) = 20.8 \text{ m}^2$$

$$\text{Soil cost} = \frac{\$6.25}{1 \text{ m}^2} \times 20.8 \text{ m}^2 = \$130.00$$

Total cost = $57.23 + $130.00 = $187.23

Therefore, the total cost to lay the garden is $187.23.

w = 3.2 m

l = 6.5 m

Example 7.3-c   **Finding the Area of a Dental X-ray Film**

A dental x-ray film in the shape of a rectangle measures 24 mm × 40 mm. Find the area of the x-ray film.

Solution

Dimensions of the rectangular x-ray film: l = 24 mm, w = 40 mm.

Using A = l × w,

$$A = 24 \text{ mm} \times 40 \text{ mm} = 960 \text{ mm}^2$$

Therefore, the area of the x-ray film is 960 mm².

Rhombuses and Parallelograms

A **rhombus** is a quadrilateral whose sides are all equal in length – it is differentiated from a square by the property that the angles are not right angles. We denote the length of each side by the letter b, and the perpendicular **height** by the letter h.

Rhombuses, like squares, have four equal side lengths, which makes the calculation of the perimeter of a rhombus equal to that of a square.

The area of a rhombus is determined as follows:

Draw a perpendicular line from the top corner of the rhombus to its base. This is the "height", h, of the rhombus. "Cut" the resulting triangle that is created and "paste" it on the opposite side. The result is a rectangle with length b and width h, as shown in the diagram below:

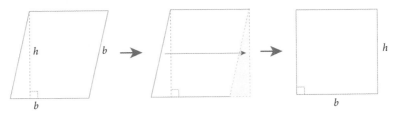

A **parallelogram** is a quadrilateral whose opposite sides are equal and parallel. It is differentiated from a rectangle by the property that the angles are not right angles. We denote the length of the **base** by the letter b, the length of the slant side by the letter a, and the perpendicular **height** by the letter h.

The calculation of the perimeter of a parallelogram is equal to that of a rectangle, replacing the letters l and w with a and b.

The area of a parallelogram is determined using the same procedure as that of a rhombus.

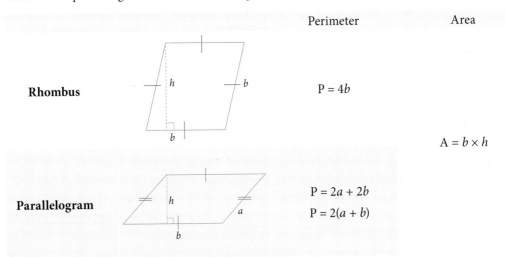

		Perimeter	Area
Rhombus		$P = 4b$	
			$A = b \times h$
Parallelogram		$P = 2a + 2b$ $P = 2(a + b)$	

Example 7.3-d | **Calculating the Perimeter and Area of Rhombuses and Parallelograms**

Find the perimeter and area of the following figures:

(i)

22 cm 25 cm

(ii)

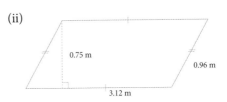

0.75 m 0.96 m

3.12 m

Solution

(i) The figure is a rhombus.

Using $P = 4b$,

$$P = 4(25 \text{ cm}) = 100 \text{ cm}$$

Using $A = b \times h$,

$$A = (25 \text{ cm})(22 \text{ cm}) = 550 \text{ cm}^2$$

Therefore, the perimeter is 100 cm and the area is 550 cm².

(ii) The figure is a parallelogram.

Using P = 2a + 2b,

P = 2(0.96 m) + 2(3.12 m) = 8.16 m

Using A = b × h,

A = (3.12 m)(0.75 m) = 2.34 m²

Therefore, the perimeter is 8.16 m and the area is 2.34 m².

Trapezoids

A **trapezoid** is a quadrilateral with one pair of opposite sides that are parallel – it is differentiated from a parallelogram by the property that the other pair of opposite sides are not parallel. Since all four sides may have different lengths, we denote the length of the smaller parallel side by the letter a, the length of the larger parallel side by the letter b, and the lengths of the other two sides by the letters c and d. Again, we denote the perpendicular height by the letter h.

The perimeter of a trapezoid is the sum of the four side lengths, a, b, c, and d.

To calculate the area of a trapezoid, "copy" the trapezoid, rotate the image by 180°, and "paste" it to the original trapezoid, as shown below. The result will be a parallelogram with an area of $(a + b) × h$.

The area of the trapezoid is half the area of the parallelogram $= \frac{1}{2}(a + b) × h$.

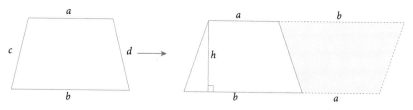

	Perimeter	Area
Trapezoid 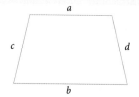	$P = a + b + c + d$	$A = \frac{1}{2}(a + b) × h$

Example 7.3-e **Calculating the Perimeter and Area of a Trapezoid**

Find the perimeter and area of the following trapezoid:

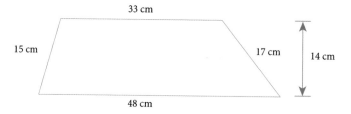

Solution

Using   P = a + b + c + d,

P = 33 cm + 48 cm + 15 cm + 17 cm = 113 cm

Solution
continued

Using $A = \dfrac{1}{2}(a + b) \times h$,

$$A = \dfrac{1}{2}(33 \text{ cm} + 48 \text{ cm})(14 \text{ cm})$$

$$= \dfrac{1}{2}(81 \text{ cm})(14 \text{ cm}) = 567 \text{ cm}^2$$

Therefore, the perimeter of the trapezoid is 113 cm and the area of the trapezoid is 567 cm².

Example 7.3-f | **Determining the Area of A Wound**

A patient comes to the ER with a burn wound in the shape of a trapezoid with the dimensions given on the figure below. Determine the perimeter and area of the burn.

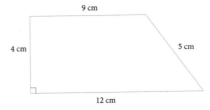

Solution

Using $P = a + b + c + d$,

$$P = 9 \text{ cm} + 12 \text{ cm} + 4 \text{ cm} + 5 \text{ cm} = 30 \text{ cm}$$

Using $A = \dfrac{1}{2}(a + b) \times h$,

$$A = \dfrac{1}{2}(9 \text{ cm} + 12 \text{ cm}) \times 4 \text{ cm}$$

$$= \dfrac{1}{2}(21 \text{ cm})(4 \text{ cm}) = 42 \text{ cm}^2$$

Therefore, the perimeter of the burn is 30 cm and the area is 42 cm².

Triangles

A **triangle** is a closed figure formed by three sides and three internal angles. We use the letters a, b, and c to denote the side lengths, and h to denote the height.

The perimeter of a triangle (P), regardless of whether it is acute, right, or obtuse, is the sum of the three side lengths a, b, and c.

$$P = a + b + c$$

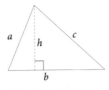

(i) Acute Triangle

(ii) Right Triangle

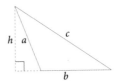

(iii) Obtuse Triangle

Calculating the area of a triangle (acute, right, or obtuse) when the length of the base and height are known.

To calculate the area of a triangle (regardless of whether it is acute, right, or obtuse), "copy" the triangle, rotate the image by 180°, and "paste" it to the original triangle as shown below. The result in all three cases will be a parallelogram, with base b and height h.

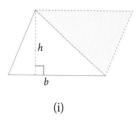 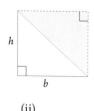 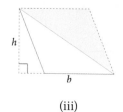

(i)   (ii)   (iii)

Thus, the area of a triangle is half that of a parallelogram.

$$A = \frac{1}{2}(b \times h)$$

Calculating the area of a triangle (acute, right, or obtuse) when the length of all three sides are known (using Heron's formula)

Heron's formula states that if a, b, and c, are the lengths of the sides of the triangle, the area is given by:

$$A = \sqrt{p(p-a)(p-b)(p-c)}$$

Where p is half the perimeter (P), $p = \dfrac{a+b+c}{2}$

		Perimeter	Area
Triangle	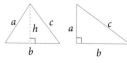	$P = a + b + c$	$A = \frac{1}{2}(b \times h)$ Or, using Heron's Formula, $A = \sqrt{p(p-a)(p-b)(p-c)}$ where, $p = \dfrac{a+b+c}{2}$

Example 7.3-g **Calculating the Perimeter and Area of a Triangle**

Find the perimeter and area of the following triangles:

(i)
16 cm   41.6 cm
38.4 cm

(ii)
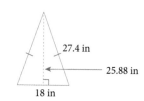
27.4 in
25.88 in
18 in

Solution

(i)   Using P = a + b + c,

P = 16 cm + 38.4 cm + 41.6 cm = 96 cm

Using $A = \dfrac{1}{2}(b \times h)$,

$A = \dfrac{1}{2}(38.4 \text{ cm} \times 16 \text{ cm})$

= 307.2 cm²

or

Using $A = \sqrt{p(p-a)(p-b)(p-c)}$,

where $p = \dfrac{a+b+c}{2} = \dfrac{96 \text{ cm}}{2} = 48$ cm

$A = \sqrt{48(48-16)(48-38.4)(48-41.6)}$

= 307.2 cm²

Therefore, the perimeter of the triangle is 96 cm and the area is 307.2 cm².

Solution
continued

(ii) P = 27.4 in + 18 in + 27.4 in = 72.8 in

$$A = \frac{1}{2}(18 \text{ in} \times 25.88 \text{ in})$$

$$= 232.92 \text{ in}^2$$

or

$$p = \frac{72.8 \text{ in}}{2} = 36.4 \text{ in}$$

$$A = \sqrt{36.4(36.4 - 27.4)(36.4 - 18)(36.4 - 27.4)}$$

$$= 232.917496... = 232.92 \text{ in}^2$$

Therefore, the perimeter of the triangle is 72.8 in. and the area of the triangle is 232.92 in².

Example 7.3-h **Finding the Area of a Kite**

Calculate the area of the kite shown in the figure below:

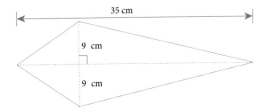

Solution

Since the adjacent sides of a kite are equal and the diagonals meet at right angles, the kite consists of two identical triangles, each with a base of 35 cm and a height of 9 cm.

First we find the area of each of the two triangles, using $A = \frac{1}{2}(b \times h)$

$$A = \frac{1}{2}(35 \text{ cm} \times 9 \text{ cm}) = 157.5 \text{ cm}^2$$

Therefore, the area of the kite is 2 × 157.5 cm² = 315 cm².

Circles and Sectors

Circles

A **circle** is a closed plane curve such that any point on the curve lies within a fixed distance (known as the **radius**) from a fixed point (the **centre**).

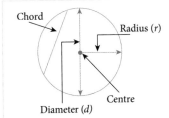

The **radius** *(r)* is the distance from the centre point of the circle to any point on the boundary of the circle.

A **chord** is a line segment that connects any two points on the boundary of the circle.

The **diameter** *(d)* is the length of the largest chord on the circle: the one that passes through the centre point. Notice that the diameter is exactly twice the radius: $d = 2r$.

Exhibit 7.3 A circle and its components

To describe the boundary length of the circle, the word **circumference**, rather than perimeter, is used. For any circle, the ratio of the circumference, *C*, to its diameter, *d*, is a constant special irrational number discovered by the ancient Greeks, known as π (*pi*, pronounced "pie").

$$C = \pi d$$

i.e., $\dfrac{C}{d} = \pi$; hence,

$$C = \pi(2r)$$

$$C = 2\pi r$$

Note: 'π' is an irrational number, which means that we cannot express its exact value as a fraction or decimal; an approximation of pi is π ≈ 3.14159, or more simply, π ≈ 3.14. However, in calculations involving 'π' in the examples and exercise questions within this chapter, we use the 'π' button that can be found on any scientific calculator.

The area of a circle is calculated, as follows:

$2\pi r$

πr

h

$b = \pi r$

Step 1: Cut a circle into an even number of equal slices (for example, 16).

Step 2: Take half of the slices and arrange them end-to-end in the shape of "teeth". Do the same with the other half and place it on each end to make the interlocking shape symmetrical.

Step 3: The result is approximately a parallelogram. The length of the parallelogram is half of the circumference of the circle; i.e., $b = \dfrac{2\pi r}{2} = \pi r$. The height of the parallelogram is the distance from the boundary of the circle to the centre, which is the radius, r. The area of the circle, therefore, is approximately equal to the area of the parallelogram: $A \approx b \times h = (\pi r) \times r = \pi r^2$.

Note: The more slices used in the circle, the closer the approximation gets. Therefore, the formula in Step 3 is indeed the exact formula for the area of a circle:

		Circumference	Area
Circle		$C = \pi d$ $C = 2\pi r$	$A = \pi r^2$

Example 7.3-i Calculating Circumference and Area of a Circle

Find the circumference and area of the following circles (round the answer to 2 decimal places):

(i)

radius
15 cm

(ii)

diameter
1.24 m

Solution

(i) Using $C = 2\pi r$ and $A = \pi r^2$,

$C = 2\pi r = 2(\pi)(15 \text{ cm}) = 94.247779... = 94.25$ cm

$A = \pi r^2 = (\pi)(15 \text{ cm})^2 = 706.858347... = 706.86$ cm²

Therefore, the circumference of the circle is 94.25 cm and the area is 706.86 cm².

(ii) Using $C = \pi d$ and $A = \pi r^2$,

$C = \pi d = \pi(1.24 \text{ m}) = 3.895574... = 3.90$ m

$r = \dfrac{d}{2} = \dfrac{1.24 \text{ m}}{2} = 0.62$ m

$A = \pi r^2 = \pi(0.62 \text{ m})^2 = 1.207628... = 1.21$ m²

Therefore, the circumference of the circle is 3.90 m and the area is 1.21 m².

Example 7.3-j | Calculating the Distance Travelled on an Exercise Bicycle

A stationary exercise bicycle has a wheel with a 622 mm diameter. If the wheel spins at 192 rpm (revolutions per minute), determine the distance the cyclist travels in 1 hour and 20 minutes, rounded to the nearest tenth of a km.

Solution

The distance travelled in one revolution of the wheel is equivalent to the circumference of the wheel.

Distance travelled in one revolution = $C = \pi d = \pi(622 \text{ mm}) \approx 1,954 \text{ mm} = 1.954 \text{ m}$

Since it spins at 192 rpm (revolutions per minute), the distance travelled in 1 minute is equal to,

$$\frac{192 \text{ rev}}{1 \text{ min}} \times \frac{1.954 \text{ m}}{1 \text{ rev}} \approx 375.2 \text{ m/min}$$

The total distance travelled in 1 hour and 20 minutes (= 80 minutes) is,

$$80 \text{ min} \times \frac{375.2 \text{ m}}{1 \text{ min}} = 30,016 \text{ m} \approx 30.0 \text{ km}$$

Therefore, the cyclist travelled approximately 30.0 km in 1 hour and 20 minutes.

Example 7.3-k | Determining the Amount of Iodine Needed

A circular area with a diameter of 12 inches of a patient's body is being prepped for surgery. A surgical resident spreads iodine solution on the area at a rate of 1.5 mL of iodine solution per square inch (in²) of skin. How much iodine solution (rounded to the nearest 10 mL) is required to cover the entire surgical area, if an additional 1-inch section around the surgical area is also to be covered in iodine?

Solution

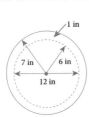

Radius of surgical area surface $= \dfrac{d}{2} = \dfrac{12 \text{ in}}{2} = 6 \text{ in}$

Since there is a 1-inch section to be included around the edge of the surgical area, the radius of the surface to be covered with iodine solution is 7 inches.

The area of the surgical section to be covered with the iodine is:
$A = \pi r^2 = \pi(7 \text{ in})^2 \approx 154 \text{ in}^2$

The quantity of iodine solution needed to cover the surgical area is:

$$154 \text{ in}^2 \times \frac{1.5 \text{ mL}}{1 \text{ in}^2} \approx 230 \text{ mL}$$

Therefore, approximately 230 mL of iodine solution is needed to cover the surgical area.

Sectors

A **sector** (denoted by a capital S) is a portion of a circle that is bounded by two radii from the centre of the circle to the boundary of the circle, as shown in the diagram below. The section of the circumference that bounds the sector is known as the **arc** (denoted by a capital L). The internal angle of the sector inscribed by the two radii is known as the **angle subtended by the arc** (denoted by the Greek letter θ).

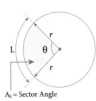

A_S = Sector Angle

In a sector of a circle with sector angle θ:

(i) The arc length, L, of the sector is proportional to the circumference of the circle, πd, as θ is to 360°.

i.e., $\dfrac{\theta}{360°} = \dfrac{L}{\pi d} \longrightarrow L = \pi d \times \dfrac{\theta}{360°}$

Thus, the perimeter of the sector $P_S = r + r + L = 2r + L$

(ii) The area, A, of the sector is proportional to the area of the circle, πr^2, as θ is to 360°.

i.e., $\dfrac{\theta}{360°} = \dfrac{A_S}{\pi r^2} \longrightarrow A_S = \pi r^2 \times \dfrac{\theta}{360°}$

		Arc length	Area
Sector	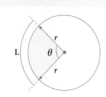	$L = \pi d \times \dfrac{\theta}{360°}$ Perimeter $P_S = 2r + L$	$A_S = \pi r^2 \times \dfrac{\theta}{360°}$

Example 7.3-l

Calculating the Perimeter and Area of a Sector

Calculate the perimeter and area (rounded to the nearest mm and mm², respectively) of a sector of a circle with a radius of 75 mm and an inscribed angle of 75°.

Solution

Using $\quad P_S = 2r + L$ and $L = \pi d \times \dfrac{\theta}{360°}$,

$$P_S = 2(75 \text{ mm}) + \pi(2)(75 \text{ mm})\left(\frac{75°}{360°}\right) \approx 150 \text{ mm} + 98 \text{ mm} = 248 \text{ mm}$$

Using $\quad A_S = \pi r^2 \times \dfrac{\theta}{360°}$,

$$= \pi(75 \text{ mm})^2 \left(\frac{75°}{360°}\right) \approx 3,682^2 \text{ mm}^2$$

Example 7.3-m

Determining the Speed of a Lab Sample in a Centrifuge

A centrifuge has a diameter of 50.5 cm. If the centrifuge rotates at a maximum speed of 9° per millisecond (i.e., one-thousandth of a second), determine the speed at which the lab samples on the rim of the centrifuge are moving (in m/s, rounded to the nearest hundredth of a m).

Solution

Using $\quad L = \pi d \times \dfrac{\theta}{360°}$,

$$L = \pi(50.5 \text{ cm})\left(\frac{9°}{360°}\right) \approx 3.97 \text{ cm}$$

A centrifuge is a device used in health sciences that spins liquids at a very high speed to separate the substances in the liquid by density.

Hence, the lab samples travel at a maximum speed of 3.97 cm/ms.

Converting cm/ms to m/s:

$$\frac{3.97 \text{ cm}}{1 \text{ ms}} \times \frac{1 \text{ m}}{100 \text{ cm}}$$

$$= \frac{0.0397 \text{ m}}{1 \text{ ms}} \times \frac{1,000 \text{ ms}}{1 \text{ s}}$$

$$= 39.7 \text{ m/s}$$

Therefore, the lab samples travel at a maximum speed of 39.7 m/s.

Composite Figures

It is quite common, when solving application problems, to see a complex geometric figure constructed out of two or more simple, geometric figures that have been previously described. Such figures are called **composite figures**.

To determine the perimeter of a composite figure, simply calculate the length of the boundary, by adding up all the straight lengths and sector lengths along the boundary.

To determine the area of a composite figure, break the figure up into simple figures and add up all the areas.

Example 7.3-n — Calculating the Perimeter and Area of a Parking Lot

A new parking lot is to be created around a hospital (see image to the right). The edge of the parking lot is to be enclosed with concrete curbs and the surface of the parking lot is to be paved with asphalt. Determine how many linear metres of concrete curbing and square metres of asphalt are required to create the parking lot.

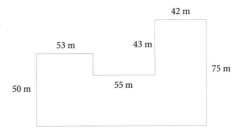

Solution

Let x, y, and z be the unknown lengths as marked in the diagram below:

$x = 53\text{ m} + 55\text{ m} + 42\text{ m} = 150\text{ m}$

$y = 75\text{ m} - 43\text{ m} = 32\text{ m}$

$z = 50\text{ m} - y = 50\text{ m} - 32\text{ m} = 18\text{ m}$

$P = 50 + 53 + z + 55 + 43 + 42 + 75 + x = 486\text{ m}$

$A_1 = (50\text{ m})(53\text{ m}) = 2{,}650\text{ m}^2$

$A_2 = (y)(55\text{ m}) = (32\text{ m})(55\text{ m}) = 1{,}760\text{ m}^2$

$A_3 = (75\text{ m})(42\text{ m}) = 3{,}150\text{ m}^2$

$A = 2{,}650 + 1{,}760 + 3{,}150 = 7{,}560\text{ m}^2$

To calculate the amount of asphalt needed, we calculate the area of the parking lot by breaking it up into three rectangular components, (1), (2) and (3):

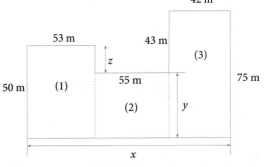

Therefore, 486 m of concrete curbing and 7,560 m² of asphalt are needed to create the parking lot.

Example 7.3-o — Calculating the Perimeter and Area

A pool used for physiotherapy is rectangular in shape with two semi-circular ends (see sketch below). Determine the amount of material required (rounded to the nearest square metre) for the pool cover if it is 60 m from end to end at its longest and 20 m wide.

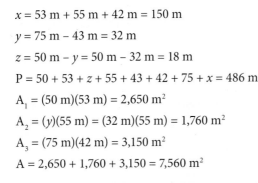

Solution

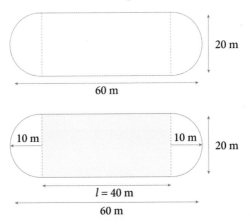

The width of the rectangle = 20 m.

Since the pool is 20 m wide, the diameters of each of the end semi-circles = 20 m; hence the radius = 10 m.

The length of the rectangle is the full length of the pool minus the radius of the two semi-circles at each end = 60 − 2(10) = 40 m.

$$A_{\text{rectangle}} = (40\text{ m})(20\text{ m}) = 800\text{ m}^2$$

$$A_{\text{semi-circle at both ends}} = 2\left[\frac{1}{2}\pi(10\text{ m})^2\right] \approx 314\text{ m}^2$$

Therefore, $A \approx 800 + 314 = 1{,}114\text{ m}^2$.

In some cases, it may be easier to think of the composite figure as a "cut-out" shape; i.e., as a simple geometric figure with another simple geometric figure cut out of it. In such cases, subtraction may be more convenient to calculate the perimeter or area of the composite figure.

| Example 7.3-p | **Calculating the Perimeter and Area of a "Cut-Out" Shape** |

Find the area of the following "cut-out" shape:

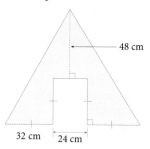

Solution

The shape is a triangle with a rectangle cut out of it. As with the previous question, we need the dimensions of both simple shapes:

The dimensions of the rectangle at the centre are $l = 32$ cm and $w = 24$ cm.

The height of the triangle is $h = 48$ cm + 32 cm = 80 cm

The base of the triangle is $b = 2(32$ cm$) + 24$ cm = 88 cm

$$A_{triangle} = \frac{1}{2}(88 \text{ cm})(80 \text{ cm}) = 3{,}520 \text{ cm}^2$$

$$A_{rectangle} = (32 \text{ cm})(24 \text{ cm}) = 768 \text{ cm}^2$$

Therefore, the area of the 'cut-out' figure = 3,520 – 768 = 2,752 cm²

7.3 | Exercises

Answers to odd-numbered problems are available at the end of the textbook.

For Problems 1 to 10, calculate the perimeter and area of the plane figures:

1. a. A square with sides 8 mm long.   b. A rectangle with sides of 6.4 m and 4.5 m.

2. a. A square with sides 22.5 cm long.   b. A rectangle with sides of 15 m and 20 m.

3. A rhombus with sides of 16.25 cm and a height of 12.75 cm.

4. A rhombus with sides of 6.75 m and a height of 5.25 m.

5. A parallelogram with a base of 12 cm, slant sides of 4 cm, and a height of 3.5 cm.

6. A parallelogram with a base of 14 cm, slant sides of 7 cm, and a height of 5.5 cm.

7. A trapezoid with parallel sides 2.45 m and 1.55 m long, slant sides that are both 0.75 m long, and a perpendicular height of 0.6 m.

8. A trapezoid with parallel sides 98 mm and 73 mm, one side measuring 60 mm that is perpendicular to the parallel sides, and a slant side that is 65 mm long.

9. An isosceles triangle with a base of 9 cm, slant sides of 7.5 cm, and a height of 6 cm.

10. An equilateral triangle with sides 52.5 mm long and a height of 45.5 mm.

For Problems 11 to 14, calculate the circumference and area of the circles (rounded to the indicated place value):

11. A circle with a radius of 8 cm (to the nearest hundredth).

12. A circle with a radius of 25 cm (to the nearest tenth).

13. A circle with a diameter of 1.84 m (to the nearest thousandth).

14. A circle with a diameter of 95 mm (to the nearest whole number).

For Problem 15 to 18, calculate the perimeter and area of the given sectors (rounded to the indicated place value):

15. A sector of a circle with radius 72 cm, inscribed by an angle of 135° (to the nearest whole number).

16. A sector of a circle with radius 2.5 m, inscribed by an angle of 40° (to the nearest hundredth).

17. A sector of a circle with diameter 64 mm, inscribed by an angle of 12° (to the nearest tenth).

18. A sector of a circle with diameter 48 km, inscribed by an angle of 75° (to the nearest thousandth).

19. A waiting room is being built on a rectangular piece of land, 35 m long by 28 m wide. If there is to be a 2 m wide walkway around the entire waiting room, determine the area available to build the inner section of the room.

20. A cross section of a portal vein has a diameter of 2 mm. Calculate the cross-sectional area of the vein through which blood can flow.

21. A cross section of a jugular vein has an area of 2.25 cm². Determine its circumference.

22. A square surgical area has an area of 225 cm². Determine the perimeter of the surgical section.

23. A square piece of gauze has a perimeter of 144 cm. Calculate the area of the gauze in cm².

24. A Band-Aid that is three times as long as it is wide has a perimeter of 24 cm. Determine the area of the Band-Aid in cm².

25. A hospital window is constructed using a simple frame of two pieces of metal, one long piece measuring 60 cm and one short piece measuring 32 cm, fashioned together in the shape of a perpendicular cross (see diagram to the right). Glass panes are then fitted to the frame to make the window. Determine the total area of glass needed.

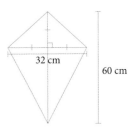

32 cm

60 cm

26. If the dimensions in problem 25 were doubled, what would happen to the amount of glass needed to construct the window? What total area of glass would be required?

27. A garden is planted on a right-triangular plot that is 6.5 m long and 6.5 m wide, at the corner of a main intersection coming into a town. If soil for the garden costs $2.75/m², determine the total cost to lay the soil in the garden.

28. A quilt for a new baby is constructed using triangular pieces of fabric, each 16 cm long at the base and 10 cm high. How many triangular pieces of fabric are needed to make a quilt that has an area of 1 m²?

29. An exercise bike with a wheel diameter of 32 cm makes a complete revolution in 0.4 seconds. Determine the speed of the wheel, in km/h, rounded to the nearest tenth.

30. A car tire has a diameter of 68 cm and the car is travelling at a speed of 100 km/h. Determine the number of revolutions the tire makes in one minute (rpm), rounded to the nearest rpm.

For Problems 31 to 40, determine the perimeter and area of the composite plain figures. Round your answer to two decimal places, as needed.

31.

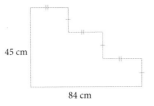

45 cm

84 cm

32.

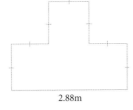

2.88m

33.

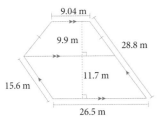

9.04 m

9.9 m

28.8 m

11.7 m

15.6 m

26.5 m

34.

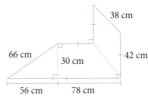

38 cm

66 cm

30 cm

42 cm

56 cm   78 cm

35.

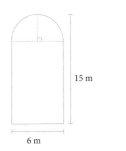

15 m

6 m

36.

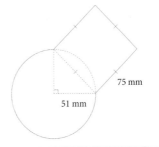

75 mm

51 mm

37.

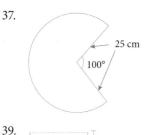

38.

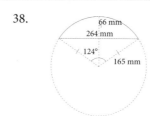

39.

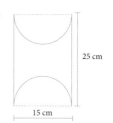

40.

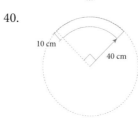

7.4 | Surface Areas and Volumes of Common Solid Objects

All the shapes and figures outlined in the previous sections were 2-dimensional. In this section, the general classification of common solid objects that occupy 3-dimensions will be discussed, along with the two important measurements of these objects: surface area and volume. The 3-dimensions most-commonly referred to are length (l), width (w), and height (h). Sometimes, these terms are interchanged with breadth, thickness, and depth, respectively.

The **surface area** of a solid is the total area of the external surface of a solid, including its ends or bases. It is measured in square units (cm^2, m^2, ft^2, etc.).

The **volume** of a solid is a measure of the space it occupies or encloses. It is measured in cubic units (cm^3, m^3, ft^3, etc.), or in the case of liquids, in litres, gallons, or some other unit of volume measurement.

In the health sciences, surface area and volume measurements are required to effectively use medical tools.

The different types of common solid objects that are classified based on their shapes are shown in Exhibit 7.4-a.

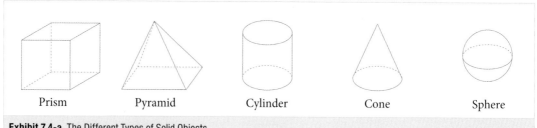

Exhibit 7.4-a The Different Types of Solid Objects

A **polyhedron** is a 3-dimensional object in which all the faces are polygons (flat surfaces with straight edges). For example, prisms and pyramids are bounded by polygons (flat surfaces), and therefore, they are polyhedrons. However, cylinders, cones, and spheres are not polyhedrons because they are formed by curved surfaces.

A polyhedron with congruent faces is known as a **platonic solid**. There are only 5 possible platonic solids:

- Tetrahedron: 4 faces, congruent equilateral triangles (a special type of pyramid)

- Cube: 6 faces, congruent squares (a special type of prism)

- Octahedron: 8 faces, congruent equilateral triangles

- Dodecahedron: 12 faces, congruent pentagons

- Icosahedron: 20 faces, congruent equilateral triangles

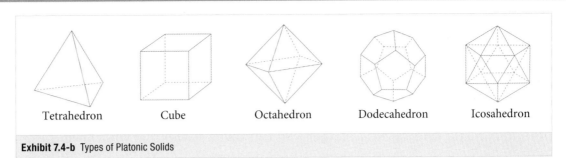

Exhibit 7.4-b Types of Platonic Solids

Prisms

A **prism** is a polyhedron with two parallel and congruent end-faces (bases). The height of a prism is the perpendicular distance between its bases.

In a **right prism**, all the lateral faces are rectangles. The height of a rectangular prism is the length of a lateral edge. In an **oblique prism**, all lateral faces are parallelograms (see diagram below). This chapter will only examine right prisms.

Prisms are named according to the shape of the bases. For example, a prism with a rectangular base is a **rectangular prism**, while a prism with a triangular base is a **triangular prism**.

> Lateral faces are faces in a solid object that are not bases (top or bottom).

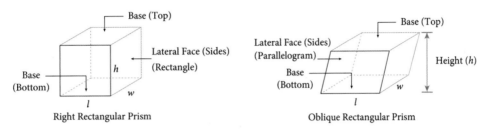

Surface Area of a prism = 2 × Base Area + Sum of the area of all lateral faces

Volume of a prism = Base Area × Height of the prism

Right Prisms

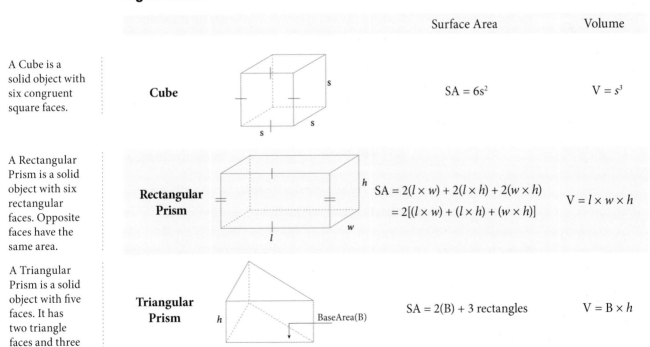

		Surface Area	Volume
A Cube is a solid object with six congruent square faces.	**Cube**	$SA = 6s^2$	$V = s^3$
A Rectangular Prism is a solid object with six rectangular faces. Opposite faces have the same area.	**Rectangular Prism**	$SA = 2(l \times w) + 2(l \times h) + 2(w \times h)$ $= 2[(l \times w) + (l \times h) + (w \times h)]$	$V = l \times w \times h$
A Triangular Prism is a solid object with five faces. It has two triangle faces and three rectangular faces.	**Triangular Prism**	$SA = 2(B) + 3$ rectangles	$V = B \times h$

Example 7.4-a **Calculating the Surface Area and Volume of Rectangular Prisms**

The dimensions of a microscope slide used in a lab to analyze blood samples are 75 mm by 26 mm by 1 mm. Determine the surface area and volume of the slide.

Solution

Using SA = $2(l \times w) + 2(l \times h) + 2(w \times h)$,

SA = $2(75 \text{ mm} \times 26 \text{ mm}) + 2(75 \text{ mm} \times 1 \text{ mm}) + 2(26 \text{ mm} \times 1 \text{ mm})$

= $3{,}900 \text{ mm}^2 + 150 \text{ mm}^2 + 52 \text{ mm}^2$

= $4{,}102 \text{ mm}^2$

Using V = $l \times w \times h$,

V = $(75 \text{ mm} \times 26 \text{ mm} \times 1 \text{ mm})$

= $1{,}950 \text{ mm}^3$

Therefore, the surface area of the microscope slide is $4{,}102 \text{ mm}^2$ and the volume is $1{,}950 \text{ mm}^3$.

Pyramids

A **pyramid** is a polyhedron in which the base is a polygon and all lateral faces are triangles, meeting at a common point called the **apex** (vertex).

A **regular right pyramid** is a pyramid whose base is a regular polygon and the line connecting the apex to the centre of the base forms a right-angle with the base; this is the height of the regular pyramid.

A **right rectangular pyramid** is a right pyramid with a rectangular base, in which all triangular side faces are isosceles triangles and opposite side faces are congruent (the term **rectangular pyramid** is commonly used to describe a right rectangular pyramid). If the base happens to be a square, then it is called a **right square pyramid**.

A **right triangular pyramid** is a right pyramid with a triangular base. If all the faces of the triangular pyramid are equilateral triangles, then it is called a **tetrahderon**.

The slant heights of the four triangular faces of a right rectangular pyramid are usually denoted by s_1 for the slant height on the length side and s_2 for the slant height on the width side. In a right square pyramid, since all four triangular sides are identical, there is only one slant height, denoted by s.

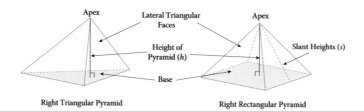

Apex	Lateral Triangular Faces	Apex
	Height of Pyramid (h)	Slant Heights (s)
	Base	
Right Triangular Pyramid		Right Rectangular Pyramid

Surface Area = (Sum of the area of all lateral triangular faces) + (Base area)

Volume = $\dfrac{1}{3}$(Base area × Height of the pyramid)

Right Pyramids

		Surface Area	Volume
Square Pyramid		$SA = 4\left(\dfrac{l \times s}{2}\right) + l^2$	$V = \dfrac{1}{3}(l \times l)h$
		$SA = 2(l \times s) + l^2$	$V = \dfrac{l^2 \times h}{3}$

		Surface Area	Volume
Rectangular Pyramid	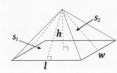	$SA = 2\left(\dfrac{l \times s_1}{2} + \dfrac{w \times s_2}{2}\right) + l \times w$ $SA = (l \times s_1 + w \times s_2) + l \times w$	$V = \dfrac{1}{3}(l \times w)h$ $V = \dfrac{l \times w \times h}{3}$
Triangular Pyramid	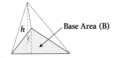	$SA =$ Area of all 3 lateral sides + Base Area (B)	$V = \dfrac{1}{3}(B)h$ $V = \dfrac{B \times h}{3}$

Example 7.4-b | **Calculating the Surface Area and Volume of Pyramids**

A herbal tea bag used for medicinal purposes is manufactured in the shape of a square-based pyramid, with side length 30 mm, height 20 mm, and slant height 25 mm. Find the following:

(i) The amount of mesh (in mm²) needed to manufacture the tea bag

(ii) The volume of tea (in cm³) the bag can hold

Solution

Since the tea bag has a square base, the slant heights are equal on all sides.

(i) Using $SA = 2(l \times s) + l^2$,

$\quad SA = 2(30 \text{ mm} \times 25 \text{ mm}) + (30 \text{ mm})^2$

$\quad\quad = 2{,}400 \text{ mm}^2$

Therefore 2,400 mm² of mesh is needed to manufacture the tea bag.

(ii) The length is 30 mm = 3 cm, and the height is 20 mm = 2 cm.

$\quad$ Using $V = \dfrac{l^2 \times h}{3}$,

$\quad\quad V = \dfrac{(3 \text{ cm})^2 \times (2 \text{ cm})}{3}$

$\quad\quad\quad = 6 \text{ cm}^3$

Therefore, the tea bag can hold 6 cm³ of tea.

Cylinders

A **cylinder** is a prism with 2 parallel and congruent circular bases and a curved lateral surface connecting the two bases. The height (altitude), h, of the cylinder is the perpendicular distance between the two bases. The radius, r, of the cylinder is the radius of the base circle.

In a **right cylinder**, the line joining the centre of the bases is perpendicular to the bases.

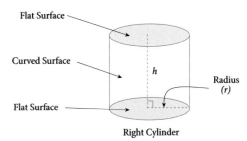

Right Cylinder

If the lateral side of a right circular cylinder is unwrapped, as in Exhibit 7.4-b, we see that it is a rectangle with a length equal to the circumference of the circular base ($C = 2\pi r$) and width equal to the height of the cylinder.

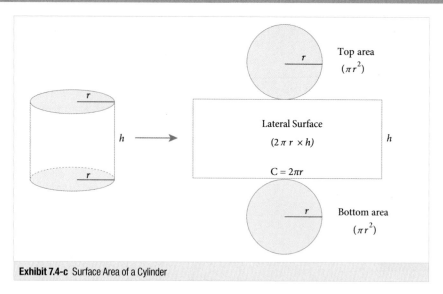

Exhibit 7.4-c Surface Area of a Cylinder

That is, we can take a rectangle and wrap it around to create a circular tube, which can then be "capped" at either or both ends with circles. This leads us to the following three definitions:

- A **closed cylinder** (or **can**) is a cylinder that has a lateral face and two end-faces.
- A **semi-closed cylinder** (or **cup**) is a cylinder that has a lateral face and one end-face.
- An **open cylinder** (or **tube**) is a cylinder that only has a lateral face with no end-faces.

Surface Area of a cylinder = 2 × Circular base area + Area of the curved lateral face

Volume of a cylinder = Base area × Height of the cylinder

Closed, Semi-closed, and Open Cylinders

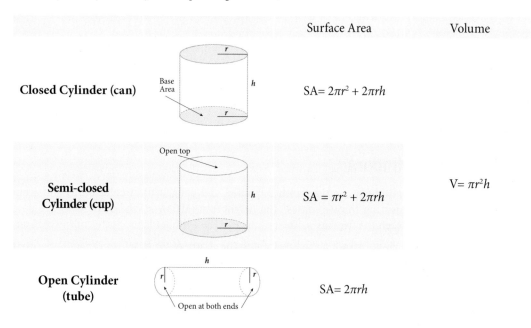

		Surface Area	Volume
Closed Cylinder (can)		SA = $2\pi r^2 + 2\pi rh$	
Semi-closed Cylinder (cup)		SA = $\pi r^2 + 2\pi rh$	V = $\pi r^2 h$
Open Cylinder (tube)		SA = $2\pi rh$	

Example 7.4-c	Calculating the Surface Area and Volume of a Closed Cylinder

A cylindrical can of prepared baby formula used in the pediatric-care unit in a hospital has a diameter of 10 cm and a height of 10 cm. Find the following, rounded to the nearest whole number:

(i) The area of metal needed for the can, including the lid, in cm².

(ii) The volume of baby formula the can holds, in mL.

Solution

Since the can has both a top and a bottom face, it represents a closed cylinder. Also, since the diameter of the can is 10 cm, the radius is 5 cm.

(i) Using SA = $2\pi r^2 + 2\pi rh$,

$$SA = 2\pi(5 \text{ cm})^2 + 2\pi(5 \text{ cm})(10 \text{ cm})$$

$$\approx 157 \text{ cm}^2 + 314 \text{ cm}^2$$

$$= 471 \text{ cm}^2$$

Therefore, the area of metal needed for the can is 471 cm².

(ii) Using V = $\pi r^2 h$,

$$V = \pi(5 \text{ cm})^2(10 \text{ cm})$$

$$\approx 785 \text{ cm}^3$$

Recall that 1 cm³ = 1 mL; therefore, V ≈ 785 mL.

Therefore, the volume of baby formula that the can holds is 785 mL.

Example 7.4-d | Calculating the Surface Area and Volume of a Semi-Closed Cylinder

A cylindrical bucket used for cleaning a hospital floor has a radius of 40 cm and a height of 90 cm. Find the following, rounded to the nearest whole number:

(i)   The area of plastic needed for the bucket, in cm² (rounded to the nearest whole unit).

(ii) The volume the bucket is able to hold, in L (rounded to the nearest tenth).

Solution

Since the bucket has a base but no top, it is a semi-closed cylinder.

(i) Using SA = $\pi r^2 + 2\pi rh$,

$$SA = \pi (40 \text{ cm})^2 + 2\pi(40 \text{ cm})(90 \text{ cm})$$

$$\approx 5{,}026.5 \text{ cm}^2 + 22{,}619.5 \text{ cm}^2$$

$$\approx 27{,}646 \text{ cm}^2$$

Therefore, the area of plastic needed for the bucket is 27,646 cm².

(ii) Using V = $\pi r^2 h$,

$$V = \pi(40 \text{ cm})^2(90 \text{ cm})$$

$$\approx 452{,}389 \text{ cm}^3$$

Recall that 1 cm³ = 1 mL; therefore, V ≈ 452,389 mL ≈ 452.4 L.

Therefore, the volume the bucket can hold is 452.4 L.

Example 7.4-e | Calculating the Surface Area and Volume of an Open Cylinder

A PVC tube has a diameter of 16 cm and a length of 1.2 m. Find the amount of plastic needed for the tube, in cm² (rounded to the nearest whole unit).

Solution

Since the tube has no base or top, it is an open cylinder. Before we can calculate the surface area, we need to get all the dimensions in a common unit:

d = 16 cm, therefore r = 8 cm, l = 1.2 m = 120 cm

Using SA = $2\pi rh$

$$SA = 2\pi(8 \text{ cm})(120 \text{ cm})$$

$$= 6{,}032 \text{ cm}^2$$

Therefore, the amount of plastic needed for the PVC tube is 6,032 cm².

Cones

A **cone** is a pyramid with a circular base and a curved lateral surface, which extends from the base to a point called the vertex. The height (altitude), h, of the cone is the perpendicular distance from the vertex to the base. The radius, r, of the cylinder is the radius of the base circle. The slant height of the cone, s, is the distance from the vertex to any point on the edge of the base.

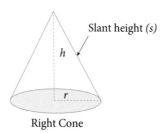

Right Cone

The surface area of a closed cone is the sum of the area of the circular base and the area of the lateral face. The area of the lateral face is $A = \pi \times r \times s$; the explanation of this formula is beyond the scope of this textbook.

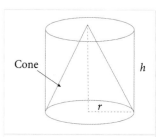

As with cylinders, closed cones have "lids" while open cones do not. Therefore, the surface area of an open cone is simply the area of the lateral face.

Surface Area = (Area of the circular base) + (Area of the lateral face)

Volume = $\frac{1}{3}$ (Area of circular base × Height of the cone)

The volume of a cone is exactly one third that of the cylinder with the same base and height.

Closed and Open Cones

		Surface Area	Volume
Cone (closed)		$SA = \pi r^2 + \pi rs$	$V = \dfrac{1}{3}\pi r^2 h$
Cone (open)		$SA = \pi rs$	$= \dfrac{\pi r^2 h}{3}$

Example 7.4-f	Calculating the Surface Area and Volume of Cones

A paper water cup used for a water cooler is in the shape of a cone, with a diameter of 6.4 cm, a height of 10.8 cm, and a slant height of 11.3 cm. Find the following:

(i)   The area of the paper needed to make the cup (rounded to the nearest cm²).

(ii) The volume of water the cup can hold (rounded to the nearest mL).

Solution

Since the cup has no lid, we need the formula for an open cone. We also need the length of the radius, which is half of the diameter: $r = 3.2$ cm.

(i) Using SA = πrs,

$$SA = \pi(3.2 \text{ cm})(11.3 \text{ cm})$$
$$\approx 114 \text{ cm}^2$$

Therefore, the area of the paper needed to make the cup is 114 cm².

(ii) Using $V = \dfrac{\pi r^2 h}{3}$,

$$V = \frac{\pi(3.2 \text{ cm})^2(10.8 \text{ cm})}{3}$$
$$\approx 116 \text{ cm}^3$$
$$= 116 \text{ mL}$$

Therefore, the volume of water the cup can hold is 116 mL.

Spheres

A sphere is a 3-dimensional object shaped like a ball. It is a solid bounded by curved surfaces and every surface point is a fixed distance (called the **radius**) away from a centre.

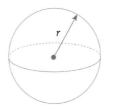

The surface area of a sphere is exactly equal to the surface area of the smallest **open** cylinder that inscribes the sphere. The volume of the sphere is exactly $\dfrac{2}{3}$ of the volume of the smallest cylinder that inscribes it.

Surface Area = (Surface area of inscribing open cylinder)

$$SA = 2\pi rh$$
$$= 2\pi r(2r)$$
$$= 4\pi r^2$$

Volume = $\dfrac{2}{3}$ (Volume of the inscribing cyclinder)

$$V = \frac{2}{3}\pi r^2 h$$
$$= \frac{2}{3}\pi r^2(2r)$$
$$= \frac{4}{3}\pi r^3$$

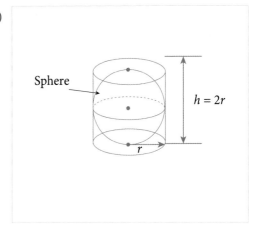

Sphere

$h = 2r$

r

	Surface Area	Volume
Sphere	$SA = 4\pi r^2$	$V = \dfrac{4}{3}(\pi r^3)$

	Surface Area	Volume
Half-sphere (solid also called a hemisphere) 	$SA = \dfrac{1}{2}(4\pi r^2) + \pi r^2$ $= 3\pi r^2$	$V = \dfrac{1}{2}(\dfrac{4}{3}\pi r^3)$ $= \dfrac{2}{3}(\pi r^3)$

Example 7.4-g | Calculating the Surface Area and Volume of Spheres

A spherical yoga ball has a height of 75 cm. Find the following:

(i)   The area of rubber needed to construct the ball (in m², rounded to the nearest thousandth).

(ii) The volume of air that the ball can hold when fully inflated (rounded to the nearest L).

Solution

The height of the yoga ball is the same as the diameter of the ball, which is twice the radius; therefore, $r = 37.5$ cm $= 0.375$ m.

(i)   Using $SA = 4\pi r^2$,

$$SA = 4\pi(0.375 \text{ m})^2$$

$$\approx 1.767 \text{ m}^2$$

Therefore, the amount of rubber needed to construct the ball is 1.767 m².

(ii) Since 1 mL = 1 cm³, 1 L = 1,000 mL = 1,000 cm³.

Using $V = \dfrac{4}{3} \times \pi r^3$,

$$V = \dfrac{4}{3}\pi(37.5 \text{ cm})^3$$

$$\approx 220,893 \text{ cm}^3$$

$$\approx 221 \text{ L}$$

Therefore, the volume of air that the ball can hold when fully inflated is 221 L.

Composite Figures

As in 2-dimensional plane geometry, there are many complex 3-dimensional solids which are composed of simpler solids like prisms, cylinders, pyramids, cones, and spheres. We will consider some examples of these below:

Example 7.4-h | Calculating the Surface Area of a Composite Shape

A greenhouse is built 5.0 m long, 3.0 m wide, 2.55 m tall at the sides and 3.2 m tall in the middle, with a roof that has a slant height of 1.6 m, as per the following diagram:

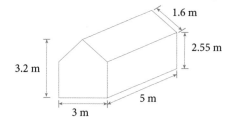

If the glass to build the greenhouse costs $3.96/m², find the total cost of the glass needed to build the greenhouse.

First, we need to determine the amount of glass needed to build the greenhouse, in m², which is the surface area of the greenhouse. This is a pentagonal prism, which we do not have a formula for. However, we can analyze the shape as a prism with 2 rectangular side faces, 2 rectangular roof faces, (no bottom face, since the floor is not constructed out of glass), and two end-faces that are each comprised of a rectangle and a triangle:

Using $SA = 2A_{side} + 2A_{roof} + 2(A_{end\ rectangle} + A_{end\ triangle})$

$$SA = 2(5.0\ m)(2.55\ m) + 2(5.0\ m)(1.6\ m) + 2\left((3.0\ m)(2.55\ m) + \frac{1}{2}(3.0\ m)(3.2\ m - 2.55\ m)\right)$$

$$= 25.5\ m^2 + 16.0\ m^2 + 2(8.625\ m^2)$$

$$= 58.75\ m^2$$

$$Cost = 58.75\ m^2 \times \frac{\$3.96}{m^2} = \$232.65$$

Therefore, the total cost of the glass needed to build the greenhouse is $232.65.

Example 7.4-i | **Calculating the Surface Area and Volume of a Composite Shape**

After a tonsillectomy, a child patient receives an ice-cream cone with a diameter of 8.5 cm at the opening, a perpendicular height of 17.5 cm, and a slant height of 18 cm. Ice-cream is scooped and packed into the cone until it is completely filled with ice cream and an additional hemi-sphere of ice cream sits on top, as in the figure below:

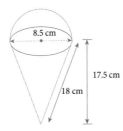

Find the following:

(i) The surface area of the cone (rounded to the nearest cm²).

(ii) The volume of ice-cream the cone can hold, including the hemi-sphere on top (rounded to the nearest mL).

(i) Since the cone does not have a lid, we use the formula for an open cone, and the radius is half of the diameter, so r = 4.25 cm.

Using $SA = \pi rs$

$$SA = \pi(4.25\ cm)(18\ cm)$$

$$\approx 240\ cm^2$$

Therefore, the surface area of the waffle cone is 240 cm².

(ii) The volume of ice-cream is equal to the volume of the cone, $\frac{\pi r^2 h}{3}$, plus the volume of a hemi-sphere, $\frac{2}{3}\pi r^3$. Since the flat circular face of the hemisphere lines up with the open circular face of the cone, the radii of the two solids are equal (i.e., r = 4.25 cm for both the cone and hemi-sphere).

$$V = \frac{\pi r^2 h}{3} + \frac{2}{3}\pi r^3$$

Solution
continued

$$V = \frac{\pi(4.25 \text{ cm})^2(17.5 \text{ cm})}{3} + \frac{2}{3}\pi(4.25 \text{ cm})^3$$

$$\approx 331.0 \text{ cm}^3 + 160.8 \text{ cm}^3$$

$$\approx 492 \text{ cm}^3$$

$$= 492 \text{ mL}$$

Therefore, the volume of ice-cream the cone can hold, including the hemi-sphere on top is 492 mL.

7.4 | Exercises

Answers to odd-numbered problems are available at the end of the textbook.

For the following problems, round your answer to two decimal places (unless otherwise indicated).

For Problems 1 to 16, determine the surface area and volume of the given solids:

1. A cube with sides 25 mm long.

2. A cube with sides 8 cm long.

3. A rectangular prism with sides of 3 m, 6 m, and 12.5 m.

4. A rectangular prism with sides of 40 cm, 80 cm, and 150 cm.

5. A semi-open cylinder with a height of 15 cm and a base with a diameter of 12 cm.

6. An open cylinder with a height of 51 cm and a base with a radius of 5 cm.

7. A closed cylinder with a height of 85 mm and a base with a radius of 32 mm.

8. A semi-open cylinder with a height of 1.5 m and a base with a diameter of 64 cm.

9. An open cone with a perpendicular height of 22 cm, a slant height of 22.5 cm, and a base with a radius of 4.5 cm.

10. A closed cone with a perpendicular height of 94 mm, a slant height of 98 mm, and a base with a diameter of 56 mm.

11. A sphere with a radius of 22 cm.

12. A sphere with a radius of 8 mm.

13. A sphere with a diameter of 1.3 m.

14. A sphere with a diameter of 7.5 cm.

15. A rectangular pyramid with base dimensions of 40 cm × 16 cm, a perpendicular height of 15 cm, and slant heights of 17 cm up from the 40 cm base and 25 cm up from the 16 cm base.

16. A square-based pyramid with base length of 5 m, a perpendicular height of 6 m, and slant heights of 6.5 m.

For Problems 17 to 20, determine the volume of the given solids:

17. A square pyramid with sides 4.5 m long and a height of 2.8 m.

18. A rectangular pyramid with side lengths of 48 cm and 60 cm, and a height of 55 cm.

19. A triangular prism with a base area of 7 cm² and a height of 36 cm.

20. A triangular pyramid with a base area of 270 m² and a height of 15 m.

21. Calculate the volume of a rectangular box measuring 1.44 m by 1.25 m by 75 cm. How much cardboard is needed to construct the box?

22. Calculate the volume of a can of baby formula that has a base with a diameter of 7.4 cm and a height of 11 cm. How much aluminum is needed to create the can?

23. Determine the volume of air held in a spherical bag valve mask (BVM) that has a surface area of 1,800 cm².

24. A spherical Ambu bag has a surface area of 277 mm². Determine the volume of the bag.

25. A cylindrical PVC tube with a height that is ten times its base diameter has a volume of 2.5 m³. Determine the surface area of the (open) cylindrical tube, rounded to the nearest tenth of a square metre.

26. A fish tank in a doctor's office in the shape of a rectangular prism with a width that is twice its height and two-thirds its length has a volume of 93,750 cm³. Determine the surface area of the fish tank, which is open at the top.

27. A decoration in a pediatrician's waiting room is made from an open plastic cone that has a slant height of 70 cm and a base diameter of 25 cm. Determine the amount of plastic needed to create the object.

28. A blood sample is placed on a 48 mm × 28 mm microscope slide, and filled the entire slide with a depth of 0.5 mm. What is the volume of blood in the sample? Express the volume in cc.

29. The diameter of a piece of a patient's portal vein is 2.5 mm. What volume of blood in cm³ is in a section of vein that is 4 mm long? Express the answer in mL, rounded to the nearest thousandth.

30. A spherical bowling ball is made up of a polyurethane core and a reactive resin cover, and must have a circumference of 68 cm. Determine the cost to manufacture the ball if the polyurethane for the core costs \$0.0065/cm³ and the reactive resin coating costs \$0.0105/cm². Round your answer to the nearest cent.

For Problems 31 to 34, determine the surface area and volume of the composite figures:

Note: For Problems 31 and 32, do not include the floor of the buildings in your surface area calculations.

31. A children's hospital playhouse consisting of a square prism base and a square-pyramid roof:

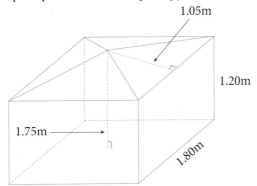

1.05m

1.20m

1.75m

1.80m

32. A naturopathic clinic has a greenhouse consisting of a rectangular base and a half-cylindrical roof:

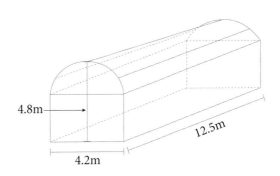

4.8m

12.5m

4.2m

33. A metal implant consisting of a cylindrical base and a hemispherical roof:

10.6 mm

3.2 mm

34. A pill capsule with two hemispheres on either side and an open cylinder

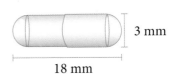

3 mm

18 mm

7.5 | Pythagorean Theorem

The Pythagorean Theorem is a famous theorem in mathematics. It is named after a Greek philosopher and mathematician, Pythagoras, who discovered[1] it thousands of years ago. It describes a special relationship between the lengths of the three sides of a right triangle. The theorem states that the squares of the lengths of the two shorter sides that meet at the right angle (called the **legs** of the right triangle) equal the square of the longest side opposite the right angle (called the **hypotenuse** of the right triangle).

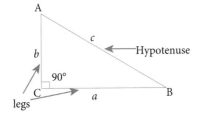

In a right-triangle, for example, ABC with the right angle at C, the Pythagorean Theorem is written as an equation relating the lengths of the sides of the right triangle a, b, and c, where a and b represent the legs, and c represents the hypotenuse, as follows:

$$a^2 + b^2 = c^2$$

[1] Although Pythagoras is credited with the discovery of the theorem, there is evidence to suggest that it was known by the ancient Babylonians, over 1,000 years prior to Pythagoras.

Using this equation, if the lengths of both legs (*a* and *b*) are known, then the hypotenuse (*c*) can be calculated as follows:

$$c = \sqrt{a^2 + b^2}$$

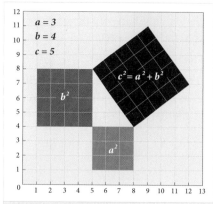

Exhibit 7.5 Pythagorean Theorem

Similarly, if the lengths of the hypotenuse (*c*) and one leg (*a* or *b*) are known, then the length of the other leg can be calculated as follows:

$$a = \sqrt{c^2 - b^2} \quad \text{or} \quad b = \sqrt{c^2 - a^2}$$

A set of positive integers that satisfies the Pythagorean Theorem are known as Pythagorean triples. For example, the integers 3, 4, and 5 are Pythagorean triples.

$$3^2 + 4^2 = 5^2$$

$$(9 + 16 = 25)$$

Some of the other Pythagorean triples are: (5, 12, 13), (7, 24, 25), (8, 15, 17), (9, 40, 41), (12, 35, 37), etc.

Example 7.5-a Calculating the Length of the Hypotenuse of a Right Triangle

Using the Pythagorean Theorem, calculate the length (rounded to the nearest hundredth, as needed) of the hypotenuse, *c*, of the following right triangles, given the lengths of the two legs, *a* and *b*.

(i) *a* = 3 m and *b* = 4 m

(ii) *a* = 10 cm and *b* = 12 cm

Solution

(i) Using $a^2 + b^2 = c^2$,

$$c^2 = a^2 + b^2 = 3^2 + 4^2 = 9 + 16 = 25$$

$$c = \sqrt{25} = 5 \text{ m}$$

(ii) Using $a^2 + b^2 = c^2$,

$$c^2 = a^2 + b^2 = 10^2 + 12^2 = 100 + 144 = 244$$

$$c = \sqrt{244} = 15.620499... = 15.62 \text{ cm}$$

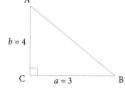

Example 7.5-b Calculating the Length of One of the Legs of a Right-Triangle

Using the Pythagorean Theorem, calculate the length (rounded to the nearest hundredth, as needed) of the missing leg of the following right-triangles, given the lengths of the hypotenuse, *c*, and one leg.

(i) *a* = 5 cm and *c* = 13 cm

(ii) *b* = 8 m and *c* = 16 m

Solution

(i) Using $a^2 + b^2 = c^2$

$$b^2 = c^2 - a^2 = 13^2 - 5^2 = 169 - 25 = 144$$

$$b = \sqrt{144} = 12 \text{ cm}$$

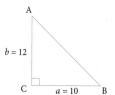

Solution
continued

(ii) Using $a^2 + b^2 = c^2$

$a^2 = c^2 - b^2 = 16^2 - 8^2 = 256 - 64 = 192$

$a = \sqrt{192} = 13.856406... = 13.86$ m

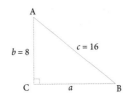

Example 7.5-c | **Calculate the Unknown Lengths in Right Triangles**

In the following figures, calculate the lengths of x and y (rounded to the nearest tenth, as needed):

(i)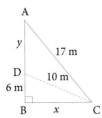

(ii)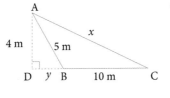

(iii)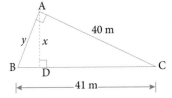

Solution

(i)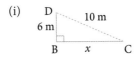

In the right triangle BCD, using the Pythagorean Theorem,

$x^2 + 6^2 = 10^2$

$x^2 = 10^2 - 6^2$

$= 100 - 36 = 64$

$x = \sqrt{64} = 8$ m

In the right triangle ABC, using the Pythagorean Theorem,

$(y + 6)^2 + 8^2 = 17^2$

$(y + 6)^2 = 17^2 - 8^2$

$= 289 - 64 = 225$

$(y + 6) = \sqrt{225} = 15$

$y = 15 - 6 = 9$ m

Therefore, $x = 8$ m and $y = 9$ m.

(ii)

In the right triangle ADB, using the Pythagorean Theorem,

$y^2 + 4^2 = 5^2$

$y^2 = 5^2 - 4^2$

$= 25 - 16 = 9$

$y = \sqrt{9} = 3$ m

In the right triangle ADC, using the Pythagorean Theorem,

$4^2 + 13^2 = x^2$

$x^2 = 16 + 169 = 185$

$x = \sqrt{185} = 13.601470... = 13.6$ m

Therefore, $x = 13.6$ m and $y = 3$ m.

(iii)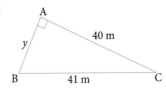

In the right triangle ABC, using the Pythagorean Theorem,

$y^2 + 40^2 = 41^2$

$y^2 = 41^2 - 40^2$

$= 1,681 - 1,600 = 81$

$y = \sqrt{81} = 9$ m

Solution
continued

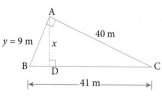

Using Heron's Formula, we can calculate the area of the triangle.

$$p = \frac{a+b+c}{2} = \frac{9+40+41}{2} = 45$$

$$A = \sqrt{p(p-a)(p-b)(p-c)}$$

$$= \sqrt{45(45-9)(45-40)(45-41)}$$

$$= \sqrt{32,400} = 180 \text{ m}^2$$

Now that we know area, we can use the formula for the area of a triangle to solve for height (x).

$$A = \frac{1}{2}(b \times h)$$

$$180 = \frac{1}{2}(41x)$$

$$180 = 20.5x$$

$$x = 8.780487... = 8.8 \text{ m}$$

Therefore, $x = 8.8$ m and $y = 9$ m.

Applications of the Pythagorean Theorem

Example 7.5-d   **Calculating the Distance Between Two Hospitals**

Hospital A is 45 km north and 26 km west of Hospital B. Find the shortest flying distance (rounded to the nearest kilometre) between the two hospitals.

Solution

Using the Pythagorean theorem,

$$d^2 = 45^2 + 26^2$$

$$= 2,025 + 676$$

$$= 2,701$$

$$d = \sqrt{2,701}$$

$$= 51.971145... = 52 \text{ km}$$

Therefore, the shortest flying distance between the two hospitals is 52 km.

Example 7.5-e   **Determining the Dimensions of a Television**

A 42 inch television, with a length to height ratio of 16 : 9, measures 42 inches across the diagonal. Find the length and the height of the TV, to the nearest tenth of an inch.

Solution

Since the ratio of the length of the TV to the height of the TV is 16 : 9, let $16x$ represent the length of the TV and $9x$ represent the height of the TV.

Using the Pythagorean Theorem,

$$42^2 = (16x)^2 + (9x)^2$$

$$1,764 = 256x^2 + 81x^2$$

$$1,764 = 337x^2$$

$$x^2 = \frac{1,764}{337} = 5.234421...$$

$$x = \sqrt{5.24421...} = 2.287885...$$

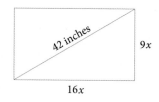

Length of the TV = $16x$ = 16(2.287885...) = 36.606172... = 36.6 inches

Height of the TV = $9x$ = 9(2.287885...) = 20.590972... = 20.6 inches

Therefore, the length of the TV is 36.6 inches and the height is 20.6 inches.

Example 7.5-f | **Calculating the Height, Surface Area, and Volume of a Pyramid**

The Great Pyramids of Giza in Egypt have certain special properties: the ratio of the slant height (s) of the pyramid to the semi-base (b_1) of the pyramid adheres to the "Golden Ratio," which is approximately 1.618 : 1.

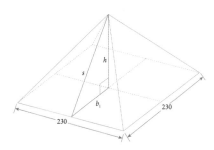

Jorge wishes to know the height (h) and volume (V) of the largest pyramid. If he measures the length of one side of the base to be 230 m, find the height of the pyramid, rounded to the nearest metre. Then, find the surface area and volume of the pyramid, rounded to the nearest square metre and cubic metre, respectively.

Solution

Since the base is 230 m, $b_1 = \dfrac{230}{2} = 115$ m.

Step 1: Calculate the slant height of the pyramid, s, using the Golden Ratio $\dfrac{s}{b_1} = 1.618$.

$$s = 1.618(115) = 186.07 = 186 \text{ m}$$

Therefore, the slant height of the pyramid is 186 m.

Step 2: Calculate the height of the pyramid using the Pythagorean Theorem.

$$s^2 = b_1^2 + h^2$$
$$(186)^2 = (115)^2 + (h)^2$$
$$34{,}596 = 13{,}225 + h^2$$
$$h^2 = 21{,}371$$
$$h = \sqrt{21{,}371} = 146.188234... = 146 \text{ m}$$

Therefore, the height of the pyramid is 146 m.

Step 3: Calculate the surface area of the 4 equal triangular sides using slant height $s = 186$ m and $b = 230$ m.

$$SA = 4 \times \left[\frac{(230 \text{ m})(186 \text{ m})}{2} \right] = 85{,}560 \text{ m}^2$$

Step 4: Calculate the volume of the pyramid using the formula for a square-based pyramid.

$$V = \frac{(230 \text{ m})^2(146 \text{ m})}{3} = 2{,}574{,}466.666... = 2{,}574{,}467 \text{ m}^3$$

Therefore, the surface area of the pyramid is 85,560 m² and the volume of the pyramid is 2,574,467 m³.

7.5 | Exercises

In Problems 1 to 4, use the Pythagorean Theorem to determine the length (express the answers rounded to the nearest hundredth, wherever applicable) of the missing side in the given right-angled triangles, where a and b represent the legs of the triangle and c represents the hypotenuse of the triangle.

1.

	a	b	c
a.	15 cm	20 cm	?
b.	2.5 cm	?	6.5 cm
c.	?	6 cm	6.25 cm

2.

	a	b	c
a.	7 cm	24 cm	?
b.	7.5 cm	?	12.5 cm
c.	?	20 cm	20.5 cm

3.

	a	b	c
a.	12 cm	15 cm	?
b.	8 cm	?	17 cm
c.	?	15 cm	16 cm

4.

	a	b	c
a.	16 cm	18 cm	?
b.	20 cm	?	29 cm
c.	?	17 cm	23 cm

In Problems 5 to 8, calculate the length of the missing side for each of the diagrams.

5.

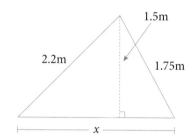

6.

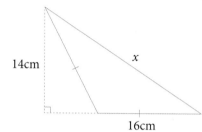

7.

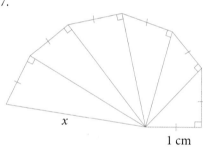

8.

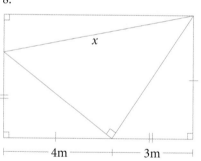

For Problems 9 and 10, use the Pythagorean Theoram and Heron's Formula to determine the missing side length.

9.

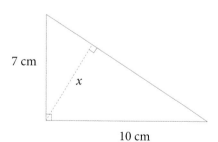

10.

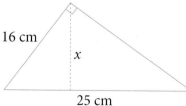

In Problems 11 to 14, calculate the perimeter and area of each of the given diagrams.

11.

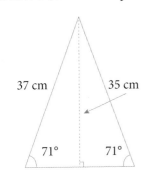

12.

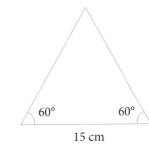

13.

14.

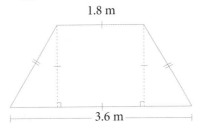

15. A laptop screen measures 31 cm long by 17.5 cm high. Determine the diagonal length of the laptop screen, rounded to the nearest tenth of a cm.

16. From a point 'X', a person walked 850 m due west and then turned and walked for another 1.7 km due south to reach point 'Y'. Calculate the shortest distance between X and Y, rounded to the nearest hundredth of a km.

17. A 2.5 m tent pole is secured using a 4.3 m long guy rope from the top of the pole. How far away from the base of the pole will the rope need to be secured to the ground, assuming it is pulled taut? Round your answer to the nearest centimetre.

18. A 5 m ladder is leaned up against a wall. If the base of the ladder is placed on the ground 1.7 m away from the wall, how high up against the wall will the ladder reach, rounded to the nearest tenth of a metre?

19. A skateboard ramp that is 3.5 m long is built with a maximum slope of $\frac{3}{5}$. Determine the maximum height of the ramp, rounded to the nearest cm.

20. A wheelchair ramp is to be constructed to the top of a set of stairs that is 1.75 m tall, with a maximum slope of $\frac{1}{12}$.

Determine the minimum ramp length required, in order for the ramp to be built according to specifications. Can you suggest a way to build the ramp that would save space?

21. A towel rack that is 1 m long is to be placed in a box measuring 75 cm × 60 cm × 45 cm. Will the towel rack fit along the diagonal at the bottom of the box? Will it fit in the box if placed on the 3-dimensional diagonal?

22. Will a 16-foot-long piece of lumber fit in a truck with interior cargo dimensions of 12.5 feet by 8 feet by 7.5 feet?

In Problems 23 to 26, calculate the perpendicular height (to the nearest tenth), surface area (to the nearest whole number), and volume (to the nearest whole number) of the solids.

Note: Use your rounded height value when calculating volume.

23. A cone with a base diameter of 24 cm and a slant height of 30 cm.

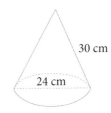

24. A cone with a base diameter of 64 mm and a slant height of 105 mm.

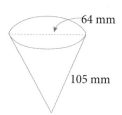

25. A square pyramid with a base length and corner edge length all equal to 98 m.

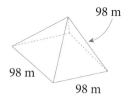

26. A pyramid with a rectangular base that has a length of 50 cm, a width of 36 cm, and a corner edge length of 45 cm.

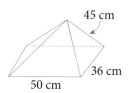

- 27. A truncated cone with a top diameter of 24 cm, a base diameter of 40 cm, and a slant height of 18 cm.

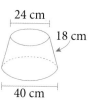

- 28. A truncated square pyramid with a top side length of 75 m, a base side length of 225 m, and a slant height of 120 m.

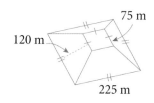

7 | Review Exercises

For the following problems, round your answer to two decimal places (unless otherwise indicated).

For Problems 1 and 2, determine (i) the measure of angle θ using a protractor and (ii) calculate the supplement and complement of the angle θ.

1.　a.

　　b.

2.　a.

　　b.

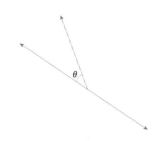

3.　Given the following diagram:

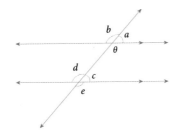

a. State the relationship of θ to each of the angles, *a, b, c, d,* and *e.*

b. Calculate the angle measure of each of the unknown angles given that θ = 113 °.

4.　Given the following diagram:

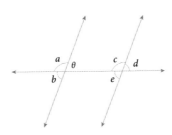

a. State the relationship of θ to each of the angles, *a, b, c, d,* and *e.*

b. Calculate the angle measure of each of the unknown angles given that θ = 89 °.

In Problems 5 and 6, determine the unknown angles a, b, and c in each of the diagrams.

5.　a.

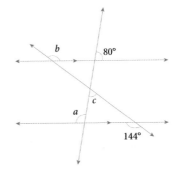

　　b.

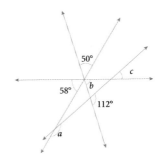

6. a.

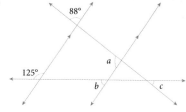

    b.

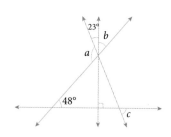

In Problems 7 and 8, classify the quadrilaterals.

7. a.

    b.

    c.

8. a.

    b.

    c.

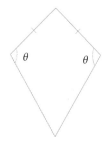

For the triangles in Problems 9 and 10:

i. Determine all the missing angles.

ii. Classify the triangle by side length and by angle.

9. a.

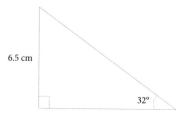

    b.

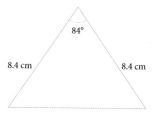

10. a.

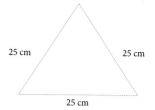

    b.

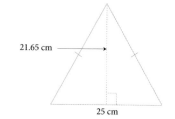

In Problems 11 and 12, calculate the perimeter and the area of the given triangles. (Hint: you will need the Pythagorean Theorem)

11. a.

    b.

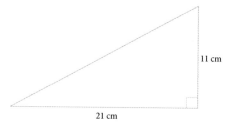

12. a.

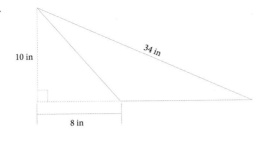

b.

13. Calculate the perimeter of a rectangle with a length that is twice its width and an area of 392 cm².

14. Calculate the volume (to the nearest cm³) of a sphere with a surface area of 452 cm².

In Problems 15 to 18, calculate the perimeter and area of the given shapes.

15. A parallelogram with a base of 32 cm, a perpendicular height of 15 cm, and a slant height of 18 cm.

16. A rhombus with a side length of 45 cm and a perpendicular height of 36 cm.

17. a. A circle with a radius of 23.6 m.

b. A sector of a circle with a diameter of 125 cm and an inscribed angle of 30°.

18. a. A circle with a diameter of 3.5 m.

b. A sector of a circle with a radius of 78 cm and an inscribed angle of 115°.

19. Calculate the surface area of a closed cylinder (to the nearest cm²) that has a volume of 3,220 cm³ and a height that is equal to its diameter.

20. A box that holds gauze is 10 cm long, 5 cm high, and 5 cm deep. What is the surface area and volume of the box?

21. The centre of the eye is composed of two parts: the pupil (the black circle at the center of the eye which is the aperture that light enters through) and the iris (the coloured band around the pupil). Together, the pupil and iris form a circle with a fixed diameter of 8 mm. What is the total area of the pupil and iris?

22. A circular Petri dish has a diameter of 60 mm. Determine the area of the dish.

In Problems 23 to 26, determine the perimeter and area of the given composite shapes.

23. A knee wrap

24. A first-aid patch

25. An Erlenmeyer flask

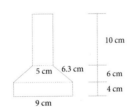

26. A hospital hallway sign

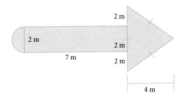

In Problems 27 to 30, determine the surface area and volume of the following 3-dimensional objects.

27. A cylindrical lens with a radius of 32 mm and a height of 12 mm.

28. A cylindrical inner-cardboard of a paper towel roll with a diameter of 38 mm and a length of 28 cm.

29. A medical tent pitched in the shape of a square-based pyramid, with a base length of 4.2 m, a slant height of 3.5 m, and a height of 2.8 m. [*Note: Include floor of tent in SA.*]

30. A tetrahedral (equilateral triangular prism) mesh used in medical imaging, with side lengths of 22 mm each, and a height of 18 mm.

For the composite figures in Problems 31 and 32, determine the surface area and volume. (Hint: you will need the Pythagorean Theorem).

31. A surgical drill tip

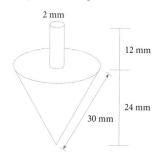

32. A neonatal intensive care unit

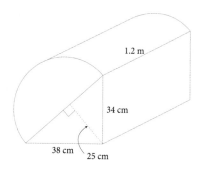

For Problems 33 to 36, find the missing side lengths:

33. a.

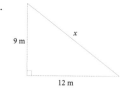

b.

34. a.

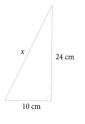

b.

35.

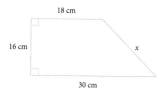

36.

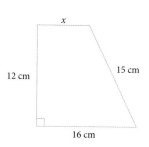

37. Use the Pythagorean Theorem to calculate the perimeter and area of a right trapezoid, with parallel sides that are 64 cm and 40 cm long, and a perpendicular height of 18 cm.

38. Use the Pythagorean Theorem to calculate the perimeter and area of an isosceles trapezoid, with parallel sides that are 6.5 m and 4.2 m long, and slant heights that are both 2.3 m long.

39. At the gym of a physiotherapy clinic, a patient recovering from a shoulder injury is doing "pull-down" shoulder extensions on a machine that is 2.2 m tall, with a cable that is 1.8 m long. If he is standing 1.3 m from the machine, and he is supposed to pull the cable down to his waist, which is 0.9 m above the floor, will he be able to properly perform the exercise where he is currently standing? If not, what could he do to correct this situation in order to perform the exercise properly?

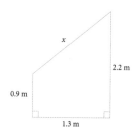

40. An athlete training for the Olympics is doing an aerobic rowing exercise where she sits on a sliding bench, holding a bar attached to a cable attached to the resistance machine at her feet, and extends her legs to slide backwards. If she is holding the bar 0.8 m above the seat, and her legs are 1.2 m long, how much cable will she need when it is at its greatest extension, assuming she needs an additional 10 cm of cable for slack at the end? If the cable is 1.5 m long, will this be sufficient? If not, how can she adjust her exercise appropriately so that it will be sufficient?

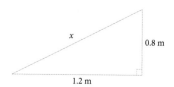

7 | Self-Test Exercises

1. For the following angles:

   a. $\theta = 34°$
   c. $\theta = 67°$
   b. $\theta = 116°$
   d. $\theta = 90°$

   i. Classify the angle as acute, right, or obtuse.

   ii. Calculate the supplement of the angle.

   iii. Calculate the complement of the angle (if applicable).

2. Determine the unknown angles for a, b, and c in the following figures:

   a.

   b.

3. Classify the following triangles by angle measure and by side length:

   a. 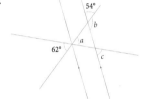   b.

   c.

4. Classify the following quadrilaterals:

   a. 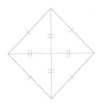   b.

   c.

   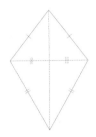

5. Calculate the perimeter and area of the following triangles. (*Hint: you will need the Pythagorean Theorem*).

   a.

   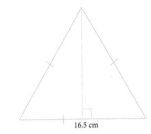

   b.

   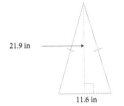

6. In the following triangles, (i) find the missing side lengths, then (ii) compute the perimeter, and (iii) compute the area.

   a.

   b.

   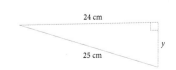

7. Find the area of the following figures:

   a. A nicotine patch shaped like a rhombus with a side length of 8.5 cm and a perpendicular height of 7.2 cm.

   b. A surgical device shaped like a parallelogram with a base of 1.75 m, a perpendicular height of 84 cm, and a slant height of 1.12 m.

   c. A circular pacemaker with a radius of 16 cm.

8. Determine the circumference (or perimeter) and area of the following figures:

   a. A circle with a diameter of 2.5 m.

   b. A sector of a circle with a radius of 36 cm and an inscribed angle of 65°.

9. In order to calculate the speed to display on an ambulance's speedometer, the on-board computer must be programmed with the size of the ambulance tire installed. Following this, it can compute the speed (in km/h) based on the number of revolutions per minute (rpm) at which the wheel turns. If the factory-installed tires on a new ambulance have a diameter of 63 cm and the wheels are turning at a rate of 960 rpm, determine the speed displayed on the ambulance speedometer, in km/h.

10. Determine the area of the shaded regions in the following composite figure:

11. Calculate the volume of the following common medical objects:

   a. A cylindrical PVC tube with a radius of 18 mm and a length of 175 mm.

   b. A cone-shaped paper cup with a diameter of 6.8 cm at the opening and a height of 9.2 cm.

   c. A spherical tissue expander with a circumference of 32 cm.

12. A closed cylinder with a height of 15 cm has a volume of 3,000 cm³.

   a. Find its base radius, rounded to 2 decimal places.

   b. Find its surface area, rounded to the nearest cm² [*Use rounded r from part a.*].

13. A sphere has a surface area of 450 cm².

   a. Find its radius, rounded to 2 decimal places.

   b. Find its volume, rounded to the nearest cm³ [*Use rounded r from part a.*].

14. A closed cylinder of a given volume has an optimal (minimal) surface area when its height is exactly the same as its diameter. Calculate the minimum possible surface area of a cylinder with a volume of 170 cm³.

15. Calculate the surface area and volume of the following objects:

   (*Hint: for part a, you will need the Pythagorean Theorem*).

   a.

   b.

16. Find the volume of a person's trachea if its diameter is 2.6 cm and its length is 13 cm.

17. Find the volume of a person's small intestine if its diameter is 3 in. and its length is 60 in.

18. Find the surface area and volume of a bucket (semi-closed cylinder) that has a radius of 38 cm and a height of 53 cm.

19. Find the surface area and volume of a breathing tube with a length of 16 cm and a diameter of 3 cm.

20. A coccus (spherical) bacteria in an isotonic solution has a radius of 14 μm. What is the bacterium's volume?

21. A rod (cylindrical) bacterium in an isotonic solution has a radius of 10 μm and a length of 18 μm. What is the bacterium's volume?

22. A sling is fashioned from a bandage by paramedics for a patient with a dislocated shoulder. The bandage must be cut so that the longest edge is twice the distance from the hand to the shoulder. If the arm is 45 cm from the hand to the elbow and 35 cm from the elbow to the shoulder, what length must the longest edge of the bandage be cut to, assuming the elbow is at a 90° angle?

23. Determine the unknown side lengths of the following figure:

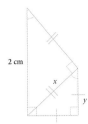

24. Use the Pythagorean Theorem to find the perimeter and area of the following figures:

a. A right trapezoid, with parallel sides that are 5.3 m and 9.7 m long, and a perpendicular height of 2.4m.

b. An isosceles triangle with a base length of 32 cm and slant heights that are each 34 cm.

25. Use the Pythagorean Theorem to determine the surface area and volume of the following 3-dimensional objects:

a. An ice-cream cone with a diameter of 4.4 cm and a height of 11.8 cm.

b. A conical candy container with a radius of 15 cm and a height of 25 cm.

26. Determine the value for x, as well as the perimeter and area of the inner triangle in the following diagram (*hint: you will require Heron's formula*).

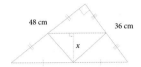

7 | Summary of Notation and Formulas

FORMULAS	COMMON PLANE FIGURES	NOTATION

Square:

$P = 4s$

$A = s^2$

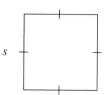

P = Perimeter

A = Area

s = length of the sides

Rectangle:

$P = 2l + 2w = 2(l + w)$

$A = l \times w$

P = Perimeter

A = Area

l = length

w = width

Rhombus:

$P = 4b$

$A = b \times h$

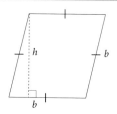

P = Perimeter

A = Area

b = length of each side

h = perpendicular height

Parallelogram:

$P = 2a + 2b = 2(a + b)$

$A = b \times h$

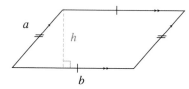

P = Perimeter

A = Area

a = length of the slant

b = length of the base

h = perpendicular height

Trapezoid

$P = a + b + c + d$

$A = \frac{1}{2}(a + b) \times h$

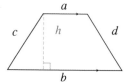

P = Perimeter

A = Area

a = length of the smaller parallel side

b = length of the larger parallel side

c, d = other sides

h = perpendicular height

Triangle:

$$P = a + b + c$$

$$A = \frac{1}{2}(b \times h)$$

Heron's Formula:

$$A = \sqrt{p(p-a)(p-b)(p-c)}$$

$$\text{where, } p = \frac{a+b+c}{2}$$

P = Perimeter

A = Area

a, b, c = side lengths

h = height

p = half of the Perimeter

Circle:

$$P = C$$

$$C = \pi d = 2\pi r$$

$$A = \pi r^2$$

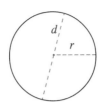

P = Perimeter

C = Circumference

A = Area

d = diameter = 2r

r = radius

Sector:

$$L = \pi d \times \frac{\theta}{360°}$$

$$P_S = 2r + L$$

$$A_S = \pi r^2 \times \frac{\theta}{360°}$$

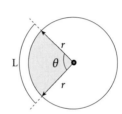

L = Arc length

P_S = Perimeter of sector

A_S = Area of sector

θ = angle subtended by the arc

d = diameter = 2r

r = radius

Pythagorean Theorem:

$$a^2 = b^2 + c^2$$

$$c = \sqrt{a^2 + b^2}$$

$$a = \sqrt{c^2 - b^2}$$

$$b = \sqrt{c^2 - a^2}$$

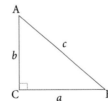

a, b = legs of a right angle triangle

c = hypotenuse of a right angle triangle

FORMULAS	COMMON SOLID OBJECTS	NOTATION

Cube:

$$SA = 6s^2$$
$$V = s^3$$

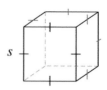

SA = Surface Area

V = Volume

s = side length

Rectangular Prism:

$$SA = 2(l \times w) + 2(l \times h) + 2(w \times h)$$
$$= 2[(l \times w) + (l \times h) + (w \times h)]$$
$$V = l \times w \times h$$

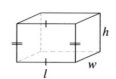

SA = Surface Area

V = Volume

l = length

w = width

h = height

Triangular Prism:

$$SA = 2(B) + 3 \text{ rectangles}$$
$$V = B \times h$$

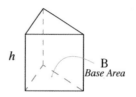

SA = Surface Area

V = Volume

B = Base Area

h = height

Square Pyramid:

$$SA = 4\left(\frac{l \times s}{2}\right) + l^2$$
$$SA = 2(l \times s) + l^2$$
$$V = \frac{1}{3}(l \times l)h$$
$$V = \frac{l^2 \times h}{3}$$

SA = Surface Area

V = Volume

s = slant height

h = height

l = length

w = width

Rectangular Pyramid:

$$SA = 2\left(\frac{l \times s_1}{2} + \frac{w \times s_2}{2}\right) + l \times w$$
$$SA = (l \times s_1 + w \times s_2) + l \times w$$
$$V = \frac{1}{3}(l \times w)h$$
$$V = \frac{l \times w \times h}{3}$$

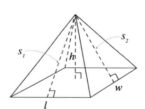

SA = Surface Area

V = Volume

h = height

l = length

w = width

s_1 = slant height on the length side

s_2 = slant height on the width side

Triangular Pyramid:

SA = Area of all 3 lateral

    sides + Base Area (B)

$V = \dfrac{1}{3}(B)h$

$V = \dfrac{B \times h}{3}$

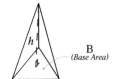

SA = Surface Area

V = Volume

B = Base Area

h = height

Cylinder:

$SA = 2\pi r^2 + 2\pi rh$ (closed)

   $= \pi r^2 + 2\pi rh$ (semi-closed)

   $= 2\pi rh$ (open)

$V = \pi r^2 h$

SA = Surface Area

V = Volume

r = radius

h = height

Cone:

$SA = \pi r^2 + \pi rs$ (closed)

   $= \pi rs$ (open)

$V = \dfrac{1}{3}\pi r^2 h$

SA = Surface Area

V = Volume

r = radius

s = slant height

h = height

Sphere:

$SA = 4\pi r^2$

$V = \dfrac{4}{3}(\pi r^3)$

SA = Surface Area

V = Volume

r = radius

8

GRAPHS AND SYSTEMS OF LINEAR EQUATIONS

LEARNING OBJECTIVES

- Identify the basic terminology of rectangular coordinate systems.

- Express linear equations in standard form and slope-intercept form.

- Determine the slope and y-intercept of a line from its equation.

- Construct a table of values for a linear equation.

- Graph a linear equation using a table of values, the slope and y-intercept, and x- and y- intercepts.

- Determine the equation of a line from a graph.

- Determine the equations of parallel and perpendicular lines.

- Classify systems of linear equations.

- Solve linear systems graphically.

- Solve linear systems using the method of substitution or elimination.

- Set up and solve systems of linear equations to solve application problems.

CHAPTER OUTLINE

8.1 Rectangular Coordinate System

8.2 Graphing Linear Equations

8.3 Solving Systems of Linear Equations with Two Variables, Graphically

8.4 Solving Systems of Linear Equations with Two Variables, Algebraically

8.5 Using Systems of Linear Equations to Solve Application Problems With Two Unknowns

Introduction

Linear equations describe relationships between constant numeric values and one or more variables, in which all variables appear in separate terms with real-number coefficients and exponents of 1. Graphing linear equations provides an illustrative way of expressing the relationship between the variables defined by the equation.

When more than one relationship exists between the variables, a system of linear equations, which is a set of linear equations that are considered simultaneously, can be used to model the various relationships. Many practical scenarios in life can be modeled by a linear equation or system of linear equations.

In this chapter, you will learn how to graph linear equations with two unknown variables and understand how the graphs of these relationships represent the solutions to the corresponding equations. You will also learn how to solve systems of two linear equations with two unknown variables by a variety of methods, including both graphical and algebraic approaches.

8.1 | Rectangular Coordinate System

Graphs provide information in a visual form and they are most commonly drawn on a rectangular coordinate system known as the **Cartesian coordinate system** (invented by René Descartes). Understanding the rectangular coordinate system is crucial in order to be able to read and draw graphs, which is essential to understanding the concepts of functions and statistics, both of which are important branches of mathematics in the health sciences.

The rectangular coordinate system uses a horizontal and a vertical number line, each known as an axis. These two perpendicular axes cross at the point (O), known as the origin.

The horizontal number line (moving to the left or the right) is called the **X-axis** and the vertical number line (moving up or down) is called the **Y-axis**, as illustrated in Exhibit 8.1-a.

The numbers to the **right** of the origin along the X-axis are **positive (+)** and those to the left are **negative (−)**. The numbers **above** the origin along the Y-axis are **positive (+)** and those below are **negative (−)**.

The purpose of the rectangular coordinate system and the sign convention is to locate a point relative to the X- and Y-axes and in reference to the origin 'O'.

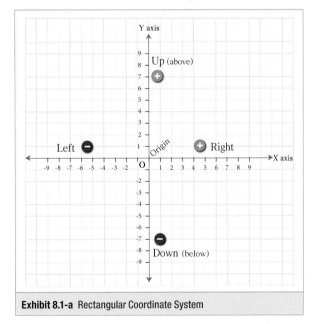

Exhibit 8.1-a Rectangular Coordinate System

Points in the Cartesian Coordinate System

Each ordered pair, (x, y), represents only one point on a graph. The x and y values of the ordered pair determine the location of that point.

A **point** in the Cartesian coordinate system is a location in the plane, represented as an **ordered pair** of numbers inside a set of brackets, called **coordinates**. The first number is called the **x-coordinate**, representing its horizontal position with respect to the origin, and the second number is called the **y-coordinate**, representing its vertical position with respect to the origin. The ordered pair of coordinates for a given point P is written as follows: P(x, y) or simply (x, y). For example, the **origin** (i.e., the point where the x-axis and y-axis intersect) is identified by the coordinates (0, 0) since both its x and y coordinates are 0.

As illustrated in Exhibit 8.1-b, the ordered pair (2, 3) refers to the coordinates of the point P which is 2 units to the right and 3 units above, in reference to the origin.

It is called a rectangular coordinate system because the x- and y-coordinates form a rectangle with the X- and Y-axes.

It is important to identify the coordinate numbers in their order. They are called ordered pairs because the order in which they appear determines their position on the graph. Changing the order of the coordinates will result in a different point.

For example, (2, 3) and (3, 2) are different points.

Pay close attention to the order in which coordinate pairs are written - the first coordinate always refers to the x-coordinate (horizontal distance) and the second coordinate always refers to the y-coordinate (vertical distance).

- (2, 3) refers to a point 'P', which is 2 units to the right of the origin and 3 units above the origin.
- (3, 2) refers to a point 'Q', which is 3 units to the right of the origin and 2 units above the origin.

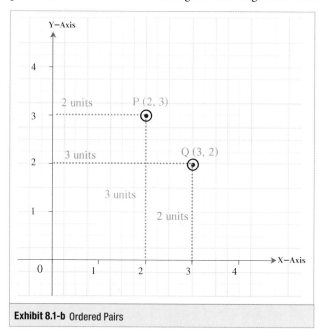

Exhibit 8.1-b Ordered Pairs

Quadrants

The X- and Y- axes divide the coordinate plane into 4 regions, called **quadrants**. Quadrants are numbered counter-clockwise from one (I) to four (IV), starting from the upper-right quadrant, as illustrated in Exhibit 8.1-c.

Points with one or more zeros (0) as coordinates are on axes and not in quadrants.

That is, the upper-right quadrant is Quadrant I, the upper-left quadrant is Quadrant II, the lower-left quadrant is Quadrant III, and the lower-right quadrant is Quadrant IV. Table 8.1 shows the sign convention of coordinates in each of the quadrants with examples that are plotted on the graph in Exhibit 8.1-d.

Table 8.1 — Sign Convention of Coordinates in Different Quadrants, Axes, and Origin

Quadrant, Axis, Origin	Sign of x-coordinate	Sign of y-coordinate	Example (plotted in Exhibit 8.1-d)
Quadrant I	Positive (+)	Positive (+)	A (3, 2)
Quadrant II	Negative (−)	Positive (+)	B (−3, 4)
Quadrant III	Negative (−)	Negative (−)	C (−5, −2)
Quadrant IV	Positive (+)	Negative (−)	D (5, −3)
X–Axis	Positive (+) or Negative (−)	Zero (0)	E (4,0), F (−2,0)
Y–Axis	Zero (0)	Positive (+) or Negative (−)	G (0,3), H (0,−4)
Origin	Zero (0)	Zero (0)	O (0,0)

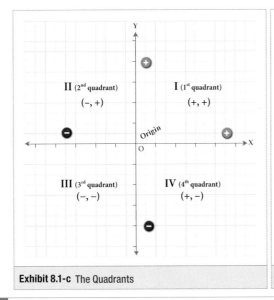

Exhibit 8.1-c The Quadrants

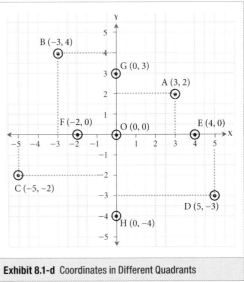

Exhibit 8.1-d Coordinates in Different Quadrants

Example 8.1-a — Identifying x- and y-coordinates

Find the x- and y-coordinates of the points A, B, C, D, E, F, G and H labelled on the graph below.

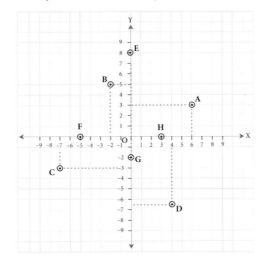

Solution   A: (6, 3)   B: (−2, 5)   C: (−7, −3)   D: (4, −6.5)

E: (0, 8)   F: (−5, 0)   G: (0, −2)   H: (3, 0)

Example 8.1-b	Identifying the Quadrant or the Axis

Identify the quadrant or the axis in which the following points are located:

(i) A (−15, 20)   (ii) B (20, 5)   (iii) C (0.45, 0)   (iv) D (0, 30.8)

(v) E $(12, -\frac{8}{17})$ (vi) F $(0, -\frac{23}{6})$ (vii) G (−30, −15)   (viii) H (−1, 0)

Solution

(i)   A (−15, 20) $\longrightarrow$ (−, +)   = 2nd Quadrant

(ii)   B (20, 5) $\longrightarrow$ (+, +)   = 1st Quadrant

(iii)   C (0.45, 0) $\longrightarrow$ (+, 0)   = X-Axis (Right)

(iv)   D (0, 30.8) $\longrightarrow$ (0, +)   = Y-Axis (Up)

(v)   E $(12, -\frac{8}{17})$ $\longrightarrow$ (+, −)   = 4th Quadrant

(vi)   F $(0, -\frac{23}{6})$ $\longrightarrow$ (0, −)   = Y-Axis (Down)

(vii)   G (−30, −15) $\longrightarrow$ (−, −)   = 3rd Quadrant

(viii)   H (−1, 0) $\longrightarrow$ (−, 0)   = X-Axis (Left)

Relations and Functions

When one or more points (i.e., ordered pairs) are plotted together on a graph, they form a set called a **relation**. A relation can be expressed in three ways:

(i) As a set

(ii) As a graph

(iii) As an algebraic equation

For example, consider the relation between x and y, where x and y are whole numbers whose sum is 4. It can be expressed as follows:

(i) {(0,4), (1,3), (2,2), (3,1), (4,0)}

(ii)

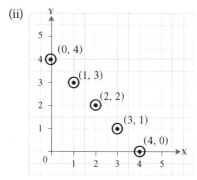

(iii) $x + y = 4$, where x, y are whole numbers

If the relation has only one *y*-value for every *x*-value, then it is known as a **function**. A function can be identified in its three forms as follows:

(i) As a set, a function has the property that every ordered pair will have a unique *x*-value.

(ii) As a graph, a function will pass the "vertical line test" meaning that no vertical line will pass through the graph more than once.

(iii) As an equation, a function can be solved for *y* (i.e., *y* = some formula of *x*).

Example 8.1-c	Identifying Functions

Determine whether the following relations are functions:

(i)   {(0, 4), (1, 1), (2, 0), (3, 1), (4, 4)}

(ii)   {(5, 1), (4, 2), (3, 3), (4, 4), (5, 5)}

(iii) $3x + 4y = 12$, where *x* and *y* are real numbers.

(iv)

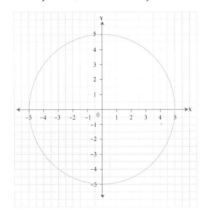

Solution

(i)   Since each ordered pair has a unique *x*-value, this relation represents a function.

(ii)   In this relation, there are ordered pairs with repeated *x*-values (for example, 4 and 5), but with different *y*-values. Therefore, this relation does not represent a function.

(iii)   The equation $3x + 4y = 12$ can be solved for *y* as follows:

$$3x + 4y = 12$$

$$4y = -3x + 12$$

$$y = -\left(\frac{3}{4}\right)x + 3$$

Therefore, this relation represents a function.

(iv)   The graph of the circle does not pass the vertical line test, as there are vertical lines that pass through the graph more than once. Therefore, this relation does not represent a function.

Domain and Range

The **domain** of a relation is defined as the set of all the '*x*' values in the ordered pairs.

The **range** of a relation is defined as the set of all the '*y*' values in the ordered pairs.

In mathematics, the domain and range are essential to identify function families, plot important points, and understand graphs of complex functions.

Note: When listing out all the values in the domain and range, they should be listed in increasing order, with any duplicates removed.

| Example 8.1-d | Expressing Domain and Range |

Find the domain and range for each relation.

(i) $\{(-4, 3), (-2, 5), (0, 2), (-3, 1), (1, 2)\}$

(ii) $\{(x, y) \mid x, y \in \mathbf{Z}, x + y = 7, -4 < x < 5\}$

Solution

(i) $\{(-4, 3), (-2, 5), (0, 2), (-3, 1), (1, 2)\}$

Domain: $\{-4, -3, -2, 0, 1\}$

Range: $\{1, 2, 3, 5\}$

(ii) $\{(x, y) \mid x, y \in \mathbf{Z}, x + y = 7, -4 < x < 5\}$

This relation can be interpreted as follows:

"The set of all coordinates (x, y), such that x and y are integers, $x + y = 7$, and x is greater than -4 and less than 5."

The domain is given by the condition $-4 < x < 5$, and x is an integer.

Domain: $\{-3, -2, -1, 0, 1, 2, 3, 4\}$

The range can be determined by inserting each of our values for x into the equation $x + y = 7$, and solving for y.

Range: $\{3, 4, 5, 6, 7, 8, 9, 10\}$

> In set notation,
>
> **N** is a symbol for natural numbers.
>
> **W** is a symbol for whole numbers.
>
> **Z** is a symbol for integers.
>
> **R** is a symbol for real numbers.

8.1 | Exercises

Answers to odd-numbered problems are available at the end of the textbook.

For Problems 1 to 4, plot the points on a graph:

1. a. A $(-3, 5)$ b. B $(5, -3)$ c. C $(0, -4)$

2. a. A $(-6, 4)$ b. B $(4, -2)$ c. C $(0, -7)$

3. a. D $(6, 0)$ b. E $(-2, -4.5)$ c. F $\left(\frac{5}{2}, 2\right)$

4. a. D $(8, 0)$ b. E $(-3.2, -5)$ c. F $\left(\frac{2}{3}, 5\right)$

For Problems 5 to 8, determine the quadrant in which the points lie.

5. a. A $(-1, 2)$ b. B $(5, -1)$ c. C $(3, 5)$

6. a. A $(1, 6)$ b. B $(4, -3)$ c. C $(-7, 3)$

7. a. D $(-4, 0)$ b. E $(-2.2, -7.8)$ c. F $\left(0, 5\frac{1}{3}\right)$

8. a. D $(6, 0)$ b. E $(-1.3, -13)$ c. F $\left(0, -\frac{7}{8}\right)$

For Problems 9 to 12, plot the pairs of points on a graph and calculate the length of each horizontal line joining the pair of points:

9. a. $(3, 4)$ and $(5, 4)$ b. $(-7, 1)$ and $(2, 1)$

10. a. $(2, -6)$ and $(7, -6)$ b. $(-5, -4)$ and $(3, -4)$

11. a. $(-5.4, 3)$ and $(0, 3)$ b. $(-2.2, -2)$ and $(-6.5, -2)$

12. a. $(-6.8, 8)$ and $(0, 8)$ b. $(7, -5)$ and $(2.1, -5)$

For Problems 13 to 16, plot the pairs of points on a graph and calculate the length of each vertical line joining the pair of points:

13. a. $(3, 6)$ and $(3, 1)$ b. $(5, 2)$ and $(5, -5)$

14. a. $(2, -5)$ and $(2, -9)$ b. $(-3, 4)$ and $(-3, 6)$

15. a. $(-5, 6\frac{1}{2})$ and $(-5, 2)$ b. $(7, \frac{2}{3})$ and $(7, -\frac{4}{5})$

16. a. $(1, 5\frac{3}{4})$ and $(1, -4)$ b. $(-3, \frac{5}{6})$ and $(-3, 0)$

17. Three vertices of a square ABCD have points A $(-3, 3)$, B $(1, 3)$, and C $(1, -1)$. Find the coordinates of the 4th vertex D.

18. Three vertices of a square EFGH have points E $(-1, -2)$, F $(6, -2)$, and G $(6, 5)$. Find the coordinates of the 4th vertex H.

19. Three vertices of a rectangle PQRS have points P $(-3, 4)$, Q $(6, 4)$, and R $(6, -1)$. Find the coordinates of the 4th vertex S.

20. Three vertices of a rectangle TUVW have points T $(-4, 7)$, U $(5, 7)$, and V $(5, 4)$. Find the coordinates of the 4th vertex W.

21. A vertical line segment has a length of 7 units and the coordinates of one end of the line are $(1, 5)$. Find two possible coordinates of the point on the other end of the line segment.

22. A horizontal line segment has a length of 5 units and the coordinates of one end of the line are $(-3, 1)$. Find two possible coordinates of the point on the other end of the line segment.

23. A line segment has a length of 6 units and the coordinates of one end of the line are $(-1, 3)$. Find four possible coordinates of the point on the other end of the line segment.

24. A line segment has a length of 8 units and the coordinates of one end of the line are $(-1, -2)$. Find four possible coordinates of the point on the other end of the line segment.

For Problems 25 to 38, find the domain and range for each relation and determine whether it is a function.

25. $\{(0, 0), (1, 1), (1, -1), (4, 2), (4, -2)\}$

26. $\{(1, 4), (2, 3), (3, 2), (4, 1), (-1, -4), (-2, -3), (-3, -2), (-4, -1)\}$

27. $\{(-1, 3), (-2, 3), (-4, 3), (0, 3), (4, 3), (6, 3)\}$

28. $\{(5, 3), (5, 4), (5, 5), (5, 6), (5, 7)\}$

29.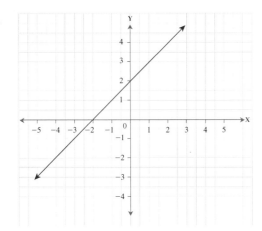

30.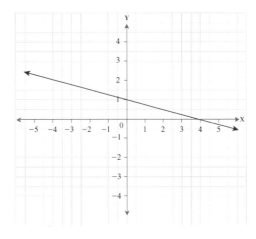

31.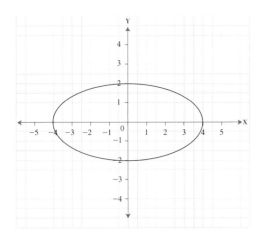

32.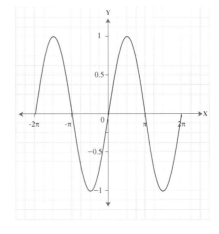

33.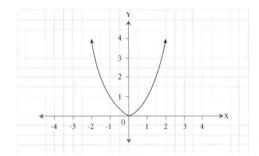

34.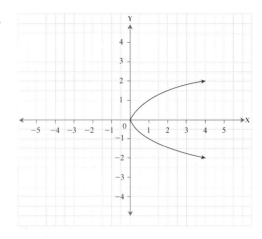

35. $\{(x, y) \mid x, y \in \mathbb{Z}, y = x - 3, -4 \le x \le 5\}$

36. $\{(x, y) \mid x, y \in \mathbb{N}, y = 2x + 1, 1 \le x \le 7\}$

37. $\{(x, y) \mid x, y \in \mathbb{R}, x - 2y = -4, -6 < x < 1\}$

38. $\{(x, y) \mid x, y \in \mathbb{R}, 3x + y = 2, -3 < x < 3\}$

8.2 | Graphing Linear Equations

A 2-dimensional linear equation is an algebraic equation with one or two variables (each with an exponent of one), which produces a straight line when plotted on a graph.

Examples of linear equations with one variable in the rectangular coordinate system are:

(a) $x = 3$ (b) $y = -2$

Examples of linear equations with two variables in the rectangular coordinate system are:

(c) $2x - 3y + 3 = 0$ (d) $y = \dfrac{3}{4} x$

The process of finding the value of the variables for which the equation is true is known as solving the equation. Linear equations with two variables have infinitely many pairs of values as solutions; therefore, it is usually more convenient to represent these solutions by drawing a graph.

Linear equations with two variables are generally represented by the variables x and y and are expressed either in the form of $Ax + By = C$ (where A, B, and C are integers and A is positive), known as **standard form**, or in the form of $y = mx + b$ (where m and b are integers or fractions), known as **slope-intercept** form.

Linear Equations in Standard Form

For an equation in standard form, the value of A is usually positive.

The 'standard' form of a linear equation with two variables, x and y, is written as $\boldsymbol{Ax + By = C}$, where A, B, and C are integers, A is positive, and A, B, and C have no common factors other than 1.

For example, consider the following simple linear equation with two variables: $2x - y = -3$

This equation is in the standard form of $Ax + By = C$, where $A = 2$, $B = -1$, and $C = -3$.

- If a given equation has fractions, then multiply each term by the least common denominator (LCD), divide each term by any common factors, and rearrange the equation into standard form.
- If a given equation has decimals, then multiply each term by a power of 10 to eliminate the decimals, divide each term by any common factors, and rearrange the equation into standard form.
- If a given equation has no fractions or decimals, then divide each term by any common factors and rearrange it into standard form.

Example 8.2-a   Writing Linear Equations in Standard Form

Write the following linear equations in standard form:

(i) $\frac{2}{3}x + \frac{1}{2}y - 3 = 0$ (ii) $0.3x = 1.25y - 2$ (iii) $y = \frac{2}{3}x - 5$

Solution

(i) $\frac{2}{3}x + \frac{1}{2}y - 3 = 0$ Multiplying each term by the LCD 6 and simplifying,

     $4x + 3y - 18 = 0$ Rearranging,

     $4x + 3y = 18$ This is in the form $Ax + By = C$.

Therefore, the equation $\frac{2}{3}x + \frac{1}{2}y - 3 = 0$, in standard form, is $4x + 3y = 18$.

(ii) $0.3x = 1.25y - 2$ Multiplying each term by 100,

     $30x = 125y - 200$ Dividing each term by the common factor 5 and simplifying,

     $6x = 25y - 40$ Rearranging,

     $6x - 25y = -40$ This is in the form $Ax + By = C$.

Therefore, the equation $0.3x = 1.25y - 2$, in standard form, is $6x - 25y = -40$.

(iii) $y = \frac{2}{3}x - 5$ Multiplying each term by 3 and simplifying,

     $3y = 2x - 15$ Rearranging,

     $-2x + 3y = -15$ Multiplying each term by -1 to make A positive,

     $2x - 3y = 15$ This is in the form $Ax + By = C$.

Therefore, the equation $y = \frac{2}{3}x - 5$, in standard form, is $2x - 3y = 15$.

Linear Equations in Slope-Intercept Form

The 'slope-intercept' form for a linear equation with two variables, x and y, is written in the form of $y = mx + b$, where m and b are either integers or fractions. 'm' represents the slope and 'b' represents the y-coordinate of the y-intercept.

For example, consider a simple linear equation such as $y = 2x + 3$. This equation is in the slope-intercept form of $y = mx + b$, where $m = 2$ and $b = 3$; hence, the slope is 2 and the y-intercept is $(0, 3)$.

- If a given equation has fractions, then multiply each term by the least common denominator (LCD), divide each term by any common factors and rearrange to isolate for y.

- If a given equation has decimals, then multiply each term by a power of 10 to eliminate the decimals, divide each term by any common factors and rearrange to isolate for y.

- If a given equation has no fractions or decimals, then divide each term by any common factors and rearrange to isolate for y.

Example 8.2-b   Writing Linear Equations in Slope-Intercept Form

Write the following linear equations in slope-intercept form and identify the slope and the y-intercept.

(i) $4x + 3y = 18$ (ii) $x = \frac{25}{6}y + \frac{20}{3}$

Solution

(i) $4x + 3y = 18$ Rearranging the term with y on the left,

$$3y = -4x + 18 \qquad \text{Dividing each term by 3 and simplifying,}$$

$$y = -\frac{4}{3}x + 6 \qquad \text{This is in the form, } y = mx + b$$

Therefore, the slope is $m = -\frac{4}{3}$ and the y-intercept is the point $(0, 6)$.

(ii) $\qquad x = \frac{25}{6}y + \frac{20}{3} \qquad \qquad$ Multiplying each term by the LCD of 6 and simplifying,

$$6x = 25y + 40 \qquad \qquad \text{Rearranging the term with } y \text{ on the left,}$$

$$-25y = -6x + 40 \qquad \qquad \text{Multiplying each term by } -1,$$

$$25y = 6x - 40 \qquad \qquad \text{Dividing each term by 25 and simplifying,}$$

$$y = \frac{6}{25}x - \frac{8}{5} \qquad \qquad \text{This is in the form } y = mx + b.$$

Therefore, the slope is $m = \frac{6}{25}$ and the y-intercept is the point $\left(0, -\frac{8}{5}\right)$.

Determining the Solution Set of a Linear Equation

If a linear equation has two variables, x and y, then there are infinitely many solutions to the equation, and it is not possible to solve the equation for a single value of each variable. However, it is possible to solve for a **set of values** by replacing one variable (either x or y) with any value and then solving for the value of the other variable; i.e., for every one of the infinitely many values for x, there is one and only one value for y that solves the equation.

For example, consider the equation: $y = 2x + 3$

Choosing $x = 1$ and substituting $x = 1$ in the equation: $y = 2x + 3$,

$$y = 2(1) + 3 = 5$$

Therefore, $x = 1$ and $y = 5$ is one of the infinitely-many solutions to the equation $y = 2x + 3$; i.e., $(1, 5)$ is a coordinate pair that satisfies the equation.

Choosing $x = 2$ and substituting for $x = 2$ in the equation: $y = 2x + 3$,

$$y = 2(2) + 3 = 7$$

Therefore, $x = 2$ and $y = 7$ is another solution to the equation; i.e., $(2, 7)$ is another coordinate pair that satisfies the equation.

Similarly, we can obtain any number of points that satisfy the equation by choosing different values for x, and computing the corresponding value for y.

We can represent the solution set to this linear equation as follows: $\{(x, 2x + 3) \mid x \in \mathbf{R}\}$

Alternatively, we can represent the solution set by graphing the linear equation. The graph of the linear equation will be a line formed by all the solutions to the linear equation. Conversely, any point on the line is a solution to the linear equation.

Graphing Linear Equations Using a Table of Values

Follow these steps to graph a linear equation using a table of values:

Step 1: Create a table of values by choosing any value for the variable x (0 is often a good first choice).

Drawing a linear graph requires only two points. However, at least 3 points will ensure that the graph of the line truly represents the given linear equation.

Step 2: Compute the corresponding value for the variable y (this is easiest if the equation is in slope-intercept form).

Step 3: Form the ordered pair (x, y).

Step 4: Repeat Steps 1 to 3 at least two more times to create at least 3 ordered pairs.

Step 5: Plot the ordered pairs (points) on the coordinate system, using an appropriate scale.

Step 6: Join the points in a straight line, continuing the line indefinitely in both directions using arrows.

Step 7: Label the graph with the equation of the line.

For example, consider the linear equation $y = 2x + 3$. We will first determine the coordinates of 4 ordered pairs that are on this line by choosing values for x and finding the corresponding values for y; then we will draw the graph.

- Choosing $x = 0$,
$$y = 2x + 3$$
$$= 2(0) + 3$$
$$= 0 + 3 = 3$$
  (0, 3) is a point on the line.

- Choosing $x = 1$,
$$y = 2x + 3$$
$$= 2(1) + 3$$
$$= 2 + 3 = 5$$
  (1, 5) is a point on the line.

- Choosing $x = 2$,
$$y = 2x + 3$$
$$= 2(2) + 3$$
$$= 4 + 3 = 7$$
  (2, 7) is a point on the line.

- Choosing $x = 3$,
$$y = 2x + 3$$
$$= 2(3) + 3$$
$$= 6 + 3 = 9$$
  (3, 9) is a point on the line.

$y = 2x + 3$		
x	y	(x, y)
0	3	(0, 3)
1	5	(1, 5)
2	7	(2, 7)
3	9	(3, 9)

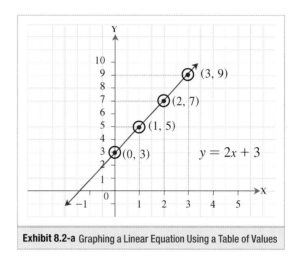

Exhibit 8.2-a Graphing a Linear Equation Using a Table of Values

Since all the points fall on a line when joined, it verifies that the plotted line represents the equation.

Graphing Linear Equations Using the *x*-intercept and the *y*-intercept

The **x-intercept** is the point at which the line crosses the X-axis and where the y-coordinate is zero.

The **y-intercept** is the point at which the line crosses the Y-axis and where the x-coordinate is zero.

If the intercepts are not at the origin (0, 0), we may use the x-intercept and y-intercept as two points to draw a linear graph and use a 3rd point to test the plotted line.

If the intercepts are at the origin (0, 0), then we need to compute another ordered pair to use as the 2nd point (along with the origin) to draw the line with, and we use a 3rd point to test the plotted line.

For example, consider a linear equation, $3x - y = -9$, where we will use the x-intercept and y-intercept to draw the graph, and a third ordered pair to test the graph of the line.

At *x*-intercept the *y*-coordinate is zero.

First, we find the *x*-intercept:

Substituting $y = 0$ in the given equation and solving for *x*,

$3x - 0 = -9$, thus, $x = -3$.

Therefore, $(-3, 0)$ is the *x*-intercept.

At *y*-intercept the *x*-coordinate is zero.

Then, we find the *y*-intercept:

Substituting $x = 0$ in the given equation and solving for *y*,

$3(0) - y = -9$, thus, $y = 9$.

Therefore, $(0, 9)$ is the *y*-intercept.

Finally, we find another ordered pair as a 3rd point on this line to use as a test point to verify the plotted line joining the *x*-intercept and *y*-intercept.

Choosing $x = -1$, substituting this in the given equation, and solving for *y*,

$3(-1) - y = -9$, thus, $y = 6$.

Therefore, $(-1, 6)$ is a point on the line $3x - y = -9$.

- Plot the ordered pairs on the coordinate system using an appropriate scale.

- Draw a line to join the *x*-intercept and *y*-intercept.

- Verify that the test point falls on the graph of the plotted line.

$3x - y = -9$			
x	*y*	(x, y)	
−3	0	$(-3, 0)$	*x*-intercept
0	9	$(0, 9)$	*y*-intercept
−1	6	$(-1, 6)$	Test point

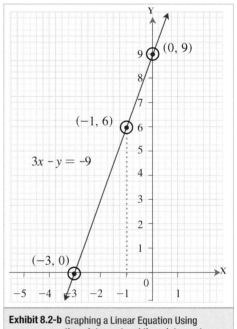

Exhibit 8.2-b Graphing a Linear Equation Using the *x*-intercept and the *y*-intercept

Since the test point $(-1, 6)$ falls on the line when plotted on the graph, it verifies that the plotted line represents the linear equation.

Graphing Linear Equations Using the Slope and the *y*-intercept

Recall that a linear equation in the form of $y = mx + b$ is known as the equation in slope-intercept form, where '*m*' is the slope and '*b*' is the *y*-coordinate of the *y*-intercept.

If the equation is in the standard form $Ax + By = C$, it can be rearranged into slope-intercept form, as follows:

$$Ax + By = C$$

$$By = -Ax + C$$

$$y = -\frac{A}{B}x + \frac{C}{B}$$

This is in the form $y = mx + b$, where the slope is given by, $m = -\dfrac{A}{B}$ and the y-intercept is the point $\left(0, \dfrac{C}{B}\right)$.

Note: *In order to rearrange a linear equation from standard form into slope-intercept form, it requires that $B \neq 0$. We will examine the case where $B = 0$ a little later on in this section when we look at Slope and Direction of a Line.*

The Slope and y-intercept of a Line

The slope (m) is the steepness of the line relative to the X-axis. It is the ratio of the change in value of y (called the 'rise' and denoted Δy) to the corresponding change in value of x (called the 'run' and denoted Δx).

If P (x_1, y_1) and Q (x_2, y_2) are two different points on a line, then the slope of the line PQ between the two points is given by:

$$m = \frac{Rise}{Run} = \frac{Change\ in\ y\ value}{Change\ in\ x\ value} = \frac{\Delta y}{\Delta x} = \frac{y_2 - y_1}{x_2 - x_1}$$

This is illustrated in Exhibit 8.2-c and Exhibit 8.2-d:

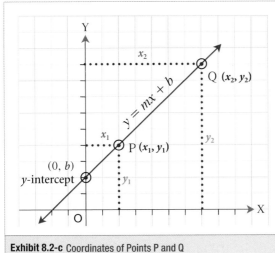

Exhibit 8.2-c Coordinates of Points P and Q

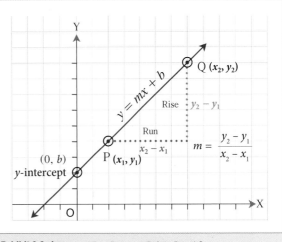

Exhibit 8.2-d Rise and Run Between Points P and Q

| Example 8.2-c | Finding the Slope and y-intercept of a Linear Equation and Graphing the Equation |

Find the slope and y-intercept of the linear equation $-2x + 3y - 12 = 0$ and graph the equation.

Solution

$$-2x + 3y - 12 = 0 \qquad \text{Rearranging the term with } y \text{ on the left,}$$

$$3y = 2x + 12 \qquad \text{Dividing each term by 3 and simplifying,}$$

$$y = \frac{2}{3}x + 4 \qquad \text{This is in the form } y = mx + b.$$

Therefore, the slope is $m = \dfrac{2}{3}$, and the y-intercept is the point $(0, 4)$.

Therefore, (0, 4) is a point on the line and the slope,

$$m = \frac{Rise}{Run} = \frac{Change\ in\ y\ value}{Change\ in\ x\ value} = \frac{2}{3}$$

represents an increase of 2 in the vertical direction ('rise') for every increase of 3 in the horizontal direction ('run').

Representing this on a graph:

(i)   First, plot the y-intercept (0, 4).

(ii)   From this point, move 3 units to the right and then move 2 units up to locate the new point (3, 6).

     Note: This is the same as moving 2 units up, and then 3 units to the right.

(iii)   Similarly, from the point (3, 6) move 3 units to the right and 2 units up to locate another point (6, 8).

(iv)   Draw the line through these points to graph the equation.

Or,

(i)   First, plot the y-intercept (0, 4).

(ii)   From this point, move 3 units to the left and then move 2 units down to locate the new point (−3, 2).

(iii)   Similarly, from the point (−3, 2) move 3 units to the left and 2 units down to locate another point (−6, 0).

(iv)   Draw the line through these points to graph the equation.

Note: All the points will lie on the same line.

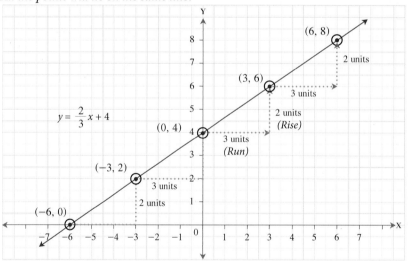

| Example 8.2-d | Graphing a Linear Equation in the Slope-Intercept Form |

Graph the equation $y = -\frac{3}{4}x - 2$.

The equation is in the form $y = mx + b$.

Therefore, $m = -\frac{3}{4}$ and $b = -2$, which means the y-intercept is the point (0, −2) and the slope is

$$m = \frac{Rise}{Run} = \frac{Change\ in\ y\ value}{Change\ in\ x\ value} = \frac{-3}{4}\ or\ \frac{3}{-4}$$

First plot the point (0, −2). Then, using the slope, $m = \frac{-3}{4}$, from the point (0, −2), move 4 units to the

right and 3 units down to locate the new point, (4, −5).

Solution
continued

Alternatively, first plot the point (0, –2). Then, using the slope, $m = \dfrac{3}{-4}$, from the point (0, –2), move 4 units to the left and 3 units up to locate another point on the line, (–4, 1).

Draw a line through these points to graph the equation.

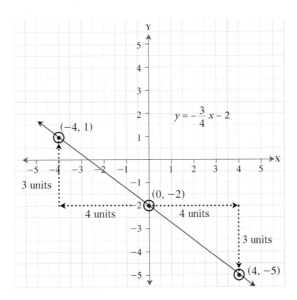

Slope and Direction of a Line

The slope, m, of a line is a number that describes the direction of the line and the steepness of the slope.

The **direction** of the line either (i) slopes upwards to the right, (ii) slopes downwards to the right, (iii) is horizontal, or (iv) is vertical, as discussed below:

If the slope of a line is positive, then the line rises to the right.

(i)   If the sign of the coefficient 'm' is positive, then the line slopes upwards to the right (i.e., the line rises from left to right), as illustrated in Exhibit 8.2-e.

If the slope of a line is negative, then the line falls to the right.

(ii)   If the sign of the coefficient 'm' is negative, then the line slopes downwards to the right (i.e., the line falls from left to right), as illustrated in Exhibit 8.2-f.

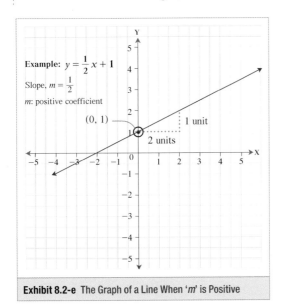

Exhibit 8.2-e The Graph of a Line When 'm' is Positive

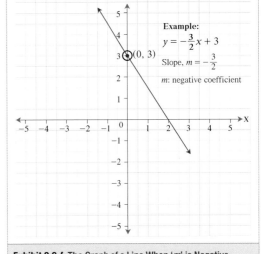

Exhibit 8.2-f The Graph of a Line When 'm' is Negative

If the slope of a line is zero, then the line is horizontal.

(iii) If the coefficient 'm' is zero, then the line is horizontal (parallel to the X-axis). A slope of zero means that when the x-coordinate increases or decreases, the y-coordinate does not change (i.e., 'rise' = 0). This is a special case of the linear equation $Ax + By = C$, where the value $A = 0$.

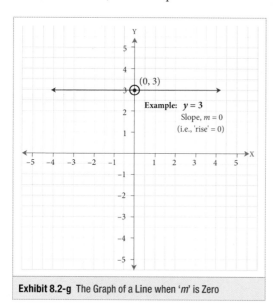

Exhibit 8.2-g The Graph of a Line when 'm' is Zero

Therefore, the equation of a horizontal line will be in the form $y = b$, and the y-intercept of the line is $(0, b)$.

For example, in the equation, **$y = 3$**, (i.e., $y = 0x + 3$), the slope is zero and the value of the y-coordinate is 3 for all values of x.

Therefore, the line is horizontal and passes through the y-intercept $(0, 3)$, as illustrated in Exhibit 8.2-g.

If the slope of a line is undefined, then the line is vertical.

(iv) If the coefficient 'm' is undefined, then the line is vertical (parallel to the Y-axis). An undefined slope means that when the y-coordinate increases or decreases, the x-coordinate does not change (i.e., 'run' = 0). This is a special case of the linear equation $Ax + By = C$, where the value $B = 0$.

As was mentioned above, an equation in this form cannot be rearranged into slope-intercept form, as it would require dividing by 0. As such, rather than isolating for y, we instead isolate for the variable x.

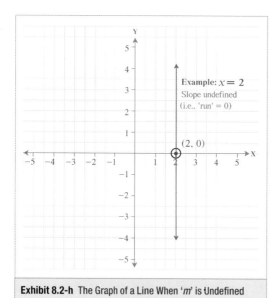

Exhibit 8.2-h The Graph of a Line When 'm' is Undefined

Therefore, the equation of a vertical line will be in the form $x = a$, and the x-intercept of the line is $(a, 0)$.

For example, in the equation, **$x = 2$**, the slope is undefined and the value of the x-coordinate is 2 for all values of y.

Therefore, the line is vertical and passes through the x-intercept $(2, 0)$, as illustrated in Exhibit 8.2-h.

Slope and Steepness of a Line

The **steepness** of the line is also measured by the coefficient of the slope ('m') of the line. The farther the coefficient 'm' is away from zero, the steeper is the slope. The closer the coefficient 'm' is to zero, the flatter is the slope.

A greater value for a positive slope indicates a steeper rise.

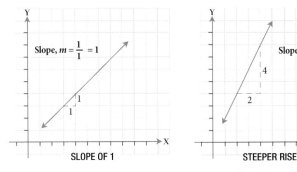

SLOPE OF 1   STEEPER RISE   FLATTER RISE

Positive slopes

A lesser value for a negative slope indicates a steeper fall.

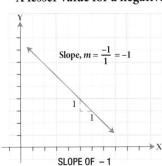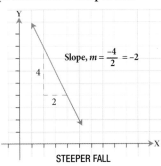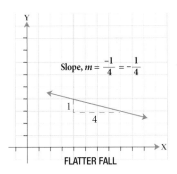

SLOPE OF – 1   STEEPER FALL   FLATTER FALL

Negative slopes

As discussed earlier, a slope of 0 indicates a horizontal line (no steepness) and an undefined slope indicates a vertical line (infinite steepness).

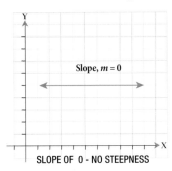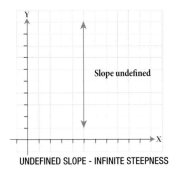

SLOPE OF 0 - NO STEEPNESS   UNDEFINED SLOPE - INFINITE STEEPNESS

Special slopes

Lines Passing Through the Origin

An equation with a y-intercept (or x-intercept) equal to 0 will have the graph passing through the origin.

Lines passing through the origin means that the point $(0, 0)$ is on the line. That is, the coordinates of both the x- and y-intercepts are $(0, 0)$. Hence, the equation of a line passing through the origin will be in the form $y = mx$, with the exception of two special cases:

$y = 0$ - **the equation of the x-axis** (i.e., the horizontal line passing through the origin)

$x = 0$ - **the equation of the y-axis** (i.e., the vertical line passing through the origin)

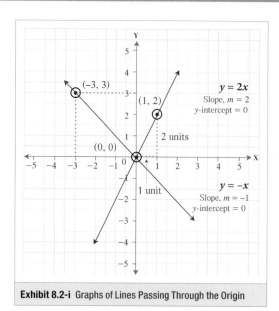

Exhibit 8.2-i Graphs of Lines Passing Through the Origin

For example, in the equation, $y = 2x$, $m = 2$, and $b = 0$; hence the slope is 2 and the y-intercept is the point $(0, 0)$.

Similarly, in the equation $y = -x$, $m = -1$, and $b = 0$; hence the slope is -1 and the y-intercept is the point $(0, 0)$.

Therefore, both of the lines above pass through the origin $(0, 0)$, as illustrated in Exhibit 8.2-i.

Determining Equations of Lines

In order to determine the equation of a line, we need both the slope and the y-intercept. If we do not know this information, we can determine by following these steps:

Step 1: If the slope is not given, determine it by computing the rise and run between two points on the graph.

Step 2: Replace the unknown m in the slope-intercept form of the equation with the slope value from Step 1.

Step 3: If the y-intercept is unknown, determine it by substituting the coordinates of a point on the line in for the x and y values in the slope-intercept form of the equation from Step 2, and solve for b.

Step 4: We replace the unknown b in the slope-intercept form of the equation from Step 2 with the y-intercept value from Step 3 to get the final equation of the line.

| Example 8.2-e | **Finding the Equation of a Line Given the Slope and One Point** |

Find the equation of a line having a slope of -2 and passing through the point $(3, 5)$.

Solution

Step 1: In this case, the slope is already known: $m = -2$.

Step 2: Replace m in the equation $y = mx + b$ with the value given.

Substituting for m in the slope-intercept equation $y = mx + b$, we obtain $y = -2x + b$.

Step 3: Substitute the coordinates of the given point into the equation to solve for b.

Substituting the x- and y- coordinates of the point $(3, 5)$ into the above equation, we obtain,

$$5 = -2(3) + b$$
$$b = 5 + 6 = 11$$

Step 4: Write the equation in slope-intercept form, $y = mx + b$, by substituting for the values of m and b determined in the steps above.

Therefore, the equation of the line is $y = -2x + 11$.

Example 8.2-f — Finding the Slope and the Equation of a Line Given Two Points

Find the equation of a line that passes through points (3, 2) and (4, 5).

Solution

Step 1: Calculate the slope.

$$m = \frac{\text{Change in } y \text{ value}}{\text{Change in } x \text{ value}} = \frac{y_2 - y_1}{x_2 - x_1} = \frac{5 - 2}{4 - 3} = \frac{3}{1} = 3$$

Step 2: Replace m in the equation $y = mx + b$ with the calculated slope.

Substituting for m in the slope-intercept equation $y = mx + b$, we obtain $y = 3x + b$.

Step 3: Substitute the coordinates of one of the given points into the equation to solve for b.

Substituting the x- and y-coordinates of the point (3, 2) into the above equation, we obtain,

$$2 = 3(3) + b$$
$$b = 2 - 9 = -7$$

Step 4: Write the equation in slope-intercept form, $y = mx + b$, by substituting for the values of m and b determined in the steps above.

Therefore, the equation of the line is $y = 3x - 7$.

Example 8.2-g — Finding the Equation of a Line Given a Graph

The graph below predicts the increase in the population of a rural community near a major suburb over time (assuming linear growth), where the x-axis measures the number of years from now, and the y-axis measures the population in thousands. Determine the equation of the line in standard form that represents the population growth in terms of time, given by the graph. Then, predict the population of the community in 10 years.

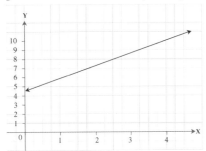

Solution

Step 1: Start by choosing any two points (with integer coordinates) on the line:

e.g., (1, 6) and (4, 10).

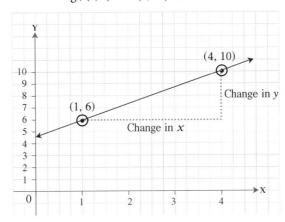

Solution
continued

The slope of the line is, $m = \dfrac{y_2 - y_1}{x_2 - x_1} = \dfrac{10 - 6}{4 - 1} = \dfrac{4}{3}.$

Step 2:   Let the equation of the line be $y = mx + b$ Substituting $m = \dfrac{4}{3}$,

Therefore, $y = \dfrac{4}{3}x + b$

Step 3:   Substituting the coordinates of one of the points $(1, 6)$ into the above equation and solving for b,

$$y = \dfrac{4}{3}(x) + b$$

$$6 = \dfrac{4}{3}(1) + b$$

$$b = 6 - \dfrac{4}{3} = \dfrac{18 - 4}{3} = \dfrac{14}{3}$$

Step 4:   Therefore, the equation of the line in slope-intercept form is: $y = \dfrac{4}{3}x + \dfrac{14}{3}.$

$$y = \dfrac{4}{3}x + \dfrac{14}{3}$$ Multiplying each term by 3, and simplifying,

$$3y = 4x + 14$$ Rearranging, ensuring that the coefficient of the x term remains positive,

$$4x - 3y = -14$$

Therefore, the equation of the line in standard form, is $4x - 3y = -14$.

Using the equation we found, we can predict the population of the community (given by y, in thousands) after a certain number of years (given by x).

After 10 years, the population of the community can be predicted using the slope-intercept form of the line:

$$y = \dfrac{4}{3}(10) + \dfrac{14}{3}$$

$$= \dfrac{40}{3} + \dfrac{14}{3}$$

$$= \dfrac{54}{3} = 18$$

Therefore, the population of the city is predicted to be 18,000 people in 10 years.

| Example 8.2-h | **Constructing Linear Models to Represent Practical Scenarios** |

A patient receives 300 mL of medication intravenously, infused at a constant rate. Thirty minutes into his treatment, the bag had 285 mL left. Write the linear equation in slope-intercept form to describe the situation and determine the amount of medication remaining in the bag 2.5 hours after the treatment began.

Solution

We first need to establish variables to model this scenario. The volume of medication remaining in the bag varies depending on the length of time that has elapsed since the treatment began. Hence, we let $x =$ time elapsed in minutes since the treatment began (independent variable) and $y =$ volume of medication in mL remaining in the bag (dependent variable).

Now, based on the information given, we can establish two ordered pairs of coordinates: $(0, 300)$ representing the 300 mL in the bag at the beginning of the treatment, and $(30, 285)$ representing the 285 mL remaining in the bag, 30 minutes into the treatment.

Plotting these two points on a graph, we get the following:

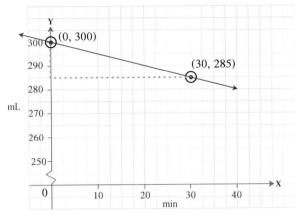

The slope of the line is, $$m = \frac{y_2 - y_1}{x_2 - x_1} = \frac{285 - 300}{30 - 0} = \frac{-15}{30} = \frac{-1}{2}$$

That is, for every two minutes, the IV medication will decrease by 1 mL.

Let the equation of the line be, $\quad y = mx + b$

Substituting $m = \frac{-1}{2}$, $\qquad\qquad y = \frac{-1}{2}x + b$

By inspection of the graph, $b = 300$ (since the y-intercept was one of the given points).

Therefore, the equation of the line in slope-intercept form is $y = \frac{-1}{2}x + 300$.

Converting hours to minutes, $\qquad\qquad$ 2.5 hours = 150 minutes

Substituting the value of x into the equation, $\qquad y = \frac{-1}{2}x + 300$

$$y = \frac{-1}{2}(150) + 300$$

$$= 225$$

Therefore, after 2.5 hours, there will be 225 mL of medication remaining in the bag.

Parallel and Perpendicular Lines

Parallel Lines

Lines that never intersect are called **parallel lines**. All lines with the same slope are parallel to each other. Similarly, all horizontal lines are all parallel to each other and all vertical lines are parallel to each other.

For example,

(i)   Lines represented by the equations $y = \frac{3}{2}x + 6$, $y = \frac{3}{2}x + 3$, and $y = \frac{3}{2}x - 6$ have the same slope (equal to $\frac{3}{2}$). Therefore, they are all parallel to each other.

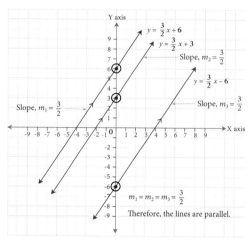

(ii) Lines represented by the equations $y = 4$, $y = 2$, and $y = -2$ are horizontal lines and have slopes equalling zero. Therefore, they are all parallel to each other. Horizontal lines are also parallel to the X-axis (which has the equation $y = 0$).

All points on a horizontal line will have the same y-coordinate and the slope is zero.

The equation of a horizontal line is in the form $y = b$, where b represents the y-coordinate of all the points of the line.

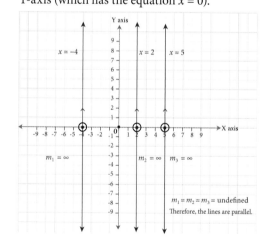

(iii) Lines represented by the equations $x = -4$, $x = 2$, and $x = 5$ are vertical lines and have undefined slopes. Therefore, they are all parallel to each other. Vertical lines are also parallel to the Y-axis (which has the equation $x = 0$).

All points on a vertical line will have the same x-coordinate and the slope is undefined.

The equation of a vertical line is in the form $x = a$, where a represents the x-coordinate of all the points on the line.

Example 8.2-i | **Writing the Equation of a Line Parallel to a Given Line and Passing Through a Given Point**

Write the equation of the line that is parallel to $3x + y = 5$ and that passes through the point P $(2, 4)$.

Solution

$$3x + y = 5 \qquad \text{Rearranging to slope-intercept form,}$$
$$y = -3x + 5 \qquad \text{Therefore, the slope is } m = -3.$$

The slope of the line parallel to this will have the same slope, $m = -3$.

> Lines that are parallel have the same slope.

Let the equation of the line parallel to $3x + y = 5$ be $y = mx + b$. It passes through $(2, 4)$ and has a slope of $m = -3$.

$$y = mx + b \qquad \text{Substituting the slope } m = -3,$$
$$y = -3x + b \qquad \text{Substituting the coordinates of the given point } (2, 4),$$
$$4 = -3(2) + b \qquad \text{Solving for } b,$$
$$4 = -6 + b$$
$$b = 10$$

Therefore, the equation of the desired line is $y = -3x + 10$, or $3x + y = 10$ in standard form.

Note: For parallel lines in standard form $Ax + By = C$, the values of A and B will always be proportional, and often will be equal.

Perpendicular Lines

Two lines that meet at a right angle are known as **perpendicular lines**. If the product of the slopes of two lines is -1, then the two lines are perpendicular to each other. This is the same as stating that if the slope of one line is the **negative reciprocal** of the other, then the two lines are perpendicular to each other.

For example, the lines represented by $y = 2x + 4$ and $y = -\dfrac{1}{2}x + 1$ are perpendicular to each other

because their slopes are negative reciprocals of each other.

> Two lines are perpendicular if the product of their slopes is –1.

$$m_1 = 2, \ m_2 = -\frac{1}{2}$$

$$m_1 \cdot m_2 = 2\left(-\frac{1}{2}\right) = -1$$

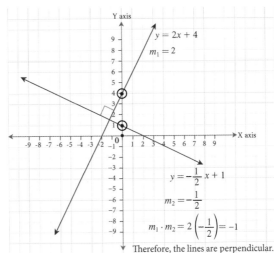

Therefore, the lines are perpendicular.

Also, all vertical lines (slope is undefined) and horizontal lines (slope is zero) are perpendicular to each other. For example, the lines represented by $y = 2$ and $x = 4$ are perpendicular to each other.

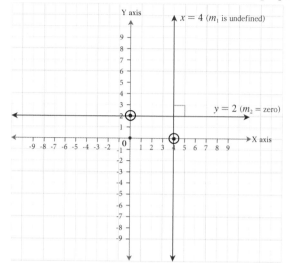

Two lines are also perpendicular if one of them is vertical (parallel to y-axis), and the other is horizontal (parallel to x-axis).

Example 8.2-j **Writing the Equation of a Line Perpendicular to a Given Line and Passing Through a Given Point**

Write the equation of the line perpendicular to $x + 3y = 9$ that passes through the point $(-4, 2)$.

Solution

$x + 3y = 9$ Rearranging to slope-intercept form,

$3y = -x + 9$

$y = \dfrac{-1}{3}x + 3$ Therefore, the slope is $m = -\dfrac{1}{3}$.

The slope of the line perpendicular to this will be the negative reciprocal of $-\dfrac{1}{3}$, which is 3.

Let the equation of the line perpendicular to $x + 3y = 9$ be $y = mx + b$. It passes through the point $(-4, 2)$ and has a slope of $m = 3$.

Lines that are perpendicular have slopes that are negative reciprocals of each other.

$y = mx + b$ Substituting the slope $m = 3$,

$y = 3x + b$ Substituting the coordinates of the given point $(-4, 2)$,

$2 = 3(-4) + b$ Solving for b,

$2 = -12 + b$

$b = 2 + 12 = 14$

Therefore, the equation of the desired line is $y = 3x + 14$, or $3x - y = -14$ in standard form.

8.2 | Exercises

Answers to odd-numbered problems are available at the end of the textbook.

1. For the equation $2x + 3y = 18$, find the missing values in the following ordered pairs:

   a. $(3, ?)$ b. $(-6, ?)$ c. $(0, ?)$

   d. $(?, 0)$ e. $(?, -4)$ f. $(?, 2)$

2. For the equation $4x + 5y = 20$, find the missing values in the following ordered pairs:

   a. $(0, ?)$ b. $(-15, ?)$ c. $(5, ?)$

   d. $(?, 8)$ e. $(?, -4)$ f. $(?, 0)$

3. For the equation $y = -\dfrac{2}{3}x + 1$, find the missing values in the following ordered pairs.

   a. $(6, ?)$ b. $(-3, ?)$ c. $(0, ?)$

   d. $(?, 0)$ e. $(?, -3)$ f. $(?, 5)$

4. For the equation $y = \frac{1}{4}x - 3$, find the missing values in the following ordered pairs.

    a. (8, ?)   b. (–4, ?)   c. (0, ?)

    d. (?, 0)   e. (?, –3)   f. (?, 9)

For Problems 5 to 10, write the equations in slope-intercept form:

5. $4y + 6x = -3$ 6. $9y + 2x = 18$

7. $3y - 2x = 15$ 8. $5y - 2x = -20$

9. $\frac{x}{2} + \frac{y}{3} = 1$ 10. $\frac{x}{4} + \frac{y}{5} = 2$

For Problems 11 to 16, write the equations in standard form:

11. $y = \frac{5}{2}x + 1$ 12. $y = \frac{2}{5}x - 1$

13. $y = -\frac{3}{4}x - 3$ 14. $y = -\frac{4}{3}x + 4$

15. $y = \frac{1}{2}x + \frac{3}{5}$ 16. $y = \frac{3}{2}x - \frac{1}{3}$

For Problems 17 to 28, graph the equations using a table of values:

17. $y = x + 3$ 18. $y = 3x + 2$

19. $y = -5x + 1$ 20. $y = -2x + 3$

21. $2x + y + 1 = 0$ 22. $4x + y + 2 = 0$

23. $2x - y - 3 = 0$ 24. $x - y - 1 = 0$

25. $y = 5$ 26. $x = -2$

27. $x + \frac{7}{2} = 0$ 28. $y - \frac{10}{3} = 0$

For Problems 29 to 34, find the x- and y-intercepts for the equations and graph the equations:

29. $y = 2x + 4$ 30. $y = 4x + 1$

31. $x + y - 3 = 4$ 32. $x + y - 4 = 7$

33. $3x + 4y = -2$ 34. $5x + 2y = -3$

35. Point 'A' is in the 3rd quadrant and Point 'B' is in the 1st quadrant. Find the sign of the slope of the line AB.

36. Point 'C' is in the 4th quadrant and Point 'D' is in the 2nd quadrant. Find the sign of the slope of the line CD.

For Problems 37 to 40, find the slopes and y-intercepts of the equations and graph the equations:

37. $2x - 3y - 18 = 0$ 38. $5x - 2y + 10 = 0$

39. $-4x + 7y - 21 = 0$ 40. $-7x + 8y - 32 = 0$

For Problems 41 to 44, find the equations of the lines that pass through the points:

41. (1, –2) and (5, –2)   42. (0, 5) and (4, 5)

43. (3, –5) and (3, 4)   44. (–4, 7) and (–4, –1)

For Problems 45 to 50, find the equations of the lines that:

45. Have a slope of –2 and pass through (2, 6).

46. Have a slope of 3 and pass through (–3, –2).

47. Have a slope of $\frac{2}{3}$ and pass through the origin.

48. Have a slope of $-\frac{4}{5}$ and pass through the origin.

49. Have an x-intercept = 4 and a y-intercept = 6.

50. Have an x-intercept = –4 and a y-intercept = 2.

For Problems 51 to 54, find the slopes of the lines passing through the points, then graph the lines.

51. (2, 1) and (6, 1)

52. (−6, 4) and (2, 4)

53. (−3, 4) and (−3, −1)

54. (5, 6) and (5, −4)

55. The slope of a line is 3. The line passes through A (4, y) and B (6, 8). Find y.

56. The slope of a line is 2. The line passes through A (x, 8) and B (2, 4). Find x.

57. Points D (3, 2), E (6, 5), and F (x, 1) are on a line. Find x.

58. Points A (2, 3), B (6, 5), and C (10, y) are on a line. Find y.

For Problems 59 to 62, find the equation of the line (in standard form) for the graphs.

59.

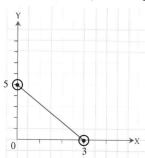

Quantity of IV fluid decreasing over time

60.

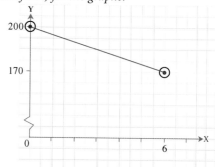

Weight of a patient on a 6-month diet

61.

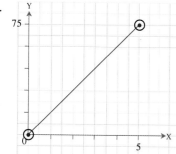

Number of calories burned per minute of exercise

62.

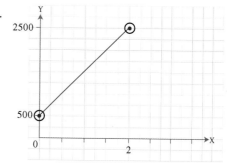

Average cost to stay in a hospital per night

For Problems 63 to 74, determine the equations for the lines:

63. A line parallel to $3x - 2y = 6$ and passing through the point P(2, −3).

64. A line parallel to $x - 3y = -1$ and passing through the point P(−2, −4).

65. A line parallel to $3x - 9y = 6$ and passing through the y-intercept of the line $5x - 4y = 20$.

66. A line parallel to $2x + 8y = -10$ and passing through the x-intercept of the line $2x + 3y = 4$.

67. A line parallel to $y = 2$ and passing through the point P(4, −7).

68. A line parallel to $x = -1$ and passing through the point P(−3, 5).

69. A line perpendicular to $x + y = -2$ and passing through the point P(−2, 5).

70. A line perpendicular to $4x + y + 1 = 0$ and passing through the point P(3, 4).

71. A line perpendicular to $2x - 5y - 5 = 0$ and passing through the x-intercept of the line $3x + 2y - 6 = 0$.

72. A line perpendicular to $3x + 4y + 9 = 0$ and passing through the y-intercept of the line $2x + 3y - 12 = 0$.

73. A line perpendicular to $y = 2$ and passing through the point P(4, −7).

74. A line perpendicular to $x = -1$ and passing through the point P(−3, 5).

For Problems 75 to 80, solve the word problems.

75. A patient was started on a saline drip with an IV bag that contained 500 mL. Thirty minutes later, the bag had 430 mL.

    a. Assuming a linear rate of decrease, at what rate (in mL/hour) is the saline flowing out of the bag?

    b. Write the linear equation to model this situation.

    c. How much saline solution will remain in the bag after 3 hours?

76. A nurse administered an IV line with an IV bag that contained 1,000 mL of solution. Fifteen minutes later, the bag had 950 mL remaining.

    a. Assuming a linear rate of decrease, at what rate (in mL/hour) is the solution flowing out of the bag?

    b. Write the linear equation to model this situation.

    c. How much solution will remain in the bag after 4.5 hours?

77. By noon, an ER nurse had already seen 35 patients. Every two hours from then, she sees another 15 patients. Model this scenario using a linear equation and use your equation to determine at what time she will have seen 80 patients.

78. A new clinic opens up with a capacity for 150 new patients. Every three weeks, the clinic enrolls 25 new patients, which decreases the capacity correspondingly. Model this scenario using a linear equation and use your equation to determine after how many weeks the capacity of the clinic will be reduced to only 50 patients.

79. A medical supplier charges $20 in shipping for the first unit ordered. However, for every additional unit ordered in the same shipment, she charges a further $15 for shipping. Write an equation that shows the relationship between her total shipping charge (y) and the number of units ordered in the shipment (x). Plot the graph of this equation, identifying both the slope and the y-intercept and what they represent.

80. A pharmacy charges a dispensing fee of $12 for the first prescription refill. However, for every additional prescription refill, ordered at the same time, the pharmacy will charge a further dispensing fee of $9. Write an equation that shows the relationship between the total dispensing fee (y) and the number of refills ordered (x). Plot the graph of this equation, identifying both the slope and the y-intercept and what they represent.

8.3 | Solving Systems of Linear Equations With Two Variables, Graphically

In the previous section, you learned that a linear equation with two variables produces a straight line when plotted on a graph. If the graph of an equation is linear, then all the points (**ordered pairs**) on the line are solutions to that linear equation.

For example, $2x + y = 4$ is a linear equation with two variables, x and y. The graph of this equation is a line and all the points (ordered pairs) on this line are solutions to this equation as shown in the diagram below:

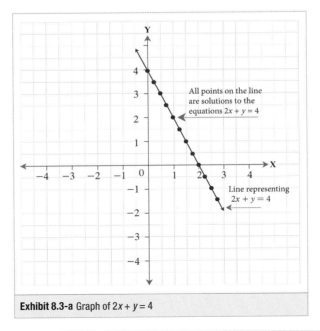

All points on the line are solutions to the equations $2x + y = 4$

Line representing $2x + y = 4$

Exhibit 8.3-a Graph of $2x + y = 4$

System of Equations

Two or more equations that are solved simultaneously form a system of equations. In this section, we will be analyzing systems of two linear equations with two variables.

The solution to a system of two linear equations with two variables is an ordered pair of numbers (coordinates) that satisfy both equations.

If we graph a system of two linear equations, the solution to the system (if it exists) will be the coordinates of the point at which the two linear equations intersect. If they do not intersect, then there is no solution to that system of equations.

For example, $2x + y = 4$ and $x - 2y = -3$ form a system of two linear equations. The graphs of these equations intersect at $(1, 2)$ as shown in the following diagram. Hence, the point $(1, 2)$ is the solution to the system of two linear equations, which can be verified by substituting $x = 1$ and $y = 2$ into the two linear equations and confirming that they make both equations true:

$$2(1) + (2) = 4 \quad \text{and} \quad (1) - 2(2) = -3$$

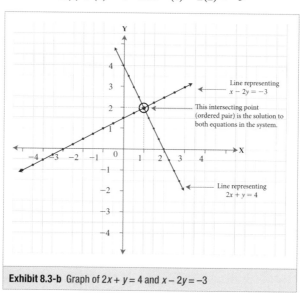

Exhibit 8.3-b Graph of $2x + y = 4$ and $x - 2y = -3$

Three Cases for a System of Two Linear Equations with Two Variables

- **If they intersect** (i.e., *the lines are not parallel*), then there is only one solution: the point of intersection.

- **If they do not intersect** (i.e., *the lines are parallel and distinct*), then there is no solution.

- **If they coincide** (i.e., *the lines are the same*), then there are an infinite number of solutions: every point on the coincident lines..

Consistent and Inconsistent Systems

A linear system of two equations that has **one or an infinite number of solutions** is known as a **consistent linear system**.

A linear system of two equations that has **no solution** is called an **inconsistent linear system**.

If the graphs of 2 linear equations intersect at one point or if the lines coincide (representing the same line) then they are "consistent" as a system. Otherwise, they are "inconsistent" as a system.

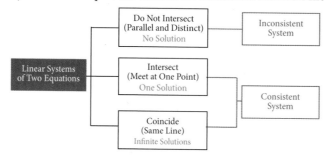

Dependent and Independent Equations

If a system of equations has an **infinite number of solutions**, then the **equations are dependent**.

If a system of equations has **one or no solution,** then the **equations are independent**.

If the graphs of 2 linear equations coincide (representing the same line), then they are known as a "dependent system of equations". Otherwise, they are known as an "independent system of equations".

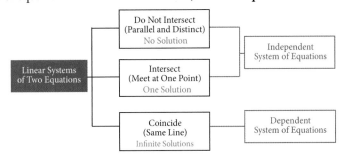

Summary of the Three Cases

Intersecting Lines

Slopes of lines:	Different
y-intercepts:	May or may not be the same. *Will be different, unless the lines intersect on the Y-axis or at the origin.*
Number of solutions:	One
System:	Consistent
Equations:	Independent

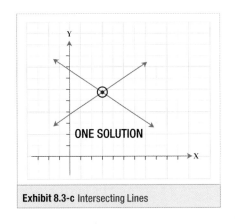

Exhibit 8.3-c Intersecting Lines

Parallel and Distinct Lines

Slopes of lines:	Same
y-intercepts:	Different
Number of solutions:	None
System:	Inconsistent
Equations:	Independent

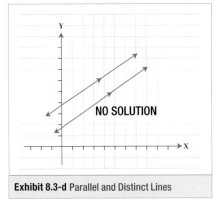

Exhibit 8.3-d Parallel and Distinct Lines

Coincident Lines

Slopes of lines:	Same
y-intercepts:	Same
Number of solutions:	Infinite
System:	Consistent
Equations:	Dependent

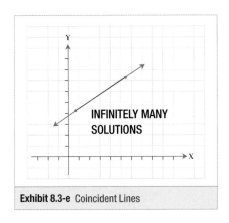

Exhibit 8.3-e Coincident Lines

Solving Linear Systems Graphically

The following steps will help to solve systems of two linear equations with two variables, graphically:

Step 1: Rewrite both equations in either the slope-intercept form of $y = mx + b$ (if you prefer to graph using the slope-intercept method or by using a table of values), or the standard form of $Ax + By = C$ (if you prefer to graph using the x- and y-intercept method).

Step 2: Graph the first equation by either using the slope-intercept method, the x- and y-intercept method, or using a table of values. The graph will be a straight line.

Step 3: Graph the second equation on the same axes as in Step 2. It will be another straight line.

Step 4: If the two lines intersect at a point, then the point of intersection (x, y) is the solution to the given system of equations. If the lines are parallel and distinct, there is no solution to the given system of equations (i.e., the system is inconsistent). If the lines are coincident, then all of the infinitely-many points on the lines are solutions to the given system of equations (i.e., the equations are dependent).

Step 5: Check the solution obtained by substituting the values for the variables in each of the original equation. If the answer satisfies **both** of the equations, then it is indeed the correct solution to the given system of equations.

Note: In Steps 2 and 3, the order in which the equations are graphed or the method(s) used to graph the equations does not matter.

Example 8.3-a	Solving and Classifying Systems of Linear Equations

Solve the following system of equations by graphing, and classify the system as consistent or inconsistent and the equations as dependent or independent.

$x - y + 1 = 0$

$x + y - 3 = 0$

Solution

Step 1: $x - y + 1 = 0$ Writing the equation in $y = mx + b$ form,

$\qquad\qquad y = x + 1$ Equation ①

$\qquad x + y - 3 = 0$ Writing the equation in $y = mx + b$ form,

$\qquad\qquad y = -x + 3$ Equation ②

Step 2: Equation ① : $y = x + 1$

$\qquad m = 1$ and $b = 1$

Therefore, the slope is $\dfrac{1}{1}$ and the y-intercept is $(0, 1)$.

Step 3: Equation ② : $y = -x + 3$

$\qquad m = -1$ and $b = 3$

Therefore, the slope is $\dfrac{-1}{1}$ and the y-intercept is $(0, 3)$.

Solution
continued

Graphing equations ① and ② using the slope-intercept method:

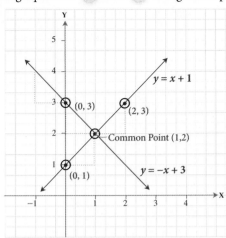

Step 4:   The two lines intersect at the common point (1, 2).

Step 5:   Check the solution (1, 2) in Equations ① and ② .

Equation ① , $y = x + 1$ Equation ② , $y = -x + 3$

LS = $y = 2$ LS = $y = 2$

RS = $x + 1 = 1 + 1 = 2$ RS = $-x + 3 = -1 + 3 = 2$

Therefore,   LS = RS   Therefore,   LS = RS

Therefore, the solution is (1, 2). The system is consistent (has a solution) and the equations are independent (lines are not coincident).

Example 8.3-b   **Classifying Systems of Linear Equations**

Solve the following system of equations by graphing, and classify the system as consistent or inconsistent and the equations as dependent or independent.

$3x + y - 3 = 0$

$3x + y + 2 = 0$

Solution

Step 1: $3x + y - 3 = 0$ Writing the equation in $y = mx + b$ form,

$y = -3x + 3$ Equation ①

$3x + y + 2 = 0$ Writing the equation in $y = mx + b$ form,

$y = -3x - 2$ Equation ②

Step 2:   Equation ① : $y = -3x + 3$

$m = -3$ and $b = 3$

> Since the slopes are the same, the lines are parallel.

Therefore, the slope is $\dfrac{-3}{1}$ and the y-intercept is (0, 3).

Step 3:   Equation ② : $y = -3x - 2$

$m = -3$ and $b = -2$

Therefore, the slope is $\dfrac{-3}{1}$ and the y-intercept is (0, -2).

Solution
continued

Graphing equations ① and ② using the slope-intercept method:

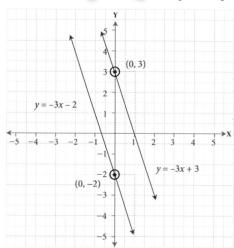

Step 4: The lines have the same slopes but different *y*-intercepts. Therefore, the lines are parallel and distinct; i.e., they have no solutions.

The system is inconsistent (no solution) and the equations are independent (lines are not coincident).

Note: Once we had the equations in slope-intercept form, we could already tell that they were parallel (same slope) and distinct (different y-intercept) and, therefore, that there were no solutions to the system of equations, without even needing to graph the system.

| Example 8.3-c | **Analyzing System of Equations** |

Without graphing, determine whether each system has one solution, no solution, or infinitely many solutions.

(i) $4x + y = 9$ (ii) $2y + x = 4$ (iii) $2x - 3y + 6 = 0$
     $2x + y = 5$ $2x + 4y = 16$ $6x - 9y = -18$

Solution

(i) Rewrite the equations in slope-intercept form ($y = mx + b$):

$4x + y = 9$

$\quad y = -4x + 9$ $\longrightarrow$ Slope (m) = -4, y-intercept (b) = 9

$2x + y = 5$

$\quad y = -2x + 5$ $\longrightarrow$ Slope (m) = -2, y-intercept (b) = 5

The slopes of the lines are different (-4 and -2).

Therefore, the lines are not parallel. They will intersect at one point. The system will have one solution.

(ii) Rewrite the equations in slope-intercept form ($y = mx + b$):

$2y + x = 4$

$\quad 2y = -x + 4$

$\quad\quad y = -\dfrac{1}{2}x + 2$ $\longrightarrow$ Slope (m) = $-\dfrac{1}{2}$, y-intercept (b) = 2

$2x + 4y = 16$

$\quad 4y = -2x + 16$

$\quad\quad y = -\dfrac{1}{2}x + 4$ $\longrightarrow$ Slope (m) = $-\dfrac{1}{2}$, y-intercept (b) = 4

Solution
continued

The slopes of the lines are the same $\left(-\dfrac{1}{2}\right)$ but the y-intercepts are different.

Therefore, the lines are parallel but distinct. The system will have no solutions.

(iii)   Rewrite the equations in slope-intercept form ($y = mx + b$):

$$2x - 3y + 6 = 0$$
$$-3y = -2x - 6$$
$$y = \frac{2}{3}x + 2 \quad \longrightarrow \quad \text{Slope } (m) = \frac{2}{3}, y\text{-intercept } (b) = 2$$

$$6x - 9y = -18$$
$$-9y = -6x - 18$$
$$y = \frac{2}{3}x + 2 \quad \longrightarrow \quad \text{Slope } (m) = \frac{2}{3}, y\text{-intercept } (b) = 2$$

The slopes of the lines are the same $\left(\dfrac{2}{3}\right)$ and the y-intercepts are also the same (2).

Therefore, the two lines coincide. The system will have infinitely many solutions.

8.3 | Exercises

Answers to odd-numbered problems are available at the end of the textbook.

For Problems 1 to 8, without graphing, using the slope property of parallel and perpendicular lines, identify whether each of the pairs of the following lines are parallel, perpendicular, or (non-perpendicular) intersecting.

1. $y = x + 1$
    $4x + 4y = -1$

2. $6x - 5y = 10$
    $y = -\dfrac{6}{5}x - 12$

3. $x - 3y = -60$
    $y = \dfrac{1}{3}x - 4$

4. $3x - 2y = -12$
    $2x + 3y = -12$

5. $2x + 5y = -5$
    $y = \dfrac{5}{2}x - 4$

6. $7x + 4y = 16$
    $y = -\dfrac{4}{7}x + 3$

7. $3x + 2y = -24$
    $y = \dfrac{3}{2}x + 3$

8. $3x - 2y = -6$
    $y = \dfrac{3}{2}x - 16$

For Problems 9 to 16, without graphing, determine whether each system has one solution, no solution, or infinitely many solutions.

9. $3x + 4y = 4$
    $2x + y = 6$

10. $3x - 2y = 6$
     $x + 2y = 6$

11. $x - y = 1$
     $2x + y = 5$

12. $x + y = 7$
     $2x - y = 8$

13. $3y - 2x = 1$
     $12y - 8x = -4$

14. $2x - y - 4 = 0$
     $6x - 3y + 12 = 0$

15. $2x = 3y + 1$
     $8x = 12y + 4$

16. $x + 2y = 5$
     $2x + 4y = 10$

17. Find the value of 'A' for which the lines $Ax - 2y - 5 = 0$ and $8x - 4y + 3 = 0$ are parallel (and distinct).

18. Find the value of 'B' for which the lines $3x - 2y + 8 = 0$ and $6x + By - 3 = 0$ are parallel (and distinct).

19. Find the value of b for which the lines $x + 3y + 6 = 0$ and $y = -\dfrac{1}{3}x + b$ are coincident.

20. Find the value of m for which the lines $y = mx + 3$ and $x - 2y + 6 = 0$ are coincident.

For Problems 21 to 40, solve the system of equations by graphing, and then classify the systems of equations as consistent or inconsistent and the equations as dependent or independent.

21. $y = 3x - 2$
    $y = -7x + 8$

22. $y = 3x + 9$
    $y = x + 1$

23. $y = -x + 2$
    $2x + 2y = 6$

24. $y = 2x + 6$
    $3x + 2y = 2$

25. $y = -4x + 7$
    $8x + 2y = 14$

26. $y = -2x + 3$
    $4x + 2y = 6$

27. $y = x - 2$
    $2x + 3y = 9$

28. $y = 2x - 4$
    $2x + 3y = 4$

29. $x - y - 1 = 0$
    $2x + -5y = 0$

30. $3x - y - 8 = 0$
    $6x - 2y - 1 = 0$

31. $5x + y + 9 = 0$
    $x - 3y + 5 = 0$

32. $3x - 2y + 1 = 0$
    $4x + y - 6 = 0$

33. $3x + 2y = -4$
    $y + \dfrac{3}{2}x + 2 = 0$

34. $2x - y = 3$
    $6x + 3y = 15$

35. $4x - 2y = 6$
    $2x - y - 4 = 0$

36. $x - 2y + 6 = 0$
    $y = \dfrac{1}{2}x + 3$

37. $x - y = 6$
    $2x + y = 3$

38. $4x - 8y = 0$
    $2x - 4y = -8$

39. $y = -\dfrac{1}{2}x + 1$
    $x - 4y = -4$

40. $y = x + 5$
    $x + 2y = 10$

8.4 | Solving Systems of Linear Equations with Two Variables, Algebraically

We have seen how to solve systems of linear equations using graphical methods, but in all the examples given, the solutions had integer coordinates. We will now be introduced to some algebraic methods for solving systems of linear equations, which are preferable for the following reasons:

1. Algebraic methods eliminate the possibility of graphing errors.

2. Algebraic methods provide the exact answer for systems of equations that have solutions with fractional coordinates.

There are two algebraic methods for solving systems of linear equations:

*   The method of Substitution
*   The method of Elimination

Substitution Method

The idea behind the substitution method is similar to what we've already seen when we evaluate an algebraic expression by substituting values in for the variables. However, with the substitution method, instead of substituting a value in for a variable, we substitute another algebraic expression to reduce our equation to having only one unknown variable, which we can then solve for.

The substitution method is the preferable algebraic method to use to solve the system if either one of the equations in the system has a variable with a coefficient of 1 or –1, which makes that variable easy to isolate in the equation.

To solve a system of two linear equations with two variables, follow these steps:

Step 1: If there is an equation with a variable that has a coefficient of +1 or –1, isolate for that variable to find an expression for that variable in terms of the other variable. If there is no variable with a coefficient of +1 or –1, choose the variable in one of the two equations with the easiest coefficient to divide by (e.g., 2, 4, 5, 10, etc.) and isolate for that variable.

Step 2: Substitute the expression for the variable from Step 1 into the other equation (the one not used in Step 1). This will result in an equation involving only one of the two variables.

Step 3: Solve the equation in Step 2 for the one unknown variable.

Step 4: Solve for the other variable by substituting the value of the known variable back into either of the original equations (it is often easiest to substitute back into the equation from Step 1 with the isolated variable).

Step 5: State the solution for the system of equations as an ordered pair of the solutions for the two variables found in Step 3 and Step 4.

Step 6: Check if the solution obtained for the variables is true by substituting these values into each of the original equations. If the solution satisfies **both** of the equations, then it is the solution to the given systems of equations.

| Example 8.4-a | Solving a System of Equations by Substituting for the Variable 'y' |

Solve the system of equations given below:

$$y - 3x + 2 = 0$$
$$3y + x - 14 = 0$$

Solution

Step 1: The coefficient of y in Equation ① is one, so we isolate for y in that equation.

$$y - 3x + 2 = 0$$
$$y = 3x - 2$$

Step 2: Substituting $(3x - 2)$ for y in Equation ②,

$$3y + x - 14 = 0$$
$$3(3x - 2) + x - 14 = 0$$

Step 3: Solving for 'x',

$$9x - 6 + x - 14 = 0$$
$$9x + x = 14 + 6$$
$$10x = 20$$
$$x = 2$$

Step 4: Substituting for $x = 2$ back into the equation that is solved for y,

$$y = 3x - 2$$
$$y = 3(2) - 2$$
$$y = 4$$

Step 5: Therefore, the solution is (2, 4).

Solution
continued

Step 6: Checking the solution in Equations ① and ② ,

$$\text{Equation ①}, y - 3x + 2 = 0 \qquad \text{Equation ②}, 3y + x - 14 = 0$$

$$LS = y - 3x + 2 \qquad\qquad LS = 3y + x - 14$$

$$= 4 - 3(2) + 2 \qquad\qquad = 3(4) + 2 - 14$$

$$= 0 \qquad\qquad\qquad\qquad = 0$$

$$= RS \text{ (True)} \qquad\qquad = RS \text{ (True)}$$

Therefore, LS = RS.   Therefore, LS = RS.

Example 8.4-b	**Solving a System of Equations by Substituting for the Variable 'x'**

Solve the system of equations given below:

$$x + 2y = 6$$
$$4x + 3y = 4$$

Solution

Step 1: The coefficient of x in Equation ① is one.

$$x + 2y = 6$$
$$x = 6 - 2y$$

Step 2: Substituting $(6 - 2y)$ for x in Equation ② ,

$$4x + 3y = 4$$
$$4(6 - 2y) + 3y = 4$$

Step 3: Solving for 'y',

$$24 - 8y + 3y = 4$$
$$-8y + 3y = 4 - 24$$
$$-5y = -20$$
$$y = 4$$

Step 4: Substituting $y = 4$ back into the equation that is solved for x,

$$x = 6 - 2y$$
$$x = 6 - 2(4)$$
$$x = -2$$

Step 5: Therefore, the solution is $(-2, 4)$.

Step 6: Checking the solution in Equations ① and ② ,

$$\text{Equation ① } x + 2y = 6 \qquad \text{Equation ② } 4x + 3y = 4$$

$$LS = x + 2y \qquad\qquad LS = 4x + 3y$$

$$= -2 + 2(4) \qquad\qquad = 4(-2) + 3(4)$$

$$= 6 \qquad\qquad\qquad\qquad = 4$$

$$= RS \text{ (True)} \qquad\qquad = RS \text{ (True)}$$

Therefore, LS = RS.   Therefore, LS = RS.

Elimination Method

The idea behind the elimination method is that adding or subtracting equations still maintains equality: if $A = B$ and $C = D$, then $A + C = B + D$ and $A - C = B - D$. If the equations are added or subtracted in such a way that one of the variables are eliminated, we will be left with an equation with one variable (which can be solved) that is equivalent to the original system of equations.

The elimination method is preferable if none of the equations in the system has a variable with a coefficient of 1 or −1. The elimination method is easier to use when equations are in the form $Ax + By = C$.

In this method, the following steps are used to solve systems of two linear equations with two variables:

Step 1: Rewrite both equations in the form of $Ax + By = C$, where A, B, and C are integers.

Note: For the elimination method, the coefficient A in front of x does not need to be positive, as it would be in standard form.

Step 2: Multiply one or both equations by a suitable integer so that it will create the same (or opposite) coefficient for any one of the variables in both equations.

The purpose is to eliminate one of the variables by subtracting (or adding) these two equations.

Step 3: Subtract (or add) the two equations from Step 2 to obtain one equation with only one variable that is equivalent to the original system of equations.

Step 4: Solve the equation in Step 3 to find the value of the one variable.

Step 5: Solve for the other variable by substituting the value of the known variable into either one of the equations in Step 1.

Step 6: State the solution for the system of equations as an ordered pair of the solutions for the two variables found in Step 4 and Step 5.

Step 7: Check if the solution obtained for the variables is true by substituting these values into each of the original equations. If the solution satisfies **both** of the equations, then it is the solution to the given systems of equations.

Note: • In Step 2, it does not matter which of the variables you choose to make the same (or opposite) coefficient. Typically, you will want to choose whichever variable will be easier to make the coefficients equal or opposite (e.g., if one coefficient is a multiple of the other).

*• In Step 3, you will **subtract** if both equations have the same coefficient for the variable to be eliminated. If the coefficients are opposite, then you will **add** to eliminate that variable.*

Example 8.4-c — Solving a System of Equations by Eliminating the Variable 'x'

Solve the system of equations given below:

$3x + 2y = 12$

$6x - 3y = 3$

Solution

Step 1: The equations are in the form of $Ax + By = C$,

$3x + 2y = 12$ Equation ①

$6x - 3y = 3$ Equation ②

Step 2: In this case, the variable 'x' will be easier to eliminate, as its coefficient in the second equation (6) is a multiple of its coefficient in the first equation (3).

Multiplying Equation ① by 2 to make the coefficients on x the same,

$2(3x + 2y) = 2(12)$

$6x + 4y = 24$ Equation ③

Solution
continued

Step 3: Since the coefficients on the variable 'x' are the same, we subtract Equation ② from Equation ③ ,

$$6x + 4y = 24$$
$$- (6x - 3y) = - (3)$$
$$7y = 21$$

Step 4: Solving for 'y',

$$7y = 21$$
$$y = \frac{21}{7} = 3$$

Step 5: Substituting $y = 3$ in Equation ① and solving for 'x',

$$3x + 2y = 12$$
$$3x + 2(3) = 12$$
$$3x = 12 - 6 = 6$$
$$x = 2$$

Step 6: Therefore, the solution is (2, 3).

Step 7: Checking the solution in Equations ① and ② ,

Equation ① , $3x + 2y = 12$ Equation ② , $6x - 3y = 3$
  LS = 3x + 2y   LS = 6x - 3y
    = 3(2) + 2(3)   = 6(2) - 3(3)
    = 6 + 6   = 12 - 9
    = 12   = 3
    = RS (True)   = RS (True)
  Therefore, LS = RS.   Therefore, LS = RS.

Example 8.4-d | **Solving a System of Equations by Eliminating the Variable 'y'**

Solve the system of equations given below:
$$3x + 2y = 22$$
$$8x - 5y = 7$$

Solution

Step 1: The equations are in the form of $Ax + By = C$,
$$3x + 2y = 22 \qquad \text{Equation } ①$$
$$8x - 5y = 7 \qquad \text{Equation } ②$$

Step 2: In this case, since neither of the variables have pairs of coefficients that are multiples of each other or even share a common factor, we choose the variable 'y' to eliminate, as the coefficients are smaller:

The variable 'y' in Equations ① and ② has coefficients of 2 and –5, respectively.

Multiplying Equation ① by 5, and multiplying Equation ② by 2 to make the coefficients on y the same:

$$5(3x + 2y) = 5(22) \qquad\qquad\qquad 2(8x - 5y) = 2(7)$$
$$15x + 10y = 110 \quad \text{Equation } ③ \qquad 16x - 10y = 14 \quad \text{Equation } ④$$

Step 3: Since the coefficients on the variable 'y' are opposite, we add Equations ③ and ④,

$$15x + 10y = 110$$
$$+ (16x - 10y) = +(14)$$
$$\overline{31x = 124}$$

Step 4: Solving for 'x',

$$31x = 124$$
$$x = \frac{124}{31} = 4$$

Step 5: Substituting $x = 4$ in Equation ① and solving for 'y',

$$3x + 2y = 22$$
$$3(4) + 2y = 22$$
$$2y = 22 - 12 = 10$$
$$y = 5$$

Step 6: Therefore, the solution is $(4, 5)$.

Step 7: Checking the solution in Equations ① and ②,

Equation ①, $3x + 2y = 22$ Equation ②, $8x - 5y = 7$

$$\begin{aligned} LS &= 3x + 2y \\ &= 3(4) + 2(5) \\ &= 12 + 10 \\ &= 22 \\ &= RS \text{ (True)} \end{aligned} \qquad \begin{aligned} LS &= 8x - 5y \\ &= 8(4) - 5(5) \\ &= 32 - 25 \\ &= 7 \\ &= RS \text{ (True)} \end{aligned}$$

Therefore, LS = RS.   Therefore, LS = RS.

Solving Systems of Equations With Fractions

When one or more of the variables in a system of equations has fractional coefficients, it is often easiest to first clear the fractions by multiplying each equation by its least common denominator (**LCD**).

For example, consider the following system of equations:

$$\frac{2}{3}x + \frac{1}{2}y = 1$$
$$\frac{1}{3}x + \frac{3}{4}y = -2$$

To clear the fractions, multiply each equation by its **LCD** (least common denominator).

$\frac{2}{3}x + \frac{1}{2}y = 1$ The LCD is 6; therefore, multiplying each term by 6,

$4x + 3y = 6$ Equation ①

$\frac{1}{3}x + \frac{3}{4}y = -2$ The LCD is 12; therefore, multiplying each term by 12,

$4x - 9y = -24$ Equation ②

Therefore, the equations of the given system are equivalent to:

$$4x + 3y = 6$$
$$4x - 9y = -24$$

This system can then easily be solved by the Elimination method.

Solving Systems of Equations With Decimal Numbers

When one or more of the variables in a system of equations has decimal numbers as coefficients, it is often easier to first clear the decimal numbers by multiplying each equation by an appropriate power of 10, depending on the number of decimal places, and then divide all the terms in the equation by any common factors.

For example, consider the following system of equations:

$$0.05x + 0.15y = 2.4$$
$$2.5x + 0.5y = 2.2$$

To clear the decimal numbers, multiply the first equation by 100 (to eliminate 2 decimal places) and the second equation by 10 (to eliminate 1 decimal place).

$0.05x + 0.15y = 2.4$	Multiplying by 100,
$5x + 15y = 240$	Dividing by 5,
$x + 3y = 48$	Equation ①
$2.5x + 0.5y = 2.2$	Multiplying by 10,
$25x + 5y = 22$	Equation ②

Therefore, the equations of the given system are equivalent to:

$$x + 3y = 48$$
$$25x + 5y = 22$$

This system can then be easily solved by the Substitution method.

Systems With No Solutions

If a false equation is obtained (such as $0 = 4$) when solving a system of two linear equations with two variables, then the system has no solutions. That is, the graphs of the linear equations will be parallel and distinct. A system of equations with no solutions is inconsistent and independent.

Example 8.4-e   **Solving a System With No Solutions**

Solve the following system of equations by using the Elimination method:
$$2x + 3y = 6$$
$$6x + 9y = 45$$

Solution

Step 1: $2x + 3y = 6$ Equation ①

               $6x + 9y = 45$ Equation ②

Step 2:   Choosing the variable to be eliminated; in this case, 'x'.

               The variable 'x' in Equations ① and ② has coefficients of 2 and 6, respectively.

               Multiplying Equation ① by 3,

$$3(2x + 3y) = 3(6)$$
$$6x + 9y = 18 \quad \text{Equation ③}$$

Step 3:   Subtracting Equation ③ from ②,

$$6x + 9y = 45$$
$$-(6x + 9y) = -(18)$$
$$\overline{}$$
$$0 = 27 \quad \text{This cannot be true.}$$

             Therefore, the system has no solution.

Solution
continued

The system is inconsistent and independent. That is, the graph of the system will have parallel and distinct lines as shown below.

Equation ①

$2x + 3y = 6$

x-intercept: $(3, 0)$

y-intercept: $(0, 2)$

Equation ②

$6x + 9y = 45$

x-intercept: $(7.5, 0)$

y-intercept: $(0, 5)$

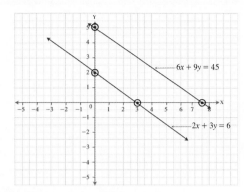

Systems With Many (Infinite) Solutions

If an identity of $0 = 0$ is obtained when solving a system of two linear equations with two variables, then the system has infinitely many solutions. A system of equations with infinitely many solutions is consistent and dependent. That is, the graphs of the two linear equations will be the same line.

Example 8.4-f	Solving a System With Many (Infinite) Solutions

Solve the following system of equations by using the Substitution method:

$2x + y = 7$

$6x + 3y = 21$

Solution

Step 1: The coefficient of y in Equation ① is 1.

Rearranging, $2x + y = 7$

$y = -2x + 7$

Step 2: Substituting $(-2x + 7)$ in for y into Equation ② ,

$$6x + 3y = 21$$

$$6x + 3(-2x + 7) = 21$$

Step 3: Solving for 'x',

$$6x - 6x + 21 = 21$$

$$6x - 6x = 21 - 21$$

$$0 = 0$$

Therefore, the system will have infinitely many solutions; i.e., the system will have coincident lines. The system is consistent and dependent.

Equation ① :

$2x + y = 7$

x-intercept: $(3.5, 0)$

y-intercept: $(0, 7)$

Equation ② :

$6x + 3y = 21$

x-intercept: $(3.5, 0)$

y-intercept: $(0, 7)$

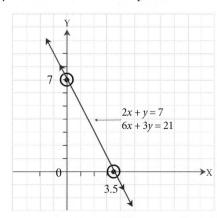

8.4 | Exercises

For Problems 1 to 14, solve the systems of equations by using the Substitution method.

1. $y - 3x + 8 = 0$
   $y - x + 4 = 0$

2. $4x - 7y + 3 = 0$
   $x - 3y + 2 = 0$

3. $3x - 2y = 12$
   $x + 3y = 15$

4. $6x - 5y + 2 = 0$
   $x - 2y + 5 = 0$

5. $x - 3y = 12$
   $5x - 15y = 60$

6. $3x + y = -8$
   $-12x - 4y = -32$

7. $5x + 4y = 14$
   $x - 3y = -1$

8. $x - 9y = 12$
   $3x - 7y = 16$

9. $3x - 2y = 20$
   $y + 4x = 23$

10. $9x - y = 15$
    $5y + 3x = 21$

11. $7x - 5y + 3 = 0$
    $3x - y - 1 = 0$

12. $6x - 5y + 13 = 0$
    $3x - y + 8 = 0$

13. $y = 2x - 5$
    $4x - 2y = 3$

14. $y = -3x + 1$
    $12x + 4y = 4$

For Problems 15 to 26, solve the systems of equations by using the Elimination method.

15. $2x + 3y = 24$
    $2x - 2y = 14$

16. $4x + 9y = 1$
    $4x + 5y = -3$

17. $5x + 3y = 19$
    $3x - 5y = -9$

18. $5x - 3y = 2$
    $3x - 5y = 7$

19. $7x - 3y = -5$
    $5x - 9y = 7$

20. $4x + 6y = 10$
    $2x + 3y = 5$

21. $5x - 15y = 10$
    $-2x + 6y = -4$

22. $12x + 8y = 10$
    $3x + 2y = 4$

23. $2y + 3x = 14$
    $9x - 4y = 2$

24. $3x - 5y = 4$
    $5x + 3y = -16$

25. $3y + 7x = 15$
    $3x + 5y + 1 = 0$

26. $5x - 2y + 1 = 0$
    $2x - 3y - 4 = 0$

For Problems 27 to 38, solve the systems of equations by using either the Substitution or the Elimination method.

27. $0.7x - 0.4y = 2.9$
    $0.6x - 0.3y = 2.4$

28. $1.5x + y = 1$
    $0.8x + 0.7y = 1.2$

29. $0.5x - 0.3y = -0.24$
    $0.2x - 0.7y = 0.02$

30. $1.2x + 0.6y = 0$
    $3.5x + 1.7y = 0.01$

31. $\dfrac{x}{5} + \dfrac{y}{6} = 3$
    $\dfrac{x}{2} + \dfrac{y}{3} = 3$

32. $\dfrac{x}{6} - \dfrac{y}{3} = \dfrac{2}{3}$
    $\dfrac{x}{4} - \dfrac{y}{12} = -\dfrac{2}{3}$

33. $\dfrac{x}{4} + \dfrac{y}{2} = \dfrac{9}{4}$
    $\dfrac{2x}{3} + \dfrac{y}{6} = \dfrac{3}{2}$

34. $\dfrac{3x}{10} + \dfrac{y}{5} = \dfrac{1}{2}$
    $\dfrac{x}{3} - \dfrac{y}{3} = \dfrac{1}{2}$

35. $4(x - 3) + 5(y + 1) = 12$
    $3(y + 7) - 2(x + 2) = 24$

36. $4(x + 3) - 3(y + 4) = 21$
    $2(x + 4) + 5(y - 3) = 10$

37. $2(x - y) - 3(y - x) = 15$
    $5(x - y) + 2(y - x) = 9$

38. $3(x + 2y) - 2(y + 2x) = 6$
    $5(2x - 5y) + 3(7y - 3x) = -17$

8.5 | Using Systems of Linear Equations to Solve Application Problems With Two Unknowns

In previous chapters, we solved application problems that could be modeled using only one variable. However, in many real-life application problems, we need to use two unknown variables to model and solve the problem. If the problem can be modeled with linear equations, then we can solve the problem by setting up and solving a system of linear equations in two variables, using one of the methods learned in the previous section.

Writing a System of Linear Equations from Word Problems With Two Unknowns

The following steps will assist in solving application problems with two unknowns:

Step 1: Choose two different variables (e.g., x and y) to represent each of the unknown quantities and specify clearly what each variable represents and its unit of measure.

Step 2: Based on the given information, translate the word expressions into mathematical equations.

Step 3: Solve the equations for the unknown variables, using one of the methods learned in the previous section.

Step 4: Indicate the solutions to the word problem, including units.

Step 5: Verify the solutions by substituting the values back into the original problem.

Example 8.5-a | **Solving Mathematical Problems**

The sum of two numbers is 46. The difference between the numbers is 8. Find the numbers.

Solution

Step 1:   Let the larger number be x and the smaller number be y.

Step 2: $x + y = 46$ Equation ①
          $x - y = 8$ Equation ②

Step 3:   We will use the Elimination method for this example, though the Substitution method would work just as well. Adding Equations ① and ② ,

$$2x = 54$$
$$x = 27$$

Substituting $x = 27$ into Equation ① ,

$$x + y = 46$$
$$27 + y = 46$$
$$y = 46 - 27$$
$$y = 19$$

Step 4:   Therefore, the numbers are 27 and 19.

Step 5:   Check:

$$27 + 19 = 46 \text{ (True)}$$
$$27 - 19 = 8 \text{ (True)}$$

Example 8.5-b	**Solving Investment Problems**

A small hospital invests $50,000 into two different funds. After one year, the rate of return on the first fund is 4% and the rate of return on the second fund is 6%. If the hospital earns a total of $2,700 in interest on its initial investment in the first year, how much did the hospital invest into each fund?

Solution

Step 1: Let the amount invested into the fund that paid 4% be $x.

Let the amount invested into the fund that paid 6% be $y.

Step 2:

$x + y = 50,000$	Equation ①
$0.04x + 0.06y = 2,700$	Multiplying by 100,
$4x + 6y = 270,000$	Dividing by 2,
$2x + 3y = 135,000$	Equation ②

Step 3: We will use the Substitution method for this example, though the Elimination method would work just as well. From Equation ①

$$x + y = 50,000$$
$$x = 50,000 - y$$

Substituting $(50,000 - y)$ for x in Equation ② ,

$$2x + 3y = 135,000$$
$$2(50,000 - y) + 3y = 135,000$$
$$100,000 - 2y + 3y = 135,000$$
$$-2y + 3y = 135,000 - 100,000$$
$$y = 35,000$$

Substituting $y = 35,000$ into the equation that is solved for x,

$$x = 50,000 - y$$
$$= 50,000 - 35,000$$
$$x = 15,000$$

Step 4: Therefore, the amount invested in the fund that paid 4% interest is $15,000 and the amount invested in the fund that paid 6% interest is $35,000.

Step 5: Check:

Total invested = $15,000 + $35,000 = $50,000 (True)

Total interest = $15,000 × 4% + $35,000 × 6%

= $600 + $2,100

= $2,700 (True)

Example 8.5-c	**Solving Purchasing Problems**

Aran, a medical office assistant, placed an order for 10 boxes of cotton swabs and 15 boxes of plastic ear otoscope tips, totalling $378, before taxes. The next month, he placed another order for 20 boxes of cotton swabs and 10 boxes of otoscope tips, totalling $358, before taxes. Determine the unit cost of a box of cotton swabs and a box of plastic ear otoscope tips.

Solution

Step 1: Let the unit cost of a box of cotton swabs be $x and the unit cost of a box of plastic ear otoscope tips be $y.

Step 2: $10x + 15y = 378$ Equation ①

$20x + 10y = 358$ Equation ②

Step 3: Eliminate the variable 'x' by multiplying Equation ① by 2 and subtracting:

Multiply Equation ① by 2:

$$2(10x + 15y) = 2(378)$$
$$20x + 30y = 756 \text{ Equation } ③$$

Subtracting Equation ② from Equation ③ :

$$\begin{aligned} 20x + 30y &= 756 \\ -\underline{(20x + 10y)} &= -(358) \\ 20y &= 398 \end{aligned}$$

Solving for y:

$$20y = 398$$
$$y = 19.90$$

Substituting $y = 19.90$ into Equation ② :

$$20x + 10(19.90) = 358$$
$$20x + 199 = 358$$
$$20x = 358 - 199$$
$$20x = 159$$
$$x = \frac{159}{20} = 7.95$$

Step 4: Therefore, the unit cost for a box of cotton swabs is $7.95 and the unit cost for a box of plastic ear otoscope tips is $19.90.

Step 5: Check:

First order total cost

$= 10(\$7.95) + 15(\$19.90)$

$= \$79.50 + \$298.50$

$= \$378$ (True)

Second order total cost

$= 20(\$7.95) + 10(\$19.90)$

$= \$159 + \$199$

$= \$358$ (True)

Example 8.5-d **Solving Mixture Problems**

A chemist needs 2 L of an 8% solution of hydrochloric acid. He has a 10% hydrochloric solution and a 5% hydrochloric solution on hand. How many litres of each solution should he use to create his desired solution?

Solution

Step 1: Let the volume (in L) of 10% acid solution be x and the volume (in L) of 5% acid solution be y.

Step 2: $\qquad x + y = 2 \qquad\qquad\qquad$ Equation ①

$\qquad 0.1x + 0.05y = 2(0.08)$

$\qquad 0.1x + 0.05y = 0.16 \qquad\qquad$ Equation ②

Solution continued

Step 3: Rearranging Equation ❶ , $x + y = 2$

$$y = 2 - x$$

Substituting $(2 - x)$ for y in Equation ❷ ,

$$0.1x + 0.05y = 0.16$$

$$0.1x + 0.05(2 - x) = 0.16$$

$$0.1x + 0.1 - 0.05x = 0.16$$

$$0.05x = 0.06$$

$$x = 1.2$$

Substituting $x = 1.2$ into the equation that is solved for y,

$$y = 2 - x$$

$$y = 2 - 1.2$$

$$y = 0.8$$

Step 4: Therefore, 1.2 L of 10% hydrochloric solution and 0.8 L of 5% hydrochloric solution are needed to make 2 L of 8% hydrochloric solution.

Step 5: Check

Total volume: $1.2 + 0.8 = 2$ (True)

Total concentration: $0.1(1.2) + 0.05(0.8) = 0.16$ (True)

8.5 | Exercises

Answers to odd-numbered problems are available at the end of the textbook.

1. Two bottles of hand sanitizer and three mini first-aid kits cost $48, whereas three bottles of hand sanitizer and two mini first-aid kits cost $52. How much does one bottle of hand sanitizer cost?

2. Three stethoscopes and four endoscopes cost $294, whereas four stethoscopes and three endoscopes cost $268. How much does one stethoscope cost?

3. A father and daughter are both doctors and decide to open a practice together. The sum of the father's age and the daughter's age, in years, is 92. The difference in their ages is 28. How old are the father and daughter, respectively?

4. Two senior nurses on staff in a particular hospital ward have a total of 56 years of work experience. If the nurse with the higher seniority has been working for 12 more years than the second nurse, how long has each nurse been working for?

5. Viktor invested $25,000: part of it at 5% per annum in a local physiotherapy clinic and the remainder in a private medical clinic at 4% per annum. If the total interest after one year was $1,150, how much did he invest into each clinic?

6. A $22,500 investment was made by Adam into two different pharmaceutical funds. Part of it was invested in a fund that earned 6% per annum and the remainder in a fund that earned 5% per annum. The total interest received after one year was $1,295. Find the amount invested into each of the two funds.

7. There are a total of 130 alcohol wipes (each costing 25 cents) and gauze strips (each costing 10 cents) in a supply room. If the materials are worth $27.70 in total, how many alcohol wipes and gauze strips are there?

8. There are a total of 175 tongue depressors (each costing 5 cents) and Band-Aids (each costing 10 cents) in a medic's bag. The materials are worth $15.00 in total. How many tongue depressors and Band-Aids are there?

9. Two angles are supplementary (i.e., they add up to 180°). One angle is 24° less than three times the other angle. Find the measure of the two angles.

10. Two angles are complementary (i.e., they add up to 90°). One angle is 15° more than twice the other angle. Find the measure of the two angles.

11. One canned juice drink contains 15% sugar and another contains 5% sugar. How many liters of each should be mixed together to get 10 liters of juice that has 8% sugar?

12. Solution A has 25% acid and solution B has 50% acid. How many liters of solutions A and B should be mixed to get 10 liters of 40% acid?

8 | Review Exercises

1. In which quadrant, or on which axis, do the following points lie?

   a. A (5, –1)   b. B (–2, 3)
   c. C (3, 0)   d. D (4, –2)
   e. E (–2, –8)   f. F (0, 4)

2. In which quadrant or axis do the following points lie?

   a. A (4, –1)   b. B (–5, 0)
   c. C (-2, –7)   d. D (0, –3)
   e. E (–6, 6)   f. F (5, 4)

3. Plot the following points and join them in the order of A, B, C, D. Identify the type of quadrilateral and find its area and perimeter.

   a. A (6, –3)   b. B (6, –6)
   c. C (-2, –6)   d. D (-2, –3)

4. Plot the following points and join them in the order of P, Q, R, S. Identify the type of quadrilateral and find its area and perimeter.

   a. P (–2, 4)   b. Q (–8, 4)
   c. R (–8, –2)   d. S (–2, –2)

Find the domain and range of the following relations:

5. a. $\{(1, 4), (2, –3), (4, –4), (9, 2)\}$

   b. $\{y = 2x + 1 \mid x \in \mathbb{R}, 5 < x < 11\}$

6. a. $\{(0, 5), (1, 2), (2, 1), (3, 2), (4, 5)\}$

   b. $\{y = 10 – x \mid x \in \mathbb{R}, 0 < x < 10\}$

Graph the following equations using a table of values with four points:

7. $4x – y = 2$ 8. $2x + 3y = 12$
9. $x + y – 4 = 0$ 10. $x + 2y – 4 = 0$
11. $y = \dfrac{1}{2}x + 2$ 12. $y = -\dfrac{1}{3}x - 2$

Graph the following equations using the x-intercept, y-intercept, and another point:

13. $3x – 4y = 12$ 14. $5x – 2y = –10$
15. $x – 2y – 6 = 0$ 16. $3x + y – 9 = 0$
17. $y = 4x$ 18. $x = 2y$

Graph the following equations using the slope and y-intercept:

19. $y = 4x + 6$ 20. $y = 5x + 4$
21. $y = -\dfrac{3}{4}x - 1$ 22. $y = -\dfrac{1}{3}x - 1$
23. $3x + 2y – 12 = 0$ 24. $2x + 3y + 6 = 0$

Find the equation of the line that passes through the following points:

25. (3, 2) and (7, 5)   26. (4, 6) and (2, 4)
27. (5, –4) and (–1, 4)   28. (0, –7) and (–6, –1)
29. (1, –2) and (1, 7)   30. (3, –4) and (–1, –4)

31. Write the equation of a line, in standard form, parallel to $3x – 4y = 12$ and that passes through the point P(–2, 3).

32. Write the equation of a line in standard form, parallel to $2x – 3y = 9$ and that passes though the point P(2, –3).

33. Write the equation of a line, in slope-intercept form perpendicular to $2y = x + 4$ and that passes through the point P(–2, 5).

34. Write the equation of a line, in slope-intercept form, perpendicular to $x + 4y + 6 = 0$ and that passes through the point P(4, –1).

Without graphing, determine whether each of the following systems of equations has one solution, no solution, or infinitely many solutions:

35. $3x – 2y + 13 = 0$
    $3x + y + 7 = 0$
36. $4x + 6y – 14 = 0$
    $2x + 3y – 7 = 0$
37. $x – 3y + 2 = 0$
    $3x – 9y + 11 = 0$
38. $15x + 3y = 10$
    $5x + y = –3$
39. $2x – 4y = 6$
    $x – 2y = 3$
40. $3x – y + 2 = 0$
    $x – 3y + 6 = 0$

Solve the following systems of equations by using the Graphical method:

41. $y = –2x – 1$
    $y = 3x – 11$
42. $y = 2x + 3$
    $y = –2x – 1$
43. $2x – 3y – 6 = 0$
    $x + 2y – 10 = 0$
44. $3x + 4y – 5 = 0$
    $2x – y + 4 = 0$
45. $2y = x$
    $y = –x + 3$
46. $3y = 2x$
    $y = –3x + 11$

Solve the following systems of equations by using the Substitution method:

47. $x + 4y = 8$
   $2x + 5y = 13$

48. $x + y = 3$
   $2x - y = 12$

49. $x + 4y + 12 = 0$
   $3x + 12y - 15 = 0$

50. $x - y - 1 = 0$
   $2x + 3y - 12 = 0$

51. $3x + 2y = 5$
   $y = 2x - 1$

52. $6x + 3y = 12$
   $y = -2x + 4$

Solve the following systems of equations by using the Elimination method:

53. $8x + 4y = 20$
   $7x + 8y = 22$

54. $2x + y = 8$
   $3x + 2y = 7$

55. $9x - 2y = -32$
   $x + 4y = -12$

56. $5x - 2y + 3 = 0$
   $3x - 2y - 1 = 0$

57. $4x + 2y = 12$
   $18 - 6x = 3y$

58. $2x + y + 2 = 0$
   $6x = -3y$

Solve the following systems of equations by using either the Substitution method or the Elimination method:

59. $0.4x - 0.5y = -0.8$
   $0.3x - 0.2y = 0.1$

60. $0.2x - 0.3y = -0.6$
   $0.5x + 0.2y = 2.3$

61. $\dfrac{5x}{3} - \dfrac{5y}{2} = -5$
   $\dfrac{x}{3} - \dfrac{y}{4} = 2$

62. $\dfrac{x}{4} + \dfrac{y}{3} = 2$
   $\dfrac{x}{6} + \dfrac{2y}{3} = \dfrac{4}{3}$

63. $(2x + 1) - 2(y + 7) = -1$
   $4(x + 5) + 3(y - 1) = 27$

64. $2(3x + 2) + 5(2y + 7) = 13$
   $3(x + 1) - 4(y - 1) = -15$

65. Find the two numbers whose sum is 95 and where the difference between the larger number and the smaller number is 35.

66. Find the two numbers whose sum is 84 and where the difference between the larger number and the smaller number is 48.

67. 300 vaccinations were given on a certain day. The shots cost $28 per adult and $15 per child. If $7,230 was collected, how many adults and how many children were vaccinated?

68. 715 flu shots were administered on a college campus. The shots cost $35 per faculty and $20 per student. If $16,250 was the total cost, how many faculty and students received the flu shots?

69. A pharmacy technician purchased 12 kg of acetaminophen tablets and 14 kg of ibuprofen tablets for a total cost of $186. A second purchase, at the same unit prices, included 10 kg of acetaminophen tablets and 15 kg of ibuprofen tablets. The cost of the second purchase was $180. Find the cost per kg of the acetaminophen tablets and ibuprofen tablets.

70. A physiotherapist purchased 10 resistance bands and 15 therapy balls for a total cost of $255. A second purchase, at the same unit prices, included 16 resistance bands and 16 therapy balls. The cost of the second purchase was $324. Find the unit cost for a resistance band and a therapy ball.

71. If a chemist wants to create 100 pounds of a 32% silver alloy mixture, how many pounds of 30% silver and 55% silver alloys must he mix?

72. A nurse needs 1 L of a 5% concentration of saline. She has a 13% saline solution and a 3% saline solution on hand. How many litres of the two solutions will she need to combine to get her desired solution?

73. A college chemistry lab experiment requires students to make 2 L of a 58% alcohol solution. If 20% and 70% concentrated alcohol solutions are available, how many L of each solution are required to create the desired mixture?

74. A chemist wants to make 5 L of a 48% saline solution. She has 20% saline and 90% saline solutions on hand. How many L of each solution does she need to make her desired mixture?

8 | Self-Test Exercises

Answers to all problems are available at the end of the textbook.

1. Write the following equations in the form $Ax + By = C$:

   a. $y = \dfrac{2}{3}x - 2$

   b. $6y - 2x + \dfrac{1}{4} = 0$

2. Three vertices of a rectangle ABCD have the points A (-3, 4), B (5, 4), and C (5, -1). Find the coordinates of the 4th vertex and the area of the rectangle.

3. Find the slope and y-intercept of the following lines:

   a. $2x - 3y + 6 = 0$

   b. $3x + 4y - 5 = 0$

4. Graph the equation $2x - 3y = 9$ using a table of values with four points.

5. Graph the equation $3y + 4x = 0$ using the x-intercept, y-intercept, and another point on the line.

6. Given the following slopes (m) and y-intercepts (b), write the linear equations in standard form and graph the lines:

   a. $m = -\dfrac{1}{2}, b = -4$

   b. $m = \dfrac{2}{3}, b = -2$

7. Graph and write the equation of the line that contains the point $(-3, 5)$ and that has a slope of $\dfrac{-3}{4}$.

8. Use the slope of the lines to determine whether the pairs of lines are parallel:

   a. $3y = 6x - 9$ and $4x - 2y = -6$

   b. $3y + 4x = 0$ and $3x + 4y = 2$

9. Write the equation of a line parallel to $2x + 3y = 6$ and that passes through the point $P(-6, -1)$.

10. Write the equation of the line perpendicular to $5x - y = 4$ and that passes through the point $P(1, 2)$.

11. Write the equation of the line passing through the points $P(-3, 5)$ and $Q(5, -1)$.

12. Write the equation of the line having an x-intercept equal to 5 and y-intercept equal to -3.

13. Write the equation of the line passing through the origin and parallel to $y = 5x - 1$.

14. Write the equation of the line that passes through the origin and that is perpendicular to the line passing through the points $P(-3, 5)$ and $Q(5, -1)$.

Without graphing, determine whether each of the following systems of equations has one solution, no solution, or many solutions:

15. $4x + 3y - 16 = 0$ and $2x - y + 2 = 0$

16. $x - 3y + 11 = 0$ and $2x - 6y + 4 = 0$

17. $y = 3x + 6$ and $6x - 2y + 12 = 0$

Solve the following systems of equations by using the Graphical method:

18. $y = 4x + 8$
    $8x - 2y + 8 = 0$

19. $2x + 3y + 1 = 0$
    $3x - y + 7 = 0$

Solve the following systems of equations by using the Substitution method:

20. $3x + 4y + 6 = 0$
    $y - 3x + 9 = 0$

21. $3x + y = -8$
    $2x + 3y = 4$

Solve the following systems of equations by using the Elimination method:

22. $6x - 4y + 3 = 0$
    $4x - 6y - 3 = 0$

23. $3x + 5y - 19 = 0$
    $5x - 2y - 11 = 0$

24. Henry works as a pharmaceutical sales representative and earns \$500 a month plus a commission of 10% on the sales he makes.

    a. Model the relationship between his earnings (y) in a month and the amount of sales he makes in a month (x) using a linear equation.

    b. What would his earnings be if his sales are \$50,000 in a month?

    c. If Henry wants to make \$90,000 per year, how much does he need to sell every month in order to meet this goal?

25. The fixed costs (FC) of a pharmaceutical factory for a month are \$5,000 and the variable costs (VC) to manufacture each medication are \$5. The total costs (TC) for the month are the sum of the fixed costs, and the variable costs per unit multiplied by the number of units produced and sold (x).

    The relationship between TC, FC, VC, and x is given by the equation $TC = (VC)x + FC$.

    a. What would be the total cost if 900 medications were produced and sold this month?

    b. How many medications were produced and sold this month if the total cost is \$11,375?

26. Find the value of two numbers if their sum is 65 and the difference between the larger number and the smaller number is 5.

27. A company produces two different boxes of Band-Aids: one that has 30 small Band-Aids and 10 large Band-Aids and sells for \$5.29, and another box that has 20 of each size of Band-Aid and sells for \$5.99. Assuming that the cost of the box is \$0.19 in both cases, what is the unit price of each of the two different sizes of Band-Aid?

28. In a first-aid box, there are three times as many alcohol wipes (each costing 25 cents) as gauze bandages (each costing 50 cents). If the total value of all these items is \$22.50, how many alcohol wipes are there?

29. Allie invests \$10,000 into a fund made up of two pharmaceutical stocks. At the end of the year, the value of Stock A increased by 16%, while that of Stock B decreased by 5%. If her investment had increased by \$865 at the end of the year, how much did she have invested in each stock?

30. Solution A has 20% acid and Solution B has 45% acid. How many litres of Solutions A and B should be mixed in order to obtain 10 L of 30% acid?

9

EXPONENTS AND LOGARITHMS

LEARNING OBJECTIVES

- Evaluate powers and exponential expressions using rules of exponents.
- Simplify basic exponential equations.
- Graph exponential functions.
- Identify common logarithms and understand properties of logarithmic expressions.
- Graph logarithmic functions.
- Solve application problems, including growth and decay, pH, hydrogen ion concentration, and sound waves.

CHAPTER OUTLINE

9.1 Exponents

9.2 Exponential Functions

9.3 Logarithms

9.4 Logarithmic Functions

9.5 Applications of Exponential and Logarithmic Functions

Introduction

In the previous chapter, we analyzed the graphs of linear functions, which increase/decrease at a constant rate (called the slope). However, in many practical "real-life" scenarios, the rate of increase/decrease of the variable being measured is not constant, which means the function that is used to model the situation should be non-linear.

In this chapter, we will examine some very common non-linear functions known as exponential and logarithmic functions. We will learn how to plot their graphs and how to solve exponentials.

We will also examine how exponential and logarithmic functions can be used to model important situations that arise in the health sciences, such as determining the pH concentrations of solutions, the rate at which bacterial infections increase (if untreated) or decrease (if treated with antibiotics), and the decay rate of medications or dyes used for medical imaging in the bloodstream.

9.1 | Exponents

The concept of exponents was covered in Chapter 3, where integer-valued exponents were used to express repeated multiplication or division of the same numbers.

For example,

When all the factors are equal, the product of the factor is a power of that factor.

$$\underbrace{(2)(2)(2)(2)(2)}_{\textbf{5 factors of 2}} = 2^5 \quad \longleftarrow \text{exponent} \atop \longleftarrow \text{base}$$

$$\underbrace{\frac{1}{(8)(8)(8)}}_{\textbf{3 factors of 8}} = \frac{1}{8^3} = 8^{-3} \quad \longleftarrow \text{exponent} \atop \longleftarrow \text{base}$$

The above exponential principle can also be applied to express repeated multiplication or division of a variable or an algebraic term.

In algebra, when 'n' is a positive integer, the general form for writing exponential expressions using variables is represented by:

$$\underbrace{(x)(x)(x)\dots (x)}_{\textbf{'}n\textbf{' factors of 'x'}} = x^n$$

$$\underbrace{\frac{1}{(x)(x)(x)\dots (x)}}_{\textbf{'}n\textbf{' factors of 'x'}} = \frac{1}{x^n} = x^{-n}$$

Some useful applications of the above with examples are provided below:

	Exponential Form	Expanded Form	Example
(i)	ax^n	$a(x)(x)(x)\dots (x)$	$2x^5 = 2(x)(x)(x)(x)(x)$
(ii)	$(ax)^n$	$(ax)(ax)(ax)\dots (ax)$	$(2x)^5 = (2x)(2x)(2x)(2x)(2x) = 32x^5$
(iii)	$-ax^n$	$-a(x)(x)(x)\dots (x)$	$-2x^5 = -2(x)(x)(x)(x)(x)$
(iv)	$(-ax)^n$	$(-ax)(-ax)(-ax)\dots (-ax)$	$(-2x)^5 = (-2x)(-2x)(-2x)(-2x)(-2x) = -32x^5$ $(-2x)^4 = (-2x)(-2x)(-2x)(-2x) = 16x^4$
(v)	$-x^n$	$-1 \cdot (x)(x)(x)\dots (x)$	$-x^5 = -1 \cdot (x)(x)(x)(x)(x)$
(vi)	$(-x)^n$	$(-x)(-x)(-x)\dots (-x)$	$(-x)^5 = (-x)(-x)(-x)(-x)(-x) = -x^5$ $(-x)^4 = (-x)(-x)(-x)(-x) = x^4$

	Exponential Form	Expanded Form	Example
(vii)	ax^{-n}	$a \cdot \dfrac{1}{(x)(x)(x)...(x)}$	$2x^{-5} = 2 \cdot \dfrac{1}{(x)(x)(x)(x)(x)} = \dfrac{2}{x^5}$
(viii)	$(ax)^{-n}$	$\dfrac{1}{(ax)(ax)(ax)...(ax)}$	$(2x)^{-5} = \dfrac{1}{(2x)(2x)(2x)(2x)(2x)} = \dfrac{1}{32x^5}$

Note: *The examples above assume that x is a positive number.*

Rules of Exponents and Evaluation of Exponents

The 'rules of exponents' introduced in Chapter 3 (also referred to as 'laws of exponents' or 'properties of exponents') all apply to algebraic terms and expressions in the same way as they did to numbers in Chapter 3. The following table revisits and summarizes the basic rules of exponents:

Table 9.1   **Rules of Exponents**

		Rule	Description	Example
	1.	Product Rule	To multiply powers of the same base, write the base and add the exponents. $$x^m \cdot x^n = x^{(m+n)}$$	$x^4 \cdot x^3 = x^{(4+3)} = x^7$
	2.	Quotient Rule	To divide powers of the same base, write the base and subtract the exponent. $$\dfrac{x^m}{x^n} = x^{(m-n)}$$	$\dfrac{x^5}{x^2} = x^{(5-2)} = x^3$
$(x^m)(x^n) = x^{m+n}$ $\dfrac{x^m}{x^n} = x^{m-n}$ $(x^m)^n = x^{mn}$ $(xy)^m = x^m y^m$ $\left(\dfrac{x}{y}\right)^m = \dfrac{x^m}{y^m}$ $\left(\dfrac{x}{y}\right)^{-m} = \left(\dfrac{y}{x}\right)^m$ $x^{-1} = \dfrac{1}{x}$ $x^0 = 1$ $x^1 = x$	3.	Power of a Power Rule	To raise a power to another power, write the base and multiply the exponents. $$(x^m)^n = x^{mn}$$	$(x^4)^2 = x^{(4 \cdot 2)} = x^8$
	4.	Power of a Product Rule	To simplify a power of a product, raise each factor to the same exponent. $$(xy)^m = x^m \cdot y^m$$	$(x \cdot y)^5 = x^5 \cdot y^5$
	5.	Power of a Quotient Rule	To simplify a power of a quotient, raise each factor in the numerator and the denominator to the same exponent. $$\left(\dfrac{x}{y}\right)^m = \dfrac{x^m}{y^m}$$	$\left(\dfrac{x}{y}\right)^4 = \dfrac{x^4}{y^4}$
	6.	Negative Exponent Rule	To simplify negative exponents, write the reciprocal of the base and use a positive exponent. $$x^{-m} = \dfrac{1}{x^m}, \quad \dfrac{1}{x^{-m}} = x^m$$ $$\left(\dfrac{x}{y}\right)^{-m} = \left(\dfrac{y}{x}\right)^m$$	$x^{-5} = \dfrac{1}{x^5}$ $\dfrac{1}{x^{-4}} = x^4$ $\left(\dfrac{x}{y}\right)^{-3} = \left(\dfrac{y}{x}\right)^3$

	Rule	Description	Example
7.	Exponent of Zero Rule	Any base (except 0) raised to an exponent of zero is equal to 1. $$x^0 = 1$$	$5^0 = 1$ $(xy)^0 = 1$ $\left(\dfrac{x}{y}\right)^0 = 1$
8.	Exponent of One Rule	Any base raised to an exponent of 1 is equal to itself. $$x^1 = x$$	$7^1 = 7$ $(xy)^1 = xy$ $\left(\dfrac{x}{y}\right)^1 = \dfrac{x}{y}$

Note: *There are no rules for addition or subtraction of exponents. These operations must be done separately.*

For example, $2^3 + 2^5 = (2 \times 2 \times 2) + (2 \times 2 \times 2 \times 2 \times 2)$
$$= 8 + 32 = 40$$

Example 9.1-a   **Multiplying Expressions Using the Product Rule**

Simplify each of the following expressions:

(i) $3x^2 \cdot 4x^5$ (ii) $-2x \cdot 4x^3 \cdot 2x^4$

(iii) $2x^2y^4 \cdot 3x^2y^2$ (iv) $x^n \cdot x^{2n} \cdot x^{(n-1)}$

Solution

(i) $3x^2 \cdot 4x^5$ Regrouping the factors,
     $= 3 \cdot 4 \cdot x^2 \cdot x^5$ Applying the Product Rule and simplifying,
     $= 12 \cdot x^{(2+5)}$
     $= 12x^7$

(ii) $-2x \cdot 4x^3 \cdot 2x^4$ Regrouping the factors,
     $= -2 \cdot 4 \cdot 2 \cdot x \cdot x^3 \cdot x^4$ Applying the Product Rule and Exponent of One Rule and simplifying,
     $= -16x^{(1+3+4)}$
     $= -16x^8$

<table>
<tr><td>Note:
$x = x^1$, not x^0</td></tr>
</table>

(iii) $2x^2y^4 \cdot 3x^2y^2$ Regrouping the factors with same bases,
     $= (2 \cdot 3) \cdot (x^2 \cdot x^2) \cdot (y^4 \cdot y^2)$ Applying the Product Rule and simplifying,
     $= 6x^{(2+2)} \cdot y^{(4+2)}$
     $= 6x^4 y^6$

(iv) $x^n \cdot x^{2n} \cdot x^{(n-1)}$ Applying the Product Rule,
     $= x^{[n + 2n + (n-1)]}$
     $= x^{4n-1}$

Example 9.1-b   **Multiplying and Dividing Expressions Using the Product and Quotient Rules**

Simplify each of the following expressions:

(i) $\dfrac{6x^5}{8x^2}$ (ii) $\dfrac{-15x^4 \cdot 8x^2}{10xy^3}$

(iii) $\dfrac{-25x^2 \cdot 3y^3}{-5xy^4}$ (iv) $\dfrac{2x^n \cdot 3y^{2n}}{4x^{n-1}y^{n-3}}$

(i) $\dfrac{6x^5}{8x^2}$

$= \dfrac{6}{8} \cdot \dfrac{x^5}{x^2}$

$= \dfrac{3}{4} \cdot x^{(5-2)}$

$= \dfrac{3x^3}{4}$

Regrouping the factors,

Applying the Quotient Rule and simplifying,

(ii) $\dfrac{-15x^4 \cdot 8x^2}{10xy^3}$

$= \dfrac{-15 \cdot 8}{10} \cdot \dfrac{x^4 \cdot x^2}{x \cdot y^3}$

$= \dfrac{-12x^{(4+2-1)}}{y^3}$

$= \dfrac{-12x^5}{y^3}$

Regrouping the factors,

Applying the Product and Quotient Rules and simplifying,

(iii) $\dfrac{-25x^2 \cdot 3y^3}{-5xy^4}$

$= \dfrac{-25 \cdot 3}{-5} \cdot \dfrac{x^2 \cdot y^3}{x \cdot y^4}$

$= 15 \cdot x^{(2-1)} \cdot y^{(3-4)}$

$= 15xy^{-1}$

$= \dfrac{15x}{y}$

Regrouping the factors,

Applying the Product and Quotient Rules and simplifying,

(iv) $\dfrac{2x^n \cdot 3y^{2n}}{4x^{n-1}y^{n-3}}$

$= \dfrac{2 \cdot 3}{4} \cdot \dfrac{x^n \cdot y^{2n}}{x^{n-1} \cdot y^{n-3}}$

$= \dfrac{3}{2} \cdot x^{[n-(n-1)]} y^{[2n-(n-3)]}$

$= \dfrac{3xy^{n+3}}{2}$

Regrouping the factors,

Applying the Product and Quotient Rules and simplifying,

Example 9.1-c   Simplifying Expressions Using the Power of a Product and Power of a Power Rules

Simplify each of the following expressions:

(i) $(2x^2)^4$

(iii) $(-3x^3)^2$

(ii) $(2x^3 \cdot 3y^2)^3$

(iv) $(-2x^2y^4)^3$

(i) $(2x^2)^4$

$= (2)^4 \cdot (x^2)^4$

$= 16 \cdot x^{(2 \cdot 4)}$

$= 16x^8$

Regrouping and raising each factor to the power of 4,

Applying the Power of a Power Rule and simplifying,

(ii) $(2x^3 \cdot 3y^2)^3$ Regrouping and raising each factor to the power of 3,

$= (2 \cdot 3 \cdot x^3 \cdot y^2)^3$ Applying the Power of a Power Rule and simplifying,

$= (6)^3 \cdot (x^3)^3 \cdot (y^2)^3$

$= 216x^9 y^6$

(iii) $(-3x^3)^2$ Regrouping and raising each factor to the power of 2,

$= (-3)^2 \cdot (x^3)^2$ Applying the Power of a Power Rule and simplifying,

$= 9x^6$

(iv) $(-2x^2 y^4)^3$ Regrouping and raising each factor to the power of 3,

$= (-2)^3 \cdot (x^2)^3 \cdot (y^4)^3$ Applying the Power of a Power Rule and simplifying,

$= -8x^6 y^{12}$

Example 9.1-d   **Simplifying Expressions using the Power of a Quotient and Power of a Power Rules**

Simplify each of the following expressions:

(i) $\left(\dfrac{x^5}{y^2}\right)^4$ (ii) $\left(\dfrac{x^3 \cdot y^4}{x^5 y}\right)^2$

Solution

(i) $\left(\dfrac{x^5}{y^2}\right)^4$ Raising the numerator and denominator to the power of 4,

$= \dfrac{(x^5)^4}{(y^2)^4}$ Applying the Power of a Power Rule and simplifying,

$= \dfrac{x^{(5 \cdot 4)}}{y^{(2 \cdot 4)}}$

$= \dfrac{x^{20}}{y^8}$

(ii) $\left(\dfrac{x^3 \cdot y^4}{x^5 y}\right)^2$ Regrouping the factors with the same base,

$= \left(\dfrac{x^3}{x^5} \cdot \dfrac{y^4}{y}\right)^2$ Simplifying using the Quotient Rule,

$= \left(x^{(3-5)} \cdot y^{(4-1)}\right)^2$

$= (x^{-2} \cdot y^3)^2$

$= \left(\dfrac{y^3}{x^2}\right)^2$ Raising the numerator and denominator to the power of 2,

$= \dfrac{(y^3)^2}{(x^2)^2}$ Applying the Power of a Power Rule and simplifying,

$= \dfrac{y^{(3 \cdot 2)}}{x^{(2 \cdot 2)}}$

$= \dfrac{y^6}{x^4}$

Rewrite the following expressions using only positive exponents:

(i) $(x^{-5})^2$

(ii) $x^{-4} \cdot y^{-2}$

(iii) $\dfrac{5x^{-4}y^{-3}}{x^{-2}y}$

Solution

(i) $(x^{-5})^2$

$= x^{-10}$

$= \dfrac{1}{x^{10}}$

(ii) $x^{-4} \cdot y^{-2}$

$= \dfrac{1}{x^4} \cdot \dfrac{1}{y^2}$

$= \dfrac{1}{x^4 y^2}$

(iii) $\dfrac{5x^{-4}y^{-3}}{x^{-2}y}$

$= \dfrac{5x^{-4}}{x^{-2}} \cdot \dfrac{y^{-3}}{y}$

$= 5 \cdot x^{[(-4 - (-2)]} \cdot y^{(-3 - 1)}$

$= 5 \cdot x^{-2} \cdot y^{-4}$

$= 5 \cdot \dfrac{1}{x^2} \cdot \dfrac{1}{y^4}$

$= \dfrac{5}{x^2 y^4}$

Fractional Exponents

Recall that when the exponent of a variable is a fraction, we call it a **fractional exponent**. A fractional exponent is another way of expressing a radical number or expression, that does not involve using the radical sign, $\sqrt{}$.

For example,

- The square root of $x = \sqrt{x} = x^{\frac{1}{2}}$.

- The cube root of $x = \sqrt[3]{x} = x^{\frac{1}{3}}$.

- Similarly, the nth root of $x = \sqrt[n]{x} = x^{\frac{1}{n}}$.

Fractional exponents obey all the rules of exponents. We summarize these in the following four "rules of fractional exponents":

$x^{\frac{1}{n}} = \sqrt[n]{x}$

$x^{-\frac{1}{n}} = \dfrac{1}{x^{\frac{1}{n}}} = \dfrac{1}{\sqrt[n]{x}}$

$x^{\frac{m}{n}} = \left(x^{\frac{1}{n}}\right)^m = \left(\sqrt[n]{x}\right)^m = \sqrt[n]{x^m}$

$x^{-\frac{m}{n}} = \dfrac{1}{x^{\frac{m}{n}}} = \dfrac{1}{\left(\sqrt[n]{x}\right)^m} = \dfrac{1}{\sqrt[n]{x^m}}$

(i) $x^{\frac{1}{n}} = \sqrt[n]{x}$

For example, if $x = 16$ and $n = 4$, then, $16^{\frac{1}{4}} = \sqrt[4]{16} = 2$

(ii) $x^{-\frac{1}{n}} = \dfrac{1}{x^{\frac{1}{n}}} = \dfrac{1}{\sqrt[n]{x}}$.

For example, if $x = 27$, and $n = 3$, then $(27)^{-\frac{1}{3}} = \dfrac{1}{27^{\frac{1}{3}}} = \dfrac{1}{\sqrt[3]{27}} = \dfrac{1}{3}$

(iii) $x^{\frac{m}{n}} = \left(x^{\frac{1}{n}}\right)^m = \left[\sqrt[n]{x}\right]^m$

This refers to finding the nth root of x, then raising the result to the power of m.

For example, if $x = 16$, $m = 3$, and $n = 4$, then, $16^{\frac{3}{4}} = \left(16^{\frac{1}{4}}\right)^3 = \left[\sqrt[4]{16}\right]^3 = [2]^3 = 8$

Alternatively, we could think of this as first raising x to the power of m, then finding the nth root of the result:

$x^{\frac{m}{n}} = \left(x^m\right)^{\frac{1}{n}} = \sqrt[n]{x^m}$

For example, if $x = 16$, $m = 3$, and $n = 4$, then, $16^{\frac{3}{4}} = \left(16^3\right)^{\frac{1}{4}} = \sqrt[4]{16^3} = \sqrt[4]{4,096} = 8$

Note: The first method is typically easier to compute because finding the nth root first results in a smaller number, which is then easier to raise to the power of 'm'.

(iv) $x^{-\frac{m}{n}} = \dfrac{1}{x^{\frac{m}{n}}} = \dfrac{1}{\left(\sqrt[n]{x}\right)^m}$

For example, if $x = 27$, $m = 4$, and $n = 3$, then, $27^{-\frac{4}{3}} = \dfrac{1}{27^{\frac{4}{3}}} = \dfrac{1}{\left(\sqrt[3]{27}\right)^4} = \dfrac{1}{(3)^4} = \dfrac{1}{81}$

Note: In all of the above examples, when dealing with fractional exponents, we assume that the base (x) is positive.

| Example 9.1-f | Simplifying Algebraic Expressions Using the Fractional Exponent Rules |

Simplify each of the following expressions:

(i) $\left(\dfrac{\sqrt[4]{x^8}}{\sqrt[2]{x^3}}\right)^2$
(ii) $\left(\sqrt[3]{x^{12}}\right)^{-\frac{1}{2}}$

Solution

(i) $\left(\dfrac{\sqrt[4]{x^8}}{\sqrt[2]{x^3}}\right)^2$ Rewriting using the Fractional Exponent Rule (iii),

$= \left(\dfrac{x^{\frac{8}{4}}}{x^{\frac{3}{2}}}\right)^2$ Simplifying the exponents within the bracket and applying the Power of a Quotient Rule,

$= \dfrac{\left(x^2\right)^2}{\left(x^{\frac{3}{2}}\right)^2}$ Applying the Power of a Power Rule and simplifying,

$= \dfrac{x^{(2\cdot2)}}{x^{\left(\frac{3}{2}\cdot2\right)}}$

$= \dfrac{x^4}{x^3}$ Applying the Quotient Rule and simplifying,

$= x^{(4-3)}$

$= x$

(ii) $\left(\sqrt[3]{x^{12}}\right)^{-\frac{1}{2}}$ Rewriting using the Fractional Exponent Rule (iii),

$= \left(x^{\frac{12}{3}}\right)^{-\frac{1}{2}}$ Simplifying the exponents within the bracket,

$= \left(x^4\right)^{-\frac{1}{2}}$ Applying the Fractional Exponent Rule (ii),

$= \dfrac{1}{x^{\left(4\cdot\frac{1}{2}\right)}}$

$= \dfrac{1}{x^2}$

9.1 | Exercises

Answers to odd-numbered problems are available at the end of the textbook.

Simplify the following expressions and write the answers with positive exponents:

1. $x^3 \cdot x^7$
2. $x^5 \cdot x^4$
3. $4x^4 \cdot 2x$
4. $3x^3 \cdot 5x^2$
5. $(-5x^6)(-3x^2)$
6. $(-4x^3)(-2x)$
7. $(-2x^3)(3x^5)$
8. $(4x^6)(-3x^3)$
9. $x^2 \cdot x^5 \cdot x^7$
10. $x^6 \cdot x^4 \cdot x$
11. $2x^3 \cdot 3x^2 \cdot 4x$
12. $3x^5 \cdot 4x^4 \cdot 5x$

13. $x^7 \div x^4$

14. $x^5 \div x^2$

15. $6x^6 \div 2x^2$

16. $8x^5 \div 4x^2$

17. $x^8 \cdot x^2 \div x^7$

18. $x^3 \cdot x^7 \div x^6$

19. $(x^2)^4 \cdot (x^3)^5$

20. $(x^3)^2 \cdot (x^4)^3$

21. $(2x^4)^3 (4x^5)^2$

22. $(5x^3)^2 (3x^4)^3$

23. $(2x^2)^{-4}$

24. $(3x^3)^{-2}$

25. $\left(\dfrac{2x^4}{3y^2}\right)^3$

26. $\left(\dfrac{3x^3}{2y^4}\right)^4$

27. $\left(\dfrac{2x^3}{5y^2}\right)^2$

28. $\left(\dfrac{3x^4}{5y^3}\right)^4$

29. $\dfrac{x^2 y^3}{(xy)^2}$

30. $\dfrac{x^4 y^6}{(xy)^2}$

31. $\dfrac{x^5 y^6}{(x^2 y^3)^2}$

32. $\dfrac{xy^5}{(x^2 y)^3}$

33. $(3x^{-3} \cdot y^3)^{-2}$

34. $(4x^4 \cdot y^{-3})^{-3}$

35. $(5x^2 \cdot y^{-4})^3$

36. $(3x^{-3} \cdot y^2)^4$

37. $\left(\dfrac{x}{y}\right)^{-2} \left(\dfrac{x}{y}\right)^3$

38. $\left(\dfrac{x}{y}\right)^{-3} \left(\dfrac{x}{y}\right)^5$

39. $\left(\dfrac{x}{y}\right)^2 \left(\dfrac{x}{y}\right)^3 \left(\dfrac{x}{y}\right)^{-4}$

40. $\left(\dfrac{x}{y}\right)^4 \left(\dfrac{x}{y}\right)^3 \left(\dfrac{x}{y}\right)^{-5}$

41. $(x^3)^2 (x^{-2})^3 (x^3)^{-1}$

42. $(x^5)^{-1} (x^3)^2 (x^2)^{-3}$

43. $-2x^2 (-2x)^2$

44. $3x^3 (-3x)^3$

45. $\left(\dfrac{4x^5 y}{16xy^4}\right)^2$

46. $\left(\dfrac{5x^3 y^2}{12xy^3}\right)^3$

47. $\dfrac{(-x^2 y)^2}{-x^2 y^3}$

48. $\dfrac{(-xy)^3}{-xy^2}$

49. $\dfrac{(-2x^2 y^3)^3}{(xy)^2}$

50. $\dfrac{(-3x^3 y^2)^3}{(xy)^3}$

51. $\dfrac{(3xy)^2}{3y^6}$

52. $\dfrac{(2xy)^3}{4y^6}$

53. $\dfrac{(3x^2 y^3)^2}{9xy}$

54. $\dfrac{(5x^4 y)^2}{25xy}$

55. $\dfrac{(-4x^5 y)^2}{(2xy)^4}$

56. $\dfrac{(-2xy^2)^4}{(2xy)^5}$

57. $\sqrt[3]{x^5}$

58. $\sqrt[5]{x^3}$

59. $\dfrac{1}{\sqrt[3]{x}}$

60. $\dfrac{1}{\sqrt{x^3}}$

61. $\sqrt{x}$

62. $\sqrt[6]{x^5}$

63. $\dfrac{1}{\sqrt[4]{x^3}}$

64. $\dfrac{1}{\sqrt[3]{x^4}}$

65. $\left(\sqrt[5]{x^3}\right)^{10}$

66. $\left(\sqrt[5]{x^3}\right)^{10}$

67. $(2x)^{-\frac{1}{3}}$

68. $(3x)^{-\frac{1}{4}}$

69. $\sqrt[4]{x^6 x^{10}}$

70. $\sqrt[6]{x^8 x^4}$

71. $\sqrt[3]{x^9 y^{12}}$

72. $\sqrt[4]{x^{12} y^8}$

73. $\sqrt[3]{x^9 y^{-12}}$

74. $\sqrt[2]{x^{10} y^{-6}}$

75. $(27x^6)^{\frac{1}{3}}$

76. $(81x^8)^{\frac{1}{4}}$

77. $\left(\dfrac{x^{14}}{x^5}\right)^{\frac{1}{3}}$

78. $\left(\dfrac{x^{19}}{x^3}\right)^{\frac{1}{4}}$

79. $\dfrac{(-x)^{-3} (-x)^4}{\sqrt[3]{x^5}}$

80. $\dfrac{(-x)^{-7} (-x)^4}{\sqrt{x^9}}$

9.2 | Exponential Functions

Exponential functions are special kinds of functions, often used to measure values that grow at a rate proportional to the current size; i.e., as the size of the measurement increases, the rate of growth increases proportionally. An exponential function follows the form $y = a^x$, where $a > 0$ and $a \neq 1$. For exponential functions, the domain is the set of real numbers, or $\{x \in \mathbf{R}\}$, and the range is all positive real numbers, or $\{y \in \mathbf{R} \mid y > 0\}$. The reason for this is because, as we have seen, a positive base raised to **any** power (even a negative power) remains positive.

Exponential functions are useful in modeling growth, such as the value of an investment subject to compound interest or the increase of a population, and decay, such as the amount of radioactive isotope present in a certain fossil or rock (which can help scientists to determine its approximate age).

In the health sciences, exponential functions are used to determine the concentration of an administered drug in the bloodstream after a certain length of time has passed, or how quickly a bacterial infection will spread, and the length of time that it should be treated with antibiotics.

Euler's Number

A special kind of exponential function is the function whose rate of growth is not just proportional to the current size of the measurement, but **exactly equal** to it. This is sometimes referred to as **natural growth** or **continuous growth**, as it is the rate of growth that occurs naturally and continuously, without intervention or obstruction. For example, if a culture of bacteria was allowed to multiply under favourable conditions, the culture would grow at a natural or continuous growth rate.

So what is this "magic" number that corresponds to natural/continuous growth? The answer was discovered by two mathematicians named the Bernoulli brothers in the 1600's, and it is an irrational number (similar to π) that is approximately equal to 2.71828... (non-repeating). It is known by the letter e, and is called **Euler's number**, for the mathematician Leonard Euler (1707-1783), not because he first discovered it or first used it, but because he made its use popular.

Calculation of Euler's Number

Imagine that you were able to invest your money so that it would double in one year, but instead of getting all the interest at the end of the year, it would be split up into many (n) small pieces, and then paid into your account n times over the course of the year. This means that the original investment would more than double, since the interest is earning interest too! At the end of the year, your investment would be multiplied by the growth factor $\left(1 + \dfrac{1}{n}\right)$, n times – i.e., $\left(1 + \dfrac{1}{n}\right)^n$.

As n gets really large (i.e., as $n \longrightarrow \infty$), the value $\left(1 + \dfrac{1}{n}\right)^n$ approaches the value 2.71828... or e (try this for yourself by letting $n = 1{,}000{,}000$ and computing the growth factor on your calculator). We call this the **limit** of the expression as n approaches infinity, and denote it using the abbreviation $\lim\limits_{n \to \infty}$. Hence,

$$e = \lim_{n \to \infty} \left(1 + \frac{1}{n}\right)^n \approx 2.71828$$

Therefore, the exponential function that relates to natural or continuous growth is expressed as: $y = e^x$. The function e^x can be found on scientific calculators.

Graphs of Exponential Functions

The graphs of basic exponential functions (i.e., $y = a^x$) all share certain characteristics:

- They all pass through the y-axis at $y = 1$; i.e., their y-intercept is (0,1).

- They all approach the x-axis (i.e., $y = 0$) in one direction, and "blow up" to infinity in the other direction.

- If the base $a > 1$, the function increases from left to right, and larger bases increase more quickly, resulting in steeper curves.

- If the base $0 < a < 1$, the function decreases from left to right, and smaller bases (i.e., closer to 0) decrease more quickly, resulting in steeper curves.

To graph basic exponential functions in the form of $y = a^x$, we first create a table of values by substituting a few different values for x near 0 (for example: –3, –2, –1, 0, 1, 2, and 3) to determine the (x, y) coordinates of the graph near the y-axis. We then plot those points on a rectangular coordinate system with an appropriate scale, and connect them to obtain the final graph.

For exponential functions with negative exponents, we first convert the expression to one with a positive exponent, using the Negative Exponent Rule from the previous section, and then create the graph. For example, $y = 2^{-x}$ can be rewritten as $y = \left(\dfrac{1}{2}\right)^x$. Now, with a positive exponent, we can substitute x-values into the expression to determine the corresponding y-values, and then draw the graph.

Example 9.2-a   **Graphing Exponential Functions with Positive Exponents**

Graph the following functions on the same set of axes:

(i) $y = 2^x$ (ii) $y = 3^x$ (iii) $y = e^x$ (iv) $y = \left(\dfrac{3}{4}\right)^x$

Solution

(i) $y = 2^x$

x	y	(x, y)
−2	0.25	(−2, 0.25)
−1	0.5	(−1, 0.5)
0	1	(0, 1)
1	2	(1, 2)
2	4	(2, 4)

(ii) $y = 3^x$

x	y	(x, y)
−2	0.1111…	(−2, 0.11)
−1	0.3333…	(−1, 0.33)
0	1	(0, 1)
1	3	(1, 3)
2	9	(2, 9)

(iii) $y = e^x$

x	y	(x, y)
−2	0.1353…	(−2, 0.14)
−1	0.3678…	(−1, 0.37)
0	1	(0, 1)
1	2.7182…	(1, 2.72)
2	7.3890…	(2, 7.39)

(iv) $y = \left(\dfrac{3}{4}\right)^x$

x	y	(x, y)
−2	1.7777…	(−2, 1.78)
−1	1.3333…	(−1, 1.33)
0	1	(0, 1)
1	0.75	(1, 0.75)
2	0.5625	(2, 0.56)

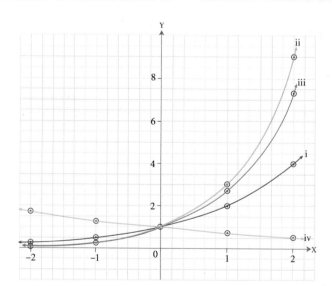

Example 9.2-b **Graphing Exponential Functions with Negative Exponents**

Graph the following functions on the same set of axes:

(i) $y = 2^{-x}$ (ii) $y = 3^{-x}$ (iii) $y = e^{-x}$ (iv) $y = \left(\dfrac{3}{4}\right)^{-x}$

Solution

First, we convert the exponential functions with negative exponents to ones with positive exponents, using the Negative Exponent Rule. Then, we plot the graph using a table of values.

(i) $y = 2^{-x} = \left(\dfrac{1}{2}\right)^{x}$

x	y	(x, y)
−2	4	(−2, 4)
−1	2	(−1, 2)
0	1	(0, 1)
1	0.5	(1, 0.5)
2	0.25	(2, 0.25)

(ii) $y = 3^{-x} = \left(\dfrac{1}{3}\right)^{x}$

x	y	(x, y)
−2	9	(−2, 9)
−1	3	(−1, 3)
0	1	(0, 1)
1	0.3333…	(1, 0.33)
2	0.1111…	(2, 0.11)

(iii) $y = e^{-x} = \left(\dfrac{1}{e}\right)^{x}$

x	y	(x, y)
−2	7.3890…	(−2, 7.39)
−1	2.7182…	(−1, 2.72)
0	1	(0, 1)
1	0.3678…	(1, 0.37)
2	0.1353…	(2, 0.14)

(iv) $y = \left(\dfrac{3}{4}\right)^{-x} = \left(\dfrac{4}{3}\right)^{x}$

x	y	(x, y)
−2	0.5625	(−2, 0.56)
−1	0.75	(−1, 0.75)
0	1	(0, 1)
1	1.3333…	(1, 1.33)
2	1.7777…	(2, 1.78)

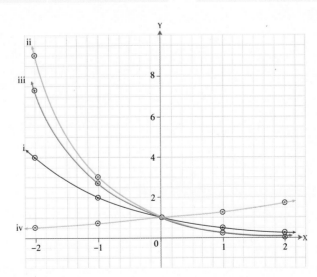

Example 9.2-c   Graphing More Exponential Functions

Graph the following functions on separate axes:

(i) $y = 10\left(\dfrac{1}{2}\right)^x$ (ii) $y = 2e^x$ (iii) $y = 5^{\frac{x}{2}}$

Solution

(i) $y = 10\left(\dfrac{1}{2}\right)^x$

> Recall BEDMAS: you must perform the exponent calculation before you multiply by the coefficient!

x	y	(x, y)
−2	40	(−2, 40)
−1	20	(−1, 20)
0	10	(0, 10)
1	5	(1, 5)
2	2.5	(2, 2.5)

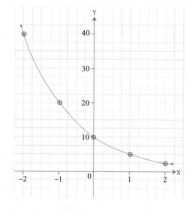

(ii) $y = 2e^x$

x	y	(x, y)
−2	0.2706…	(−2, 0.27)
−1	0.7357…	(−1, 0.74)
0	2	(0, 2)
1	5.4365…	(1, 5.44)
2	14.7781…	(2, 14.78)

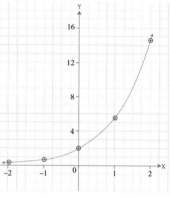

(iii) $y = 5^{\frac{x}{2}}$

x	y	(x, y)
−2	0.2	(−2, 0.2)
−1	0.4472…	(−1, 0.45)
0	1	(0, 1)
1	2.2360…	(1, 2.24)
2	5	(2, 5)

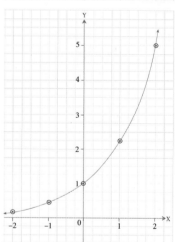

Exponential Growth and Decay

An exponential function $y = a^x$ has two basic shapes, depending on the restrictions placed on a: **exponential growth** (i.e., curving upwards to the right) if $a > 1$, and **exponential decay** (i.e., curving upwards to the left) if $0 < a < 1$.

In general, a can be written as $(1 + r)$, where $r > 0$ indicates growth and $r < 0$ indicates decay. Then, the value of a given measurement is simply its initial measurement (A) muliplied by the growth

t and k must be in the same units

factor $(1 + r)^{\frac{t}{k}}$, where t is the time since the initial measurement, and k is the length of time (in the same units as t) required for the population to grow or decay by the growth rate (known as the **growth period**). Hence,

Exponential Growth and Decay

$$y = A(1 + r)^{\frac{t}{k}}$$

Example 9.2-d | **Calculating Growth and Decay**

Solve the following word problems related to exponential growth and decay:

(i) A pharmaceutical company has a culture of 300 bacteria that grows exponentially, doubling every 35 hours. How many bacteria will be present after 4 days? Round your answer to the nearest whole number.

(ii) The pharmaceutical company in part (i) then applies an antibiotic drug treatment to the culture, which reduces the number of bacteria by one-third every 3 hours. Determine the amount of bacteria remaining in the culture after one day of drug treatment. Round your answer to the nearest whole number.

(iii) A certain radioactive isotope, used in a dye to detect blood clots, has a half-life of 13.5 minutes (i.e., the amount of radioactive material decreases by a factor of one-half every 13.5 minutes). If 20 mg of the isotope is initially injected into the bloodstream, determine the remaining mass of the isotope after 2 hours. Round your answer to two decimal places.

Solution

(i) A (initial amount) = 300

r (growth rate) = 100% = 1   Doubling in population is equivalent to 100% growth.

k (growth period) = 35 hours

t (time) = 4 days × 24 hours/day = 96 hours t and k must be in the same units.

Using Formula 9.2, $\quad y = 300(1 + 1)^{\frac{96}{35}}$

$\qquad\qquad\qquad = 300(2)^{\frac{96}{35}}$

$\qquad\qquad\qquad = 2008.184120...$

$\qquad\qquad\qquad \approx 2008$

Therefore, there will be approximately 2,008 bacteria after 4 days.

(ii) A (initial amount) = 2008

r (growth rate) = $-33\frac{1}{3}\% = -\frac{1}{3}$ The population is decaying, so r is negative.

k (growth period) = 3 hours

t (time) = 1 day × 24 hours/day = 24 hours

Using Formula 9.2, $\quad y = 2008\left(1 - \frac{1}{3}\right)^{\frac{24}{3}}$

$\qquad\qquad\qquad = 2008\left(\frac{2}{3}\right)^{8}$

$\qquad\qquad\qquad = 78.349032...$

$\qquad\qquad\qquad \approx 78$

Therefore, there will be approximately 78 bacteria remaining in the culture at the end of the day.

(iii) A (initial amount) = 20

r (growth rate) = -50% = $-\dfrac{1}{2}$ "Half-life" is equivalent to 50% decay.

k (growth period) = 13.5 minutes

t (time) = 2 hours × 60 minutes/hour = 120 minutes

Using Formula 9.2, $y = 20\left(1 - \dfrac{1}{2}\right)^{\frac{120}{13.5}}$

$$= 20\left(\dfrac{1}{2}\right)^{\frac{120}{13.5}}$$

$$= 0.042189...$$

$$\approx 0.04$$

Therefore, there will be approximately 0.04 mg of the isotope remaining in the bloodstream after 2 hours.

9.2 | Exercises

Answers to odd-numbered problems are available at the end of the textbook.

For the Problems 1 to 16, graph the functions.

1. $y = 6^x$
2. $y = 5^x$
3. $y = 0.45^x$
4. $y = 0.5^x$

5. $y = 3^{-x}$
6. $y = 2^{-x}$
7. $y = 1.6^{-x}$
8. $y = 2.5^{-x}$

9. $y = \left(\dfrac{1}{4}\right)^x$
10. $y = \left(\dfrac{5}{6}\right)^x$
11. $y = \left(\dfrac{2}{3}\right)^{-x}$
12. $y = \left(\dfrac{1}{6}\right)^{-x}$

13. $y = 1.5e^x$
14. $y = 5.2e^x$
15. $y = \left(\dfrac{e}{4}\right)^x$
16. $y = e^{\frac{x}{3}}$

17. The population of a town starts at 10,000, and grows exponentially by 10% each year. What is the town's population in seven years?

18. A population of rabbits in a favourable environment will grow exponentially at a rate of 60% each year. How big will a population of 500 rabbits grow to in 10 years?

19. A scientist studying a bacterium notices that the bacteria double every 30 minutes. The initial culture contained 100 bacteria. How many bacteria will be present in five hours?

20. A certain mold spreads in such a way that it doubles in the number of spores present every three days. The initial sample contained 2,500 spores. How many spores will be present in six weeks?

21. The half-life of the radioactive isotope Technetium-99, used in brain scans, is 6.01 hours (i.e., it loses 50% of its radioactivity every 6.01 hours). What percent of its initial radioactivity will remain after two days? Round your answer to two decimal places.

22. The half-life of the radioactive isotope Iodine-123, used in thyroid therapy, is 13.27 hours (i.e., it loses 50% of its radioactivity every 13.27 hours). What percent of its initial radioactivity will remain after seven days? Round your answer to three decimal places.

23. A certain drug is injected into a patient's bloodstream directly, and dissipates at an exponential rate once in the patient's bloodstream. If, after one minute, the amount of drug in the patient's bloodstream has decreased by 1.7%, what percent of the initial amount of drug injected will remain in the patient's bloodstream after two hours? Round your answer to two decimal places.

24. A chemist is conducting an experiment using a flask containing 50 mL of a liquid. Under extreme conditions, the liquid evaporates at an exponential rate. After one minute, the chemist notes that 2.3% of the liquid has evaporated. At this rate, how much liquid will be left in the beaker after 18 minutes? Round your answer to two decimal places.

9.3 | Logarithms

In the previous two sections, we focused on how to evaluate an exponential function $y = a^x$ for y given a value for x. But what if we wish to evaluate x in that expression for a given value of y? We could use a trial-and-error method, whereby we try to guess at the correct value for x and substitute that value into our equation to check if that yields the correct value for y, but this would be very time-consuming, and not very accurate.

Remember from earlier chapters that roots are used to isolate and solve for the base of a power, but now we will introduce an algebraic concept used to isolate and solve for the exponent of a power: the **logarithm**.

Exponential Form vs Logarithmic Form

Exponential Form

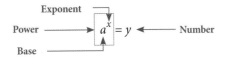

Read as: base 'a' raised to the exponent 'x' is 'y' or 'a' to the power of 'x' is 'y'.

In exponential form	Base	Exponent
$a^x = y$	a	x
$10^3 = 1,000$	10	3
$5^2 = 25$	5	2

Logarithmic Form

$$\log_a y = x \quad \longleftarrow \quad \text{Logarithm (exponent)}$$

Read as: logarithm of 'y' to the base 'a' is 'x' or log-base-'a' of 'y' is 'x'.

In logarithmic form	Base	Exponent	In exponential form
$\log_a y = x$	a	x	$a^x = y$
$\log_{10} 1,000 = 3$	10	3	$10^3 = 1,000$
$\log_5 25 = 2$	5	2	$5^2 = 25$

Converting between Exponential and Logarithmic Forms

$$a^x = y \quad \longleftrightarrow \quad \log_a y = x$$

Exponential notation — Logarithmic notation

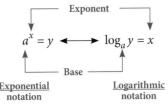

Exponents and logarithms are inverse functions.

For example,

- $10^3 = 1,000 \longleftrightarrow \log_{10} 1,000 = 3$

  $3 \xrightarrow{10^3} 1,000$, $\xleftarrow{\log_{10} 1000}$

- $5^2 = 25 \longleftrightarrow \log_5 25 = 2$

  $2 \xrightarrow{5^2} 25$, $\xleftarrow{\log_5 25}$

Example 9.3-a   Converting from Exponential Form to Logarithmic Form

Convert the following to logarithmic form:

(i) $6^2 = 36$

(ii) $2^6 = 64$

(iii) $7^3 = 343$

(iv) $2^{-5} = \dfrac{1}{32}$

(v) $16^{\frac{3}{4}} = 8$

(vi) $a^b = c$

Using $a^x = y \longleftrightarrow \log_a y = x$,

(i) $6^2 = 36$

$\log_6 36 = 2$

(ii) $2^6 = 64$

$\log_2 64 = 6$

(iii) $7^3 = 343$

$\log_7 343 = 3$

(iv) $2^{-5} = \dfrac{1}{32}$

$\log_2 \left(\dfrac{1}{32}\right) = -5$

(v) $16^{\frac{3}{4}} = 8$

$\log_{16} 8 = \dfrac{3}{4}$

(vi) $a^b = c$

$\log_a c = b$

Example 9.3-b	Converting from Logarithmic Form to Exponential Form

Convert the following to exponential form:

(i) $\log_3 81 = 4$

(ii) $\log_2 128 = 7$

(iii) $\log_3 2{,}187 = 7$

(iv) $\log_2 \left(\dfrac{1}{16}\right) = -4$

(v) $\log_{27} 9 = \dfrac{2}{3}$

(vi) $\log_a b = c$

Solution

Using $\log_a y = x \longleftrightarrow a^x = y$,

(i) $\log_3 81 = 4$

$3^4 = 81$

(ii) $\log_2 128 = 7$

$2^7 = 128$

(iii) $\log_3 2{,}187 = 7$

$3^7 = 2{,}187$

(iv) $\log_2 \left(\dfrac{1}{16}\right) = -4$

$2^{-4} = \dfrac{1}{16}$

(v) $\log_{27} 9 = \dfrac{2}{3}$

$27^{\frac{2}{3}} = 9$

(vi) $\log_a b = c$

$a^c = b$

Common Logarithms (log)

Common logarithms always have a base of 10. If no base is shown in a logarithmic expression, it is assumed to be a common logarithm of base 10 and is referred to simply by the symbol '**log**'.

Common Logarithmic Form	Exponential Form
$\log_{10} 1{,}000 = \log 1{,}000 = 3$	$10^3 = 1{,}000$
$\log_{10} 100 = \log 100 = 2$	$10^2 = 100$
$\log_{10} 10 = \log 10 = 1$	$10^1 = 10$
$\log_{10} 1 = \log 1 = 0$	$10^0 = 1$
$\log_{10} 0.1 = \log 0.1 = -1$	$10^{-1} = 0.1$
$\log_{10} 0.01 = \log 0.01 = -2$	$10^{-2} = 0.01$
$\log_{10} y = \log y = x$	$10^x = y$

Example 9.3-c	Calculating the Common Logarithm of Powers of 10

Calculate the following, without the use of a calculator:

(i) log 1,000,000   (ii) log 1   (iii) log 0.001   (iv) $\log (10^n)$

Solution

(i) log 1,000,000

$10^6 = 1{,}000{,}000$ in exponential form; hence, in logarithmic form, log 1,000,000 = 6 (ii)　log 1

　　　$10^0 = 1$ in exponential form; hence, in logarithmic form, log 1 = 0

(iii)　log 0.001

　　　$10^{-3} = 0.001$ in exponential form; hence, in logarithmic form, log 0.001 = –3

(iv)　log (10^n)

　　　Using the previous 3 examples as a pattern, we can deduce that log $10^n = n$.

Example 9.3-d　Estimating and Calculating the Common Logarithm of Arbitrary Numbers using a Calculator

First, estimate the following common logarithms without the use of a calculator. Then, calculate the exact value of each of the logarithms using a calculator, rounded to 4 decimal places (as needed).

(i)　log 10,000　　　(ii)　log 40　　　(iii)　log 6.5　　　(iv)　log 0.25

Solution

We can use the `log` button on a scientific calculator to solve common logarithms.

(i)　Since $10^4 = 10,000$, we can compute exactly that log 10,000 = 4 using the method above.
　　Using the calculator, we confirm that log 10,000 = 4.

(ii)　Since $10^1 = 10$ and $10^2 = 100$, we can estimate that log 40 will be between 1 and 2.
　　Using the calculator, we confirm that log 40 = 1.602059… = 1.6021.

(iii)　Since $10^0 = 1$ and $10^1 = 10$, we can estimate that log 6.5 will be between 0 and 1.
　　Using the calculator, we confirm that log 6.5 = 0.812913… = 0.8129.

(iv)　Since $10^{-1} = 0.1$ and $10^0 = 1$, we can estimate that log 0.25 will be between –1 and 0.
　　Using the calculator, we confirm that log 0.25 = –0.602059… = –0.6021.

Natural Logarithms (ln)

Natural logarithms always have a base of $e = 2.71828…$

If the base of a logarithmic expression is 'e', then it is called the **natural logarithm**, and is expressed by the symbol '**ln**' (pronounced "lawn").

We know $x^0 = 1$, for every $x > 0$

Thus, $10^0 = 1$ and $e^0 = 1$

Therefore,

$\log_{10} 1 = 0 \longrightarrow \log 1 = 0$
$\log_e 1 = 0 \longrightarrow \ln 1 = 0$

Natural Logarithmic Form

$\log_e 1 = \ln 1 = 0$

$\log_e e = \ln e = 1$

$\log_e 10 = \ln 10 = 2.302585…$

$\log_e 0.01 = \ln 0.01 = -4.605170…$

Exponential Form

$e^0 = 1$

$e^1 = e = 2.71828…$

$e^{2.302585…} = 10$

$e^{-4.605170…} = 0.01$

Example 9.3-e　Calculating the Natural Logarithm of Arbitrary Numbers using a Calculator

Calculate the following using a calculator, rounded to 4 decimal places (as needed):

(i)　ln 1,000　　　(ii)　ln 50　　　(iii)　ln 0.50　　　(iv)　ln e^2

Solution

Using the `LN` button on the calculator,

(i)　ln 1,000 = 6.907755…　(ii)　ln 50 = 3.912023…　(iii)　ln 0.50 = –0.693147…　(iv)　ln e^2 = 2
　　　　= 6.9078　　　　　　　　　= 3.9120　　　　　　　　　= –0.6931

Note: From Example 9.3-e (iv), we can deduce that ln $e^n = n$.

Rules of Logarithms

The rules of logarithms are used to evaluate the exponent 'n' in mathematical formulas $y = ax^n$.

Table 9.3		Rules of Logarithms		
		Rule	**Description**	**Rule in Common Logarithmic Form**
	1.	Product Rule	The logarithm of a product equals the sum of the logarithms of the factors.	$\log_a (AB) = \log_a A + \log_a B$
	2.	Quotient Rule	The logarithm of a quotient equals the difference between the logarithm of the numerator (dividend) and the logarithm of the denominator (divisor).	$\log_a \left(\dfrac{A}{B}\right) = \log_a A - \log_a B$
	3.	Power Rule	The logarithm of a number raised to an exponent equals the product of the exponent and the logarithm of the number.	$\log_a (A)^n = n \log_a A$
	4.	Logarithm of 1 Rule	The logarithm of 1 is zero.	$\log_a 1 = 0$
	5.	Logarithm of the Base Rule	The logarithm of the same number as the base is one.	$\log_a a = 1$
	6.	Logarithm of a Base Raised to a Power Rule	The logarithm of the base raised to a power is equal to the power.	$\log_a (a)^n = n$
	7.	"Change of Base" Rule	The logarithm of a number with any arbitrary (positive) base is equal to the common (or natural) logarithm of the number, divided by the common (or natural) logarithm of the original base.	$\log_a A = \dfrac{\log A}{\log a} = \dfrac{\ln A}{\ln a}$

Remember, the base of a logarithm must be positive and cannot equal 1, and the number inside a logarithm must be positive.

i.e., $a > 0$, $a \neq 1$; and $A, B > 0$

Note:

$\log_a (M + N) \neq \log_a M + \log_a N$

$\log_a (M - N) \neq \log_a M - \log_a N$

$(\log_a M)(\log_a N) \neq \log_a M + \log_a N$

$\dfrac{\log_a M}{\log_a N} \neq \log_a M - \log_a N$

1. *Rules of logarithms can be used to combine two or more logarithmic expressions into a single logarithmic expression.*

2. *Common logarithms (log) and natural logarithms (ln) follow the same rules.*

3. *Converting between common and natural logarithms, using rule 7 above, gives the following:*

$$\ln A = \frac{\log A}{\log e} \qquad \log A = \frac{\ln A}{\ln 10}$$

Example 9.3-f

Evaluating Logarithms Using Rules of Logarithms, without a Calculator

Evaluate the following logarithms, without the use of a calculator:

(i) $\log 200 + \log 5{,}000$ (ii) $\log 35{,}000 - \log 7 - \log 50$

(iii) $\log 8 + 3\log 5$ (iv) $\log_2 32^3 - \log_3 81^4 + \log_5 125^2$

(v) $\ln e^4$

Solution

(i) $\log 200 + \log 5{,}000$ Using the Product Rule,

      $= \log(200 \times 5{,}000)$

      $= \log(1{,}000{,}000)$

      $= 6$

(ii) $\log 35{,}000 - \log 7 - \log 50$ Using the Quotient Rule,

      $= \log\left[\dfrac{\left(\dfrac{35{,}000}{7}\right)}{50}\right]$

      $= \log(100)$

      $= 2$

(iii) $\log 8 + 3\log 5$ Using the Power Rule,

      $= \log 8 + \log 5^3$

      $= \log 8 + \log 125$ Using the Product Rule,

      $= \log(8 \times 125)$

      $= \log(1{,}000)$

      $= 3$

(iv) $\log_2 32^3 - \log_3 81^4 + \log_5 125^2$ Using the Power Rule,

      $= 3\log_2 32 - 4\log_3 81 + 2\log_5 125$ Switching to exponential form,

      $= 3\log_2(2^5) - 4\log_3(3^4) + 2\log_5(5^3)$ Using the Logarithm of a Base Raised to a Power Rule,

      $= 3(5) - 4(4) + 2(3)$

      $= 5$

(v) $\ln e^4$

      $= \log_e(e^4)$ Using the Logarithm of a Base Raised to a Power Rule,

      $= 4$

Example 9.3-g

Evaluating Logarithms Using Rules of Logarithms with a Calculator

Evaluate the following using natural logarithms and a calculator, rounded to 4 decimal places (as needed).

(i) $\ln(275 \times 75)$ (ii) $\log_2\left(\dfrac{4{,}750}{3{,}275}\right)$ (iii) $\log_7(4.25)^6$ (iv) $\log_{0.25}(125)^2 + \log_{0.25}(10)^{-6}$

Solution

(i) $\ln (275 \times 75)$ Using the Product Rule,

$= \ln 275 + \ln 75$

$= 5.616771... + 4.317488...$

$= 9.934259... = 9.9343$

(ii) $\log_2 \left(\dfrac{4,750}{3,275} \right)$ Using the Quotient Rule,

$= \log_2 4,750 - \log_2 3,275$ Using the Change of Base Rule,

$= \dfrac{\ln 4,750}{\ln 2} - \dfrac{\ln 3,275}{\ln 2}$

$= \dfrac{\ln 4,750 - \ln 3,275}{\ln 2}$

$= \dfrac{8.465899... - 8.094073...}{0.693147...}$

$= \dfrac{0.371826...}{0.693147...}$

$= 0.536432... = 0.5364$

(iii) $\log_7 (4.25)^6$ Using the Power Rule,

$= 6 \cdot \log_7 (4.25)$ Using the Change of Base Rule,

$= \dfrac{6 \ln (4.25)}{\ln (7)}$

$= \dfrac{6(1.446918...)}{1.945910...}$

$= 4.461415... = 4.4614$

(iv) $\log_{0.25} (125)^2 + \log_{0.25}(10)^{-6}$ Using the Power Rule,

$= 2 \cdot \log_{0.25}(125) - 6 \cdot \log_{0.25}(10)$ Using the Change of Base Rule,

$= \dfrac{2\ln (125)}{\ln (0.25)} - \dfrac{6\ln (10)}{\ln (0.25)}$

$= \dfrac{2\ln (125) - 6\ln (10)}{\ln (0.25)}$

$= \dfrac{2(4.828313...) - 6(2.302585)}{-1.386294...}$

$= \dfrac{-4.158883...}{-1.386294...}$

$= 3$

Example 9.3-h	Writing a Simple Logarithm

First, write each of the following as a single logarithm. Then, evaluate the logarithm using a calculator, rounded to 4 decimal places (as needed).

(i) $2 \log 3 + \log 5$

(ii) $3 \log 4 - \log 8$

(iii) $5 \log 2 + \log 4 - \log 8$

(iv) $\log \sqrt[3]{100} + \log \sqrt{1,000}$

(i) $2 \log 3 + \log 5$

$= \log 3^2 + \log 5$

$= \log (3^2 \times 5)$

$= \log (45)$

$= 1.653212... = 1.6532$

(ii) $3 \log 4 - \log 8$

$= \log 4^3 - \log 8$

$= \log \left(\dfrac{4^3}{8}\right)$

$= \log (8)$

$= 0.903089... = 0.9031$

(iii) $5 \log 2 + \log 4 - \log 8$

$= \log 2^5 + \log 4 - \log 8$

$= \log 32 + \log 4 - \log 8$

$= \log \left(32 \times \dfrac{4}{8}\right)$

$= \log (16)$

$= 1.204119... = 1.2041$

(iv) $\log \sqrt[3]{100} + \log \sqrt{1,000}$

$= \log (100)^{\frac{1}{3}} + \log (1,000)^{\frac{1}{2}}$

$= \log (10^2)^{\frac{1}{3}} + \log (10^3)^{\frac{1}{2}}$

$= \log (10^{\frac{2}{3}}) + \log (10^{\frac{3}{2}})$

$= \log (10^{\frac{2}{3}} \times 10^{\frac{3}{2}})$

$= \log (10^{\frac{2}{3} + \frac{3}{2}})$

$= \log 10^{\frac{13}{6}}$

$= \dfrac{13}{6} (\log 10)$

$= \dfrac{13}{6} (1)$

$= \dfrac{13}{6} = 2\dfrac{1}{6}$

9.3 | Exercises

For Problems 1 to 6, express the following in logarithmic form:

1. a. $10^5 = 100,000$ b. $4^5 = 1,024$
2. a. $10^4 = 10,000$ b. $4^4 = 256$
3. a. $2^6 = 64$ b. $6^5 = 7,776$
4. a. $2^3 = 8$ b. $6^4 = 1,296$
5. a. $3^2 = 9$ b. $9^4 = 6,561$
6. a. $3^6 = 729$ b. $8^3 = 512$

For Problems 7 to 12, express the following in exponential form:

7. a. $\log_{10} 100 = 2$ b. $\log_4 64 = 3$
8. a. $\log_{10} 1,000 = 3$ b. $\log_4 4,096 = 6$
9. a. $\log_2 32 = 5$ b. $\log_5 625 = 4$
10. a. $\log_2 4 = 2$ b. $\log_5 125 = 3$
11. a. $\log_3 729 = 6$ b. $\log_6 216 = 3$
12. a. $\log_3 243 = 5$ b. $\log_6 1,296 = 4$

For Problems 13 to 20, calculate the following (rounded to 4 decimal places):

13. a. $\log 225$ b. $\log 1.54$
14. a. $\log 27$ b. $\log 2.5$
15. a. $\log_3 35$ b. $\log_5 0.25$
16. a. $\log_8 155$ b. $\log_3 0.75$
17. a. $\ln 10.05$ b. $\ln 1.005$
18. a. $\ln 12.51$ b. $\ln 750$
19. a. $\log_{1.2} 0.165$ b. $\log_{0.75} 72$
20. a. $\log_{2.4} 0.675$ b. $\log_{0.56} 120$

For Problems 21 to 32, express the following as a sum or difference of two or more logarithms:

21. $\log\left(\dfrac{3}{7}\right)$
22. $\log\left(\dfrac{40}{13}\right)$
23. $\ln (4 \times 9)$
24. $\ln (7 \times 8)$
25. $\log\left(\dfrac{AB}{C}\right)$
26. $\log\left(\dfrac{x}{ab}\right)$
27. $\ln\left(\dfrac{X}{YZ}\right)$
28. $\ln\left(\dfrac{xy}{c}\right)$
29. $\log\left(\dfrac{3x}{2yz}\right)$
30. $\log\left(\dfrac{5x}{2ab}\right)$
31. $\ln\left(\dfrac{xy}{\sqrt{z}}\right)$
32. $\ln\left(\dfrac{x}{\sqrt{yz}}\right)$

If $\log_a x = M$ and $\log_a y = N$, express the value of each of the following in terms of M and N:

33. $\log_a \left(\dfrac{x}{y}\right)$ 34. $\log_a \left(\dfrac{y}{x}\right)$ 35. $\log_a (xy^2)$ 36. $\log_a (x^2 y)$

37. $\log_a \left(\dfrac{x^2}{y}\right)$ 38. $\log_a \left(\dfrac{x}{y^2}\right)$ 39. $\log_a (x^6 y^9)^{-\frac{2}{3}}$ 40. $\log_a (x^8 y^4)^{\frac{3}{4}}$

41. $\log_a (\sqrt[5]{x^4})$ 42. $\log_a (\sqrt[3]{y^2})$ 43. $\log_a \left(\dfrac{1}{\sqrt[3]{x^2 y}}\right)$ 44. $\log_a \left(\dfrac{1}{\sqrt{x y^3}}\right)$

For Problems 45 to 64, express the following as a single logarithm, and then evaluate using a calculator, rounded to 4 decimal places, where applicable:

45. $\log 8 + \log 5$ 46. $\log 25 + \log 4$ 47. $\ln 15 - \ln 3$ 48. $\ln 60 - \ln 15$

49. $5 \log 2 - 2 \log 3$ 50. $4 \log 5 - 3 \log 2$ 51. $2 \ln 5 + 3 \ln 3$ 52. $2 \ln 8 + 3 \ln 3$

53. $2 \log 5$ 54. $5 \log 2$ 55. $3 \ln 6$ 56. $6 \ln 3$

57. $2 \log \left(\dfrac{x}{y}\right)$ 58. $5 \log \left(\dfrac{a}{b}\right)$ 59. $4 \ln (a \times b)$ 60. $3 \ln (xy)$

61. $3 \log 2 + 4 \log 3 - 2 \log 4$ 62. $2 \log 3 + 3 \log 2 - 4 \log 2$ 63. $3 \ln a + 2 \ln b - 5 \ln c$ 64. $4 \ln x - 2 \ln y + 3 \ln z$

For Problems 65 to 72, simplify the following expressions by writing them without exponents or radicals, and then evaluate without the use of a calculator.

65. $\log_{10} \sqrt{1,000}$ 66. $\log_{10} \sqrt[4]{100,000}$ 67. $\log_2 \sqrt{64}$ 68. $\log_5 \sqrt{625}$

69. $\log_3 \sqrt[3]{9^2}$ 70. $\log_2 \sqrt[5]{32^3}$ 71. $\log_{27} \sqrt[4]{\dfrac{1}{81}}$ 72. $\log_{36} \sqrt[3]{\dfrac{1}{216}}$

9.4 | Logarithmic Functions

Important: neither the base of a logarithm nor the number inside a logarithm can be negative or zero - they must both be positive numbers (and the base cannot be equal to 1).

As we have previously seen, exponents and logarithms are inverses of each other. Where exponential functions measure the change in the value of a power with a fixed base as the exponent changes at a constant rate, logarithmic functions measure the change in the value of the exponent on a fixed base as the overall value of the power changes at a constant rate. A logarithmic function follows the form $y = \log_a x$, which means "y is the exponent to which a is raised to in order to result in a value of x", and is read as "y is the base-a logarithm of x", or more simply, "y equals log-base-a of x". Every logarithmic function is the inverse of some exponential function. For example, $y = \log_{10} x$ can be rewritten as $x = 10^y$. Since exponentials and logarithms are inverse functions, their domains and ranges are reversed; i.e., the domain of a logarithmic function $y = \log_a x$ is all positive real numbers $\{x \in \mathbf{R} \mid x > 0\}$, while the range of a logarithmic function is all real numbers $\{y \in \mathbf{R}\}$. Again, this is because in a logarithmic function, the output value y represents the exponent, which can be any number, while the input value x represents the overall value of the power with a positive base a, which therefore must be positive.

Graphs of Logarithmic Functions

To graph logarithmic functions, we follow these steps:

Step 1: Write the expression as a single logarithm.

Step 2: Convert the logarithmic function to its exponential form, with y as the exponent, and solve for x.

Step 3: Create a table of values for the exponential function by substituting values in for y and solving for x.

Step 4: Plot the graph using an appropriate scale.

Example 9.4-a **Graphing Logarithmic Functions**

Graph the following functions:

(i) $y = \log_3 x$ (ii) $y = \log_2(2x)$ (iii) $y = 2\log x$

Solution

(i) $y = \log_3 x$

$x = 3^y$

y	x	(x, y)
−2	0.1111...	(0.11, − 2)
−1	0.3333...	(0.33, − 1)
0	1	(1, 0)
1	3	(3, 1)
2	9	(9, 2)

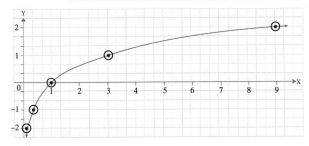

(ii) $y = \log_2(2x)$

$2x = 2^y$

$x = \dfrac{2^y}{2}$

y	x	(x, y)
−2	0.125	(0.13, − 2)
−1	0.25	(0.25, − 1)
0	0.5	(0.5, 0)
1	1	(1, 1)
2	2	(2, 2)

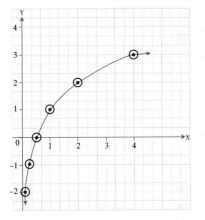

(iii) $y = 2\log x$

$\dfrac{y}{2} = \log x$

Remember, log without any base means $\log_{10}$

$x = 10^{\frac{y}{2}}$

y	x	(x, y)
−2	0.1	(0.1, − 2)
−1	0.3162...	(0.32, − 1)
0	1	(1, 0)
1	3.1622...	(3.16, 1)
2	10	(10, 2)

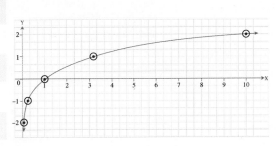

Logarithmic Scale

Logarithmic scales are commonly used when the values of measurements grow exponentially, and so would end up being so large or so small that they are not practical to work with. The use of a logarithmic scale instead brings all the numbers into a very small range, since instead of working with the actual value of the measurement, we are working with the exponent of the power of 10 that represents that measurement.

For example, if measurements could take on values from 1 to 1,000,000,000,000 on a normal scale, on a logarithmic scale, the values would only range from 0 to 12 (since $1 = 10^0$ and $1,000,000,000,000 = 10^{12}$). As such, this is a very convenient scale for any values typically expressed in scientific notation.

pH Scale

The **pH Scale** is used to measure the Hydrogen Ion concentration (denoted [H+], and usually expressed in scientific notation) in an aqueous solution. It is a scale that ranges from 0-14, and represents a measure of the solution's **acidity**, with low values (0-6) representing highly acidic solutions, while high values (8-14) represent highly alkaline (i.e., non-acidic) solutions. pH values around 7 are considered to be "neutral", which are neither acidic nor alkaline.

The formula for pH is given as follows:

$$pH = -\log([H+])$$

Example 9.4-b	pH Calculations

Find the pH of a chemical solution with a hydrogen ion concentration of 3.1627×10^{-5}, and determine whether it's an acidic or alkaline solution.

Solution

$pH = -\log [H+]$ Recall: $3.1627 \times 10^{-5} = 0.000031627$

$pH = -\log [0.000031627]$

$pH = 4.499942...$

$pH = 4.5$

Therefore, the pH of the solution is 4.5, making it acidic.

Magnitude and Intensity

Logarithmic scales are very useful for measuring the magnitudes of vibrations or "waves", such as earthquakes and sound waves. Because the intensity of these vibrations increase exponentially by powers of 10, a logarithmic scale is used to keep the numbers relatively small and easy to work with.

The two most common log scales for magnitude and intensity are the **Richter Magnitude Scale**, named for the American physicist Charles F. Richter, which measures the intensity of an earthquake, and the **Decibel Scale**, literally meaning one-tenth ("deci") of a bel, a unit named for the Scottish physicist, engineer and inventor Alexander Graham Bell, that measures the intensity or "volume" of a sound wave.

Richter Magnitude

$M = \log\left(\dfrac{I}{I_0}\right)$, where M is the Richter Magnitude of the earthquake, I is the intensity of the earthquake, and I_0 is the "threshold intensity" of an earthquake that can just barely be measured.

Decibel Gain

$G = 10 \log\left(\dfrac{P_2}{P_1}\right)$, where G is the "gain" in sound level, measured in dB (decibels), P_2 is the power of the output sound wave, and P_1 is the power of the input sound wave.

Example 9.4-c **Richter Magnitude Calculations**

If an earthquake has an intensity that is 794 times the threshold of the intensity level, what would be its Richter scale rating?

Solution

$$M = \log\left(\frac{I}{I_0}\right)$$ I_0 is the threshold intensity, and $I = 794I_0$, so therefore $\frac{I}{I_0} = 794$.

$$M = \log(794)$$

$$M = 2.899820\ldots$$

$$M = 2.9$$

Therefore, the earthquake's magnitude on the Richter scale is approximately 2.9.

Example 9.4-d **Decibels Gained or Lost**

An amplifier emits 10,238 W of power when given an input of 3,240 W. What is the decibel gain?

Solution

$$G = 10 \log\left(\frac{P_2}{P_1}\right)$$ $P_2 = 10{,}238$ W and $P_1 = 3{,}240$ W

$$G = 10 \log\left(\frac{10{,}238}{3{,}240}\right)$$

$$G = 4.996701\ldots$$

$$G = 5$$

Therefore, the gain is 5 dB.

Drug Absorption Rate

Finally, we look at a specific health sciences application of logarithmic functions: **drug absorption rates**.

The time required for a certain percentage of a drug to be absorbed by the body depends on the absorption rate of the drug. This can be modeled by the function $T = \frac{-\ln p}{K}$, where T is the elapsed time in hours, p is the percent of the drug that **remains** in the body, and K is the absorption rate of the drug.

Example 9.4-e **Drug Absorption Rate**

What is the time required for the body to absorb 35% of a drug that has an absorption rate of 7.2%?

Solution

Percent of the drug that **remains** in the body: $p = 100\% - 35\% = 65\% = 0.65$
Drug absorption rate: $K = 7.2\% = 0.072$

$$T = \frac{-\ln p}{K}$$

$$= \frac{-\ln 0.65}{0.072}$$

$$= 5.983096\ldots = 5.98 \text{ h}$$

Therefore, the time required for the body to absorb 35% of a drug that has an absorption rate of 7.2% is 5.98 hours.

9.4 | Exercises

Answers to odd-numbered problems are available at the end of the textbook.

For Problems 1 to 8, graph the logarithmic functions by first converting to exponential expressions.

1. $y = \log_4 x$
2. $y = \log_8 x$
3. $y = \log_5 (2x)$
4. $y = \log_8 (4x)$

5. $y = \ln (1.3x)$
6. $y = 2 \ln x$
7. $y = 0.5 \log (x)$
8. $y = \log (3.4x)$

9. Find the pH for the following substances and determine whether they are acidic or alkaline.
    a. pH of vinegar, where $[H+] = 3.981 \times 10^{-3}$
    b. pH of bleach, where $[H+] = 2.512 \times 10^{-13}$

10. Find the pH for the following substances and determine whether they are acidic or alkaline.
    a. pH of ammonia, where $[H+] = 3.162 \times 10^{-12}$
    b. pH of sodium carbonate, where $[H+] = 1.585 \times 10^{-4}$

11. Find the time required for 90% of an administered drug to be absorbed if the drug has an absorption rate of 8.2%.

12. Find the time required for 75% of an administered drug to be absorbed if the drug has an absorption rate of 3.5%.

13. An earthquake has an intensity that is 9,550 times the threshold intensity for tectonic vibrations to be measured. What would be its Richter scale magnitude?

14. An earthquake has an intensity that iss 199,500 times the threshold intensity for tectonic vibrations to be measured. What would be its Richter scale magnitude?

15. The 2010 earthquake in Haiti had a Richter magnitude of 7.0. The next year, in 2011, Japan was hit by one of the most powerful earthquakes on record, registering as 126 times as powerful as the 2010 Haitian earthquake. Determine the Richter magnitude of the 2011 earthquake that hit Japan.

16. The largest recorded earthquake in North America since the start of the 20th century occurred in Alaska in 1965 and had a Richter magnitude of 8.7. The earthquake with the largest ever recorded Richter magnitude occurred 5 years earlier, in 1960, in Valdivia, Chile, and is known as the "Great Chilean Earthquake." If it was 6.3 times more powerful than the Alaskan earthquake, determine the Richter Magnitude of the Great Chilean Earthquake.

17. An amplifier receives a 10μW signal and amplifies it to 5.23mW. What is the decibel gain?

18. A noise is amplified to a power of 8.32mW from its 19μW signal. What is the decibel gain?

19. Sound-dampening foam that is used for soundproofing a studio reduces a signal with a power of 125 mW/m^2 to 35.2 μW/m^2. Determine the decibel loss caused by the dampening foam.

20. A rock concert produces sound at a power level of 5.011 W/m^2 in the general seating area. The sound level (in decibels) is measured by the formula $L = 10 \log\left(\dfrac{I}{I_0}\right)$, where $I_0 = 10^{-12}$ W/m^2. Calculate the sound level of the rock concert. If exposure to sound levels over 120 dB can cause permanent hearing loss instantly, is the sound level at this rock concert dangerous?

9.5 | Applications of Exponential and Logarithmic Functions

When solving exponential and logarithmic application questions, often a particular variable in an equation or a formula must be isolated by rearranging the terms and simplifying, so that the required variable is on the left side of the equation and all the other variables and numbers are on the right side of the equation. Rearrangement can be performed by using the rules that you have learned in the previous sections of this chapter and the following guidelines:

- An exponential equation can be solved by taking the logarithm of both sides, and applying the power rule to bring down the unknown exponent value as a multiplication factor.

- A logarithmic equation can be solved by using the properties of logarithms to combine the log terms into a single logarithm, and then rewriting the equation in exponential form.

Solving Equations

Example 9.5-a **Solving Exponential Equations**

Solve for n in the following equations (rounded to 4 decimal places, as needed):

(i) $1{,}024 = 2^n$

(ii) $3{,}749 = 1{,}217(1.005)^n$

Solution

Using natural logarithms:

(i) $1{,}024 = 2^n$ Taking ln on both sides,

$\ln 1{,}024 = \ln 2^n$ Using Power Rule,

$\ln 1{,}024 = n \ln 2$ Isolating n,

$$n = \frac{\ln 1{,}024}{\ln 2}$$

$$= \frac{6.931471\ldots}{0.693147\ldots}$$

$$= 10$$

Using common logarithms:

$1{,}024 = 2^n$ Taking log on both sides,

$\log 1{,}024 = \log 2^n$ Using Power Rule,

or $\log 1{,}024 = n \cdot \log 2$ Isolating n,

$$n = \frac{\log 1{,}024}{\log 2}$$

$$= \frac{3.010299\ldots}{0.301029\ldots}$$

$$= 10$$

(ii) $3{,}749 = 1{,}217(1.005)^n$ Dividing both sides by 1,217,

$$\frac{3{,}749}{1{,}217} = (1.005)^n$$ Taking ln on both sides,

$$\ln\left(\frac{3{,}749}{1{,}217}\right) = \ln (1.005)^n$$ Using Power Rule,

$$\ln\left(\frac{3{,}749}{1{,}217}\right) = n \ln 1.005$$ Isolating n,

$$n = \frac{\ln\left(\dfrac{3{,}749}{1{,}217}\right)}{\ln 1.005}$$

$$= \frac{1.125100\ldots}{0.004987\ldots}$$

$$= 225.582147\ldots = 225.5821$$

or

$3{,}749 = 1{,}217(1.005)^n$ Dividing both sides by 1,217,

$$\frac{3{,}749}{1{,}217} = (1.005)^n$$ Taking log on both sides,

$$\log\left(\frac{3{,}749}{1{,}217}\right) = \log (1.005)^n$$ Using Power Rule,

$$\log\left(\frac{3{,}749}{1{,}217}\right) = n \cdot \log (1.005)$$ Isolating n,

$$n = \frac{\log\left(\dfrac{3{,}749}{1{,}217}\right)}{\log 1.005}$$

$$= \frac{0.488624\ldots}{0.002166\ldots}$$

$$= 225.582147\ldots = 225.5821$$

Example 9.5-b **Solving Logarithmic Equations**

Solve for n in the following equations (rounded to 2 decimal places, as needed):

(i) $16 \log (2n) = 40$

(ii) $-10 \ln \left(\dfrac{n-5}{3}\right) = 4$

Solution

(i) $16 \log (2n) = 40$

$$\log (2n) = \frac{40}{16}$$

$$\log (2n) = 2.5$$

$$2n = 10^{2.5}$$

$$n = \frac{10^{2.5}}{2}$$

$$n = 158.113883\ldots = 158.11$$

(ii) $-10 \ln \left(\dfrac{n-5}{3}\right) = 4$

$$\ln \left(\frac{n-5}{3}\right) = \frac{4}{-10}$$

$$\ln \left(\frac{n-5}{3}\right) = -0.4$$

$$\frac{n-5}{3} = e^{-0.4}$$

$$\frac{n-5}{3} = 0.670320\ldots$$

$$n - 5 = 2.010960\ldots$$

$$n = 7.010960\ldots = 7.01$$

Applications of Exponential Functions

Use $y = A(1 + r)^{\frac{t}{k}}$ when given a specific period of growth (for example, doubling time or half-life).

Use $y = Ae^{kt}$ when given a continuous, natural exponential growth rate, or given two different measurements at two different times.

In the health sciences, we will solve exponential equations that involve rates of growth, such as with a bacterial infection, and rates of decay, such as with a radioactive dye. Often, however, we need to calculate the length of time in the problem, which requires the use of logarithms to solve. Most of these types of problems can be modelled by the formula $y = Ae^{kt}$, where A is the initial value, t is the time elapsed, and k is a growth factor that is either given in the problem, or must be calculated.

This exponential model (with a base of e) is commonly used to model continuous growth or decay that occurs naturally, such as with bacteria growth and radioactive decay.

Note: This formula is not typically used when given the doubling time of a bacteria culture or half-life of a radioactive compound. In these cases, the rate of growth formula given in section 9.2 ($y = A(1 + r)^{\frac{t}{k}}$) is more commonly used.

Example 9.5-c	Doubling Time

There were 100 specimens in a small population of protozoa when measured at a certain time. One minute later, the same population is measured again, but now there are 117 specimens. Assuming the growth of protozoa is exponential and continuous, how long (in minutes and seconds) will it take this population to double in quantity?

Solution

Before we can compute the length of time it will take the population to double in quantity, we first need to compute the growth factor. We know the population grows from 100 to 117 specimens in the course of one minute, so we can compute the growth factor as follows:

Initial value: $A = 100$

Value after $t = 1$ minute: $y = 117$

Therefore, inputting the values into the formula $y = Ae^{kt}$:

$$117 = 100e^{k(1)}$$

$$1.17 = e^k$$

$$\ln(1.17) = k$$

$$k \approx 0.157$$

Now, we can determine the length of time it will take for the population to double:

$y = 200, A = 100, k \approx 0.157$

$$200 = 100e^{0.157t}$$

$$2 = e^{0.157t}$$

$$\ln 2 = 0.157t$$

$$t = \frac{\ln 2}{0.157}$$

$$t = \frac{0.693147...}{0.157}$$

$$t = 4.414950...$$

or 4 minutes and $(0.414950 \times 60) \approx 25$ seconds

Therefore, it will take approximately 4 minutes and 25 seconds for the culture of bacteria to double.

Example 9.5-d	Determining Current Times

The current of an electrical charge is determined in amperes (A) by the formula $I = 3.4\left(e^{-148t}\right)$, where t is the time in seconds. After how many seconds will the current be at 3.2 A? Express your answer in scientific notation, accurate to 2 significant figures.

Solution

In this case, the decay factor (since it is negative) k is given, and is equal to –148. Substituting $I = 3.2$ A into the formula $I = 3.4(e^{-148t})$, we can solve for t:

$$3.2 = 3.4\left(e^{-148t}\right)$$

$$\frac{3.2}{3.4} = e^{-148t}$$

$$\ln(0.941176...) = -148t$$

$$t = \frac{\ln(0.941176...)}{-148} = 0.000409626...$$

$$t = 4.1 \times 10^{-4}$$

Therefore, it will take 4.1×10^{-4} seconds for the current to be reduced to 3.2 A.

Applications of Logarithmic Functions

Example 9.5-e   **Determining Voltage**

The loudest volume that the human ear can withstand is 160 decibels. What would be the intensity of a noise at this volume in W/m^2, if the formula for sound level is $L = 10 \log\left(\frac{I}{I_0}\right)$, where I_0 is the threshold sound intensity, equal to 10^{-12} W/m^2?

Solution

Substituting $L = 160$ dB into the above formula, and solving for I:

$$160 = 10 \log\left(\frac{I}{I_0}\right)$$

$$\log\left(\frac{I}{I_0}\right) = 16$$

$$\left(\frac{I}{I_0}\right) = 10^{16}$$

$$I = 10^{16}\,(I_0)$$

$$= 10^{16}\,(10^{-12}\text{ W/m}^2)$$

$$= 10^4 \text{ W/m}^2 \text{ or } 10{,}000 \text{ W/m}^2$$

Therefore, the intensity would be equal to 10,000 W/m^2.

Example 9.5-f   **Intensity Calculations**

If two earthquakes register 6 and 9, respectively, on the Richter scale, by how much is the stronger earthquake more intense than the weaker one?

Solution

Formula: $M = \log\left(\frac{I}{I_0}\right)$ I_0 is the threshold intensity of a barely-measurable earthquake.

First earthquake: $6 = \log\left(\frac{I_1}{I_0}\right)$

Second earthquake: $9 = \log\left(\frac{I_2}{I_0}\right)$

$\log\left(\frac{I_2}{I_0}\right) - \log\left(\frac{I_1}{I_0}\right) = 9 - 6$ Using the Quotient Rule,

$(\log I_2 - \log I_0) - (\log I_1 - \log I_0) = 3$

$$\left(\log I_2\right) - \left(\log I_1\right) = 3$$

$$\log\left(\frac{I_2}{I_1}\right) = 3$$

$$\frac{I_2}{I_1} = 10^3 = 1{,}000$$

Therefore, the earthquake with a Richter magnitude of 9 is 1,000 times more intense than the earthquake with a Richter magnitude of 6.

Note: As shown in the previous example, we can determine how many times more intense an earthquake with a Richter Magnitude of M_2 is compared to an earthquake with a Richter Magnitude of M_1 using the following formula:

$$M_2 - M_1 = \log\left(\frac{I_2}{I_1}\right)$$

Example 9.5-g   **H+ concentration**

A solution of hydrochloric acid (HCl) has a pH of 3.01. What is its hydrogen ion [H+] concentration? Express your answer in scientific notation, accurate to 3 significant figures.

Solution

Formula: pH = –log [H+]

$$3.01 = -\log [\text{H+}]$$

$$[\text{H+}] = 10^{-3.01}$$

$$[\text{H+}] = 0.000977237\ldots = 9.77 \times 10^{-4}$$

Therefore, the [H+] concentration is 9.77×10^{-4}.

9.5 | Exercises

Answers to odd-numbered problems are available at the end of the textbook.

For Problems 1 to 16, solve for 'n' (rounding to 2 decimal places):

1. $\log_2 n = -4$
2. $\log_9 n = \dfrac{3}{2}$
3. $\log_n 1{,}225 = 7$
4. $\log_n 500 = 4$

5. $\ln\left(n^{\frac{3}{4}}\right) = 2.68$
6. $\ln\left(n^{-5}\right) = 17.9$
7. $\ln\left(\dfrac{2n+5}{3}\right) = 4.5$
8. $4\ln\left(\dfrac{n}{2-1}\right) = -0.17$

9. $250 = (30)^n$
10. $320 = (15)^n$
11. $(1.05)^n = 1.31$
12. $2.5 = (1.05)^n$

13. $7{,}500 = (45)^n + 500$
14. $8{,}000 = (35)^n + 1{,}500$
15. $10{,}000 = 2{,}000(1.2)^n$
16. $15{,}000 = 5{,}000\,(1.04)^n$

17. A hearing aid amplifies a sound from 65 decibels to 85 decibels. By what factor was the sound amplified?

18. Ear plugs worn by construction workers dampen a sound from 130 decibels to 75 decibels. By what factor do the ear plugs dampen the sound?

19. A virus spreads according to the following exponential equation: $A = Pe^{1.15t}$, where A is the size of the population affected at a given time, P is the size of the initial infected population, and t is the length of time in days. Under these assumptions, how long will it take for the virus to have infected 100 times the initial population?

20. The current in Amperes (A) of an electrical charge after t seconds is given by the formula $I = 0.24\left(e^{-124t}\right)$. How long will it take for the current to drop to 4.48 mA? (Note: 1 mA = 0.001 A)

21. The half-life for cobalt-56 is 73 days. How long does it take 34 g of cobalt-56 to become 7% of its original mass?

22. The half-life for cobalt-57 is 271 days. How long does it take 50 g of cobalt-57 to become 20% of its original mass?

23. The apparent magnitude of the full moon is –13. This is given by the formula $M = 2.5\log \dfrac{I_0}{I}$, where I_0 is the intensity of the star Vega, and I is the intensity of the celestial object, relative to Vega. What is the moon's intensity, relative to the intensity of Vega?

24. Using the formula given in the previous question, find the apparent magnitude of Jupiter (at its brightest) if it has an intensity that is 15.8 times that of Vega.

25. Two earthquakes registered 4.3 and 6.8, respectively, on the Richter scale. By what factor is the stronger earthquake greater than the weaker one?

26. Two earthquakes registered 5.2 and 9.4, respectively, on the Richter scale. By what factor is the stronger earthquake greater than the weaker one?

27. Find the [H+] concentration of the following substances (express your answer in scientific notation, accurate to 3 significant figures):
   a. Zinc hydroxide with a pH = 8.88
   b. Lactic acid with a pH = 3.51

28. Find the [H+] concentration of the following substances (express your answer in scientific notation, accurate to 3 significant figures):
   a. Boric acid with a pH = 6.12
   b. Calcium hydroxide with a pH = 11.27

29. Estimate the percent of a drug with an absorption rate of 6.2% that remains unabsorbed after 24 hours.

30. Estimate the percent of a drug with an absorption rate of 4.5% that remains unabsorbed after 8.2 hours.

The radiation dose measured through bone is: $D(x) = D_0 e^{-ux}$, where $D(x)$ is the dose at depth x, u is the dose attenuation factor, x is the bone depth measured in mm, and D_0 is the dose at the bone surface.

31. If $u = 0.257$, at what bone depth, x, would you expect the dose to be half of that as at the surface?

32. If the bone depth is 3 mm, at what dose attenuation factor, u, would you expect the dose to be 25% of that as at the surface?

9 | Review Exercises

Answers to odd-numbered problems are available at the end of the textbook.

Simplify the following and express the answer with a positive exponent:

1. a. $(-x)^2 \cdot (x)^{-4}$ b. $(-x)^3 \cdot (x)^4$

2. a. $(-x)^3 \cdot (x)^{-6}$ b. $x^3 \cdot (-x)^4$

3. a. $\dfrac{x^8}{x^4}$ b. $\dfrac{x^{-6}}{x^{-4}}$

4. a. $\dfrac{x^7}{x^5}$ b. $\dfrac{x^{-2}}{x^{-3}}$

5. a. $\left(\dfrac{x}{y}\right)^{-\frac{1}{2}}$ b. $\sqrt[3]{x^6}$

6. a. $\left(\dfrac{1}{x}\right)^{-\frac{2}{3}}$ b. $\sqrt[5]{x^{10}}$

7. a. $\dfrac{x^9}{x^5 \cdot x^2}$ b. $\dfrac{x^{-4}}{x^5 \cdot x^{-9}}$

8. a. $\dfrac{x^4 \cdot x^2}{x^3}$ b. $\dfrac{x^{-5}}{x^4 \cdot x^{-3}}$

9. a. $(x^4)(3x^3)$ b. $\dfrac{x^6}{x^2}$

10. a. $(x^3)(2x^5)$ b. $\dfrac{x^9}{x^6}$

11. a. $\left(\dfrac{x^2}{y}\right)^3 \left(\dfrac{x}{2y^2}\right)^2$ b. $\dfrac{2x^{-5}y^6}{x^3 2y^{-4}}$

12. a. $\left(\dfrac{2x^2}{y}\right)^2 \left(\dfrac{3x}{y^2}\right)^3$ b. $\dfrac{12x^{-5}y^2}{6x6y^{-8}}$

13. a. $\left(\dfrac{3x^3}{2y^2}\right)^3$ b. $\left(\dfrac{x^7}{y^0}\right)^2$

14. a. $\left(\dfrac{3x^2}{2y^3}\right)^2$ b. $\left(\dfrac{x^0}{y^3}\right)^3$

15. a. $(8x^6)^{\frac{1}{3}}$ b. $\left(\dfrac{3x^{-2}y^7}{6x^3y^{-5}}\right)^{-2}$

16. a. $(4x^8)^{\frac{1}{2}}$ b. $\left(\dfrac{6x^{-3}y^4}{2xy^{-2}}\right)^{-3}$

Graph the following functions using a table of values.

17. a. $y = 5^x$ b. $y = 0.25^x$

18. a. $y = 3^x$ b. $y = 0.5^x$

19. a. $y = 2.8^{-x}$ b. $y = 9^{-x}$

20. a. $y = 4^{-x}$ b. $y = 7.5^{-x}$

Solve for the unknown and express the answer to 2 decimal places:

21. a. $2{,}060 = 1{,}225(1.02)^n$ b. $5{,}215 = (1.005)^n + 600$

22. a. $6{,}075 = 4{,}150(1.03)^n$ b. $4{,}815 = (1.04)^n + 900$

23. a. $2{,}187 = 3^n$ b. $1{,}000 = 7^n - 1{,}401$

24. a. $15{,}625 = 5^n$ b. $6{,}000 = 3^n - 561$

25. a. $n = \log_{12} 2{,}775$ b. $n = \log_{1.05} 2$

26. a. $n = \log_8 500$ b. $n = \log_{1.02} 3$

27. $\log(2x + 5) = 2$

28. $2\ln(x + 1) = 3$

29. $4\log(2x) - 3\log(3x) = 1.5$

30. $5\log(2x) - 2(\log 5x^2) = 0.25$

31. $\ln(4x) - 1 = \ln(2x - 1)$

32. $\ln(3x + 2) - 2 = \ln(x - 4)$

Graph the following functions using a table of values.

33. a. $y = \log_3(x)$ b. $y = \log(2x)$

34. a. $y = \log_5(4x)$ b. $y = \ln(x)$

Solve the following exponential word problems.

35. A research student finds that the growth rate of a certain bacterium doubles every 4 hours. If the initial culture had 500 bacteria, how many bacteria will there be in 28 hours?

36. At the end of each year, the population of a certain town is 3% greater than it was at the beginning of the year. If the population was 4,000 in the year 2017, what will its population be in the year 2025?

37. A sample of uranium-235 that initially was 200 g has decayed to 50% of its original mass in 50 years. At this rate, how long will it take (in total) to decay to 1% of its original mass?

38. The half-life for iodine-81 is 8 days. How long does it take 50 g of iodine-81 to become 5% of its original mass?

39. A microbiologist finds that the growth rate of a bacterium doubles every 2.3 hours. If the initial culture had 8 bacteria, how many bacteria will there be in 10 hours?

40. A microbiologist finds that the growth rate of a bacterium doubles every 2.8 hours. If the initial culture had 12 bacteria, how many bacteria will there be in 16 hours?

Solve the following logarithmic word problems.

41. a. Find the [H+] concentration of saliva, where pH = 6.5 (express your answer in scientific notation, accurate to 3 significant figures).

     b. Find the pH of gastric acid, where the [H+] concentration = 0.143.

42. a. Find the [H+] concentration of blood, where pH = 7.5 (express your answer in scientific notation, accurate to 3 significant figures).

     b. Find the pH of antacids, where the [H+] concentration $= 1.0 \times 10^{-9}$.

43. Two earthquakes register 7.2 and 8.9 on the Richter scale. How much more intense is the stronger earthquake than the weaker one?

44. An earthquake registers an intensity that is 10,532 times the threshold intensity. What would be its Richter scale magnitude?

45. An amplifier receives a 7μW signal and amplifies it to 4.89mW. What is the decibel gain?

46. An amplifier has an output of 1,200 mW with an input of 80 mW. What is the decibel gain?

47. A healing law for skin wounds states that $A = A_0 e^{-0.1t}$, where A is the number of cm^2 of unhealed skin after t days when the original area of the wound was A_0.

     a. Estimate the area of a 5.6 cm^2 wound after 5 days.

     b. How many days does it take for half of the wound to heal?

48. At a coffee shop, a cup of coffee was observed to cool at the following rate: $T(t) = 24.5 + 68e^{-0.0426t}$, where t is the time in minutes, and T is the temperature in °C.

     a. After how many minutes is the temperature at 70°C?

     b. How long does it take for the coffee to lose half of its temperature?

49. A piece of art supposedly painted by Vermeer (1632-1675) contains 99.5% of its carbon-14 (which has a half-life of 5,370 years). From this information, decide whether the painting is a fake.

50. A piece of art supposedly painted by Rembrandt (1606-1669) contains 95.6% of its carbon-14 (which has a half-life of 5,370 years). From this information, decide whether the painting is a fake.

9 | Self-Test Exercises

Answers to all problems are available at the end of the textbook.

Simplify the following and express the answer with a positive exponent:

1. a. $(-x)^3(-x)^4$ b. $(x^0 y^4)^5 (-y)^{-2}$

2. a. $\dfrac{(-x)^5}{(-x)^2}$ b. $\dfrac{(-x)^5(-x)^{-3}}{(-x)^{-4}}$

3. a. $(x^{-6})^{\frac{1}{3}}$ b. $\dfrac{x^{-3} \cdot x^{-4}}{x^2}$

4. a. $\sqrt[4]{x^8}$ b. $\dfrac{(x^{-5} \cdot x^2)^{-3}}{(x^{-2})^4}$

Simplify the following and express the answer with a positive exponent:

5. a. $(3x^3)^2$

   b. $(4x^2 y^3)^2$

6. a. $(16x^0 y^4)^{\frac{1}{2}}$

   b. $(-2x^{-2} y^{-4})^{-1} (2x^{-2})^2$

7. a. $\left(\dfrac{x^6}{x^2}\right)^{-\frac{1}{2}}$

   b. $(x^{-3}y)^2$

8. a. $\dfrac{x^{-5}x^{-3}}{x^{-10}}$

   b. $(x^4 y^4) (-2x^{-3}y)(2x^2)^{-2}$

Graph the following functions using a table of values.

9. a. $y = 5^x$ b. $y = 0.2^x$

10. a. $y = 2^{-x}$ b. $y = e^{-x}$

Solve and graph the following exponential word problems.

11. The growth rate of a certain algae doubles every 45 minutes. If the initial culture had 8 organisms, how many algae will there be in 7 hours?

12. A sample of 100 g uranium-235 has a half-life of 100 years. How long until the uranium has decayed to 20% of its original mass?

Solve for 'n' and express the answer to 2 decimal places:

13. a. $n = \log_3 5{,}000$ b. $n = \log_{1.5} 1{,}250$

14. a. $460 = 240(1.05)^n$ b. $750 = (1.05)^n + 600$

Graph the following functions using a table of values.

15. a. $y = \log_6(3x)$ b. $y = \log(10x)$

16. a. $y = [\log_2(5x + 0.5)]$ b. $y = [\log_2(x)] - 6$

Solve for 'x' and express the answer to 2 decimal places.

17. $\log\left(\dfrac{x}{4}\right) = 5$

18. $\log(x + 4) - \log x = 1.2$

19. $\ln 4 + \ln x = \ln(x - 1)$

20. $\ln\left(\dfrac{5}{x+1}\right) = 1$

Solve the following logarithmic word problems.

21. The pH of freshly-squeezed orange juice is approximately 3.6. Freshly-squeezed lemon juice, on the other hand, is approximately 40 times more acidic than orange juice. Using this information, find the pH of freshly-squeezed lemon juice.

22. An earthquake registers an intensity that is 7,902 times the threshold intensity. What would be its Richter scale magnitude?

23. Two sounds have decibel levels of 30 and 60, respectively. What is the ratio of the sound intensities?

24. Estimate the percent of a drug with an absorption rate of 5.5% that remains unabsorbed after 16 hours.

25. The radiation dose measured through bone is $D(x) = D_0 e^{-ux}$, where $D(x)$ is the dose at depth x, $u = 0.257$ is the dose attenuation factor, x is the bone depth measured in mm, and D_0 is the dose at the bone surface. At what bone depth, x, would you expect the dose to be one-third of that as at the surface?

The signal ratio in decibels of a system is modeled by the formula $S = 10 \log\left(\dfrac{P_o}{P_i}\right)$, where P_i and P_o are the input power and output power, respectively.

26. Find the signal ratio of a medical machine's electronic system if the input power is 15 mW and the output power is 20 mW.

27. What input power (in kW) is needed to produce 2750 kW of output power with an amplifier having a 3.25 dB gain?

28. If an amplifier loses 12 dB with an input of 70 W, what is the output power (in W)?

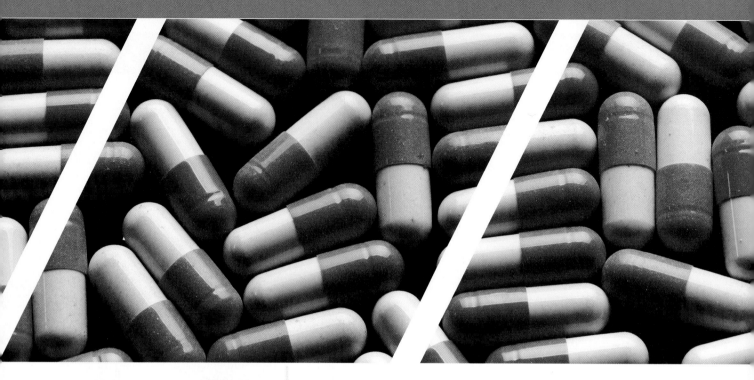

10

DOSAGE CALCULATIONS AND MEDICATION ADMINISTRATION

LEARNING OBJECTIVES

- Describe the "Six Rights" of safe medication administration.
- Interpret information found on drug labels and on drug orders.
- Calculate doses of oral medication, both in solid and liquid form.
- Calculate doses based on body weight and body surface area.
- Identify various types of syringes, and interpret the calibrations on syringes of various sizes.
- Calculate doses of parenteral medication administered via intramuscular and subcutaneous routes, both in liquid and powder form.
- Calculate doses of parenteral medication administered via intravenous routes, for both replacement/maintenance of fluids and piggyback drug infusions.

CHAPTER OUTLINE

Introduction

We conclude our study of mathematics for the health sciences by looking at some direct applications of some of the mathematics we have learned in the previous 9 chapters: dosage calculations and administration of medications. This chapter will rely heavily on the material learned in the chapters that examined ratios, proportions and percents, units of measurement, and solving algebraic equations, and provide some specific context for these concepts in the fields of nursing and pharmacy.

Note: *This is **not** intended to be a medical textbook, and is only designed to provide students who wish to pursue careers in the health sciences with an introduction and overview of the core concepts in the field.*

10.1 | Medication Administration

The Six 'Rights' of Medication Administration

The safety of the patient is always the primary concern when administering any type of medication. While calculating the correct dosage is vital, ensuring the safety of the patient goes beyond simply making the correct dosage calculations. The **six 'rights' of medication administration** outline six critical checks which must be made before administering a drug to a patient, in any circumstance. The six rights are listed as follows:

1. Right drug
2. Right dosage
3. Right route
4. Right time
5. Right patient
6. Right documentation

Right Drug

While this may seem obvious, it is crucial to always ensure that the patient is receiving the **right drug**.

In Canada, drugs are regulated as per Canada's Food and Drugs Act. This act outlines the proper manufacturing, labeling, and selling procedures of drugs in Canada. Since many drugs sold in Canada are manufactured outside of Canada (e.g., the US), it also outlines the proper trade standards that incoming drugs must be held to.

Drugs have two different names: the **generic name** and the **trade/brand name**. The generic name is the official, medical name of the drug, while the trade name is the name given to the drug by a pharmaceutical company who sells it. A trade name is often recognizable as it will be followed by a trademark or registered trademark symbol: ™ or ®.

Since many companies can sell the same drug, a drug can have multiple trade names. However, it can have only one generic name. For example, Advil and Motrin (trade names) are both Ibuprofen (generic name). The generic name of the drug is always given on a drug label.

Right Dosage

In this chapter, we will learn the proper procedures for calculating the **right dosage** for various types of drugs which are administered in various ways. Precision is incredibly important when calculating the right dosage; for example, mistaking mcg (micrograms) for mg (milligrams) when administering drugs can result in a thousand-fold overdose!

A drug label (or accompanying insert) will always contain the following dosage information:

- Dosage strength: the amount of drug per a specific unit of measurement.

- Standard adult dosage: the recommended dosage amount/range for an average adult.

- Safe dosage range: the maximum safe dosage amount for a given time frame for an average adult.

For example, a drug label may state that an average adult can take 1-2 tablets, each containing 200 mg of a drug, every 4-6 hours, but not exceed 6 tablets per 24 hours. Here, the dosage strength is 200 mg/tablet, the standard adult dosage is 1-2 tablets every 4-6 hours, and the safe dosage range is a maximum of 6 tablets in 24 hours.

Right Route

The route of a medication refers to how the drug is administered to the body of the patient and the method of drug delivery. There are many routes that a drug may enter the body; it is important to ensure that the drug is administered using the **right route**. In this chapter, we will learn dosage calculations for drugs administered orally and through injection. These routes (and more) are categorized in the following exhibit:

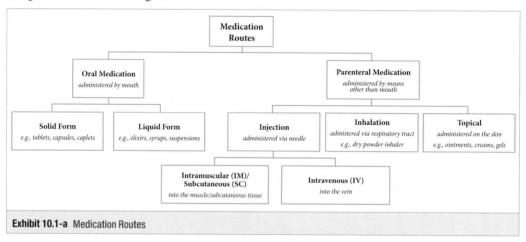

Exhibit 10.1-a Medication Routes

Note: Exhibit 10.1-a is not an exhaustive list of medication routes. Other routes include:

- *epidural injection: administered via needle into lower spine (e.g., during childbirth)*

- *intradermal injection: administered via needle beneath the skin (e.g., for allergy tests)*

- *transdermal: administered via patch on skin (e.g., nicotine patch)*

- *solution/ointment: administered to eyes, ears, nose, or mouth (e.g., antibiotic eye/ear drops)*

- *suppository: administered into body cavity*

Right Time

The **right time** to administer a drug can be presented in a couple of ways:

- **How many times:** i.e., once a day, twice a day, three times a day, four times a day, etc.

- **How frequently:** i.e., every four hours, every six hours, every eight hours, every twelve hours, etc.

If a medication is prescribed on a times-per-day basis, then there is more leniency on when the medication can be taken. For example, if a patient is prescribed to take a capsule four times a day, she may do so when she wakes up, at lunch, at dinner, and before she goes to bed.

If a medication is prescribed at a specific frequency, it must be taken in precise time intervals, regardless of whether the patient is sleeping, etc. For example, if a patient must receive medication via intravenous every six hours starting at 0900 h, then she must receive it at 0900 h, 1500 h, 2100 h, and 0300 h.

Therefore, while four times a day and every six hours may seem like the same thing, they actually have different meanings. 'Every six hours' is four times a day, but 'four times a day' is not necessarily every six hours.

Note: Military time (as discussed in Chapter 6) is used when specifying the right time to administer drugs, to ensure there cannot be confusion between AM and PM times.

Right Patient

Before administering a drug, it is critical to ensure that the drug is being administered to the **right patient**. In hospitals, patients wear electronic bracelets that can be scanned by doctors, nurses, etc. to obtain their medical information, as seen in Exhibit 10.1-b.

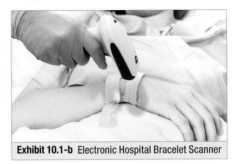

Exhibit 10.1-b Electronic Hospital Bracelet Scanner

Right Documentation

In order to be administered, all medication must have the **right documentation**, outlining all information on how to safely prepare, administer, and store the medication. In addition to this, documentation must also include the expiration date, as well as any side effects of the medication that the patient may experience.

The right documentation for a drug is either located on the drug label or on a package insert inside the drug packaging. It is very important that any documentation for a prepared prescription is written carefully, so that it is accurate and legible.

If a medication does not include the right documentation, it *cannot* be administered to a patient.

Drug Labels

It is necessary to be able to properly identify drug and dosage information from a prescription drug label in order to administer medication to patients. While all drug labels are required to include certain documentation, they can look different, and so it is important to know what information to look for. In this section, we will practice identifying key information from a drug label. This information can include the following:

1. Trade name
2. Generic name
3. Unique drug code number
4. Form of the drug
5. Dosage strength
6. Standard adult dosage
7. Storage directions
8. Expiration date

Drugs are labeled with a unique drug code number. In Canada, this is an 8-digit **Drug Identification Number (DIN)**. In the US, this is a 10-digit **National Drug Code (NDC)** number.

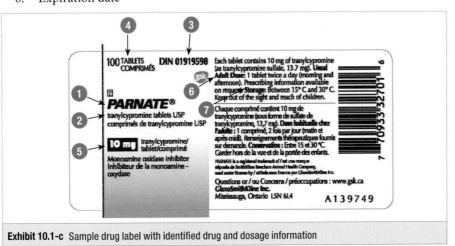

Exhibit 10.1-c Sample drug label with identified drug and dosage information

Example 10.1-a   **Identifying Drug Labels**

Identify the following information on the drug label below:

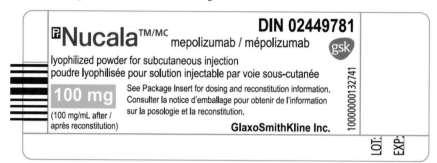

(i) Trade name	(ii) Generic name	(iii) Drug Identification Number (DIN)
(iv) Form of drug	(v) Dosage strength	(vi) Standard adult dosage

Solution

(i)   Trade name: Nucala

(ii)   Generic name: mepolizumab

(iii)   Drug Identification Number (DIN): 02449781

(iv)   Form of drug: Iyophilized powder for subcutaneous injection

(v)   Dosage strength: 100 mg/mL after reconstitution

(vi)   Standard adult dosage: see package insert

Note: In the previous example, the drug label did not include the standard adult dosage. When full dosage information is not given on the label, it is always included in the package insert.

Example 10.1-b   **Identifying Drug Labels**

Identify the following information on the drug label below:

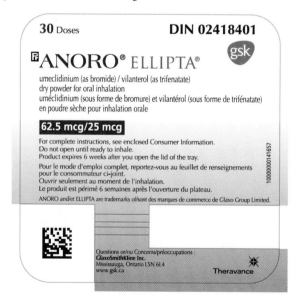

(i) Trade name	(ii) Generic name	(iii) Drug Identification Number (DIN)
(iv) Form of drug	(v) Dosage strength	(vi) Standard adult dosage
(vii) Expiration date		

Solution

(i) Trade name: Anoro Ellipta

(ii) Generic name: umeclidinium / vilanterol

(iii) Drug Identification Number (DIN): 02418401

(iv) Form of drug: dry powder for oral inhalation

(v) Dosage strength: 62.5 mcg / 25 mcg per dose

(vi) Standard adult dosage: see enclosed consumer information

(vii) Expiration date: product expires 6 weeks after you open the lid of the tray

> It is common to express the dosage strength of a medication containing more than one drug using a slash '/', as seen on the drug label.
>
> Here, each dose of the medication contains 62.5 mcg of umeclidinium and 25 mcg of vilanterol.

Abbreviations for Drug Orders

Physicians are very busy people. As such, they have developed an extensive shorthand system to save time when writing drug orders, consisting of abbreviations for medication routes, frequencies, dosages, and more.

It is necessary to be able to read and interpret these abbreviations properly when administering drugs to a patient. Although the abbreviations may be similar, they can have vastly different meanings, and there is no room for error when it comes to the safety of a patient. For example, mistaking 'q.o.d.' (every other day) for 'q.i.d.' (four times a day) could have dire consequences.

Some common abbreviations are outlined in the following four tables:

Table 10.1-a Route Abbreviations

Route	
Abbreviation	Meaning
p.o.	By mouth (orally)
n.p.o.	Nothing by mouth
ID	Intradermal
IM	Intramuscular
IV	Intravenous
IVP	Intravenous push
IVPB	Intravenous piggyback
SC	Subcutaneous
INH	Inhalation
p.r.	By rectum
supp	Suppository

Table 10.1-b Frequency Abbreviations

Frequency	
Abbreviation	Meaning
a.c.	before meal
p.c.	after meal
h.s.	at bedtime
q.d.	every day
q.o.d.	every other day
b.i.d.	2 times a day
t.i.d.	3 times a day
q.i.d.	4 times a day
q.x.h.	every x hours (e.g., q.4.h. = every 4 hours)
p.r.n. (p.r.n. pain)	as needed (as needed for pain)
stat	immediately

Recall:
q.12.h. ≠ b.i.d.

Table 10.1-c	Dosage Abbreviations

Dosage	
Abbreviation	Meaning
cap	capsule
tab	tablet
gtt	drop
mcg	microgram
mg	milligram
mL	millilitre
t, or tsp	teaspoon
T, or tbsp	tablespoon

Microgams are abbreviated to mcg instead of µg in medication administration, to avoid confusion and misidentification.

Table 10.1-d	General Abbreviations

General	
Abbreviation	Meaning
D5W	5% dextrose solution
NaCl	sodium chloride
NS	normal saline
n.k.a.	no known allergy

Note: Some of these abbreviations, such as q.d. and q.o.d., are often no longer used in hospitals, as they were too often mistaken for other abbreviations. Instead, the words are now to be written out in full.

p.r.n. (As Needed)

Typically, when a p.r.n. order is given, it is also accompanied by a q.x.h. order which will provide the maximum dosage guidelines. In other words, q.4.h. p.r.n. pain means "take every four hours, or as needed for pain," which should be interpreted as "take only as needed for pain, but no more frequently than every four hours." This is a common practice when prescribing pain medications to help patients slowly wean themselves off the medication as the pain subsides, to avoid creating a dependency.

Interpreting Drug Orders

When a drug order is given, it is usually presented in the following format:

Drug name, Dosage amount, Route, Frequency

For example, consider the following drug order:

Amoxil   250 mg   p.o.   t.i.d.

Drug name   Dosage amount   Route   Frequency

- Drug name: Amoxil

- Dosage amount: 250 mg = 250 milligrams

- Route: p.o. = 'orally' or 'by mouth'

- Frequency: t.i.d. = three times a day

Therefore, the order is 250 mg of Amoxil to be taken by mouth, three times a day.

Example 10.1-c | **Interpreting Drug Orders**

Fully interpret the following drug orders:

(i)   Insulin (U-40) 5 gtt SC q.i.d.

(ii)   Epinephrine 0.5 mg IM stat.

(iii) D5W 1,000 mL IV q.6.h.

(iv)   Naproxen 500 mg p.o. b.i.d. p.r.n. pain.

Solution

(i)   Insulin (U-40) 5 gtt SC q.i.d.

- Drug name: U-40 Insulin
- Dosage amount: 5 gtt = 5 drops
- Route: SC = subcutaneously
- Frequency: q.i.d. = four times a day

Therefore, the order is five drops of U-40 insulin to be administered subcutaneously, four times a day.

(ii)   Epinephrine 0.5 mg IM stat.

- Drug name: Epinephrine
- Dosage amount: 0.5 mg = 0.5 milligrams
- Route: IM = intramuscularly
- Frequency: stat = immediately

Therefore, the order is 0.5 mg of Epinephrine to be administered intramuscularly, immediately.

(iii) D5W 1,000 mL IV q.6.h.

- Drug name: D5W = 5% dextrose solution
- Dosage amount: 1,000 mL = 1,000 millilitres
- Route: IV = intravenously
- Frequency: q.6.h. = every six hours

Therefore, the order is 1,000 mL of 5% dextrose solution to be administered intravenously, every six hours.

(iv)   Naproxen 500 mg p.o. b.i.d. p.r.n. pain.

- Drug name: Naproxen
- Dosage amount: 500 mg = 500 milligrams
- Route: p.o. = 'orally' or 'by mouth'
- Frequency: b.i.d. p.r.n. pain = twice a day, as needed for pain

Therefore, the order is 500 mg of Naproxen to be administered orally, as needed for pain, but no more frequently than twice a day.

10.1 | Exercises

For Problems 1 to 8, identify the following pieces of information on the drug labels, as applicable:

(i)	Trade name	(ii)	Generic name	(iii)	Drug Identification Number (DIN)
(iv)	Form of drug	(v)	Dosage strength	(vi)	Standard adult dosage
(vii)	Storage directions	(viii)	Expiration date		

Note: not all pieces of information will appear on all drug labels.

1.

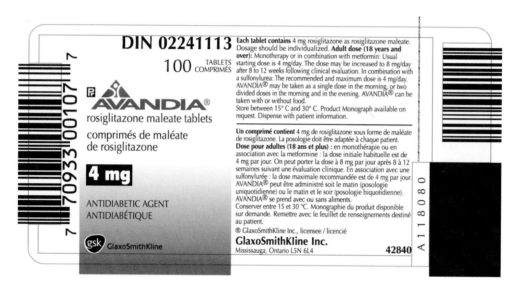

DIN 02241113

100 TABLETS COMPRIMÉS

AVANDIA®
rosiglitazone maleate tablets
comprimés de maléate de rosiglitazone

4 mg

ANTIDIABETIC AGENT
ANTIDIABÉTIQUE

gsk GlaxoSmithKline

Each tablet contains 4 mg rosiglitazone as rosiglitazone maleate. Dosage should be individualized. **Adult dose (18 years and over):** Monotherapy or in combination with metformin: Usual starting dose is 4 mg/day. The dose may be increased to 8 mg/day after 8 to 12 weeks following clinical evaluation. In combination with a sulfonylurea: The recommended and maximum dose is 4 mg/day. AVANDIA® may be taken as a single dose in the morning, or two divided doses in the morning and in the evening. AVANDIA® can be taken with or without food. Store between 15° C and 30° C. Product Monograph available on request. Dispense with patient information.

Un comprimé contient 4 mg de rosiglitazone sous forme de maléate de rosiglitazone. La posologie doit être adaptée à chaque patient. **Dose pour adultes (18 ans et plus) :** en monothérapie ou en association avec la metformine : la dose initiale habituelle est de 4 mg par jour. On peut porter la dose à 8 mg par jour après 8 à 12 semaines suivant une évaluation clinique. En association avec une sulfonylurée : la dose maximale recommandée est de 4 mg par jour. AVANDIA® peut être administré soit le matin (posologie uniquotidienne) ou le matin et le soir (posologie biquotidienne). AVANDIA® se prend avec ou sans aliments. Conserver entre 15 et 30 °C. Monographie du produit disponible sur demande. Remettre avec le feuillet de renseignements destiné au patient.

® GlaxoSmithKline Inc., licensee / licencié

GlaxoSmithKline Inc.
Mississauga, Ontario L5N 6L4   42840

A118080

2.

30 CAPSULES   DIN 02372010

gsk

®Jalyn®

dutasteride / tamsulosin hydrochloride modified release capsules

capsules de dutastéride/chlorhydrate de tamsulosine à libération modifiée

0.5 mg / 0.4 mg

Type I and II 5-Alpha-reductase Inhibitor and Alpha₁-adrenoreceptor Antagonist

Inhibiteur de la 5 alpha-réductase des types I et II et antagoniste des récepteurs alpha₁-adrénergiques

Each capsule contains 0.5 mg dutasteride and 0.4 mg tamsulosin hydrochloride. **DOSAGE: Adult Males:** One capsule taken orally once daily, approximately 30 minutes after the same meal each day. **Not for use in women and children. Do not handle JALYN® if you are or may become pregnant. DIRECTIONS FOR USE:** Swallow whole. Do not chew. Do not store above 30° C. Pharmacist: Dispense with leaflet. Product Monograph available on request.

Chaque capsule renferme 0,5 mg de dutastéride et 0,4 mg de chlorhydrate de tamsulosine. **POSOLOGIE : Hommes adultes :** une capsule par voie orale une fois par jour, environ 30 minutes après le même repas chaque jour. **Ne pas employer chez les femmes ni chez les enfants. Ne pas manipuler les capsules JALYN® si vous êtes enceinte ou susceptible de l'être. MODE D'EMPLOI :** Avaler en entier. Ne pas croquer. Ne pas conserver à une température supérieure à 30 °C. **Pharmacien :** Veuillez remettre avec le feuillet de renseignements. Monographie du produit fournie sur demande.

JALYN is a registered trademark of / est une marque déposée de Glaxo Group Limited, used under license by / utilisée sous licence par GlaxoSmithKline Inc.

GlaxoSmithKline Inc.
Mississauga, Ontario L5N 6L4

A430166

LOT:
EXP:

3.

Ouvrir en appuyant sur le bouchon et en tournant. Refermer hermétiquement.

AGITER DOUCEMENT AVANT L'EMPLOI.

Chaque cuillerée à thé (5 mL) contient 750 mg d'atovaquone.

Dose habituelle :
Consulter la notice de conditionnement pour obtenir de l'information complète sur l'indication et la posologie.

POSOLOGIE CHEZ L'ADULTE : Pneumonie à *Pneumocystis carinii* : 750 mg (5 mL) administrés avec des aliments 2 fois par jour ou 1 500 mg (10 mL) administrés avec des aliments 1 fois par jour si un seul repas est pris par jour. Prendre ce médicament pendant 21 jours.

L'innocuité et l'efficacité chez les enfants n'ont pas été établies.

Pharmacien : Remettre avec le feuillet de renseignements destinés aux patients.

Monographie de produit fournie sur demande.

Conserver à la température ambiante (de 15 °C à 25 °C) et à l'abri de la lumière. NE PAS CONGELER.

Questions ou préoccupations : www.gsk.ca

MEPRON est une marque déposée de Glaxo Group Limited, utilisée sous licence par GlaxoSmithKline Inc.

210 mL   DIN 02217422

gsk

®Mepron®

atovaquone oral suspension, USP
suspension orale d'atovaquone, USP

750 mg / 5 mL

ANTIPROTOZOAL
AGENT ANTIPROTOZOAIRE

To open, push down on cap and turn. Close tightly.
SHAKE GENTLY BEFORE USING.

Each teaspoonful (5 mL) contains 750 mg of atovaquone.

Usual dose:
For complete information on indication and dosing, please see Package Insert.

ADULT DOSAGE: *Pneumocystis carinii* pneumonia: 750 mg (5 mL) administered with food twice a day or 1500 mg (10 mL) administered with food once daily if you eat only one meal a day. Take this medicine for 21 days.

Safety and efficacy in children has not been established.

Pharmacist: Dispense with patient medication information (leaflet).

Product Monograph available on request.

Store at room temperature (15° C – 25° C). Protect from light. DO NOT FREEZE.

Questions or concerns: www.gsk.ca

MEPRON is a registered trademark of Glaxo Group Limited, used under license by GlaxoSmithKline Inc.

GlaxoSmithKline Inc.
Mississauga, Ontario L5N 6L4   A144345

4.

Benlysta®
belimumab
lyophilized powder for intravenous infusion
poudre lyophilisée pour perfusion intraveineuse
120 mg
(80 mg/mL after/après reconstitution)

DIN 02370050

10000000140262

For dosing and recommended use, see insert.
Pour la posologie et l'utilisation recommandée,
voir la notice.
GlaxoSmithKline Inc.
Mississauga, Ontario L5N 6L4

LOT:
EXP:

5.

1 x 38.5 µg (mcg) in a single-use vial
1 x 10 mL I.V. Solution Stabilizer in a single-use vial

DIN 02450283

AMGEN®

 **BLINCYTO™**
blinatumomab

38.5
µg (mcg)

For intravenous infusion only
BLINCYTO™: 38.5 µg (mcg) in 1 single-use vial of lyophilized powder for solution for infusion
Intravenous Solution Stabilizer: 1 single-use vial of solution
Store at 2° to 8°C. Protect from light. DO NOT SHAKE reconstituted solution.
Sterile – No Preservative
Amgen Canada Inc., Mississauga, ON L5N 0A4

6.

1 x 0.6 mL Single Use Prefilled Syringe

DIN 02249790

AMGEN®

Neulasta®
pegfilgrastim

A Pegylated Recombinant Human Granulocyte Colony-Stimulating Factor (PEG-r-metHuG-CSF) derived from *E. coli*

6 mg

10 mg/mL
Sterile Solution - No Preservative
For Subcutaneous Use Only
Each 0.6 mL prefilled syringe contains: 6 mg pegfilgrastim in a sterile, preservative-free solution (pH 4.0)
containing acetate (0.35 mg), sorbitol (30.0 mg), polysorbate 20 (0.004%), and sodium (0.021 mg) in
Water for Injection, USP.
Refrigerate at 2° to 8°C. Do Not Freeze or Shake. Protect from Light.

7.

DIN 00578576

Stieva-A® **0.025%**

tretinoin cream USP
crème de trétinoïne USP

Cream / Crème

25 g

Topical acne
therapy

Traitement
topique de l'acné

$\mathfrak{M}$ Stiefel

Medicinal Ingredient: Tretinoin USP 0.025% w/w.
Dosage: Once daily before bedtime. Thoroughly cleanse and dry area to be treated. Apply cream thinly with a gentle rubbing motion.
See package insert. Product Monograph available on request.
FOR EXTERNAL USE ONLY.
Store between 15° C and 30° C. Do not freeze. Keep out of the sight and reach of children.
STIEVA-A is a registered trademark of GlaxoSmithKline Inc.

Ingrédient médicinal : Trétinoïne USP à 0,025 % p/p.
Posologie : Utiliser une fois par jour au coucher. Bien nettoyer et sécher la zone à traiter. Appliquer une mince couche de crème en
massant doucement. Voir la notice d'emballage. Monographie du produit fournie sur demande.
POUR USAGE EXTERNE SEULEMENT.
Conserver entre 15 et 30 °C. Ne pas congeler. Garder hors de la vue et de la portée des enfants.
STIEVA-A est une marque déposée de GlaxoSmithKline Inc.

Mfd. by / Fabr. par :
GlaxoSmithKline Inc.
Mississauga, Ontario L5N 6L4

www.stiefel.ca

8.

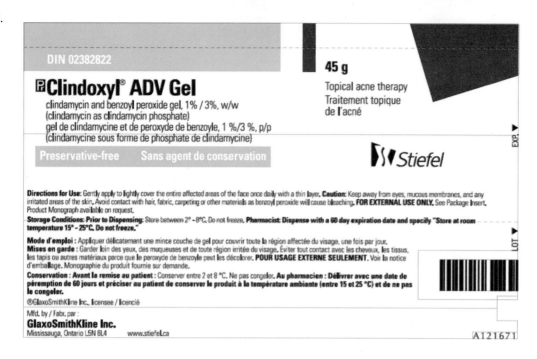

For Problems 9 to 20, fully interpret the given drug orders.

9.   Demerol 100 mg SC q.3.h. p.r.n. pain.

10. Morphine Sulfate 10 mg IM q.4.h. p.r.n. pain.

11. Synthroid 125 mcg p.o. q.d.

12. Levothyroxin 75 mcg p.o. q.o.d.

13. Gentamicin 175 mg IM b.i.d.

14. Amoxicillin 500 mg p.o. q.8.h.

15. Codeine 15 mg p.o. q.4.h. p.r.n. pain.

16. Ketorolac Tromethamine 15 mg IM q.6.h. p.r.n. pain.

17. Ancef 300 mg IV q.8.h.

18. Teriparatide 20 mcg SC q.d.

19. Hydrocortisone 1% cream q.i.d. p.r.n. affected area

20. Albuterol 2.5 mg INH t.i.d.-q.i.d.

10.2 | Oral Medication Administration

In this section, we will discuss how to administer oral medication that is in solid form and liquid form.

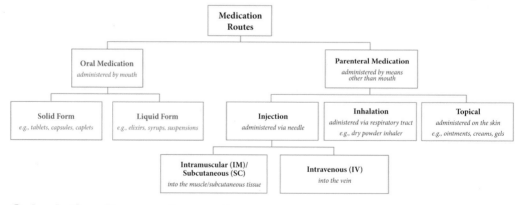

Calculating Dosage Amounts

In general, regardless of the form of medication, the proper dosage amount is calculated using the following formula:

Formula 10.2 — Dosage Amount

$$\text{Amount of Medication Given } (X) = \text{Dosage Ordered } (D) \times \frac{\text{Quantity } (Q)}{\text{Strength on Hand } (H)}$$

Hence, $X = D \times \dfrac{Q}{H}$, where,

- D, *Dosage Ordered*, is the **amount of drug prescribed or ordered** by the physician to be administered to the patient;

- H, *Strength on Hand,* is the available **strength of one dose** of the drug to be administered to the patient; and

- Q, *Quantity*, is the available **form of one dose** of the drug.

Oral Medication in Solid Form

Oral medications can come in many solid forms. The following table contains the most common:

Table 10.2 — Solid Medication Forms

Picture	Name	Description
Regular Tablet Scored Tablet	**Tablet**	Medication is compressed into a solid disk; can be scored or unscored.
	Capsule	Medication is in powder form, contained inside a hard gelatin shell.
	Gel Tab	Medication is in a liquid or gel form, contained inside a soft gelatin shell.
Scored Caplet Regular Caplet	**Caplet**	Mix between a tablet and a capsule. Medication is compressed in the shape of a capsule and coated for easy swallowing; can be scored or unscored.

Solid oral medication which is **scored** contains breakage lines to easily break the medication into smaller (e.g., half, quarter) doses. Tablets and caplets can be scored; however, capsules and gel tabs cannot be scored and can never be broken into smaller pieces, as the medication is in powder, liquid, or gel form.

*Note: Tablets and caplets which are unscored **cannot** be broken into smaller doses. Attempting to do so will result in unequal dosage amounts.*

Calculating Dosage Amounts for Oral Medication in Solid Form

Consider the following drug order: *Lamictal 200 mg p.o. b.i.d.*

We can interpret the drug order to mean "200 mg of Lamictal to be taken by mouth, twice a day." Now, we need to be able to combine this information with the dosage information given on the drug label for the ordered drug, to determine the proper amount of medication that is to be given to the patient for a single dose.

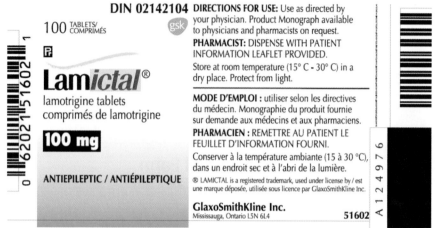

From the drug order and drug label,

> *Dosage Ordered (D)* = 200 mg (from the drug order)

> *Strength on Hand (H)* per *Quantity (Q)* = 100 mg/tablet (from the drug label)

Using Formula 10.2 and dimensional analysis (as learned in Chapter 6),

$$X = D \times \frac{Q}{H}$$

$$= 200 \text{ mg} \times \frac{1 \text{ tab}}{100 \text{ mg}}$$

$$= \frac{200}{100} \text{ tab}$$

$$= 2 \text{ tablets}$$

The dosage amount can also be calculated using proportions (as learned in Chapter 5), as follows:

$$\frac{100 \text{ mg}}{1 \text{ tab}} = \frac{200 \text{ mg}}{x \text{ tab}}$$

$$100x = 200$$

$$x = 2 \text{ tablets}$$

Therefore, a single dose of medication for the patient is two tablets.

Note: While dosage amounts can be calculated using either of these two methods, in the following examples we will be using the dimensional analysis (i.e., Formula 10.2) method.

Example 10.2-a | Determining the Dosage Amount for Oral Medication in Solid Form when the Dosage Ordered and Strength have Different Units

Determine the number of tablets that would contain a dose of 1.2 g.

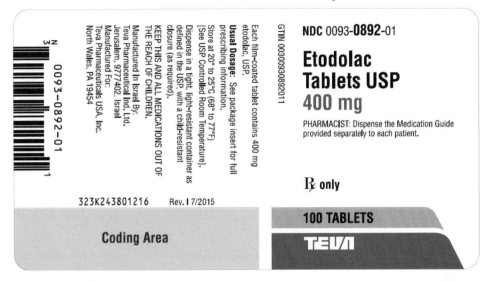

Solution

Dosage Ordered (D) = 1.2 g

Strength on Hand (H) per Quantity (Q) = 400 mg/tablet

Using Formula 10.2, $X = 1.2 \text{ g} \times \dfrac{1 \text{ tab}}{400 \text{ mg}}$

The dosage ordered and the strength of one dose of the drug are measured in different units: grams and milligrams, respectively. We need to add an additional conversion factor to our dimensional analysis to convert g to mg.

Therefore, $X = 1.2 \text{ g} \times \dfrac{1{,}000 \text{ mg}}{1 \text{ g}} \times \dfrac{1 \text{ tab}}{400 \text{ mg}}$ [1 g = 1,000 mg]

$= 1{,}200 \text{ mg} \times \dfrac{1 \text{ tab}}{400 \text{ mg}}$

$= 3 \text{ tablets}$

Therefore, three tablets contain a dose of 1.2 g.

Example 10.2-b | Determining the Dosage Amount for Oral Medication in Solid Form when a Medication Contains More than One Drug

A doctor prescribes *Percocet (oxycodone/actaminophen) 5/650 p.o. q.4.h. p.r.n. pain, 7-day supply* for a post-operative patient. The pharmacist filling the order has the following dosages on hand: 2/325, 2.5/325, 5/325.

(i)   Which tablet should the pharmacist choose to fill the order?

(ii) How many tablets should the patient take per dose?

(iii) What is the maximum number of tablets the patient should take in one day?

(iv) How many tablets should the pharmacist dispense to fill the prescription?

Solution

(i) When a medication contains more than one type of drug, the ratio of the drugs in the dosage ordered and the dosage strength on hand must always be proportional.

$$\frac{5}{650} = \frac{x}{325}$$

$$x = \frac{5 \times 325}{650} = 2.5$$

Hence, the pharmacist should use the 2.5/325 tablets to fill the prescription.

(ii) We can use either the oxycodone or acetaminophen measurements to perform this calculation (both will be shown for thoroughness, but only one calculation is necessary):

Using oxycodone measurements, $X = 5 \text{ mg} \times \dfrac{1 \text{ tab}}{2.5 \text{ mg}}$

$$= \frac{5}{2.5} \text{ tab}$$

$$= 2 \text{ tablets}$$

Using acetaminophen measurements, $X = 650 \text{ mg} \times \dfrac{1 \text{ tab}}{325 \text{ mg}}$

$$= \frac{650}{325} \text{ tab}$$

$$= 2 \text{ tablets}$$

You arrive at the same answer, regardless of which of the two drug measurements you use in your calculations.

Therefore, two 2.5/325 mg tablets of Percocet are required per dose.

(iii) To determine the maximum number of tablets the patient can take in one day, we multiply the single dose by the maximum number of doses in one day:

$$\frac{2 \text{ tab}}{1 \text{ dose}} \times \frac{1 \text{ dose}}{4 \text{ h}} \times \frac{24 \text{ h}}{1 \text{ day}}$$

$$= \frac{2 \times 24}{4} \text{ tab/day}$$

$$= 12 \text{ tablets/day}$$

Therefore, a maximum of 12 tablets can be taken in one day.

(iv) To fill the prescription, multiply the daily maximum number of tablets by the number of days prescribed:

12 tablets/day × 7 days = 84 tablets

Example 10.2-c **Determining the Dosage Amount for Oral Medication in Solid Form Required in a Day**

A physician orders *Xanax (alprazolam) 0.25 mg p.o. t.i.d.* for a patient with anxiety. The drug on hand is in the form of 0.5 mg scored tablets. Calculate the correct dosage to give the patient, and determine how many tablets the patient will receive in one day.

Solution

Using Formula 10.2, $X = 0.25 \text{ mg} \times \dfrac{1 \text{ tab}}{0.5 \text{ mg}}$

$$= \frac{0.25}{0.5} \text{ tab}$$

$$= 0.5 \text{ tablets}$$

Since the tablets are scored, it is possible for one dose to contain half a tablet. If the tablets were unscored, it would be necessary to find a drug with a smaller strength per dose.

Therefore, the patient would receive half a scored tablet per dose.

Since the medication is to be received three times a day (t.i.d.), the patient would receive 3 × 0.5 = 1.5 tablets in one day.

Oral Medication in Liquid Form

The following are the three most common types of oral medication taken in liquid form:

- **Syrup:** medication is dissolved in a thick, water-and-sugar based solution
- **Elixir:** medication is dissolved in a clear, water-and-alcohol based solution
- **Suspension:** very fine, solid particles of medication are suspended in a liquid; if left to sit, the medication particles will separate from the liquid

Calculating Dosage Amounts for Oral Medication in Liquid Form

In liquid form, the dosage strength on hand *(H)* will be presented as a number of milligrams of medication per dosage quantity *(Q)* expressed in millilitres (mg/mL). This is demonstrated in the following examples:

Example 10.2-d — Determining the Dosage Amount for Oral Medication in Liquid Form

A physician orders *Mepron 1,500 mg p.o. daily.* Read the label below to determine the number of millilitres you would administer for a single dose for the patient.

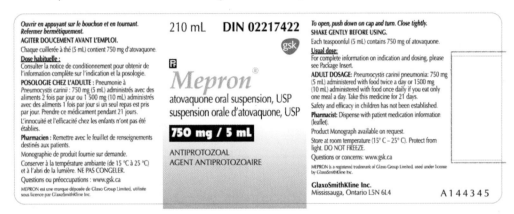

Solution

Dosage Ordered (D) = 1,500 mg

Strength on Hand (H) per *Quantity (Q)* = 750 mg/5 mL

Using Formula 10.2,
$$X = 1{,}500 \text{ mg} \times \frac{5 \text{ mL}}{750 \text{ mg}}$$

$$= \frac{1{,}500 \times 5}{750} \text{ mL}$$

$$= 10 \text{ mL}$$

Therefore, 10 mL of Mepron would be administered to the patient in a single dose.

Example 10.2-e — Determining the Dosage Amount for Oral Medication in Liquid Form

A patient with bronchitis is given a 10-day prescription for *Biaxin (clarithromycin), 375 mg p.o. q.12.h.* The pharmacist has an oral suspension of Biaxin on hand with a concentration of 250 mg/5 mL. How many mL should the pharmacist instruct the patient to take per dose, and how many mL should the pharmacist dispense to fill the prescription?

Solution

Using Formula 10.2,
$$X = 375 \text{ mg} \times \frac{5 \text{ mL}}{250 \text{ mg}}$$

$$= \frac{375 \times 5}{250} \text{ mL}$$

$$= 7.5 \text{ mL}$$

> Partial units of liquid medication can be properly measured as long as the measuring tool is precise enough.

Since the medication is to be taken every 12 hours (i.e., two doses per day) for 10 days, the total volume of medication needed to fill the prescription is calculated as follows:

$$\frac{7.5 \text{ mL}}{1 \text{ dose}} \times \frac{2 \text{ doses}}{1 \text{ day}} \times 10 \text{ days}$$

$$= 7.5 \times 2 \times 10 \text{ mL}$$

$$= 150 \text{ mL}$$

Therefore, the pharmacist should instruct the patient to take 7.5 mL per dose and must dispense 150 mL of the medication to fill the prescription.

Example 10.2-f | **Determining the Divided Dosage Amounts for Oral Medication in Liquid Form**

A physician orders the following drug order for a child with chickenpox: *Zovirax 1,600 mg p.o. daily in 4 divided doses.*

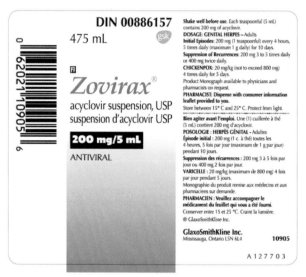

Determine the number of teaspoons of the drug you should administer per dose.

Solution

The drug order of "1,600 mg of *Zovirax* to be taken by mouth daily in four divided doses" indicates that 1,600 mg is the amount required per day, not the amount per dose.

Dosage Ordered (D) = 1,600 mg in 4 divided doses

Strength on Hand (H) per *Quantity (Q)* = 200 mg/5 mL

In order to calculate the medication administered per dose, expressed in mL, we have to add an additional conversion factor to our dimensional analysis to convert 'day' into 'doses'.

$$X = \frac{1,600 \text{ mg}}{1 \text{ day}} \times \frac{5 \text{ mL}}{200 \text{ mg}} \times \frac{1 \text{ day}}{4 \text{ doses}}$$

$$= \frac{1,600 \times 5}{200 \times 4} \text{ mL/dose}$$

$$= 10 \text{ mL/dose}$$

Now, to convert from mL to teaspoons, using 1 tsp = 5 mL,

$$X = 10 \text{ mL} \times \frac{1 \text{ tsp}}{5 \text{ mL}}$$

$$= \frac{10}{5} \text{ tsp}$$

$$= 2 \text{ tsp}$$

Solution
continued

Alternatively, this could be determined in one dimensional analysis:

$$X = \frac{1{,}600 \text{ mg}}{1 \text{ day}} \times \frac{5 \text{ mL}}{200 \text{ mg}} \times \frac{1 \text{ day}}{4 \text{ doses}} \times \frac{1 \text{ tsp}}{5 \text{ mL}}$$

$$= \frac{1{,}600 \times 5}{200 \times 4 \times 5} \text{ tsp/dose}$$

$$= 2 \text{ tsp/dose}$$

Therefore, two teaspoons of the drug should be administered per dose.

Note: "1,600 mg p.o. daily in 4 divided dosages" = "400 mg p.o. q.6.h." (≠ "400 mg p.o. q.i.d.")

Oral Medication Measured by Body Weight

A person with a greater body weight may require more of a drug than a person with a lesser body weight; therefore, physicians will sometimes order a drug per kilogram (or per pound).

The following example illustrates how to calculate the medication given based on the patient's body weight:

Example 10.2-g	Determining the Dosage Amount for Oral Medication Measured by Body Weight

A physician orders *Methylprednisolone 1.2 mg/kg p.o. q.d.* for a pediatric patient with asthma. If the patient weighs 45 lb and the drug is available in 16 mg scored tablets, how many tablets will the patient receive in a single dose?

Solution

Body Weight = 45 lb

Dosage Ordered (D) = 1.2 mg/kg

Strength on Hand (H) per *Quantity (Q)* = 16 mg/tablet

Body weight is expressed in pounds, while dosage ordered is expressed in kilograms. We need to add an additional conversion factor (1 kg = 2.2 lb) to our dimensional analysis to convert pounds to kilograms.

$$X = 45 \text{ lb} \times \frac{1 \text{ kg}}{2.2 \text{ lb}} \times \frac{1.2 \text{ mg}}{1 \text{ kg}} \times \frac{1 \text{ tab}}{16 \text{ mg}}$$

$$= 20.454545\ldots \text{ kg} \times \frac{1.2 \text{ mg}}{1 \text{ kg}} \times \frac{1 \text{ tab}}{16 \text{ mg}}$$

$$= 24.545454\ldots \text{ mg} \times \frac{1 \text{ tab}}{16 \text{ mg}}$$

$$= 1.534090\ldots \text{ tablets}$$

Therefore, the patient will receive 1.5 tablets per dose.

*Note: When calculating dosage amounts, if the calculation results in an unachievable measurement (e.g., 1.534090... tablets), **always round the dosage amount down**. Rounding the dosage amount up results in an overdose.*

Oral Medication Measured by Body Surface Area (BSA)

Body surface area (BSA) is also used in determining appropriate drug dosages. Common uses of this include cancer treatment and pediatric medication administration.

A person's BSA can be estimated using two methods: nomograms and formulas.

A nomogram is a tool consisting of three measures: one for height (on the left), one for weight (on the right), and one for BSA placed in between. Using a nomogram, you can mark the points on the left and right measures that correspond to a person's height and weight, respectively, and connect the points using a straight line; the point where the straight line intersects the BSA measure is an estimate of the person's body surface area. For example, an estimate of a person's BSA who is 180 cm tall and weighs 80 kg is 2.0 m², as seen in Exhibit 10.2.

However, it is more common to use formulas to estimate BSA, because they are more precise and more convenient to use.

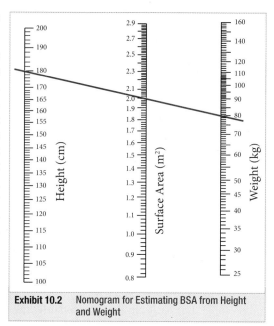

Exhibit 10.2 Nomogram for Estimating BSA from Height and Weight

Estimates for a person's body surface area, measured in square metres (m²), can be made using the following formulas:

$$\text{Metric units: } BSA \text{ (in m}^2) = \sqrt{\frac{weight\ (in\ kg) \times height\ (in\ cm)}{3,600}}$$

$$\text{US Customary units: } BSA \text{ (in m}^2) = \sqrt{\frac{weight\ (in\ lb) \times height\ (in\ inches)}{3,131}}$$

Example 10.2-h **Estimating a Person's BSA**

Estimate the body surface areas (BSA's) of the following patients:

(i)   A man who is 175 cm tall and weighs 92 kg.

(ii) An adolescent girl who is 64 inches tall and weighs 124 lb.

Solution

(i)   The man's measurements are given in metric units.

$$\text{Therefore, } BSA \text{ (in m}^2) = \sqrt{\frac{weight\ (in\ kg) \times height\ (in\ cm)}{3,600}}$$

$$= \sqrt{\frac{92 \times 175}{3,600}}$$

$$= \sqrt{4.472222\ldots}$$

$$= 2.114762\ldots = 2.11 \text{ m}^2$$

Solution
continued

(ii) The girl's measurements are given is US Customary units.

$$\text{Therefore,} \quad BSA \text{ (in m}^2\text{)} = \sqrt{\frac{weight \text{ (in lb)} \times height \text{ (in inches)}}{3{,}131}}$$

$$= \sqrt{\frac{124 \times 64}{3{,}131}}$$

$$= \sqrt{2.534653\ldots}$$

$$= 1.592059\ldots = 1.59 \text{ m}^2$$

Therefore, the man has an approximate BSA of 2.11 m² and the girl has an approximate BSA of 1.59 m².

Example 10.2-i | **Determining the Dosage Amount for Oral Medication Measured by BSA**

A physician orders *Haloperidol 1.5 mg/m² BSA p.o. b.i.d.* for a patient with severe schizophrenia. How many mL of oral suspension will the patient receive per dose if he is 170 cm tall, weighs 187 lb, and the concentration of the solution on hand is 2 mg/mL?

Solution

The patient's height is given in metric units, but the patient's weight is given in US Customary units. Therefore, in order to calculate BSA, we need to first convert one measurement to match the other.

Method 1: Converting 187 lb to kg

Using 1 kg = 2.2 lb,

$$187 \text{ lb} = 187 \text{ lb} \times \frac{1 \text{ kg}}{2.2 \text{ lb}}$$

$$= \frac{187}{2.2} \text{ kg}$$

$$= 85 \text{ kg}$$

Now, both measurements are in metric units.

> Since we are calculating an *estimate* for *BSA*, it is okay to round our intermediate calculations to two decimal places.

Method 2: Converting 170 cm to inches

Using 1 in. = 2.54 cm,

$$170 \text{ cm} = 170 \text{ cm} \times \frac{1 \text{ in.}}{2.54 \text{ cm}}$$

$$= \frac{170}{2.54} \text{ in.}$$

$$= 66.929133\ldots = 66.93 \text{ in.}$$

Now, both measurements are in US Customary units.

$$BSA \text{ (in m}^2\text{)} = \sqrt{\frac{weight \text{ (in kg)} \times height \text{ (in cm)}}{3{,}600}}$$

$$= \sqrt{\frac{85 \times 170}{3{,}600}}$$

$$= \sqrt{4.013888\ldots}$$

$$= 2.003469\ldots = 2.00 \text{ m}^2$$

$$BSA \text{(in m}^2\text{)} = \sqrt{\frac{weight \text{ (in lb)} \times height \text{ (in inches)}}{3{,}131}}$$

$$= \sqrt{\frac{187 \times 66.93}{3{,}131}}$$

$$= \sqrt{3.997416\ldots}$$

$$= 1.999353\ldots = 2.00 \text{ m}^2$$

Finally, calculating dosage amount:

BSA = 2.00 m²

Dosage Ordered (D) = 1.5 mg/m²

Strength on Hand (H) per *Quantity (Q)* = 2 mg/mL

$$X = 2.00 \text{ m}^2 \times \frac{1.5 \text{ mg}}{1 \text{ m}^2} \times \frac{1 \text{ mL}}{2 \text{ mg}}$$

$$= 3 \text{ mg} \times \frac{1 \text{ mL}}{2 \text{ mg}}$$

$$= 1.5 \text{ mL}$$

Therefore, the patient would receive 1.5 mL of solution per dose.

10.2 | Exercises

For Problems 1 to 6, read the drug labels provided and determine the amount of each drug to be administered to the patient per dose, based on the dosage ordered by the physician.

1. *Paxil 40 mg p.o. daily*

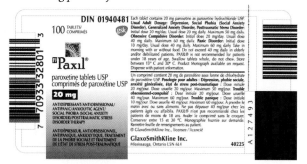

2. *Avandia 8 mg p.o. daily*

3. *Sensipar 180 mg p.o. daily in 2 divided doses*

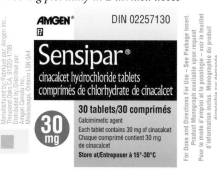

4. *Parnate 60 mg p.o. daily in 3 divided doses*

5. *Zovirax 560 mg p.o. q.i.d.*

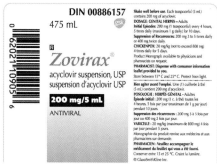

6. *Ceftin 195 mg p.o. b.i.d.*

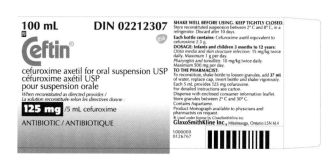

7. A physician orders codeine 75 mg p.o. q.6.h. p.r.n. for a patient with a severe cough. The medicine on hand is in the form of 30 mg scored caplets.

    a. How many caplets should the patient take per dose?

    b. How many caplets should the patient take per day?

8. A physician orders levothyroxin 225 mcg p.o. q.8.h. for a pregnant patient with a hypoactive thyroid. The medicine on hand is in the form of 150 mcg scored tablets.

    a. How many tablets should the patient take per dose?

    b. How many tablets should the patient take per day?

9. A doctor prescribes penicillin v potassium 0.5 g p.o. q.8.h. for 10 days. The available drug is in the form of 250 mg capsules. Determine the number of capsules that the patient should take per dose and the total number of capsules to dispense for a 10-day prescription.

10. A doctor prescribes 375 mg phenytoin p.o. q.d. 30-day supply. The available drug is in the form of 125 mg extended-release capsules. How many capsules should the patient take per dose? How many capsules should be dispensed for the full 30 days?

11. A physician orders amoxicillin 400 mg p.o. q.8.h. for a patient. The amoxicillin is suspended in a liquid solution with a concentration of 160 mg/5 mL. Interpret the order and determine the size of the dose to give to the patient.

12. A physician orders acetaminophen 120 mg p.o. q.4.h. p.r.n. pain for an infant patient. The infant acetaminophen is suspended in a liquid solution with a concentration of 80 mg/mL. Interpret the order and determine the amount of the solution to administer.

13. A doctor prescribes furosemide 60 mg p.o. b.i.d. The label of the drug on hand reads "20 mg/tab" and the bottle contains 90 tablets. Determine the number of tablets the patient needs to take per dose, and how long the bottle of pills will last.

14. A rheumatologist recommends that a patient with an autoimmune disorder takes 2,000 IU of Vitamin D p.o. q.d. The bottle of Vitamin D sold at the drug store contains 180 tablets, each containing 400 IU of Vitamin D. Determine the number of tablets the patient needs to take each day and how long the bottle of pills will last.

15. A physician prescribes oxycodone 15 mg p.o. q.6.h. for the management of severe pain. The drug comes in the form of a concentrated liquid solution with a concentration of 20 mg/mL.

    a. How much of the solution must be given per dose?

    b. How much of the solution must be given per day?

16. A neurologist prescribes memantine hydrochloride 10 mg p.o. q.8.h. to treat and reduce the symptoms of Alzheimer's disease in a geriatric patient. The drug comes in the form of a liquid solution with a concentration of 2 mg/mL.

    a. How much of the solution must be given per dose?

    b. How much of the solution must be given per day?

17. A doctor prescribes Tylenol 3 (acetaminophen/codeine) 650/60 mg p.o. q.4.h. p.r.n. pain, 10-day supply. The tablets available at the pharmacy are 300/30 mg, 300/60 mg, 325/30 mg, and 325/60 mg.

    a. Which tablets should be used?

    b. How many tablets should the patient be instructed to take every dose?

    c. How many tablets should be dispensed to fill the prescription?

18. A doctor prescribes Soma (aspirin/carisoprodol) 650/400 mg p.o. q.6.h. p.r.n. pain, 14-day supply. The tablets available at the pharmacy are 300/200 mg, 325/100 mg, 325/200 mg, and 650/200 mg.

    a. Which tablets should be used?

    b. How many tablets should the patient be instructed to take every dose?

    c. How many tablets should be dispensed to fill the prescription?

19. A doctor prescribes ampicillin 1 g p.o. divided q.i.d. 14-day supply. The pharmacy has 500 mg half-scored caplets on hand. Interpret the order and determine the amount of the available drug needed per dose, and the number of caplets to be dispensed to fill the prescription.

20. A doctor prescribes methylprednisolone 40 mg/day p.o. divided b.i.d. 30-day supply. The pharmacy has 16 mg quarter-scored tablets on hand. Interpret the order and determine the amount of the available drug needed per dose, and the number of tablets to be dispensed to fill the prescription.

21. A pediatric drug label with a concentration of 75 mg/5 mL comes with dosing instructions of 1.5 mg/kg. How much of the solution should be administered to a child who weighs 22 kg?

22. A drug label with a concentration of 25 mg/5 mL comes with dosing instructions of 0.2 mg/kg. How much of the solution should be administered to a patient who weighs 65 kg?

23. An antifungal drug has a recommended dosage range of 15-25 mg/kg/day, administered q.8.h., and is available on hand in 250 mg capsules.

    a. What is the recommended dosage range (in mg) of the drug that a patient weighing 178 pounds can take per dose? [Use 1 kg = 2.2 lb]

    b. Determine the number of capsules the patient may take per dose to stay within the safe dosing guidelines above.

24. A tranquilizer used to treat and prevent seizures in children has a recommended safe dosage range of 0.01-0.05 mg/kg/day, divided b.i.d, and is available on hand in 0.5 mg scored tablets.

    a. What is the recommended dosage range (in mg) of the drug that a 10-year-old patient weighing 82 lbs can take per dose? [Use 1 kg = 2.2 lb]

    b. Determine the range in the number of tablets the patient can be given per dose to stay within the safe pediatric dosing guidelines above.

25. Estimate the body surface areas (BSA) of the following patients, rounded to 2 decimal places:

    a. A girl who is 105 cm tall and weighs 31.8 kg.

    b. A man who is 6 feet 5 inches tall and weighs 190 pounds.

26. Estimate the body surface areas (BSA) of the following patients, rounded to 2 decimal places:

    a. A woman who is 5 feet 9 inches tall and weighs 172 pounds.

    b. A man who is 170 cm tall and weighs 78 kg.

27. What is the safe daily dosage range of Cyclophosphamide for an adult with a BSA of 2.24 m^2, if the recommended dosage range is 400-600 mg/m^2/day?

28. What is the safe daily dosage range of Mitomycin for a child with a BSA of 0.95 m^2, if the recommended dosage range is 10 to 20 mg/m^2/day?

29. Find the BSA of an adult who is 183 cm tall and weighs 205 pounds. A 25 mg/m^2/day p.o. divided t.i.d drug is ordered for this patient. How many mL per dose will a patient receive if the concentration of the solution is 2 mg/mL?

30. Find the BSA of an adult who is 5 feet 3 inches tall and weighs 51.5 kg. A 30 mg/m^2/day p.o. divided b.i.d drug is ordered for this patient. How many mL per dose will a patient receive if the concentration of the solution is 1.5 mg/mL?

10.3 | Syringes

A **syringe** is a tubular device designed to draw in, measure, and eject a liquid in a narrow stream. In medical uses, there are two main types of syringes: oral syringes and hypodermic syringes.

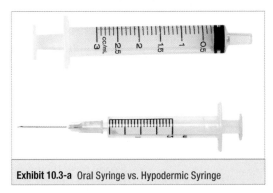

Exhibit 10.3-a Oral Syringe vs. Hypodermic Syringe

- **Oral syringes** are used to draw in and measure oral medication in a liquid form, and eject it in the mouth of the patient; oral syringes are primarily used for babies and small children.

- **Hypodermic syringes** are used to draw in and measure parenteral medication, and inject it in the body of the patient via a needle; hypodermic syringes are used for parenteral medication that enters the body through the muscle (intramuscular, IM), through subcutaneous tissue (subcutaneous, SC), and through the vein (intravenous, IV).

Before administering medication through intramuscular, subcutaneous, or intravenous injections, it is first essential to know how to properly use and measure liquid with a hypodermic syringe, as well as be able to identify the best type of syringe to use in a given scenario.

Hypodermic Syringes

Hypodermic syringes are used to inject medication into the body via a needle. The first uses of a syringe with a needle that could pierce skin occurred in the 1850's, by Dr. Alexander Wood and Dr. Charles Pravaz. Since then, the hypodermic syringe has been improved upon, and has become a popularized method of medication administration.

The calibrations can also be marked in cubic centimetres (cm³ or cc). Recall:

1 mL = 1 cc.

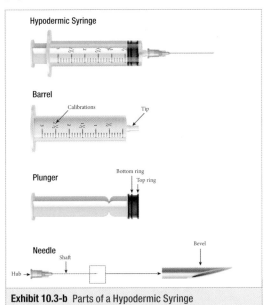

Exhibit 10.3-b Parts of a Hypodermic Syringe

The hypodermic syringe consists of three main components: the barrel, the plunger, and the needle.

The **barrel** is the tube where the medication is drawn in and measured before it is injected into the body. Therefore, the barrel contains measurements, or **calibrations**, marked in millilitres (mL) to measure a liquid. The **tip** of the barrel is where the needle is properly secured to the barrel.

The **plunger** is the rod inserted into the barrel, which is *pulled* to draw in a liquid from the needle into the barrel, and *pushed* to eject a liquid from the barrel through the needle. The **top ring** is used to measure the amount of liquid in the barrel.

The **needle** is the point from which the liquid is drawn into the barrel, and injected into the body. The **hub** is where the needle attaches to the barrel (at the tip), the **shaft** is the long, hollow stem of the needle which is inserted into the body, and the **bevel** is the fine, sharp point at the end of the shaft which breaks the skin, allowing the shaft to enter the body.

To **draw in** a liquid into the syringe:

- Insert the plunger all the way into the barrel, and the shaft of the needle into a vial containing the liquid.

- Slowly pull back on the plunger, allowing the liquid to be pulled through the needle into the barrel. Keep pulling until the **top ring** on the plunger aligns with the desired volume, as measured by the **calibrations** on the barrel.

To **eject** a liquid from the syringe:

- Slowly push the plunger all the way back into the barrel, allowing all the liquid to be pushed from the barrel through the needle, and ejected from the bevel to the body site.

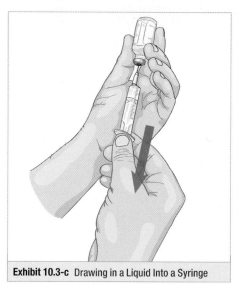

Exhibit 10.3-c Drawing in a Liquid Into a Syringe

Note: Different body sites are used for different types of injections. We will learn more about how IM, SC, and IV injections are administered to the body in sections 10.4 and 10.5

Types of Hypodermic Syringes

Categorizing of hypodermic syringes is based on the amount of liquid they can hold. Recall that the calibrations are measured in millilitres, mL (or cubic centimetres, cc).

Table 10.3 **Types of Syringes**

Type	Size	Uses	Calibration
Tuberculin Syringes	0.5 and 1 mL	ID, IV, and SC injections	hundredths of a millilitre (0.01 mL)
Small Capacity Syringes	2, 2.5, and 3 mL	ID, IM, and SC injections	tenths of a millilitre (0.1 mL)
Large Capacity Syringes	5, 6, 10, and 12 mL	draw blood, prepare medications for IV administration	increments from 0.2 mL to 1 mL
Extra Large Capacity Syringes	20 mL and larger	inject large volume of solution	typically in increments of 1 mL

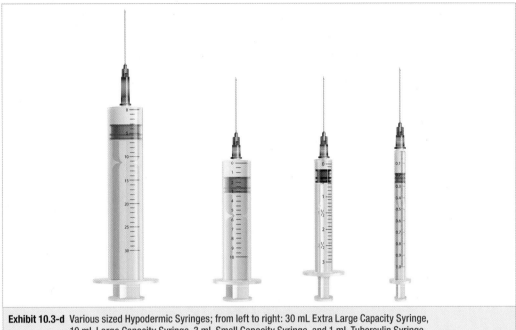

Exhibit 10.3-d Various sized Hypodermic Syringes; from left to right: 30 mL Extra Large Capacity Syringe, 10 mL Large Capacity Syringe, 3 mL Small Capacity Syringe, and 1 mL Tuberculin Syringe

Note: The syringes in the previous exhibit are not drawn to scale in order to show the different calibrations.

Reading From Various Sized Syringes

Recall that the measurements are read from the **top ring** of the plunger. We will practice reading the amount of liquid in various sized syringes in the following examples.

Example 10.3-a	Reading from a 3 mL Syringe

Identify the calibration and the amount of liquid in the following syringe:

Solution

The numbers on the barrel increase by 0.5. There are 5 notches to increase from one number to the next. Therefore, the calibration is $\dfrac{0.5}{5} = 0.1$ (i.e., each notch represents 0.1 mL).

The top ring of the plunger aligns with the 4th notch past the 1.5 marking. Therefore, the amount of liquid in the syringe is $1.5 + (4 \times 0.1) = 1.9$ mL.

Example 10.3-b | **Reading from a 0.5 mL Syringe**

Identify the calibration and the amount of liquid in the following syringe:

Solution

The numbers on the barrel increase by 0.1. There are 10 notches to increase from one number to the next. Therefore, the calibration is $\dfrac{0.1}{10} = 0.01$ (i.e., each notch represents 0.01 mL).

The top ring of the plunger aligns with the 2nd notch past the 0.3 marking. Therefore, the amount of liquid in the syringe is $0.3 + (2 \times 0.01) = 0.32$ mL.

Example 10.3-c | **Reading from a 12 mL Syringe**

Identify the calibration and the amount of liquid in the following syringe:

Solution

The numbers on the barrel increase by 1. There are 5 notches to increase from one number to the next. Therefore, the calibration is $\dfrac{1}{5} = 0.2$ (i.e., each notch represents 0.2 mL).

The top ring of the plunger aligns with the 1st notch past the 8 marking. Therefore, the amount of liquid in the syringe is $8 + (1 \times 0.2) = 8.2$ mL.

Choosing the Right Syringe

When administering a dose, the syringe with the smallest possible capacity such that the entire dose fits in the syringe should be used. However, it is best to avoid filling a syringe to its maximum capacity.

For example, if you are required to administer 0.8 mL of a medication, the smallest capacity syringe that can fit the entire dose is a 1 mL syringe. However, if you are required to administer 1 mL of a medication, since a syringe should not be filled to its maximum capacity, the next smallest capacity syringe that can fit the entire dose is a 2 mL syringe.

The reason for this is that the calibrations on a larger syringe are less precise than on a smaller syringe, and so measuring a small dosage on a larger syringe may result in an incorrect dosage amount.

Consider an order for 0.35 mL of a medication. Using a 0.5 mL or 1 mL syringe, with calibrations to the 0.01 mL, you are able to measure the exact amount of medication. However, using a 3 mL or 5mL syringe, with calibrations only to the 0.1 or 0.2, it would be easy to under or overestimate the dosage amount. If the syringe is filled to 0.4 mL instead of 0.35 mL, for example, this would result in an overdose of $\dfrac{0.4 - 0.35}{0.35} = 14.29\%$.

In order to avoid overdoses when administering using a syringe, dosage amounts under 1 mL are typically rounded **down** to the nearest 0.01 mL, and dosage amounts over 1 mL are typically rounded **down** to the nearest 0.1 mL.

10.3 | Exercises

For Problems 1 to 8, identify (i) the total capacity of the syringe, (ii) the calibration of the syringe, and (iii) the amount of liquid in the syringe.

1.

2.

3.

4.

5.

6.

7.

8.

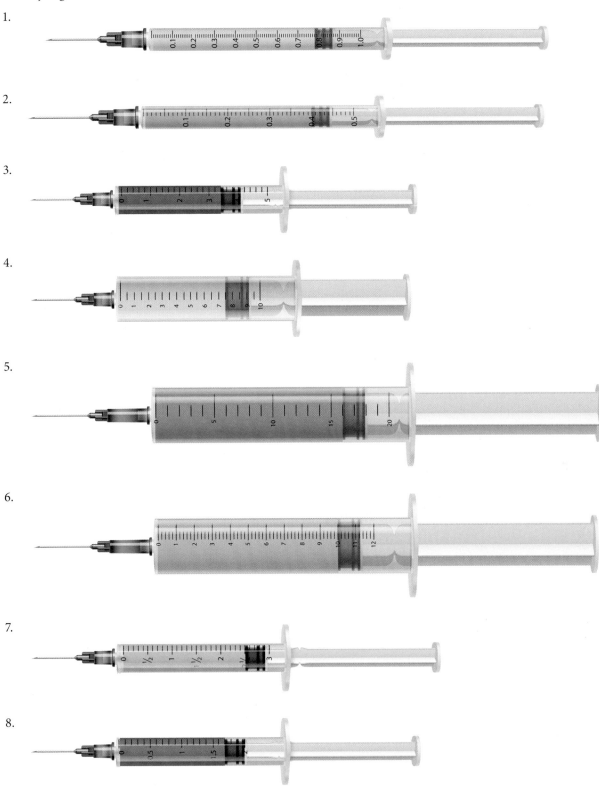

For Problems 9 to 16, choose the appropriate syringe from the image below for each of the medication volumes to be administered.

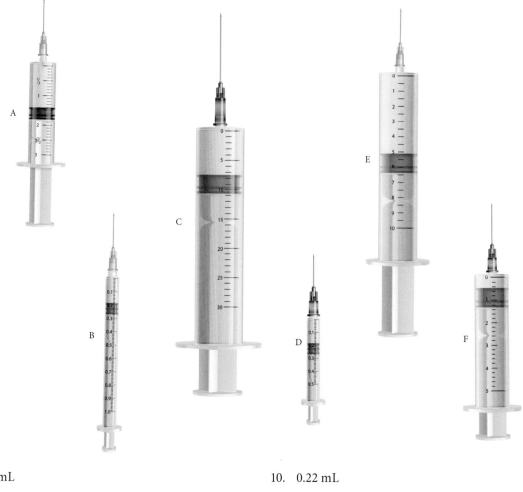

9. 2.2 mL

11. 7.5 mL

13. 0.88 mL

15. 3 mL

10. 0.22 mL

12. 3.8 mL

14. 25 mL

16. 5 mL

10.4 | Parenteral Medication Administration - IM/SC Injections

We will now begin to examine medications that are given by some other means than orally (i.e., by mouth). These types of medication are administered through **parenteral routes**, and are absorbed faster and more fully than drugs administered orally.

In this section, we will discuss how to administer parenteral medication that is injected, via a syringe, into the patient's muscle (intramuscularly) and subcutaneous tissue (subcutaneously). Intramuscular (IM) injections are injected into the patient at a 90° angle, while subcutaneous (SC) injections are injected into the patient at a 45° angle, as shown in Exhibit 10.4-a.

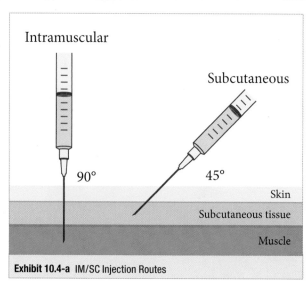

Exhibit 10.4-a IM/SC Injection Routes

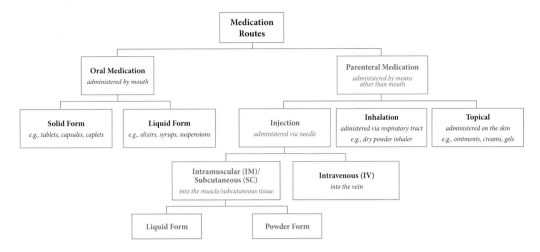

The medication that is used for IM and SC injections can be packaged in an ampule or a vial.

- An **ampule** is a glass container which contains exactly **one dose** of medication. This type of container requires a special type of opener to safely extract the medication without shattering the glass.
- A **vial** is a glass or plastic container with a rubber membrane on top, designed to hold **multiple doses** of medication; it can contain the medication in either **liquid** or **powder form**. The needle used for administering the medication is inserted directly into the top of the vial. The rubber membrane maintains the integrity of the medication, so that it can be extracted multiple times.

Exhibit 10.4-b Ampule vs. Vial

Parenteral Medications in Liquid Form

Calculating the proper dosage amount of a parenteral medication in liquid form to be administered via an IM or SC injection is the same process as for oral medication.

Recall Formula 10.2: *Medication Given (X) = Dosage Ordered (D) ×* $\dfrac{Quantity\ (Q)}{Strength\ on\ Hand\ (H)}$

We will use the same formula when calculating the dosage amount for an IM or SC injection.

In general, the amount of medication administered via an injection depends on the age of the patient and the method of entry into the patient's body. The following table outlines the guidelines for proper medication for IM and SC dosages for different ages:

<table>
<tr><th>Table 10.4</th><th colspan="2">Guidelines for Administering IM and SC Medications</th></tr>
</table>

	Intramuscular (IM)	Subcutaneous (SC)
Infant	< 1 mL	< 0.1 mL
Child	< 2 mL	< 0.5 mL
Adult	< 3 mL	< 1 mL

Therefore, intramuscular injections typically require a 1, 2, or 3 mL syringe, and subcutaneous injections typically require a 0.5 or 1 mL syringe.

Example 10.4-a **Determining the Dosage Amount for Parenteral Medication to be Administered SC**

A drug order reads as follows: *Neupogen 270 mcg SC daily.*

Read the label on the drug label below and determine how many mL of this analgesic drug are to be extracted and administered:

Solution

Dosage Ordered (D) = 270 mcg

Strength on Hand (H) per *Quantity (Q)* = 480 mcg/1.6 mL

Using Formula 10.2,

$$X = D \times \frac{Q}{H}$$

$$X = 270 \text{ mcg} \times \frac{1.6 \text{ mL}}{480 \text{ mcg}}$$

$$= \frac{270 \times 1.6}{480} \text{ mL}$$

$$= 0.90 \text{ mL}$$

Therefore, 0.90 mL of the drug should be extracted from the vial and administered to the patient.

Example 10.4-b **Dosage Calculations for Parenteral Medication to be Administered IM**

A physician orders *ketorolac tromethamine 15 mg IM q.6.h. p.r.n. pain.* The stock solution is available in a 5 mL, multi-dose vial with a label that reads 20 mg/mL.

(i)   How many mL of this analgesic drug will the patient receive?

(ii) What size syringe should be used to administer the drug?

(iii) If the manufacturer states not to exceed 60 mg/day, is this a safe dosage amount?

(iv) How many doses of the same size as calculated in (i) can be administered from one multi-dose vial?

Solution

(i) Using Formula 10.2, $\quad X = 15 \text{ mg} \times \dfrac{1 \text{ mL}}{20 \text{ mg}}$

$$= \frac{15}{20} \text{ mL}$$

$$= 0.75 \text{ mL}$$

Therefore, the patient will receive 0.75 mL of the drug.

(ii) Recall from section 10.3 that the nurse should use the smallest syringe that can accommodate a 0.75 mL dose, without reaching its full capacity. In this case, that would be a 1 mL syringe.

(iii) From the drug order: *q.6.h. p.r.n. pain* = take as needed for pain, but no more frequently than every 6 hours.

Therefore, the drug can be administered a maximum of $\dfrac{24}{6} = 4$ times per day.

15 mg × 4 times per day = 60 mg/day

The maximum dosage amount ordered by the physician is equal to 60 mg/day. Therefore, the dosage amount is safe, but **cannot** be increased.

(iv) The medication is available in a 5 mL, multi-dose vial.

$$\frac{5 \text{ mL}}{0.75 \text{ mL}} = 6.666666...$$

Therefore, six 0.75 mL doses can be administered from one multi-dose vial.

Note: When administering parenteral medication, it is not advisable to mix medication from multiple vials; i.e., the 0.5 mL left remaining after the sixth 0.75 mL dose is extracted from the 5 mL multi-dose vial in the example above should be discarded and not mixed with medication from another vial.

Parenteral Medications in Powder Form

Some medications cannot be properly maintained and stored in liquid form. These types of medication instead come in a powder form, which must first be **reconstituted** into a liquid, using a **diluent** (or solvent), before it can be injected into the patient, as illustrated in the following steps:

Step 1: Using a syringe, extract the proper amount of diluent, as indicated on the powder medication vial, from the diluent vial. Inject the extracted diluent into the powder medication vial. Medications given in powder form will always indicate the type and amount of diluent needed; the most commonly used diluents are sterile water and 0.9% sodium chloride, known as normal saline (NS).

Step 2: Remove the needle from the powder medication vial, and gently swirl the vial, allowing the powder medication to mix with the diluent. Once the medication is reconstituted, the amount of liquid in the vial may be different than the amount of diluent added. The difference between the reconstituted volume and the amount of diluent added to the vial is known as the **displacement factor**.

Step 3: Using a syringe, extract the proper dosage amount of the reconstituted medication from the powder medication vial, and inject it into the patient.

Exhibit 10.4-c shows an example of a drug label for a parenteral medication in powder form. As shown on the label, the medication is to be administered intramuscularly (IM), and is to be reconstituted with 0.9% NaCl diluent; the amount of diluent required for reconstitution will be given on the package insert. After reconstitution, the strength of the medication will be 10 mcg/0.5 mL.

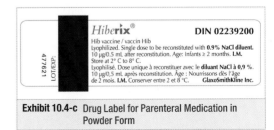

Exhibit 10.4-c Drug Label for Parenteral Medication in Powder Form

Powder medication will often come in different-sized vials. When choosing which vial to use, it is important to consider the dosage amount prescribed, the number of doses to be administered, and how long the medication is good for once reconstituted (as indicated on the drug label/package insert).

| Example 10.4-c | Reconstituting a Parenteral Medication in Powder Form, and Determining the Dosage Amount and Syringe Used |

A doctor prescribes *Pfizerpen (Penicillin G potassium) 300,000 units IM q.4.h.* The vial contains 1,000,000 units and lists three different reconstitutions:

- Add 20 mL NS (normal saline) to reconsitute to a strength of 50,000 units/mL

- Add 10 mL NS (normal saline) to reconsitute to a strength of 100,000 units/mL

- Add 5 mL NS (normal saline) to reconsitute to a strength of 200,000 units/mL

(i) Which reconstitution should be used to prepare the drug for injection?

(ii) How many mL of the reconstituted solution should be drawn out of the vial for injection?

(iii) What size syringe should be used to administer the injection?

Solution

(i) Since the drug is to be injected intramuscularly, the total volume to be injected should be less than 3 mL. Hence, the 200,000 unit/mL strength should be prepared by reconstituting the powder with 5 mL of normal saline.

(ii) Using Formula 10.2,
$$X = 300,000 \text{ units} \times \frac{1 \text{ mL}}{200,000 \text{ units}}$$
$$= \frac{300,000}{200,000} \text{ mL}$$
$$= 1.5 \text{ mL}$$

Therefore, 1.5 mL of the reconstituted solution should be drawn out for injection.

(iii) We need to use a syringe with the smallest possible capacity such that the entire 1.5 mL dose fits in the syringe, without reaching the capacity of the syringe.

Therefore, a 2 mL syringe should be used to administer the medication.

| Example 10.4-d | Determining the Strength and Dosage Amount of a Parenteral Medication in Powder Form |

A doctor orders *Kefzol (Cefazolin sodium) 375 mg IM stat* into the knee joint. The 1 g vial provides the following instructions:

For reconstitution, add 4 mL of sterile water for a total approximate volume of 4.4 mL.

(i) What is the strength of the reconstituted solution?

(ii) How many mL should be administered?

Solution

(i) The strength is calculated using the reconstituted volume, **not** the amount of diluent added.

Therefore, the strength $= \dfrac{1 \text{ g}}{4.4 \text{ mL}}$, which is approximately 227 mg/mL.

(ii) Using Formula 10.2,
$$X = 375 \text{ mg} \times \frac{4.4 \text{ mL}}{1 \text{ g}}$$

Adding an additional conversion factor to the dimension analysis to convert mg to g,

$$X = 375 \text{ mg} \times \frac{1 \text{ g}}{1,000 \text{ mg}} \times \frac{4.4 \text{ mL}}{1 \text{ g}} \quad [1 \text{ g} = 1,000 \text{ mg}]$$
$$= \frac{375 \times 4.4}{1,000} \text{ mL}$$
$$= 1.65 \text{ mL}$$

Therefore, 1.6 mL of medication should be administered.

*Note: Recall that dosage amounts over 1 mL are typically rounded **down** to the nearest 0.1 mL.*

10.4 | Exercises

Answers to odd-numbered problems are available at the end of the textbook.

For Problems 1 to 6, read the drug labels and determine the amount of each drug to administer to the patient per dose, based on the dosage ordered by the physician.

1. *Neupogen 180 mcg SC daily*

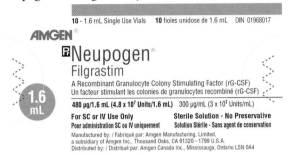

2. *Xgeva 60 mg SC q.4.week*

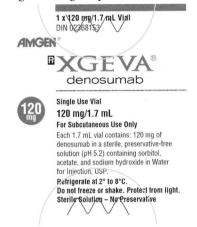

3. *Engerix-B 5 mcg IM stat.*

4. *Nucala 100 mg SC stat.*

5. *Enbrel 20 mg SC weekly*

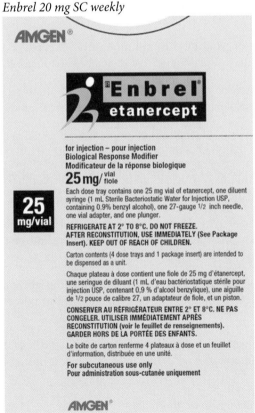

6. *Nplate 160 mcg SC weekly*

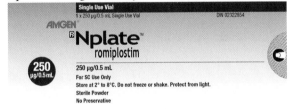

7. A pediatrician orders hydroxyzine 30 mg IM for a child with severe and persistent vomitting. The child weighs 54 pounds and the safe dosage range listed on the drug label is 1-1.5 mg/kg. [Use 1 kg = 2.2 lb]

   a. Determine the safe dosage range of hydroxyzine for this child.

   b. Is the dose ordered by the pediatrician in the safe range?

   c. If the concentration of hydroxyzine available on hand is 50 mg/mL, what volume of solution should be prepared to fill this order?

   d. What size syringe should be used?

8. An anesthesiologist orders midazolam 4 mg IM for a child patient as a pre-operative sedative for a minor procedure. The child weighs 75 pounds and the safe dosage range listed on the drug label is 0.1-0.15 mg/kg. [Use 1 kg = 2.2 lb]

   a. Determine the safe dosage range of midazolam for this child.

   b. Is the dose ordered by the anesthesiologist in the safe range?

   c. If the concentration of midazolam available on hand is 5 mg/mL, what volume of solution should be prepared to fill this order?

   d. What size syringe should be used?

9. A physician orders ampicillin 375 mg IM q.6.h. to treat pneumonia. The pharmacist prepares the order from a 1-gram vial of ampicillin powder with the following instructions: "reconstitute powder with 3.7 mL of 0.9% Sodium Chloride Solution (i.e., normal saline) to a total reconstituted volume of 4 mL."

   a. What is the concentration of the reconstituted solution (in mg/mL)?

   b. What volume of solution should be prepared for injection per dose and per day?

   c. What size syringe should be used?

10. A physician orders oxacillin 1.5 g IM q.4.h. to treat a severe skin infection. The pharmacist prepares the order from a 2-gram vial of oxacillin powder with the following instructions: "reconstitute powder with 11.4 mL of sterile water to a total reconstituted volume of 12 mL."

    a. What is the concentration of the reconstituted solution (in mg/mL)?

    b. What volume of solution should be prepared for injection per dose and per day?

    c. What size syringe should be used?

11. A diabetic patient is prescribed insulin 16 units SC q.i.d. The insulin on hand is U-40 (i.e., 40 units/mL). Interpret the order and determine both the syringe size to be used and the volume of the insulin solution that should be self-administered.

12. A physician orders 0.3 mg epinephrine IM stat. The available solution contains 0.5 mg/mL. Interpret the order and determine both the syringe size to be used and the volume of the epinephrine solution that should be administered to the patient.

13. A physician orders morphine sulfate 20 mg IM stat. The stock solution contains 40 mg of morphine sulfate in a 5 mL vial. Interpret the order and determine the volume of the solution to administer to the patient.

14. A physician orders 20 mcg teriparatide SC q.d. The stock vial contains 750 mcg/15 mL solution. Interpret the order and determine the volume of the solution to administer to the patient.

15. A physician orders that a pediatric patient be given morphine 150 mcg/kg IM q.4.h. p.r.n. pain. The label on the vial of stock solution reads 40 mg/5 mL and the patient weighs 32 kg. Interpret the order and determine how much of the solution should be added to the patient's IV line per dose and per day.

16. A physician orders that a pediatric patient is to be given codeine 0.5 mg/kg SC q.6.h. p.r.n. pain. The label on the vial of stock solution reads 30 mg/mL and the patient weighs 24 kg. Interpret the order and determine how much of the solution should be given per dose and per day.

17. A physician orders enoxaparin 1 mg/kg SC b.i.d. for a patient with deep vein thrombosis. The in-stock solution of enoxaparin is 300 mg/3 mL and the patient weighs 85 kg. Interpret the order and determine how much of the solution to administer.

18. A pediatrician orders lorazepam 75 mcg/kg IM t.i.d. for a child patient with severe anxiety. The child weighs 24 kg and the stock solution contains 20 mg/10 mL. Interpret the order and determine how much of the solution to administer.

10.5 | Parenteral Medication Administration – IV Injections

The final medication route we will learn about in this chapter is intravenous (IV) injections; this refers to the administration of fluids, nutrients, and medication through a patient's vein. This form of parenteral administration can be broken into three major functions: replacement, maintenance, and medication.

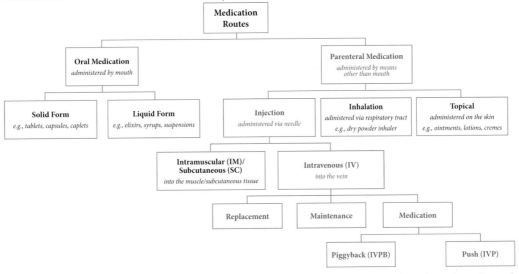

- **Replacement** refers to transferring necessary fluids to a patient who has lost them (i.e., through severe dehydration, hemorrhage, diarrhea, etc.).

- **Maintenance** refers to helping a patient sustain a healthy amount of necessary fluids; maintenance is most commonly required for patients who cannot swallow (n.p.o.) and therefore cannot drink water to stay hydrated.

- **Medication** can be injected intravenously through a **piggyback (IVPB)** or a **push (IVP)**. IVPB refers to administering a drug through an IV site that already exists for replacement or maintenance purposes. IVP refers to administering a drug directly into the vein of a patient in urgent care to ensure the medication moves through the body as quickly as possible.

In this section, we will focus on IV injections for replacement and maintenance, as well as IV piggyback (IVPB).

IV Injections for Replacement and Maintenance

The most common method of injecting fluids intravenously for replacement and maintenance reasons is using a **gravity system**, as pictured in Exhibit 10.5-a.

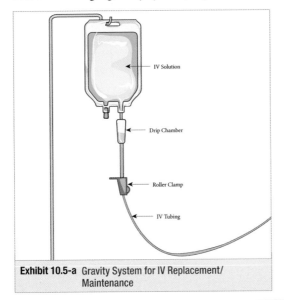

Exhibit 10.5-a Gravity System for IV Replacement/ Maintenance

In the gravity system, the **IV solution** (e.g., sterile water, 5% dextrose solution (D5W), normal saline (NS), etc.) is suspended in a bag on a metal hook above the **infusion site** (where the needle is injected into the vein of the patient, usually in the patient's hand or arm).

The IV solution passes through the **drip chamber**, which moderates the flow of the fluid into controlled drips, then runs through the **IV tubing** into the patient at the infusion site.

The IV tubing controls the size of the drops which run from the IV solution bag to the infusion site of the patient; this is called the **drop factor**. The drop factor can differ between IV tubing purchased from different manufacturers; the manufacturer must provide the drop factor, as it is used in IV calculations.

The **roller clamp** can be adjusted to decrease or increase the rate of flow of the IV solution into the infusion site.

It is the responsibility of the nurse to regularly check in on a patient receiving IV replacement/maintenance (every 30-60 minutes), to ensure that the infusion site is properly connected (with no infection), and the IV solution is being infused at an appropriate rate.

Calculating an Appropriate Rate of IV Infusion

When a fluid is being injected intravenously for replacement/maintenance purposes, it must be gradually infused in the patient over a period of time, instead of all at once, as was the case with oral, intramuscular (IM), and subcutaneous (SC) medication administration. Therefore, we must ensure that the IV solution is being administered at an appropriate rate. This rate is known as the **flow rate**.

The flow rate can be expressed in two different ways: millilitres per hour (mL/h) or drops per minute (gtt/min).

When IV infusion for replacement/maintenance is ordered, the flow rate will be expressed in the number of milliliters to be infused over the number of hours specified in the order (mL/h).

$$\textit{Flow Rate (mL/h)} = \frac{\textit{Volume to be Infused (mL)}}{\textit{Time specified (h)}}$$

However, when IV infusions are administered, the flow rate must be converted to drops per minute (gtt/min), in order to account for the drop factor of the IV tubing. This conversion is given by the following formula, which makes use of dimensional analysis:

Formula 10.5	**Flow Rate (gtt/min)**

$$\textit{Flow Rate (gtt/min)} = \textit{Flow Rate (mL/h)} \times \textit{Drop Factor (gtt/mL)} \times \frac{\textbf{1 h}}{\textbf{60 min}}$$

Drop factor is standardized to be 10, 15, or 20 drops per millilitre (gtt/mL), or 60 microdrops per millilitre (mcgtt/mL), depending on the size of the IV tubing.

Example 10.5-a	Determining Flow Rate in gtt/min

An IV solution bag containing 500 mL of D5W solution is set to run over a six-hour period. If the drop factor is 20 gtt/mL, determine the flow rate in drops per minute.

Solution

Flow Rate (mL/h) = 500 mL/6 h

Drop Factor = 20 gtt/mL

Using Formula 10.5, $\quad \textit{Flow Rate (gtt/min)} = \dfrac{500 \text{ mL}}{6 \text{ h}} \times \dfrac{20 \text{ gtt}}{1 \text{ mL}} \times \dfrac{1 \text{ h}}{60 \text{ min}}$

$$= \frac{500 \times 20}{6 \times 60} \text{ gtt/min}$$

$$= 27.777777... \text{ gtt/min}$$

Therefore, the flow rate is 28 drops per minute.

*Note: Since we cannot measure partial drops, flow rate is typically rounded **up** to the next drop. It is not rounded down because in replacement/maintenance infusion, no drugs are being administered to the patient, and so there is no risk of overdose.*

Example 10.5-b | Determining Flow Rate in mcgtt/min

Consider the following drug order: $\frac{1}{2}$ NS 500 mL IV infuse over 24 h. Determine the flow rate in microdrops per minute.

Solution

Here, the drop factor is not explicitly stated. However, since we are to determine the flow rate in microdrops per minute, and only one of the standardized drop factors are measured in microdrops, we can infer that the drop factor is 60 microdrops per millilitre (mcgtt/mL).

Flow Rate (mL/h) = 500 mL/24 h

Drop Factor = 60 mcgtt/mL

Using Formula 10.5,
$$Flow\ Rate\ (mcgtt/min) = \frac{500\ \cancel{mL}}{24\ \cancel{h}} \times \frac{60\ mcgtt}{1\ \cancel{mL}} \times \frac{1\ \cancel{h}}{60\ min}$$

$$= \frac{500 \times \cancel{60}}{24 \times \cancel{60}}\ mcgtt/min$$

$$= 20.833333\ldots\ mcgtt/min$$

Therefore, the flow rate is 21 microdrops per minute.

Notice in the example above that the drop factor $\frac{60\ mcgtt}{1\ mL}$ cancels with the conversion factor $\frac{1\ h}{60\ min}$. Therefore, the flow rate in mcgtt/min is the same as the flow rate in mL/h:

$$Flow\ Rate = \frac{500\ mL}{24\ h} = 20.833333\ldots\ mL/h = 20.833333\ldots\ mcgtt/min \approx 21\ mcgtt/min.$$

Example 10.5-c | Determining Amount of IV Solution Received in a Time Period

An IV infusion rate is 32 microdrops per minute. How many millilitres of this solution will the patient receive in six hours?

Solution

Flow Rate (mcgtt/min) = 32 mcgtt/min

As we learned in Example 10.5-b, Flow Rate (mcgtt/min) = Flow Rate (mL/h).

Therefore, Flow Rate (mL/h) = 32 mL/h

Determining the millilitres received in six hours,
$$\frac{32\ mL}{1\ h} = \frac{x\ mL}{6\ h}$$

$$x = 32 \times 6 = 192\ mL$$

Therefore, the patient will receive 192 mL in six hours.

Example 10.5-d Determining Flow Rate in Millilitres per Hour

An IV infusion rate is 30 drops per minute and the drop factor is 15 gtt/mL. Calculate the flow rate in millilitres per hour (mL/h).

Solution

Here, we are given the flow rate in gtt/min, and asked to determine the flow rate in mL/h.

Flow Rate (gtt/min) = 30 gtt/min

Drop Factor = 15 gtt/mL

Using Formula 10.5,

$$\frac{30 \text{ gtt}}{1 \text{ min}} = Flow\ Rate\ (mL/h) \times \frac{15 \text{ gtt}}{1 \text{ mL}} \times \frac{1 \text{ h}}{60 \text{ min}}$$

Rearranging,

$$Flow\ Rate\ (mL/h) = \frac{\dfrac{30 \text{ gtt}}{1 \text{ min}}}{\dfrac{15 \text{ gtt}}{1 \text{ mL}} \times \dfrac{1 \text{ h}}{60 \text{ min}}}$$

$$Flow\ Rate\ (mL/h) = \frac{30 \text{ gtt}}{1 \text{ min}} \times \frac{1 \text{ mL}}{15 \text{ gtt}} \times \frac{60 \text{ min}}{1 \text{ h}}$$

$$= \frac{30 \times 60}{15} \text{ mL/h}$$

$$= 120 \text{ mL/h}$$

Recall:

$$\frac{\dfrac{a}{b}}{\dfrac{c}{d}} = \frac{a}{b} \div \frac{c}{d} = \frac{a}{b} \times \frac{d}{c}$$

Therefore, the flow rate in millilitres per hour is 120 mL/h.

In the example above, we rearranged Formula 10.5 to determine *Flow Rate* in millilitres per hour (mL/h) when given *Flow Rate* in drops per minute (gtt/min):

$$\textbf{Flow Rate (mL/h)} = \textbf{Flow Rate (gtt/min)} \times \frac{1}{\textbf{Drop Factor}} \textbf{ (mL/gtt)} \times \frac{\textbf{60 min}}{\textbf{1 h}}$$

$\dfrac{1}{Drop\ Factor}$ is the inverse of the drop factor; therefore, it has the units mL/gtt.

Example 10.5-e Determining When an IV Solution is Finished Infusing

An IV of 1,000 mL of D5W is started at 8 AM. The flow rate is 40 drops per minute and the drop factor is 10 drops per millilitre. At what time will this infusion finish?

Solution

Method 1:

Flow Rate (gtt/min) = 40 gtt/min

Drop Factor = 10 gtt/mL

Using rearranged Formula 10.5,

$$Flow\ Rate\ (mL/h) = \frac{40 \text{ gtt}}{1 \text{ min}} \times \frac{1 \text{ mL}}{10 \text{ gtt}} \times \frac{60 \text{ min}}{1 \text{ h}}$$

$$= \frac{40 \times 60}{10} \text{ mL/h}$$

$$= 240 \text{ mL/h}$$

Solution
continued

Determining the amount of time to receive 1,000 mL,

$$\frac{240\ \text{mL}}{1\ \text{h}} = \frac{1,000\ \text{mL}}{x\ \text{h}}$$

$$240x = 1,000$$

$$x = 4.166666\ldots\ \text{h}$$

Expressing the amount of time in hours and minutes,

$$= 4\ \text{h} + (0.166666\ldots \times 60)\ \text{min}$$

$$= 4\ \text{h}\ 10\ \text{min}$$

Method 2:

Through dimensional analysis, convert the number of mL to number of drops using the drop factor, then convert the number of drops to number of minutes using the flow rate:

$$1,000\ \text{mL} \times \frac{10\ \text{gtt}}{1\ \text{mL}} \times \frac{1\ \text{min}}{40\ \text{gtt}} = \frac{1,000 \times 10}{40}\ \text{min} = 250\ \text{min}$$

Converting 250 minutes to hours,

$$250\ \text{min} = 250\ \text{min} \times \frac{1\ \text{h}}{60\ \text{min}}$$

$$= \frac{250}{60}\ \text{h}$$

$$= 4\frac{10}{60}\ \text{h}$$

$$= 4\ \text{h and }10\ \text{min}$$

Therefore, the infusion will finish 4 hours and 10 minutes after 0800 h, which is 1210 h.

Note: Recall that military time is commonly used in health sciences to avoid confusion between AM and PM.

Example 10.5-f | **Determining the Drop Factor**

At 6:00 PM, an IV tube connected to a 1,000 mL IV solution bag is started with a flow rate of 50 gtt/min. At 8:00 PM, the bag contains 600 mL of solution. Determine the drop factor of the IV tubing.

Solution

Flow Rate (gtt/min) = 50 gtt/min

$$\textit{Flow Rate}\ (\text{mL/h}) = \frac{1,000 - 600\ \text{mL}}{6:00\ \text{PM to }8:00\ \text{PM}} = \frac{400\ \text{mL}}{2\ \text{h}} = 200\ \text{mL/h}$$

Using Formula 10.5,

$$\frac{50\ \text{gtt}}{1\ \text{min}} = \frac{200\ \text{mL}}{1\ \text{h}} \times \textit{Drop Factor} \times \frac{1\ \text{h}}{60\ \text{min}}$$

Rearranging,

$$\textit{Drop Factor} = \frac{\dfrac{50\ \text{gtt}}{1\ \text{min}}}{\dfrac{200\ \text{mL}}{1\ \text{h}} \times \dfrac{1\ \text{h}}{60\ \text{min}}}$$

$$\textit{Drop Factor} = \frac{50\ \text{gtt}}{1\ \text{min}} \times \frac{1\ \text{h}}{200\ \text{mL}} \times \frac{60\ \text{min}}{1\ \text{h}}$$

$$= \frac{50 \times 60}{200}\ \text{gtt/mL}$$

$$= 15\ \text{gtt/mL}$$

Therefore, the drop factor of the IV tubing is 15 gtt/mL.

This gives us the third and final rearrangement of Formula 10.5:

$$\textbf{\textit{Drop Factor}} \textbf{ (gtt/mL)} = \textbf{\textit{Flow Rate}} \textbf{ (gtt/min)} \times \frac{1}{\textbf{\textit{Flow Rate}}} \textbf{ (h/mL)} \times \frac{\textbf{60 min}}{\textbf{1 h}}$$

$\frac{1}{\textit{Flow Rate}}$ is the inverse of the flow rate expressed in mL/h; therefore, it has the units h/mL.

Increasing/Decreasing the Flow Rate

Sometimes, the flow rate must be increased or decreased mid-infusion, by adjusting the roller clamp, in order for the IV infusion to finish at the scheduled time. This is illustrated in the following examples.

Example 10.5-g | **Determining the Amount of IV Solution Remaining After a Time Period and the Amount of Time to Finish Infusion when Flow Rate Changes**

A 1,500 mL IV with a drop factor of 20 gtt/mL is set to run at 50 gtt/min.

(i)   What volume of solution remains in the bag after four hours?

(ii) If the flow rate is slightly decreased to 45 gtt/min, how much time remains until the bag is empty?

Solution

(i)   We are given the flow rate in gtt/min. In order to determine the amount of solution that remains in the bag after four hours, we first require the flow rate in mL/h.

Flow Rate (gtt/min) = 50 gtt/min

Drop Factor = 20 gtt/mL

$$\textit{Flow Rate (mL/h)} = \frac{50 \text{ gtt}}{1 \text{ min}} \times \frac{1 \text{ mL}}{20 \text{ gtt}} \times \frac{60 \text{ min}}{1 \text{ h}}$$

$$= \frac{50 \times 60}{20} \text{ mL/h}$$

$$= 150 \text{ mL/h}$$

Determining the millilitres received in four hours, $\dfrac{150 \text{ mL}}{1 \text{ h}} = \dfrac{x \text{ mL}}{4 \text{ h}}$

$$x = 150 \times 4 = 600 \text{ mL}$$

Therefore, the volume of solution remaining in the bag after four hours is 1,500 – 600 = 900 mL.

(ii) We need to determine the new flow rate in mL/h.

$$\textit{Flow Rate (mL/h)} = \frac{45 \text{ gtt}}{1 \text{ min}} \times \frac{1 \text{ mL}}{20 \text{ gtt}} \times \frac{60 \text{ min}}{1 \text{ h}}$$

$$= \frac{45 \times 60}{20} \text{ mL/h}$$

$$= 135 \text{ mL/h}$$

There are 900 mL remaining in the bag.

Determining the amount of time to administer 900 mL, $\dfrac{135 \text{ mL}}{1 \text{ h}} = \dfrac{900 \text{ mL}}{x \text{ h}}$

$$135x = 900$$

$$x = 6.666666\dots \text{ h}$$

Expressing the amount of time in hours and minutes, $= 6 \text{ h} + (0.666666\dots \times 60) \text{ min}$

$$= 6 \text{ h } 40 \text{ min}$$

Therefore, 6 hours and 40 minutes remain until the bag is empty.

| Example 10.5-h | Determining the Amount of IV Solution Remaining After a Time Period and Increasing the Flow Rate |

A physician orders 1,000 mL of IV solution over eight hours with a drop factor of 15 gtt/mL. The IV line is set to run at 30 gtt/min.

(i) What volume of solution remains in the bag after six hours?

(ii) What level must the flow rate be increased to (in drops per minute) so that the volume of the IV bag is completely infused based on the time ordered?

Solution

Flow Rate (gtt/min) = 30 gtt/min

Drop Factor = 15 gtt/mL

(i)
$$Flow\ Rate\ (mL/h) = \frac{30\ gtt}{1\ min} \times \frac{1\ mL}{15\ gtt} \times \frac{60\ min}{1\ h}$$

$$= \frac{30 \times 60}{15}\ mL/h$$

$$= 120\ mL/h$$

Determining the millilitres received in six hours, $\qquad \dfrac{120\ mL}{1\ h} = \dfrac{x\ mL}{6\ h}$

$$x = 120 \times 6 = 720\ mL$$

Therefore, the volume of solution remaining in the bag after six hours is 1,000 − 720 = 280 mL.

(ii) The IV solution was to be administered over eight hours. After six hours, 720 mL of solution is administered. Over the remaining two hours, 280 mL must be administered.

$$Flow\ Rate\ (gtt/min) = \frac{280\ mL}{2\ h} \times \frac{15\ gtt}{1\ mL} \times \frac{1\ h}{60\ min}$$

$$= \frac{280 \times 15}{2 \times 60}\ gtt/min$$

$$= 35\ gtt/min$$

Therefore, the flow rate must be increased to 35 gtt/min in order to finish on time.

IV Piggyback (IVPB)

So far, we have examined IV injections for the purpose of replacing and maintaining bodily fluids in a patient. We will now examine the use of IV injections for the purpose of administering medication to a patient.

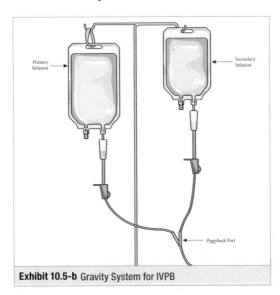

Primary Infusion

Secondary Infusion

Piggyback Port

Exhibit 10.5-b Gravity System for IVPB

In an IV piggyback (IVPB), the medication is administered via an IV site that already exists for replacement or maintenance purposes. Using the gravity system, a smaller, secondary infusion bag containing the medication is suspended on the same metal hook holding the primary IV solution bag, but at a greater height, as seen in Exhibit 10.5-b. The greater height allows the medication solution to drop faster than the primary solution, ensuring that the medication solution infuses first. Once it is done, the primary solution infusion continues. The medication bags typically hold 10-250 mL of dissolved medication, and is usually infused over a period of 20-60 minutes.

Calculating the Dosage Rate of an IV Infusion

In an IV infusion for replacement/maintenance purposes, we were interested in calculating the **flow rate**, which is the rate at which the IV solution enters the body of the patient, measured in drops per minute. In an IVPB, we are also interested in calculating the **dosage rate**, which is the rate at which the medication enters the body of the patient.

$$Dosage\ Rate = \frac{Dosage\ Ordered}{Time\ Specified}$$

Dosage rates are commonly expressed in milligrams per minute (mg/min) or micrograms per minute (mcg/min).

Example 10.5-i **Determining Dosage Rate**

Consider the following drug order: *morphine 10 mg IVPB q.4.h. infuse in 5 minutes.* Determine the dosage rate of this drug in mg/min.

Solution

Dosage Ordered = 10 mg

Time Specified = 5 min

Therefore, $\qquad Dosage\ Rate = \dfrac{10\ mg}{5\ min} = 2\ mg/min$

Therefore, the dosage rate is 2 mg/min.

Example 10.5-j **Determining Dosage Rate Measured by Body Weight**

Consider the following drug order: *gentimicin sulfate 5 mg/kg IVPB q.d. infuse in 30 minutes.* Determine the dosage rate of this antibiotic in mg/min if the patient weighs 198 pounds.

Solution

Just like how oral medication can be ordered by body weight, a patient with a greater body weight may require more of a parenterally administered drug than a patient with a lower body weight.

Body Weight = 198 lb

Dosage Ordered (mg/kg) = 5 mg/kg

Body weight is expressed in pounds, while dosage quantity is expressed in kilograms. We need to add an additional conversion factor to our dimensional analysis to convert lb into kg.

$$Dosage\ Ordered = 198\ \cancel{lb} \times \frac{1\ kg}{2.2\ \cancel{lb}} \times \frac{5\ mg}{1\ kg} \qquad [1\ kg = 2.2\ lb]$$

$$= 90\ \cancel{kg} \times \frac{5\ mg}{1\ \cancel{kg}}$$

$$= 450\ mg$$

Therefore, $\qquad Dosage\ Rate = \dfrac{450\ mg}{30\ min}$

$$= 15\ mg/min$$

Therefore, the dosage rate is 15 mg/min.

Dosage rate is most commonly expressed in milligrams per minute (mg/min). Recall, **flow rate** can be expressed in millilitres per hour (mL/h). In order to calculate the dosage rate from the flow rate (or vice versa), we require a conversion factor which can relate the two. This conversion factor is the **concentration** of the medication, which is the amount of drug in milligrams per millilitre of dissolved medication:

$$Concentration = \frac{Amount\ of\ Drug\ \textbf{(mg)}}{Amount\ of\ Fluid\ \textbf{(mL)}}$$

In general, the relationship between flow rate, dosage rate, and concentration is as follows:

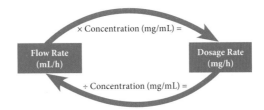

| Example 10.5-k | Calculating Dosage Rate Given Flow Rate in mL/h |

An IVPB is infusing at 100 mL/h. The concentration of the solution is 200 mg in 500 mL. Determine the dosage rate in mg/min.

Solution

Instead of a dosage quantity, we are given a flow rate, measured in millilitres per hour (mL/h).

$$Dosage\ Rate = Flow\ Rate \times Concentration$$

$$= \frac{100\ \text{mL}}{1\ \text{h}} \times \frac{200\ \text{mg}}{500\ \text{mL}}$$

$$= \frac{100 \times 200}{500}\ \text{mg/h}$$

$$= 40\ \text{mg/h}$$

However, the dosage rate is to be expressed in milligrams per minute (mg/min). Therefore, we need to add an additional conversion factor to convert hours to minutes.

$$Dosage\ Rate = \frac{40\ \text{mg}}{1\ \text{h}} \times \frac{1\ \text{h}}{60\ \text{min}} \qquad [1\ \text{h} = 60\ \text{min}]$$

$$= \frac{40}{60}\ \text{mg/min}$$

$$= 0.666666\ldots\ \text{mg/min}$$

Therefore, the dosage rate is approximately 0.66 mg/min.

| Example 10.5-l | Calculating Dosage Rate Given Flow Rate in gtt/min |

An IV bag contains 1,000 mL of NS with 500 mg of a drug (IVPB). It is infusing at 15 gtt/min. The drop factor is 10 gtt/mL.

(i)   Determine the dosage rate in mg/min.

(ii) If the recommended dosage range is between 0.5 - 2.5 mg/min, is this infusion rate safe?

Solution

(i) We are given the flow rate in drops per minute (gtt/min). Therefore, first convert the flow rate to mL/min using the drop factor, and then multiply by the concentration.

$$Dosage\ Rate = \frac{15\ gtt}{1\ min} \times \frac{1\ mL}{10\ gtt} \times \frac{500\ mg}{1,000\ mL}$$

$$= \frac{15 \times 500}{10 \times 1,000}\ mg/min$$

$$= 0.75\ mg/min$$

Therefore, the dosage rate is 0.75 mg/min.

(ii) The dosage rate falls within the recommended range. Therefore, the infusion rate is safe.

Example 10.5-m   Calculating Dosage Rate in mcg Given Flow Rate in gtt/min

An IVPB is infusing at 20 gtt/min. The concentration of the solution is 40 mg in 250 mL of D5W. The drop factor is 10 gtt/mL. What is the dosage rate in mcg/min?

Solution

The dosage rate is to be expressed in micrograms per minute (mcg/min). Therefore, we need to add an additional conversion factor to convert milligrams to micrograms.

$$Dosage\ Rate = \frac{20\ gtt}{1\ min} \times \frac{1\ mL}{10\ gtt} \times \frac{40\ mg}{250\ mL} \times \frac{1,000\ mcg}{1\ mg} \qquad [1\ mg = 1,000\ mcg]$$

$$= \frac{20 \times 40 \times 1,000}{10 \times 250}\ mcg/min$$

$$= 320\ mcg/min$$

Therefore, the dosage rate is 320 mcg/min.

Example 10.5-n   Calculating Dosage Rate and Flow Rate

A surgeon orders *dobutamine hydrochloride 5 mcg/kg/min IVPB*. The suspension solution on hand comes in a 10 mL vial with a concentration of 20 mg/10 mL with instructions to dilute with 40 mL of D5W to a total volume of 50 mL.

(i) How many mcg/min will the patient receive if the patient weighs 143 lb?

(ii) How many gtt/min will the patient receive if the drop factor is 60 gtt/mL?

Solution

(i) We need to calculate the dosage rate.

Body Weight = 143 lb

Dosage Ordered = 5 mcg/kg/min

Body weight is expressed in pounds, while dosage ordered is expressed in kilograms. We need to add an additional conversion factor to our dimensional analysis to convert lb into kg [1 kg = 2.2 lb].

$$Dosage\ Rate\ (mcg/min) = 143\ lb \times \frac{1\ kg}{2.2\ lb} \times \frac{5\ mcg}{kg \times min}$$

$$= \frac{143 \times 5}{2.2}\ mcg/min$$

$$= 325\ mcg/min$$

Therefore, the patient will receive 325 mcg/min.

Solution
continued

(ii) We need to calculate the flow rate.

$$Flow\ Rate = \frac{Dosage\ Rate}{Concentration}$$

$Dosage\ Rate = 325\ mcg/min$

$Concentration = 20\ mg/50\ mL$

Therefore, $\quad Flow\ Rate = \dfrac{325\ mcg}{1\ min} \times \dfrac{50\ mL}{20\ mg}$

Adding a conversion factor to convert mcg to mg [1 mg = 1,000 mcg],

$$Flow\ Rate = \frac{325\ mcg}{1\ min} \times \frac{1\ mg}{1,000\ mcg} \times \frac{50\ mL}{20\ mg}$$

Adding the drop factor as a conversion factor to convert mL to gtt,

$$Flow\ Rate = \frac{325\ mcg}{1\ min} \times \frac{1\ mg}{1,000\ mcg} \times \frac{50\ mL}{20\ mg} \times \frac{60\ gtt}{1\ mL}$$

$$= \frac{325 \times 50 \times 60}{1,000 \times 20}\ gtt/min$$

$$= 48.75\ gtt/min$$

Therefore, the patient will receive 48 gtt/min.

> Flow rate is rounded **down** to the nearest drop when it contains medication.

10.5 | Exercises

Answers to odd-numbered problems are available at the end of the textbook.

1. An I.V. bag containing 1,500 mL of NS solution is set to run over an 8-hour period. If the drop factor is 15 gtt/mL, determine the flow rate (in gtt/min) that needs to be set.

2. A 1 L I.V. bag is set to infuse over 6 hours. If the drop factor is 20 gtt/mL, determine the flow rate (in gtt/min) that needs to be set.

3. An IV bag has 350 mL to be infused. It is infusing at a rate of 35 gtt/min, and a drop factor of 15 gtt/mL is being used. How long will it take to finish?

4. An IV bag has 1,500 mL to be infused. If the drop factor is 20 gtt/mL and it is infusing at a rate of 50 gtt/min, how long will it take to finish?

5. 450 mL of blood is to be infused at 30 gtt/min. The drop factor on the administration set is 20 gtt/mL. How long will it take to complete the infusion?

6. A unit of 300 mL of blood is to be infused at a rate of 20 gtt/min. The drop factor is set at 10 gtt/mL. How long will it take to complete the infusion?

7. 500 mL of intravenous solution is set to infuse at 25 gtt/min, with a drop factor of 20 gtt/mL. How much solution will remain in the bag after 2 hours and 30 minutes? How long will it take for the entire bag of solution to infuse into the patient's bloodstream, in hours and minutes?

8. 250 mL of intravenous solution is set to infuse at 40 gtt/min, with a drop factor of 60 gtt/mL. How much solution will remain in the bag after 1 hour and 30 minutes? How long will it take for the entire bag of solution to infuse into the patient's bloodstream, in hours and minutes?

9. An I.V. bag containing 1,000 mL of NS solution, with instructions to run over 6 hours, started running at 11:00 PM with a flow rate of 45 gtt/min. At 3:00 AM, 280 mL remained in the bag. Find the drop factor and calculate the adjusted flow rate to run in the required time.

10. An I.V. bag containing 1,500 mL of solution is to be infused over 12 hours. The I.V. started running at 7:00 AM with a flow rate of 40 gtt/min. At 3:00 PM, 540 mL of solution remained in the bag. Find the drop factor and calculate the adjusted flow rate to set on the I.V. line to run the remaining solution in the required time.

11. An I.V. bag containing 100 mL of solution started running at 1:00 PM at a flow rate of 30 gtt/min. At 3:00 PM, the bag contained 40 mL of solution. Determine the drop factor and when the I.V. bag will be empty.

12. An I.V. bag containing 750 mL of D5W solution started running at 9:00 AM with a flow rate of 15 gtt/min. At 12:00 PM, 480 mL of solution remained in the bag. Find the drop factor and determine when the bag will be empty.

13. An I.V. bag is filled with 1,200 mL of NS containing 750 mg and set to infuse at 20 gtt/min, with a drop factor of 10 gtt/mL. The recommended safe dosage range is 0.5-1.5 mg/min.

    a. Calculate the dosage rate in mg/min.

    b. Is this dosage rate within the specified safe range?

14. An I.V. bag is filled with 500 mL of NS containing 400 mg and set to infuse at 50 gtt/min, with a drop factor of 15 gtt/mL. The recommended safe dosage range is 1.0-2.5 mg/min.

    a. Calculate the dosage rate in mg/min.

    b. Is this dosage rate within the specified safe range?

For Problems 15 and 16, you will need to use the conversion 1 mL = 60 mcgtt.

15. A physician orders ampicillin 200 mg/kg/day infused continuously through IVPB over 24 hours, for a patient with septicemia. If the patient weighs 90 kg and the concentration of the I.V. solution is 10 mg/mL, determine the flow rate of ampicillin in mcgtt/min.

16. A physician orders morphine sulfate 75 mcg/kg infused continuously through IVPB over 30 minutes, for a pediatric patient for pain relief. If the patient weighs 30 kg and the concentration of the I.V. solution is 100 mcg/mL, determine the flow rate of morphine sulfate in mcgtt/min.

17. A physician orders Invanz (ertapenem sodium) 1 g IVPB, to be infused over 30 minutes. The label on the vial indicates the concentration of the stock solution is 1 g/10 mL, to be diluted for intravenous administration using 50 mL of NS.

    a. Calculate the dosage rate in mg/min.

    b. If the drop factor is set to 10 gtt/mL, determine the flow rate in gtt/min.

18. An anesthesiologist orders Demerol (meperhydrochloride) 125 mg IVPB, to be infused over 2.5 hours while the patient is under general anesthetic. The label on the vial indicates the concentration of the stock solution is 125 mg/5 mL, to be diluted for intravenous administration using 120 mL of NS.

    a. Calculate the dosage rate in mg/min.

    b. If the drop factor is set to 60 gtt/mL, determine the flow rate in gtt/min.

19. A physician orders dopamine hydrochloride IVPB, infused at a rate of 0.5 mg/m^2/min. The patient is 165 cm tall and weighs 84 kg. The available stock solution on hand contains 200 mg of dopamine hydrochloride in 500 mL of D5W.

    a. Calculate the dosage rate in mg/min.

    b. Determine the flow rate in mL/hour.

20. A physician orders cyclophosphamide IVPB, infused at a rate of 600 mg/m^2 over the course of 2 hours. The patient is 187 cm tall and weighs 102 kg. The available stock solution on hand contains 2 g of cyclophosphamide in 1,000 mL of NS.

    a. Calculate the dosage rate in mg/min.

    b. Determine the flow rate in mL/hour.

10 | Review Exercises

For Problems 1 to 8, do the following:

(a)   *Identify the following pieces of information on the drug labels, as applicable:*

    (i)   *Trade name*

    (ii)   *Generic name*

    (iii)   *Drug Identification Number (DIN) or National Drug Code (NDC)*

    (iv)   *Form of drug*

    (v)   *Dosage strength*

    (vi)   *Storage Direction*

(b)   *Determine the amount of each drug to administer to the patient per dose, based on the dosage ordered by the physician.*

1. Order: Sensipar 30 mg p.o. t.i.d.

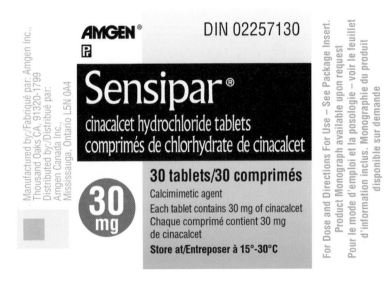

2. Order: Etodolac 0.8 g p.o. q.d.

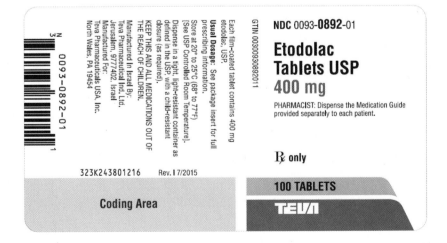

3. Order: Ceftin 250 mg p.o. b.i.d.

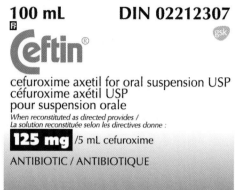

100 mL   DIN 02212307

gsk

Ceftin®

cefuroxime axetil for oral suspension USP
céfuroxime axétil USP
pour suspension orale

When reconstituted as directed provides /
La solution reconstituée selon les directives donne :

125 mg /5 mL cefuroxime

ANTIBIOTIC / ANTIBIOTIQUE

SHAKE WELL BEFORE USING. KEEP TIGHTLY CLOSED.
Store reconstituted suspension between 2° C and 8° C, in a
refrigerator. Discard after 10 days.
Each bottle contains: Cefuroxime axetil equivalent to
cefuroxime 2.5 g.
DOSAGE: Infants and children 3 months to 12 years:
Otitis media and skin structure infection: 15 mg/kg twice
daily. Maximum 1 g per day.
Pharyngitis and tonsillitis: 10 mg/kg twice daily.
Maximum 500 mg per day.
TO THE PHARMACIST:
To reconstitute, shake bottle to loosen granules, add **37 mL**
of water, replace cap, invert bottle and shake vigorously.
Each 5 mL provides 125 mg cefuroxime.
For detailed instructions see carton.
Dispense with enclosed consumer information leaflet.
Store granules between 2° C and 30° C.
Contains Aspartame.
Product Monograph available to physicians and
pharmacists on request.
® Used under license by GlaxoSmithKline Inc.
GlaxoSmithKline Inc., Mississauga, Ontario L5N 6L4

1000000
0126767

4. Order: Clavulin 750 mg/day p.o. divided t.i.d.

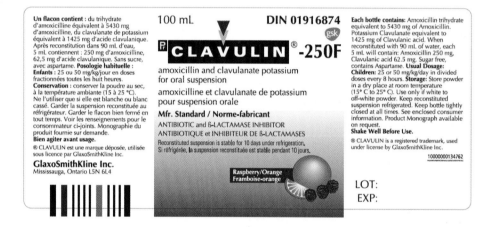

Un flacon contient : du trihydrate
d'amoxicilline équivalent à 5430 mg
d'amoxicilline, du clavulanate de potassium
équivalent à 1425 mg d'acide clavulanique.
Après reconstitution dans 90 mL d'eau,
5 mL contiennent : 250 mg d'amoxicilline,
62,5 mg d'acide clavulanique. Sans sucre,
avec aspartame. **Posologie habituelle :**
Enfants : 25 ou 50 mg/kg/jour en doses
fractionnées toutes les huit heures.
Conservation : conserver la poudre au sec,
à la température ambiante (15 à 25 °C).
Ne l'utiliser que si elle est blanche ou blanc
cassé. Garder la suspension reconstituée au
réfrigérateur. Garder le flacon bien fermé en
tout temps. Voir les renseignements pour le
consommateur ci-joints. Monographie du
produit fournie sur demande.
Bien agiter avant usage.
® CLAVULIN est une marque déposée, utilisée
sous licence par GlaxoSmithKline Inc.
GlaxoSmithKline Inc.
Mississauga, Ontario L5N 6L4

100 mL   DIN 01916874

gsk

CLAVULIN®**-250F**

amoxicillin and clavulanate potassium
for oral suspension

amoxicilline et clavulanate de potassium
pour suspension orale

Mfr. Standard / Norme-fabricant

ANTIBIOTIC and ß-LACTAMASE INHIBITOR
ANTIBIOTIQUE et INHIBITEUR DE ß-LACTAMASES

Reconstituted suspension is stable for 10 days under refrigeration.
Si réfrigérée, la suspension reconstituée est stable pendant 10 jours.

Raspberry/Orange
Framboise-orange

Each bottle contains: Amoxicillin trihydrate
equivalent to 5430 mg of Amoxicillin.
Potassium Clavulanate equivalent to
1425 mg of Clavulanic acid. When
reconstituted with 90 mL of water, each
5 mL will contain: Amoxicillin 250 mg,
Clavulanic acid 62.5 mg. Sugar free,
contains Aspartame. **Usual Dosage:**
Children: 25 or 50 mg/kg/day in divided
doses every 8 hours. **Storage:** Store powder
in a dry place at room temperature
(15° C to 25° C). Use only if white to
off-white powder. Keep reconstituted
suspension refrigerated. Keep bottle tightly
closed at all times. See enclosed consumer
information. Product Monograph available
on request.
Shake Well Before Use.
® CLAVULIN is a registered trademark, used
under license by GlaxoSmithKline Inc.

10000000134762

LOT:
EXP:

5. Order: Nucala 250 mg SC q.d.

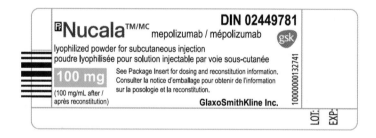

Nucala™/MC   mepolizumab / mépolizumab   DIN 02449781

gsk

lyophilized powder for subcutaneous injection
poudre lyophilisée pour solution injectable par voie sous-cutanée

100 mg

(100 mg/mL after /
après reconstitution)

See Package Insert for dosing and reconstitution information.
Consulter la notice d'emballage pour obtenir de l'information
sur la posologie et la reconstitution.

GlaxoSmithKline Inc.

10000000132741

LOT:
EXP:

6. Order: Nplate 250 mcg SC b.i.d.

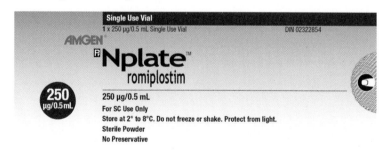

Single Use Vial

1 x 250 μg/0.5 mL Single Use Vial   DIN 02322854

AMGEN

Nplate™
romiplostim

250
μg/0.5 mL

250 μg/0.5 mL
For SC Use Only
Store at 2° to 8°C. Do not freeze or shake. Protect from light.
Sterile Powder
No Preservative

7. Order: Typherix 25 mcg IM

DIN 02242727
Single Dose 0.5 mL
Dose unique de 0,5 mL
TYPHERIX®

Typh-I vaccine / vaccin Typh-I
25 µg/0.5 mL. Age: ≥2 years.
I.M. Store at 2° C to 8° C.
25 µg/0,5 mL. Âge : ≥2 ans.
I.M. Conserver entre 2 et 8 °C.
GlaxoSmithKline Inc.   471336

8. Order: Hiberix 10 mcg IM

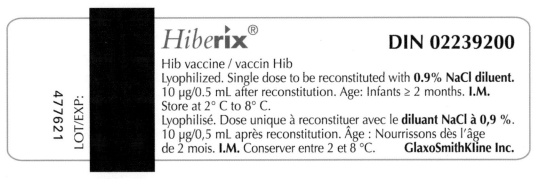

Hiberix®

DIN 02239200

Hib vaccine / vaccin Hib
Lyophilized. Single dose to be reconstituted with **0.9% NaCl diluent.**
10 µg/0.5 mL after reconstitution. Age: Infants ≥ 2 months. **I.M.**
Store at 2° C to 8° C.
Lyophilisé. Dose unique à reconstituer avec le **diluant NaCl à 0,9 %.**
10 µg/0,5 mL après reconstitution. Âge : Nourrissons dès l'âge
de 2 mois. **I.M.** Conserver entre 2 et 8 °C.   **GlaxoSmithKline Inc.**

477621   LOT/EXP:

For Problems 9 to 16, (i) interpret the drug order, and (ii) determine the amount of each drug to administer to the patient per dose, based on the dosage ordered by the physician.

9. Order: Cephalexin 1 g p.o. t.i.d.

   Dose available on hand: 500 mg/capsule

10. Order: Minoxidil 7.5 mg p.o. stat

    Dose available on hand: 2.5 mg/tab

11. Order: Acetaminophen 0.32 g p.o. q.4.h. p.r.n for fever

    Dose available on hand: 160 mg/5 mL

12. Order: Digoxin Elixir 0.5 mg p.o. q.d.

    Dose available on hand: 50 mcg/mL

13. Order: Nalbuphine Hydrochloride 5 mg SC q.6.h. p.r.n for pain

    Dose available on hand: 10 mg/mL

14. Order: Heparin Sodium 4,000 units SC b.i.d.

    Dose available on hand: 5,000 units/mL

15. Order: Hydroxyzine Hydrochloride 100 mg IM stat

    Dose available on hand: 50 mg/mL

16. Order: Morphine Sulfate 10 mg IM q.8.h. p.r.n. for pain

    Dose available on hand: 100 mg/4 mL

For Problems 17 and 18, identify (i) the total capacity of the syringe, (ii) the calibration of the syringe, and (iii) the volume of solution in the syringe:

17.

18.

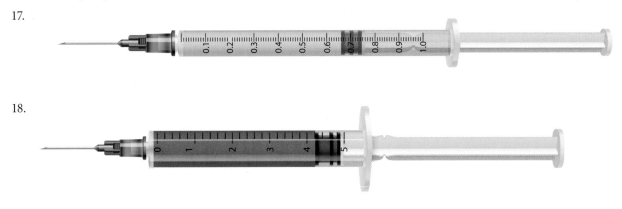

For the following problems, round your answer to 2 decimal places, unless otherwise indicated.

19. Calculate the BSA of the following patients:

    a. A man who is 5' 9" tall and weighs 185 lb.

    b. A woman who is 165 cm tall and weighs 64.8 kg.

    c. A child who is 4' 4" tall and weighs 28.2 kg.

20. Calculate the BSA of the following patients:

    a. A man who is 188 cm tall and weighs 215 lb.

    b. A woman who is 5' 4" tall and weighs 122 lb.

    c. A child who is 102 cm tall and weighs 17.5 kg.

For Problems 21 to 28, calculate the correct dosage to be administered.

21. A doctor prescribes hydrocodone 15 mg p.o. q.12.h. p.r.n. pain, 14-day supply. The dose on hand is a scored tablet (meaning it can safely be cut in half) containing 10 mg of hydrocodone. Interpret the order, calculate the number of tablets the patient should take per dose, and determine the number of tablets to be dispensed to fill the prescription.

22. A doctor prescribes levothyroxin 37.5 mcg p.o. q.d., 60-day supply. The drug comes in 0.075 mg scored tablets. Interpret the order, calculate the number of tablets the patient should take per dose, and determine the number of tablets to be dispensed to fill the prescription.

23. A physician orders acetaminophen 15 mg/kg p.o. q.4-6.h. p.r.n. pain for an infant patient weighing 8.8 kg. The infant acetaminophen is suspended in a liquid solution with a concentration of 80 mg/mL. Interpret the order and determine the amount of the solution to administer per dose.

24. A physician orders azithromycin 12 mg/kg p.o. q.d. for a child patient who weighs 10 kg to fight an infection. The azithromycin is suspended in a liquid solution with a concentration of 200 mg/5 mL. Interpret the order and determine the amount of the solution to administer per dose.

25. A physician orders cefaclor 250 mg, p.o. q.8.h. The vial of liquid medication on hand has a drug concentration of 375 mg/5 mL. How much solution must be given per dose? Per day?

26. A doctor prescribes atovaquone 750 mg, p.o. q.12.h., 21-day supply to treat Pnuemocystis pneumonia in a patient. The drug comes suspended in a liquid with a concentration of 150 mg/mL. Determine the dosing instructions and the amount of the liquid medication that should be dispensed to fill the prescription.

27. An oncologist orders rituximab 375 mg/m^2 IV infusion q.week for 4-8 weeks to be administered to an adult patient undergoing treatment for Non-Hodgkin's Lymphoma. The patient weighs 175 lbs and is 172 cm tall. Determine the correct dose of the drug to give to the patient.

28. A pediatrician orders acyclovir 500 mg/m^2 IV infusion q.8.h. for 7-10 days to be administered to a child patient undergoing treatment for Varicella. The patient weighs 23 kg and is 3' 11" tall. Determine the correct dose of the drug to give to the patient.

29. A physician orders diazepam 4 mg IM q.3.h. for an adult with moderate anxiety. The vial on hand contains 10 mg of Diazepam in powdered form, with instructions to reconstitute with 2 mL of 0.9% Sodium Chloride Injection (Normal Saline).

    a. What is the resulting concentration of the reconstituted solution (in mg/mL)?

    b. Determine the amount of solution to administer to the patient.

    c. What size syringe should be used to administer the dose calculated in part (b)?

30. A physician orders morphine 15 mg IM q.4.h. p.r.n. pain for a patient recovering from a major surgery. The vial on hand contains 50 mg of morphine in powdered form, with instructions to reconstitute with 5 mL of sterile water.

    a. What is the resulting concentration of the reconstituted solution (in mg/mL)?

    b. Determine the amount of solution to administer to the patient.

    c. What size syringe should be used to administer the dose calculated in part (b)?

31. A 1,500 mL I.V. bag of D5W is set to infuse over 8 hours with a drop factor of 15 gtt/mL. Determine the flow rate to be set in gtt/min so that the infusion will complete on time.

32. A 500 mL I.V. bag of NS is set to infuse over 4 hours with a drop factor of 20 gtt/mL. Determine the flow rate to be set in gtt/min so that the infusion will complete on time.

33. A 1 L I.V. bag of NS started running at 11:00 PM at a flow rate of 50 gtt/min. If the drop factor is 10 gtt/mL, when will the infusion be complete?

34. A 2 L I.V. bag of D5W started running at 9:00 AM at a flow rate of 75 gtt/min. If the drop factor is 15 gtt/mL, when will the infusion be complete?

35. At 1:40 PM, an anesthesiologist sets 300 mL of I.V. solution to infuse over the course of the 4-hour surgery, at a rate of 20 gtt/min. At 3:10 PM, 180 mL of solution remains in the I.V. bag. Determine the drop factor used in this I.V. infusion, and adjust the flow rate so that the infusion will be completed in the correct amount of time.

36. At 8:55 AM, an anesthesiologist sets 500 mL of I.V. solution to infuse over the course of the 3-hour surgery, at a rate of 55 gtt/min. At 10:15 AM, 280 mL of solution remains in the I.V. bag. Determine the drop factor used in this I.V. infusion, and adjust the flow rate so that the infusion will be completed in the correct amount of time.

37. An I.V. mini-bag containing 50 mL of solution and 20 mg of drug is infused at a rate of 25 gtt/min using a drop factor of 10 gtt/mL.

   a. Find the dosage rate in mg/min.

   b. If the recommended dosage range is 0.5-1 mg/min, is the administered dose safe?

38. An I.V. mini-bag containing 100 mL of solution and 40 mg of drug is infused at a rate of 50 gtt/min using a drop factor of 15 gtt/mL.

   a. Find the dosage rate in mg/min.

   b. If the recommended dosage range is 0.5-1 mg/min, is the administered dose safe?

39. A pediatrician at a hospital orders levofloxacin 8 mg/kg for a child patient weighing 30 kg. The I.V. solution of levofloxacin has a concentration of 2.5 mg/mL.

   a. Determine the volume of I.V. solution to administer to the patient.

   b. If the infusion is to be administered over the course of 80 minutes, what is the flow rate of the I.V. solution in mL/h?

   c. If the drop factor used is 15 gtt/mL, what is the flow rate of the I.V. solution in gtt/min?

40. An oncologist orders mitomycin 20 mg/m^2 for a patient with a BSA of 1.65 m^2. The I.V. solution of mitomycin has a concentration of 0.5 mg/mL.

   a. Determine the volume of I.V. solution to administer to the patient.

   b. If the infusion is to be administered over the course of 40 minutes, what is the flow rate of the I.V. solution in mL/h?

   c. If the drop factor used is 20 gtt/mL, what is the flow rate of the I.V. solution in gtt/min?

10 | Self-Test Exercises

Answers to all problems are available at the end of the textbook.

Identify the following information on the drug label below:

   (i) Trade name
   (ii) Generic name
   (iii) Drug Identification Number (DIN)

   (iv) Form of drug
   (v) Dosage strength
   (vi) Storage Direction

1.

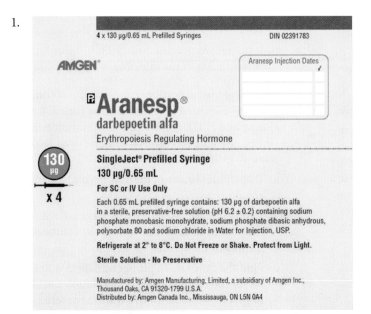

2. Determine the amount of medicine (in cc) in the syringe below:

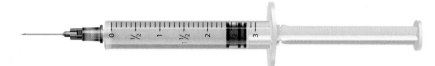

3. Fully interpret the given drug order:
    a. Solu-Medrol 200 mg IV q.i.d.
    b. Acetaminophen 650 mg p.o. q.4.h. p.r.n. for headache

4. The physician orders 7.5 mg of Tranxene SD p.o. b.i.d. for an elderly patient. The drug is available in 15 mg scored tablets. How many tablet(s) would the patient receive in each dose and in one week?

5. A physician orders 0.06 mg/day of Baraclude p.o. divided t.i.d. The oral solution contains 10 mcg/5 mL. How many teaspoons would you deliver in each dose and in 24 hours? [1 tsp = 5 mL]

6. Find the BSA of an adult who is 6 feet 6 inches tall and weighs 105 kg. A drug is ordered 15 mg/m^2 p.o. b.i.d. for this patient. How many mL will a patient receive if the concentration of the solution is 3 mg/mL?

7. A physician orders dexamethasone sodium phosphate 5 mg IM q.12.h. for an adult who had adrenal insufficiency. The patient weighs 190 pounds, and the strength in the vial is 4 mg/mL. If the recommended daily dose is 0.05 – 0.15 mg/kg, is the prescribed dosage safe? How many mL will you administer per day?

8. The recommended dose of Kanamycin to treat tuberculosis is 15 mg/kg/day for an IM injection. A patient weighs 220 pounds and is to receive IM injections q.12.h. Kanamycin for injection contains 500 mg/2 mL.
    a. How many mg should the patient receive per injection? [Use 1 kg = 2.2 lb]
    b. How many mL should the patient receive per injection?

9. A 500 mg vial of powdered Solu-Medrol for IM injection has directions on the label that state "Reconstitute with 8 mL Bacteriostatic Water for Injection with Benzyl Alcohol. When reconstituted as directed, each 8 mL contains: Methylprednisolone sodium succinate equivalent to 500 mg methylprednisolone." If a physician orders Solu-Medrol 150 mg IM q.6.h., how many mL should the nurse administer with each dose?

10. 250 mL of IV solution is set to infuse at 50 gtt/min, with a drop factor of 20 gtt/mL. How much solution will remain in the bag after 1 hour and 30 minutes?

11. An IV bag has 350 mL of solution remaining in it. It is infusing at 30 gtt/min, and a 15 gtt/mL drop factor is being used. How long (in hours and minutes) will it take to finish?

12. An order reads 1,200 mL D5W IV over 8 hours, starting at 2 PM. The drop factor is 10 gtt/mL.
    a. Find the flow rate in gtt/min for this infusion.
    b. The IV was stopped at 3:20 PM for 40 minutes. Determine the amount of fluid remaining in the I.V. bag.
    c. Determine the new flow rate in gtt/min so that the infusion will finish on time?
    d. If the facility has a policy that flow rate adjustments must not exceed 20% of the original rate, is the adjustment required in part (c) within the guidelines?

13. An I.V. bag containing 800 mL of NS solution, with instructions to run over 6 hours, started running at 8:00 AM with a flow rate of 40 gtt/min. At 12:00 PM, 160 mL remained in the bag. Find the drop factor and calculate the adjusted flow rate required for the entire volume of solution to infuse in the required time.

14. An IV bag contains 50 mL of NS with 1 mg of a drug. It is infusing at 45 gtt/min. The drop factor is 15 gtt/mL.
    a. Find the dosage rate in mg/min.
    b. If the recommended dose is 25 – 75 mcg/min, is this infusion in the safe dose range? Explain.

15. The dosage instruction for a cancer drug is 400 mg/m^2 IVPB to be infused over 3 hours. The patient weighs 89.2 kg and is 178 cm tall. The concentration in the IV bag is 1 g in 250 mL NS, and the drop factor is set to 15 gtt/mL.
    a. Determine the size of the dose (in mg) the patient should receive.
    b. Determine the volume of solution (in mL) that the patient should receive over the course of the infusion.
    c. Find the flow rate in gtt per minute that must be set for the required volume of solution calculated in part (b) to be infused in the time ordered.

Answer Key

Chapter 1

Exercises 1.1

1. a. hundreds ; 600

    b. tens ; 80

    c. ten thousands ; 90,000

3. a. thousands ; 4,000

    b. millions ; 5,000,000

    c. hundred thousands ; 300,000

5. a. 800 + 60 ; eight hundred sixty

    b. 7,000 + 800 + 5 ; seven thousand, eight hundred five

7. a. 90,000 + 4,000 + 900 + 70 + 5; ninety-four thousand, nine hundred seventy-five

    b. 600,000 + 80,000 + 4,000 + 100 + 30 + 7; six hundred eighty-four thousand, one hundred thirty-seven

9. a. 9,000,000 + 80,000 + 4,000 + 300 + 50 + 1 ; nine million, eighty-four thousand, three hundred fifty-one

    b. 20,000,000 + 3,000,000 + 6,000 + 40 + 5 ; twenty-three million, six thousand, forty-five

11. a. 456 ; four hundred fifty-six

    b. 1,932 ; one thousand, nine hundred thirty-two

13. a. 5,301 ; five thousand, three hundred one

    b. 7,088 ; seven thousand, eighty-eight

15. a. 60,780 ; sixty thousand, seven hundred eighty

    b. 20,104 ; twenty thousand, one hundred four

17. a. 1,005 ; 1,000 + 5

    b. 7,020 ; 7000 + 20

19. a. 65,244 ; 60,000 + 5,000 + 200 + 40 + 4

    b. 833,641 ; 800,000 + 30,000 + 3,000 + 600 + 40 + 1

21. a. 2,000,001,000 ; 2,000,000,000 + 1,000

    b. 1,000,025,000 ; 1,000,000,000 + 20,000 + 5,000

23. a. 500,000,000

    b. 100,000,000

25. a.

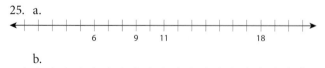

    b.

27. a. <   b. >   c. >   d. <

29. a. 4 is less than 7   b. 16 is greater than 7

    c. 10 is less than 16   d. 0 is less than 4

31. a. 49, 58, 68, 129, 147

    b. 805, 820, 836, 873, 875

33. a. 2,579 ; 2,630 ; 2,668 ; 2,759

    b. 68,336 ; 68,942 ; 69,067 ; 69,999

35. a. 167 ; 761

    b. 4,589 ; 9,854

    c. 24,567 ; 76,542

37. a. 1,630 ; 1,600 ; 2,000

    b. 9,160 ; 9,200 ; 9,000

    c. 25,970 ; 26,000 ; 26,000

    d. 139,840 ; 139,800 ; 140,000

39. a. 760,000 ; 800,000 ; 1,000,000

    b. 3,250,000 ; 3,300,000 ; 3,000,000

    c. 7,560,000 ; 7,600,000 ; 8,000,000

    d. 2,960,000 ; 3,000,000 ; 3,000,000

Exercises 1.2

1. a. 100 ; 95   b. 120 ; 116

3. a. 490 ; 486   b. 430 ; 421

5. a. 1,240 ; 1,229   b. 1,050 ; 1,047

7. a. 1,550 ; 1,547   b. 1,730 ; 1,727

9. a. 600 ; 602   b. 1,100 ; 1,096

11. a. 9,400 ; 9,317   b. 5,800; 5,757

13. a. 4,400 ; 4,339   b. 7,200 ; 7,131

15. a. 10; 16   b. 10; 12

17. a. 300; 299   b. 430; 427

19. a. 270; 275   b. 410; 417

21. a. 2,460; 2,457   b. 4,990; 4,988

23. a. 200; 123   b. 100; 138

25. a. 1,600; 1,605   b. 1,600; 1,615

27. a. 3,700; 3,707   b. 200; 163

29. a. 4,000; 3,395   b. 7,000; 6,745

31. a. 48,000; 45,790   b. 45,600; 41,525

33. a. 90,000; 95,872   b. 120,000 ; 113,810

35. a. 7; 9, remainder 6   b. 9; 9, remainder 4

37. a. 6; 4, remainder 11   b. 5; 5, remainder 5

39. a. 39; 48, remainder 9   b. 13; 13, remainder 8

41. a. 35; 38, remainder 7   b. 30; 28, remainder 3

43. a. 15; 14, remainder 199 b. 20; 20, remainder 95

45. a. $408   b. $149

47. a. $2,019   b. $180

49. $1,500   51. 35 tables

53. 18 weeks   55. $576

57. $1,073   59. 168 students

61. a. $2,130   b. $2,130

63. a. 770 patients   b. 762 patients

     c. 460 patients   d. 449 patients

65. a. 200 patients   b. 227 patients

67. 14 pounds   69. 10 nurses

Exercises 1.3

1. 23, 29, 31, 37

3. 32, 33, 34, 35, 36, 38, 39, 40, 42, 44, 45, 46, 48, 49

5. a. 31, 41, 59   b. 23, 37, 53

7. a. 1, 2, 4, 7, 14, 28; 2, 7   b. 1, 5, 7, 35; 5, 7

9. a. 1, 2, 4, 7, 8, 14, 28, 56; 2, 7

     b. 1, 2, 4, 5, 8, 10, 16, 20, 40, 80; 2, 5

11. a. 1, 2, 3, 5, 6, 10, 15 ,30; 2, 3, 5

     b. 1, 2, 3, 6, 7, 14, 21, 42; 2, 3, 7

13. a. 1, 2, 4, 5, 8, 10, 20, 40; 2, 5

     b. 1, 7, 49; 7

15. a. 5, 10, 15, 20, 25, 30   b. 12, 24, 36, 48, 60, 72

17. a. 7, 14, 21, 28, 35, 42   b. 15, 30, 45, 60, 75, 90

19. a. 48   b. 252

21. a. 50   b. 180

23. a. 60   b. 150

25. a. 120   b. 60

27. a. 40   b. 48

29. a. 84   b. 84

31. a. 60   b. 240

33. a. 14 : 1, 2, 7, 14; 35 : 1, 5, 7, 35 ; Common : 1, 7 ; GCF : 7

     b. 8 : 1, 2, 4, 8 ; 36 : 1, 2, 3, 4, 6, 9, 12, 18, 36; Common : 1, 2, 4; GCF: 4

35. a. 16: 1, 2, 4, 8, 16; 30: 1, 2, 3, 5, 6, 10, 15, 30; Common: 1, 2 ; GCF: 2

     b. 36: 1, 2, 3, 4, 6, 9, 12, 18, 36; 42: 1, 2, 3, 6, 7, 14, 21, 42; Common: 1, 2, 3, 6; GCF: 6

37. a. 35: 1, 5, 7, 35 ; 75: 1, 3, 5, 15, 25, 75; Common: 1,5 ; GCF: 5

     b. 24: 1, 2, 3, 4, 6, 8, 12, 24 ; 72: 1, 2, 3, 4, 6, 8, 9, 12, 18, 24, 36, 72; Common: 1, 2, 3, 4, 6, 8, 12, 24; GCF: 24

39. a. 6: 1, 2, 3, 6 ; 8: 1, 2, 4, 8 ; 10: 1, 2, 5, 10; Common: 1, 2 ; GCF: 2

     b. 10: 1, 2, 5, 10 ; 15: 1, 3, 5, 15 ; 25: 1, 5, 25; Common: 1, 5 ; GCF: 5

41. a. 24: 1, 2, 3, 4, 6, 8, 12, 24; 36: 1, 2, 3, 4, 6, 9, 12, 18, 36; 40: 1, 2, 4, 5, 8, 10, 20, 40 ; Common: 1, 2, 4 ; GCF: 4

     b. 12: 1, 2, 3, 4, 6, 12; 36: 1, 2, 3,4, 6, 9, 12, 18, 36; 48: 1, 2, 3, 4, 6, 8, 12, 16, 24, 48; Common: 1, 2, 3, 4, 6, 12; GCF: 12

43. a. 50: 1, 2, 5, 10, 25, 50; 75: 1, 3, 5, 15, 25, 75; 125: 1, 5, 25, 125; Common: 1, 5, 25; GCF: 25

     b. 60: 1, 2, 3, 4, 5, 6, 10, 12, 15, 20, 30, 60; 90: 1, 2, 3, 5, 6, 9, 10, 15, 18, 30, 45, 90; 120: 1, 2, 3, 4, 5, 6, 8, 10, 12, 15, 20, 24, 30, 40, 60, 120; Common: 1, 2, 3, 5, 6, 10, 15, 30; GCF: 30

45. 14 fl oz   47. April 12th

49. 18 syringes   51. 15 days

Exercises 1.4

1. a. 5^3 b. 7^5

3. a. 8^5 b. 4^5

5. a. Base 6 ; Exponent 2   b. Base 10 ; Exponent 9

7. a. Base 7 ; Exponent 5   b. Base 12 ; Exponent 1

9. a. $2 \times 2 \times 2 \times 2 \times 2 \times 2 \times 2 \times 2 = 256$

     b. $5 \times 5 \times 5 \times 5 = 625$

11. a. $7 \times 7 \times 7 \times 7 = 2,401$

     b. $4 \times 4 \times 4 \times 4 \times 4 \times 4 \times 4 = 16,384$

13. a. 200   b. 432

15. a. 0   b. 81

17. a. 61   b. 28

19. a. 60   b. 36

21. a. 17   b. 9

23. a. 40   b. 99

25. a. 7   b. 5

27. a. 3   b. 13

29. a. 8   b. 3

31. a. 12   b. 45

33. a. 40   b. 81

35. a. 64   b. 510

37. a. 27   b. 35

39. a. 5   b. 186

41. a. 32   b. 61

43. a. 250   b. 52,020

45. a. 64   b. 10

47. a. 5   b. 94

49. 123

Review Exercises 1

1. a. 9,000 + 20 + 4; nine thousand, twenty-four
   b. 30,000 + 8,000 + 20 + 4; thirty-eight thousand, twenty-four
   c. 400,000 + 5,000 + 30 + 7; four hundred five thousand, thirty-seven
   d. 2,000,000 + 600,000 + 1,000 + 70 + 1; two million, six hundred one thousand, seventy-one

3. a. 9,903; 9,000 + 900 + 3
   b. 59,303; 50,000 + 9,000 + 300 + 3
   c. 700,888; 700,000 + 800 + 80 + 8
   d. 7,076,055; 7,000,000 + 70,000 + 6,000 + 55 + 5

5. a. >   b. <   c. >   d. <

7. a. 9,100; 9,078   b. 4,200; 4,145
   c. 4,300; 4,369   d. 1,700; 1,612

9. a. 11,730   b. 5,925
   c. 46   d. 318, remainder: 13

11. a. 80   b. 108   c. 96

13. a. 1   b. 24   c. 4

15. a. 5   b. 9

17. a. 8   b. 9

19. a. 78   b. 49

21. a. 537   b. 18

23. a. 4   b. 10

25. a. 0   b. 9

27. a. 703   b. 16

29. $516   31. 650 coats

33. $3,015   35. $18,975

37. 61 boxes   39. 8 metres

41. 9:00 AM

Self-test Exercises 1

1. a. 7,300; 7,264   b. 6,900; 6,864
   c. 520,000; 445,900   d. 67; 59, remainder: 42

2. a. 24   b. 34   c. 3   d. 2

3. a. 6   b. 56   c. 36   d. 2

4. a. 54   b. 4   c. 108   d. 40

5. a. 18   b. 2   c. 20   d. 9

6. 2,550 boys; 5,100 girls

7. a. 37,278 deaths   b. 884

8. 25,995 kg   9. $1,212

10. $937.50   11. 394 cars

12. a. 707 patients   b. 582 patients

13. 320   14. 243 pounds

15. After 1,008 seconds   16. 6 m

Chapter 2

Exercises 2.1

1. a. Proper   b. Mixed

3. a. Improper   b. Mixed

5. a. Mixed   b. Improper

7. a. $\dfrac{16}{7}$ b. $\dfrac{25}{8}$ 9. a. $\dfrac{29}{5}$ b. $\dfrac{27}{4}$

11. a. $2\dfrac{5}{7}$ b. $5\dfrac{5}{8}$ 13. a. $7\dfrac{2}{3}$ b. $5\dfrac{1}{6}$

15. $\dfrac{44}{5}$; Equivalent   17. $\dfrac{54}{7}$; Not equivalent

19. $\dfrac{54}{7}$; Equivalent   21. $\dfrac{37}{9}$; Equivalent

23. $3\dfrac{3}{4}$; Not Equivalent   25. $3\dfrac{3}{5}$; Equivalent

27. $3\dfrac{8}{9}$; Equivalent   29. $3\dfrac{5}{12}$; Equivalent

31. a. $\dfrac{8}{5}$; $\dfrac{5}{8}$ b. $\dfrac{4}{7}$; $\dfrac{7}{4}$

33. a. $\dfrac{7}{6}$; $\dfrac{6}{7}$ b. 4; $\dfrac{1}{4}$

35. a. $\dfrac{4}{7}$; $\dfrac{7}{4}$ b. $\dfrac{5}{8}$; $\dfrac{8}{5}$

37. Equivalent   39. Not Equivalent

41. Not Equivalent   43. Equivalent

45. a. 12   b. 45

47. a. 24   b. 3

49. a. 15   b. 30

51. $\dfrac{1}{3}$ 53. $\dfrac{3}{4}$ 55. $\dfrac{3}{4}$ 57. $\dfrac{149}{240}$

Exercises 2.2

1. $\dfrac{2}{5}$ 3. $\dfrac{12}{15}$ 5. $\dfrac{8}{7}$ 7. $\dfrac{8}{9}$

9. $\dfrac{5}{8}$; $\dfrac{3}{5}$

11. a. $1\dfrac{1}{2}$ b. $1\dfrac{1}{3}$

13. a. $2\dfrac{1}{6}$ b. $18\dfrac{2}{15}$

15. a. $15\dfrac{11}{12}$ b. $14\dfrac{5}{12}$

17. a. $\dfrac{5}{9}$ b. $\dfrac{3}{10}$

19. a. $1\dfrac{7}{24}$ b. $14\dfrac{5}{8}$

21. a. $3\dfrac{1}{2}$ b. $2\dfrac{1}{10}$

23. a. 4   b. $2\dfrac{1}{3}$

25. a. $\dfrac{15}{88}$ b. $12\dfrac{1}{2}$

27. a. $\dfrac{1}{14}$ b. $3\dfrac{1}{3}$

29. a. $1\dfrac{1}{2}$ b. $\dfrac{3}{32}$

31. a. $\dfrac{1}{10}$ b. $2\dfrac{2}{3}$

33. a. $\dfrac{2}{5}$ b. $3\dfrac{3}{4}$

35. a. $\dfrac{4}{9}$ b. $12\dfrac{2}{3}$

37. a. $\dfrac{309}{1,000}$ b. $1\dfrac{9}{10}$

39. a. $\dfrac{39}{125}$ b. $\dfrac{11}{16}$

41. a. $\dfrac{2}{3}$ b. $1\dfrac{2}{9}$

43. 4   45. $4\dfrac{2}{5}$

47. $\dfrac{2}{3}$ 49. $5\dfrac{7}{15}$ hours

51. $\dfrac{7}{8}$ pounds   53. $\dfrac{13}{28}$ kg

55. $\dfrac{1}{10}$ 57. 1,350 books

59. $11\dfrac{1}{4}$ mL   61. $3\dfrac{1}{2}$ km

63. 14 pieces   65. 200 doses

67. $10\dfrac{2}{3}$ days   69. 304 bulbs

71. $2\dfrac{2}{5}$ litres   73. A: 75 mL ; B: 190 mL

Exercises 2.3

1. a. 0.6   b. 0.007

3. a. 0.12   b. 0.0029

5. a. 7.5   b. 9.503

7. a. 3.67   b. 29.72

9. 87.2; 80 + 7 + 0.2   11. 3.04; 3 + 0.04

13. 0.0401; 0.04 + 0.0001

15. 89.0625; 80 + 9 + 0.06 + 0.002 + 0.0005

17. 1,787.025; 1,000 + 700 + 80 + 7 + 0.02 + 0.005

19. 412.65; 400 + 10 + 2 + 0.6 + 0.05

21. 1,600,000.02; 1,000,000 + 600,000 + 0.02

23. 500.023 ; 500 + 0.02 + 0.003

25. a. Forty-two and fifty-five hundredths

    b. seven hundred thirty-four and one hundred twenty-five thousandths

27. a. Twenty-five hundredths

    b. nine and five tenths

29. a. Seven and seven hundredths

    b. Fifteen and two thousandths

31. a. Sixty-two thousandths

    b. Fifty-four thousandths

33. a. 0.034 , 0.043 , 0.304 , 0.403

    b. 5.076 , 5.607 , 5.67 , 5.7

35. 415   37. 8

39. 24.2   41. 10.4

43. 14.36   45. 181.13

47. $16.78   49. $10.00

Exercises 2.4

1. 1,716.045   3. 869.593

5. 479.444   7. 964.571

9. 240.922   11. 238.192

13. 15.88   15. 281.283

17. 229.668   19. 415.01

21. 744.606   23. 259.5571

25. 0.344   27. 319.4598

29. 91.575   31. $7.53\overline{1}$

33. $24.\overline{3}$ 35. 12.4

37. 400 ; 381.2   39. 0.4 ; 0.37

41. 8 ; 7.812   43. 2 ; 1.93

45. 210 ; 238.63   47. $378.64

49. $14.86   51. $76.38

53. $64.56   55. $11.54

57. 21.85 thousand   59. $187.86

61. $86.46   63. $44.21

65. $3,469.09   67. $54.45

69. 14 pieces   71. $1,165.53

Exercises 2.5

1. a. $\dfrac{1}{5}$ b. 0.75   b. $\dfrac{3}{50}$

3. a. 0.36   b. $\dfrac{1}{250}$ c. 0.14

5. a. 0.5   b. $\dfrac{2}{5}$ c. 0.06

7. a. $\dfrac{1}{200}$ b. 0.36   c. $\dfrac{1}{100}$

9. a. $\dfrac{7}{2}$ b. 1.6   c. $\dfrac{28}{5}$

11. a. 5.05   b. $\dfrac{34}{5}$ c. 2.75

13. a. $2\dfrac{1}{4}$ b. 1.75   c. $4\dfrac{1}{50}$

15. a. 8.35   b. $16\dfrac{1}{200}$ c. 15.5

17. a. $\dfrac{2}{3}$ b. $0.2\bar{5}$ c. $\dfrac{25}{99}$

19. a. $0.\bar{4}$ b. $\dfrac{2}{9}$ c. $0.\overline{285714}$

21. a. $\dfrac{9}{25}$ b. $\dfrac{36}{49}$

23. a. $\dfrac{27}{64}$ b. $\dfrac{625}{81}$

25. a. $1\dfrac{7}{9}$ b. $42\dfrac{7}{8}$

27. a. $\dfrac{8}{75}$ b. $\dfrac{3}{256}$

29. a. 4 b. $\dfrac{9}{4}$

31. a. $\dfrac{1}{3}$ b. $\dfrac{1}{7}$

33. a. $\dfrac{2}{5}$ b. $\dfrac{9}{4}$

35. a. $\dfrac{10}{11}$ b. $\dfrac{1}{10}$

37. a. 1 b. $\dfrac{4}{5}$

39. a. $2\dfrac{1}{4}$ b. $2\dfrac{1}{2}$

41. a. 0.001 b. 1.331

43. a. 0.16 b. 0.000008

45. a. 0.5 b. 0.7

47. a. 1.1 b. 1.3

49. a. 0.1 b. 0.07

51. a. $14\dfrac{19}{25}$ b. $\dfrac{1}{4}$

53. a. $4\dfrac{44}{45}$ b. 4

55. a. 0.338 b. 0.01

57. $2\dfrac{127}{192}$ 59. $1\dfrac{5}{7}$

61. 0.1 63. 0.6

Review Exercises 2

1. a. 3 ; 48 b. 4 ; 60 c. 4 ; 15 d. 27 ; 24

3. a. < b. > c. = d. =

5. a. $1\dfrac{3}{5}$ b. $1\dfrac{1}{2}$ c. $7\dfrac{1}{3}$ d. $11\dfrac{1}{3}$

7. a. $\dfrac{5}{23}$ b. $\dfrac{31}{12}$ c. $\dfrac{14}{3}$ d. $\dfrac{4}{5}$

9. a. Five tenths

   b. Seven thousandths

   c. Twelve hundredths

   d. Twenty-nine thousandths

11. a. Thirty-two and four hundredths

    b. Two hundred and two tenths

    c. Forty-five thousand, five and one thousandth

    d. One million, five thousand, seventy-one and twenty-five hundredths

13. a. 564.667 b. 40.103 c. 79.3802 d. $12.848\bar{3}$

15. a. 500; 500.5 b. 0.4; 0.38 c. 36; 33.67 d. 3; 3.27

17. 0.189 19. 1.996

21. a. $\dfrac{1}{40}$ b. 0.625 c. $\dfrac{2}{25}$

    d. 0.28 e. $\dfrac{1}{500}$ f. 0.78

23. $11\dfrac{13}{24}$ kg 25. $5\dfrac{5}{6}$ miles

27. 399 km 29. $22,000

31. $2,201.40 33. $870.89

35. 96 37. $15\dfrac{27}{64}$

39. $1\dfrac{1}{4}$ 41. $\dfrac{21}{625}$

43. $\dfrac{30,773}{43,200}$ 45. $4\dfrac{9}{10}$

47. $5\dfrac{2}{5}$

Self-test Exercises 2

1. a. 32 ; 15 b. 11 ; 30

   c. 18 ; 96 d. 66 ; 24

2. a. $\dfrac{15}{2}$ b. $\dfrac{26}{3}$

   c. $\dfrac{16}{9}$ d. $\dfrac{9}{55}$

3. a. $13\dfrac{3}{4}$ b. $1\dfrac{13}{15}$

   c. $\dfrac{1}{2}$ d. $2\dfrac{5}{8}$

4. a. 27.9028 b. 8.133

   c. 2.13792 d. $2.297\bar{6}$

5. a. Four thousandths

   b. Six and five hundredths

   c. Three hundred and two hundredths

   d. Seven and seventy-one thousandths

6. a. $\dfrac{5}{8}$ b. $\dfrac{16}{5}$ c. $\dfrac{17}{5}$

   d. $\dfrac{8}{11}$ e. $\dfrac{7}{3}$ f. $\dfrac{26}{15}$

7. a. 0.35 b. 2.2 c. 1.8

   d. $0.\bar{8}$ e. $1.0\bar{6}$ f. $2.\bar{3}$

8. 593.75 km ; 37.8 cm 9. 13 deliveries

10. $1,500
11. $\frac{1}{3}$; $80
12. $26.67 per hour
13. $33.76
14. $1,025
15. 9 km
16. $1\frac{16}{25}$
17. $25\frac{13}{40}$
18. $\frac{2}{9}$
19. $8\frac{3}{4}$
20. $12\frac{17}{24}$
21. $7\frac{7}{150}$
22. $4\frac{21}{40}$
23. $\frac{7}{54}$
24. $4\frac{1}{8}$

Chapter 3

Exercises 3.1

1. a. $7 ; 4 ; 7^4$
   b. $9 \times 9 \times 9 \times 9 \times 9 ; 9 ; 5$
   c. $3 \times 3 \times 3 \times 3 ; 3^4$
   d. $\frac{2}{5} ; 6 ; \left(\frac{2}{5}\right)^6$
   e. $\frac{5}{7} \times \frac{5}{7} \times \frac{5}{7} \times \frac{5}{7} \times \frac{5}{7} ; \frac{5}{7} ; 5$
   f. $\frac{4}{7} \times \frac{4}{7} \times \frac{4}{7} ; \left(\frac{4}{7}\right)^3$
   g. $1.15 ; 4 ; 1.15^4$
   h. $1.6 \times 1.6 \times 1.6 ; 1.6 ; 3$
   i. $1.25 \times 1.25 \times 1.25 \times 1.25 \times 1.25 ; 1.25^5$

3. $4^9 ; 262,144$
5. $\left(\frac{1}{2}\right)^7 ; 0.01$
7. $\left(\frac{5}{2}\right)^5 ; 97.66$
9. $(3.25)^6 ; 1,178.42$
11. $6^5 ; 7,776$
13. $\left(\frac{2}{5}\right)^2 ; 0.16$
15. $(1.4)^3 ; 2.74$
17. $6^6 ; 46,656$
19. $\left(\frac{2}{3}\right)^{12} ; 0.01$
21. $(2.5)^6$ or 244.14
23. $3^6 ; 729$
25. $10^6 ; 1,000,000$
27. 2^{10}
29. 3^8
31. 2^2
33. 3^4
35. 150
37. 609
39. 240
41. 58
43. 368
45. 7
47. 609
49. 257
51. 8,000
53. 625
55. 13,168.72 or $\frac{3,200,000}{243}$

57. 91
59. 96
61. 1.375 or $\frac{11}{8}$
63. 5.41
65. 5,184
67. 2.0736
69. 104,976
71. $0.\overline{6}$ or $\frac{2}{3}$
73. 0.75 or $\frac{3}{4}$
75. $0.\overline{3}$ or $\frac{1}{3}$
77. 125
79. 0.28 or $\frac{9}{32}$
81. 0.004 or $\frac{1}{243}$

Exercises 3.2

1. a. $\sqrt{64} ; 8$ b. $\sqrt{\frac{25}{16}} ; 1.25$ or $\frac{5}{4}$
3. a. $\sqrt[3]{8} ; 2$ b. $\sqrt[3]{\frac{27}{64}} ; 0.75$ or $\frac{3}{4}$
5. a. $144^{\frac{1}{2}} ; 12$ b. $64^{\frac{1}{5}} = 2.30$
7. a. $2^{\frac{6}{2}} = 2^3 ; 8$ b. $40^{\frac{1}{2}} ; 6.32$
9. a. $8^{\frac{1}{2}} \times 12^{\frac{1}{2}} ; 9.80$ b. $7^{\frac{1}{2}} \times 14^{\frac{1}{2}} ; 9.90$
11. a. $25^{\frac{2}{4}} \times 25^{\frac{2}{4}} = 25^1 ; 25$ b. $5^{\frac{1}{4}} \times 25^{\frac{3}{4}}; 25$
13. a. $\left(\frac{25}{81}\right)^{\frac{1}{2}} ; 0.\overline{5}$ or $\frac{5}{9}$ b. $\left(\frac{48}{3}\right)^{\frac{1}{2}} = 16^{\frac{1}{2}} ; 4$
15. a. $5^{\frac{5}{4}} ; 7.48$ b. $3^{\frac{103}{72}} ; 4.81$
17. a. $8^{\frac{7}{5}} ; 18.38$ b. $5^{\frac{5}{6}} ; 3.82$
19. a. $8^2 ; 64$ b. $3^{\frac{2}{3}} ; 2.08$
21. a. $4^{\frac{3}{7}} ; 1.81$ b. $3^{\frac{2}{3}} ; 2.08$
23. a. $12^2 ; 144$ b. $7^2 ; 49$
25. a. 4.88   b. 7
27. a. 10.07   b. 7.56
29. a. 8.49   b. 51.96
31. a. $1.1\overline{6}$ or $\frac{7}{6}$ b. 0.19
33. a. $6^2 ; 36$ b. $7^2 ; 49$
35. a. $\left(\frac{1}{10}\right)^{\frac{1}{5}} ; \sqrt[5]{\frac{1}{10}} ; 0.63$ b. $\left(\frac{1}{2}\right)^{\frac{9}{7}} ; \sqrt[7]{\left(\frac{1}{2}\right)^9} ; 0.41$
37. a. $6^{\frac{2}{9}} ; \sqrt[9]{6^2} ; 1.49$ b. $7^{\frac{37}{24}} ; \sqrt[24]{7^{37}} ; 20.08$
39. a. $\left(\frac{1}{5}\right)^{\frac{8}{3}} ; \sqrt[3]{\left(\frac{1}{5}\right)^8} ; 0.01$ b. $\left(\frac{1}{6}\right)^3 ; 0.0046$
41. a. $8^4 ; 4,096$ b. $\left(\frac{1}{7}\right)^3 ; \frac{1}{343}$ or 0.0029

464

Exercises 3.3

1. a. <   b. <
3. a. >   b. >
5. a. >   b. <
7. a. −8, −6, −5, 2, 5, 8   b. −9, −8, −6, 3, 4, 7
9. a. −8, −5, 3, 7, 9, 10
    b. −13, −8, −3, 2, 12, 15
11. a. 16   b. −3
13. a. − 5   b. 9
15. a. −3   b. −5
17. a. 50   b. 5
19. a. −18   b. −4
21. a. −20   b. 6
23. a. 12   b. 14
25. a. 7   b. −3
27. a. 30   b. −24
29. a. 8   b. −9
31. a. 2   b. 17
33. a. 70   b. −72
35. a. 265   b. 30
37. a. −132   b. −111
39. a. $(-6)^8$; 1,679,616   b. 8^3 ; 512
41. a. $(-4)^2$; 16   b. $(-2)^3$; −8
43. a. −25   b. −16
45. a. −23   b. 17
47. a. −18   b. −15

Exercises 3.4

1. a. 1   b. 3
3. a. 3   b. 4
5. a. 4   b. 6
7. a. 4   b. 5
9. a. 1   b. 3
11. a. 5,060 ; 5,100   b. 1,980 ; 2,000
13. a. 589 ; 590   b. 57.4 ; 57
15. a. 48.5 ; 48   b. 25.9 ; 26
17. a. 0.775 ; 0.78   b. 6.07 ; 6.1
19. a. 0.0989 ; 0.099   b. 6.67 ; 6.7
21. a. 151.26   b. 353.2
23. a. 281.24   b. 412.1
25. a. 26.2   b. 42.4
27. a. 670   b. 6,960
29. a. 10.   b. 8.83
31. a. $3\widetilde{0}0,000$ b. 760

33. a. 2.35×10^2 b. 4.23×10^4
35. a. 1.275×10^1 b. 7.891×10^1
37. a. 5.8×10^{-1} b. 4.8×10^{-2}
39. a. 3.8×10^{-3} b. 2×10^{-4}
41. a. 6×10^6 b. 2.5×10^{-12}
43. a. 46,000   b. 2.9
45. a. 3,090,000   b. 46,540
47. a. 0.89   b. 0.000216
49. a. 0.00315   b. 0.0000615
51. a. 5.6   b. 0.0004065
53. 8.884×10^5 55. 9.978×10^{-3}
57. 2.84×10^9 59. 7.215×10^{-2}
61. 2.439×10^4 63. 9.46×10^{13}
65. 3.15×10^{-6} 67. 3.2×10^{-3}
69. 5×10^1 71. 1.4×10^3

Review Exercises 3

1. 7   3. 3^5 ; 27
5. a. 2^2 ; 4   b. 3^2 ; 9
7. a. 3^3 ; 27   b. $6^{\frac{4}{3}}$; 10.90
9. a. 27   b. 125
11. a. 400   b. −10,000,000
13. a. 0.2 or $\frac{1}{5}$ b. 0.14 or $\frac{1}{7}$ c. $0.\overline{8}$ or $\frac{8}{9}$
15. a. 49
    b. $0.8\overline{3}$ or $\frac{5}{6}$
    c. 1.2 or $\frac{6}{5}$
17. a. 3.97   b. 50
19. a. 82.29   b. 24
21. a. −19   b. 27
23. a. 7,180.08   b. 1,817.28
25. 164,593.54
27. −17,668.97
29. a. 0   b. −7
31. a. 13   b. −28
33. a. 2 ; 7.1×10^3 b. 5 ; 5.4001×10^1
    c. 2 ; 7.2×10^{-3}
35. a. 890   b. 0.056   c. 0.000964
37. a. 4.7495×10^{14} b. 7.715×10^{-2}
39. a. 3.9744×10^6 b. 2.759×10^{-3}
41. a. 2.4×10^{12} b. 4.5×10^{-10}
43. a. 5×10^{-4} b. 2.5×10^{-7}
45. 2.795×10^8 46. 8×10^{-14}

Self-test Exercises 3

1. a. 5^4 b. 3^6 c. 2^7

2. a. 3^3 b. 2^3

3. a. 3^{10} b. 10^9

4. a. $\dfrac{3^5}{2^6}$; $\dfrac{243}{64}$ or 3.80   b. $2^3 3^2$; 72

5. a. $\dfrac{1}{12}$ or 0.08   b. 1

6. a. $\dfrac{21}{8}$ or 2.625   b. $\dfrac{16}{5}$ or 3.2   c. $\dfrac{29}{5}$ or 5.8

7. a. $\dfrac{65}{3}$ or 21.67   b. $\dfrac{407}{500}$ or 0.814   c. 1

8. a. 32   b. $\dfrac{64}{5}$ or 12.8

9. a. 5.80   b. 13.92

10. a. 1,953,125   b. –100,000,000

11. a. 3   b. 12

12. a. –26   b. 42   c. 1,240.75

13. a. –61   b. –16   c. 5,468.75

14. a. 342.76   b. 424.17

15. a. 1,376.18   b. 3,762.75

16. 20,293.53   17. 65,460.89

18. a. –3   b. 16   c. 0

19. a. $\dfrac{8}{3}$ or $2.\overline{6}$ b. $\dfrac{3}{16}$ or 0.1875

20. a. 1.009×10^1 b. 5×10^{-3} c. 6.02×10^4

21. a. 2,700   b. 0.00415   c. 0.030405

22. a. 5.009×10^4 b. 9.1504×10^{-5}

23. a. 2.7888×10^6 b. -9.534×10^{-7}

24. a. 5.2×10^{-1} b. 1.4×10^{19}

Chapter 4

Exercises 4.1

1. a. $2x - 3$ b. $\dfrac{2x}{5}$ c. $25 + 3x$

3. a. 3 terms ; no constant ; Coefficients: 3, 7, –4
   b. 2 terms ; no constant ; Coefficients: 1, –5
   c. 4 terms ; Constant: 2 ; Coefficients: 9, 7, –6

5. a. 3 terms ; Constant term: 5 ; Coefficients: 5, –3
   b. 3 terms ; Constant term: 1 ; Coefficients: –2, 3
   c. 3 terms ; Constant term: 7 ; Coefficients: –2, –2

7. a. $5A + 3B$ b. $x + 5y + 7$

9. a. $-9x + 15y$ b. $8xy^2 + x^2y - 2x^2 + 4$

11. a. $3y$; 30   b. $8z$; 56

13. a. $-2x^2$; –18   b. $54x^3$; 6,750

15. $2a + 14b - 12c + 2$; 24   17. $3x^2 - 2x$; 65

19. a. $\dfrac{23}{9}$ b. 24

21. a. 30   b. 22

23. a. $11x^2 + 17x$ b. $-7y^2 + y$

25. a. $3x + 3y^2$ b. $xy^2 + x^2y^2$

27. a. $\dfrac{8x}{5y}$ b. $\dfrac{3}{2}$

29. a. 4   b. $\dfrac{3}{2}$

31. $-90x + 42$ 33. –38

35. $-5x + 7$ 37. $2x - 4$

39. $30x - 10y - 90$ 41. $-14y - 144$

43. $-7y^2 - 12y + 6$ 45. $4x + 25$

47. $-17x^2 + 58x - 36$ 49. $10x^2 - 16x - 14$

51. $-8x^2 - 16x + 15$

53. a. $x^2 + 10x + 25$ b. $4x^2 + 12xy + 9y^2$

55. a. $9 - 6x + x^2$ b. $9x^2 - 12xy + 4y^2$

57. a. $1 - 6x + 9x^2$ b. $9 - 12x + 4x^2$

59. a. $x^2 - 25$ b. $9 - 49x^2$

61. $2x^2 + 2x + 13$ 63. $8x + 25$

65. $13x^2 - 12x - 5$ 67. $4x^2 - y^2 - 16x - 6y + 7$

69. $-x - y$ 71. $5x - 3y + 1$

73. $\dfrac{x^2}{2y}$ 75. $3y(2x - 3z)$

77. $3y(5y^3 - 4y - 1)$ 79. $-40y(3y + 1)$

81. $3y(2x^2 - x - 3)$ 83. $2x^2(5x - 2)$

85. $2b(3a - 4c)$ 87. $(5x + 3)(y + 2)$

89. $(4y - x)(x - 5)$ 91. $(y + 5)(x - 2)$

93. $(x - y)(x + 1)$ 95. $(x - y)(x + 4)$

97. $\dfrac{3}{2}(x^2 + 3)$ 99. $\dfrac{3}{8}(x - 5)$

101. $\dfrac{15x(3y - 1)}{16(x + 3)}$

Exercises 4.2

1. $x + 6 = 10$; $x = 4$ 3. $6x = 72$; $x = 12$

5. $\dfrac{x}{5} = 4$; $x = 20$ 7. $\dfrac{2}{3}x = 12$; $x = 18$

9. $x = 30$ 11. $x = 18$

13. $x = -17$ 15. $x = 6$

17. $x = 1\dfrac{2}{11}$ 19. $x = 1\dfrac{2}{5}$

21. $x = 24$ 23. $x = \dfrac{-3}{20}$

25. $x = 4$ 27. $x = 24$

29. $x = 16$

31. $x = 1.72$

33. $x = 4$

35. $x = 1.8$

37. $x = -2$

39. $x = -2.2$

41. $x = 3$

43. $x = 0.41$

45. $x = 16$

47. $y = 42$

49. $y = 11$

51. $x = -5$

53. $x = 52.6$

55. 5

57. 16 metres and 9 metres

59. Andy: 33 ; Billy: 42 ; Catherine: 25

61. 12

63. a. $A = x^2 + 7x + 12$ b. 182 m^2

65. $12.50

67. $26/hour

69. 188.24 lb

71. 1.87 L 15% solution; 2.13 L water

Exercises 4.3

1. $x = \dfrac{y - 5}{4}$

3. $x = \dfrac{y + 7}{3}$

5. $C = S - M$

7. $L = \dfrac{N}{1 - d}$

9. $P = S - C - E$

11. $x = \dfrac{y + 6}{3}$

13. $a = \dfrac{bc}{c - b}$

15. $b = \dfrac{a - c}{c}$

17. $a = \dfrac{2b + c}{b - c}$

19. $b = \dfrac{ac + 4c}{a - 1}$

21. $x = a - \dfrac{y}{6}$

23. $x = \dfrac{-3a}{2}$

25. $u = \pm \sqrt{V^2 - 2as}$

27. $s = \dfrac{V^2 - u^2}{2a}$

29. $x = \dfrac{-31y}{2}$

31. $x = \dfrac{y}{1 - y}$

33. $x = \dfrac{5(y + 1)}{y - 1}$

35. $x = \dfrac{y^2 - 5}{2}$

37. $x = (8 - y)^2$

39. $A = 4\pi r^2$

41. $y = \dfrac{x}{x - 5}$

43. $a = \dfrac{2A}{h} - b$

45. $x = \pm \sqrt{(y + 16)}$

47. a. $r = \sqrt{\dfrac{V}{\pi h}}$ b. 5.35 cm

Review Exercises 4

1. a. $3x^2 + x - 2; 12$ b. $2x^2 + 6x - 8; -12$

3. a. $-10x^2 + 3xy - 7y^2; -32$ b. $x^2 + x - 2; 10$

5. a. $3x^2 + 8x - 3; 8$ b. $2x^2 - 6x; -4$

7. a. $2x(3x - 2); 2$ b. $3y^2(y - 4); -72$

9. a. $7x(y + 2x); 168$ b. $3x(3x^2 - 2x + 1); 6$

11. a. $12 + 3x$ b. $x - 5$

13. a. $10x + 15$ b. $(x + 3)x$

15. a. $5x + 17 = 42; x = 5$ b. $\dfrac{x}{15} = 45; x = 675$

17. a. $x - 10 = 10; x = 20$ b. $4x \cdot 3 = 36; x = 3$

19. a. $x = 3$ b. $x = 18$

21. a. $x = -9$ b. $x = 2$

23. a. $r = \dfrac{C}{2\pi}$ b. 11.94 cm   c. 447.88 cm^2

25. a. $h = \dfrac{3V}{\pi r^2}$ b. 35.99 cm

27. 200 lb   29. 15 L water

Self-test Exercises 4

1. a. $x^2 + 2x - 3; 5$ b. $-x^2 - 6x + 10; 19$

2. a. $19x^2 - 7xy - 5y^2; -15$ b. $4x - 11y + 7; 4$

3. $6x + 13; 31$ 4. $-5x^2 + 26x + 24; 45$

5. a. $6y(3y - 2); 96$ b. $3y(5y^2 + 4y + 1); 30$

6. a. $7x(2y - 3x); -112$ b. $2xy(4y - 3x); 14$

7. a. $3x - 25$ b. $x + 18$

8. a. $2x - 6$ b. $\dfrac{x}{x + 3}$

9. a. $2x - 9 = 21; x = 15$ b. $22 = 5x - 3; x = 5$

10. a. $4(x + 9) = 16x; x = 3$ b. $30 = 6x - 12; x = 7$

11. a. $x = 4$ b. $x = 18$

12. a. $x = 4$ b. $x = \dfrac{16}{3}$

13. a. $x = 2$ b. $x = 7$

14. a. $x = -1.5$ b. $x = 1.1$

15. a. $F = \dfrac{9C}{5} + 32$ b. 86°

16. a. $r = \dfrac{C}{2\pi}$ b. 190.99 cm

17. $2,494.12   18. $8.00

19. 30 L of Water   20. 578.95 L

Chapter 5

Exercises 5.1

1. a. 3 : 8   b. 5 : 1   c. 2 : 5

3. a. 3 : 8 : 5   b. 7 : 2 : 5   c. 9 : 20 : 40

5. a. 10 : 3   b. 36 : 5 : 9   c. 3 : 15 : 20

7. a. Not equivalent   b. Equivalent
   c. Not equivalent   d. Equivalent

9. a. Equivalent   b. Equivalent
   c. Not equivalent   d. Equivalent

11. 75 km/h   13. 41.67 mL/h

15. 2.5mg/mL   17. 62 words/min

19. 4 mg in 100mL   21. 12 mL for $1.44

23. 6 mg : 1 kg ; Safe   25. Employee *A*

27. a. Jack: $48,000 ; Steve: $56,160 ; Connor: $78,000

b. 1 : 1.17 : 1.625 ; 1.625 times greater

29. a. 5 : 7   b. 20 : 9

Exercises 5.2

1. a. Yes   b. No   c. No   d. Yes

3. a. 2.3625   b. $\frac{4}{3}$ c. $\frac{5}{3}$ d. 0.45

5. a. 5   b. 3.6875   c. $\frac{11}{18}$ d. $2\frac{5}{8}$

7. 180 litres   9. 11.625 km

11. Chemistry: $5,400 ; Calculus: $3,600

13. a. 15g   b. 50g, 40g

c. Thiamine: 56.25g; Folic Acid: 45g ; Magnesium sulfate: 33.75g

15. A: 15,000 ; B: 18,000 ; C: 12,000

17. 29:37:53   19. $496

21. $1,730.77   23. $45,000

25. a. 26 students   b. 5 : 3

Exercises 5.3

1. a. 0.75; $\frac{3}{4}$ b. 30%; $\frac{3}{10}$ c. 25%; 0.25

3. a. 0.05; $\frac{1}{20}$ b. 20%; $\frac{1}{5}$ c. 60%; 0.6

5. a. 1.5; $1\frac{1}{2}$ b. 17.5%; $\frac{7}{40}$ c. 48%; 0.48

7. a. 0.125; $\frac{1}{8}$ b. 45%; $\frac{9}{20}$ c. 450%; 4.5

9. a. 0.006; $\frac{3}{500}$ b. 0.5%; $\frac{1}{200}$ c. 460%; 4.6

11. a. 0.0005; $\frac{1}{2,000}$ b. 0.25% ; $\frac{1}{400}$ c. 112.5%; 1.125

13. a. 0.004; $\frac{2}{500}$ b. 108%; $1\frac{2}{25}$ c. 3.75% ; 0.0375

15. a. 0.0125; $\frac{1}{80}$ b. 202.5% ; $2\frac{1}{40}$ c. 0.2% ; 0.002

17. a. $0.0\overline{6}$; $\frac{1}{15}$ b. 250%; $2\frac{1}{2}$ c. $20\frac{5}{6}$%; $0.208\overline{3}$

19. a. 70   b. 100

21. a. 0.1875   b. 0.5 km

23. a. 52   b. $60.50

25. 2   27. $4

29. $0.27   31. 7.5

33. 40%   35. 400%

37. 300%   39. 30%

41. 800   43. $186

45. 130   47. $2,200

49. $246 ; $2,296   51. $25,000

53. 74%   55. $375,000

57. $315,000   59. 13%

61. $89,400

Exercises 5.4

1. a. $391.50   b. $10,687.50   c. $400

d. $620.69   e. 50%   f. 170.59%

3. a. $79.75   b. –$159.38   c. $550

d. $4,459.02   e. 45.95%   f. 69.23%

5. $2,110   7. 188L

9. 20%   11. $45

13. $163.99   15. 5.41% increase

17. $29,706.75   19. $28,737.50

21. 22.02%   23. $2.89

25. $60,800   27. 45.83%

29. $67.20   31. 8.04% increase

33. 24.95% decrease   35. 4.17%

37. 25% less

39. 1st year: Dropped 13.51%; 2nd year: Dropped 21.56%; Overall: Dropped 32.16%

41. $900   43. Tudor

Review Exercises 5

1. 3 : 100

3. a. 8.46   b. 5.33   c. 0.06   d. $3\frac{3}{5}$

5. a. Equivalent   b. Equivalent

c. Not Equivalent   d. Equivalent

7. $1,634.62   9. $162.50

11. 48 grams for $3.75

13. a. $0.33   b. $0.011

15. a. 90 sutures/hour   b. 135 sutures

17. a. $1.42/m   b. $0.97/m => Cheapest

c. $1.26/m

19. Gina ; $0.75/hour   21. 12 : 20 : 15

23. $13,625

25. Khan: $1,135.14 ; Thomas: $2,364.86

27. 25 : 12 : 15

29. Anton: $12,000 ; Cheryl: $22,500 ; Ellen: $18,000

31. a. 0.8; $\frac{4}{5}$ b. 48%; $\frac{12}{25}$ c. 150% ; 1.5

d. $0.1\overline{6}$; $\frac{1}{6}$ e. 0.75%; $\frac{3}{400}$ f. 8% ; 0.08

33. a. 36   b. 20%   c. $2.25

35. $460,000   37. 75%

39. $1,420,800

41. a. 42,875 people   b. 38,500,000 people

43. a. 306   b. $9   c. $11,250   d. 680 kg

45. a. $530   b. 7.375   c. 75%   d. 25%

47. 368 mL   49. 20%

51. 8.24% increase   53. $250,000

55. $42,000   57. $180,200

59. 13.04%

61. a. 27.45%   b. 41.46%

63. 2.32% increase

Self-test Exercises 5

1. 360 gram for $4.89

2. 74.07km/h

3. 9 hours 20 minutes

4. a. 12   b. 2.25   c. $7\frac{1}{5}$

5. 45.83 m   6. $6,035.59

7. 4.67 years   8. 22.5 litres

9. 125 g for $2.25   10. 6 : 10 : 15

11. $2,700   12. $208.33

13. Amir: $1,500 ; Brian: $2,500 ; Caterina: $2,000

14. 11 : 21

15. Alice: 18 patients ; Bill : 24 patients: Carol: 42 patients

16. a. $0.108\overline{3}$; $\frac{13}{120}$ b. 225%; $2\frac{1}{4}$ c. $0.\overline{6}$% ; $0.00\overline{6}$

    d. 0.005; $\frac{1}{200}$ e. 2.2%; $\frac{11}{500}$ f. 26.58% ; 0.2658

17. a. 12.5%   b. $337.50   c. 500

18. $70,600

19. a. 60%   b. 10%

20. a. 56.25%   b. $819.25   c. $480

21. a. 25%   b. $90.40   c. $300

22. $800   23. $1,300

24. a. –15%   b. 85%

25. $3.76   26. $27,984

27. –28%   28. $220,360.82

29. a. $18.20   b. –9%

30. a. 1st year: Dropped 7.67%; Dropped 16.61%

    b. Dropped 23.01%

Chapter 6

Exercises 6.1

1. a. 240 cm ; 2,400 mm   b. 8.6 m ; 8,600 mm

    c. 34.42 m ; 3,442 cm

3. a. 25 cm ; 250 mm   b. 0.58 m ; 580 mm

    c. 8.47 m ; 847 cm

5. a. 1,620 m ; 162,000 cm   b. 2.39 km ; 239,000 cm

    c. 0.0232 km ; 23.2 m

7. a. 650 m ; 65,000 cm   b. 0.154 km ; 15,400 cm

    c. 0.0177 km ; 17.7 m

9. a. 2,300 cm   b. 165 mm   c. 5,000 m

11. a. 3.35 m   b. 60.3 cm   c. 1.487 km

13. 0.15 km ; 150,800 mm; 15,200 cm ; 155 m

15. 4,775 m   17. 178 cm

19. a. 4,500   b. 30   c. 6,000   d. 0.45

21. 550 μm

23. a. 2,620 g   b. 6.75 kg

25. a. 840 mcg   b. 0.58 mg

27. a. 1,650 g ; 1,650,000 mg

    b. 4.95 kg ; 4,950,000 mg

    c. 0.00644 kg ; 6.44 g

29. a. 760 g ; 760,000 mg

    b. 35.76 kg ; 35,760,000 mg

    c. 0.0503 kg ; 50.3 g

31. a. 18,000 g   b. 2,000,000 mg

    c. 3,000 kg   d. 560,000 mcg

33. a. 5.903 kg   b. 2.884 g

    c. 9.704 t   d. 0.48 mg

35. 0.075 mcg, ; 850,250 mg ; 123,200 g ; 125 kg

37. 55 tablespoons   39. 175 g

41. $16.25

43. a. 3,250 mL   b. 5.06 L

45. a. 45 mL   b. 0.22 L

47. a. 0.205 L   b. 5,050 mL   c. 0.0585 kL

49. a. 270.8 L   b. 46.8 dL   c. 36,500 cL

51. 4.5 L   53. 790 mL

55. a. 428 m^2 b. 54,300 mm^3 c. 6,000 cm^3

57. a. 2.653 L   b. 2.7 daL   c. 2.9 mL

59. a. 890 cm^3 b. 0.01532 m^3 c. 0.000000045 hm^3

61. 1,650 L

63. 3 cm^3

65. a. Tap: $0.00215/L, Bottle: $2.52/L

    b. 1,172 bottles

    c. 14 times

Exercises 6.2

1. a. 126 feet , 1,512 inches   b. 16 yards ; 576 inches

    c. 18 yards ; 54 feet

3. a. 139.5 feet ; 1,674 inches

    b. 7.5 yards ; 270 inches

    c. 80 yards ; 240 feet

5. a. 5,280 yards ; 15,840 feet

    b. 3.5 miles ; 18,480 feet

    c. 2 miles ; 3,520 yards

7. a. 3,960 yards ; 11,880 feet

    b. 1.25 miles ; 6,600 feet

    c. 1.17 miles ; 2,064 yards

9. a. 37.5 feet   b. 141.96 inches c. 1,883.2 yards

11. a. 26 yards   b. 47.5 feet   c. 3.24 miles

13. 51 inches   15. 4.5 feet

17. 7.5 miles

19. a. 18 lb   b. 128 oz

21. a. 14.5 lb   b. 404 oz

23. a. 70,000 lb   b. 7.25 tons

25. a. 25,500 lb   b. 32.5 tons

27. a. 186 oz   b. 5,250 lb

29. a. 121 oz   b. 8 lbs 14 oz

31. a. 27.9125 tons   b. 9.375 lb

33. 1.2 ton ; 2,250 lb; 34,400 oz

35. 5 oz   37. 11 lb 4 oz; 3 lb 12 oz

39. 1,000 bottles

41. a. 44 pt ; 88 c   b. 19qt ; 76 c   c. 17 qt ; 34 pt

43. a. 65 pt ; 130 c   b. 22.5 qt ; 90 c   c. 23.5 qt ; 47 pt

45. a. 48 qt ; 96 pt   b. 4.5 gal ; 36 pt   c. 7 gal ; 28 qt

47. a. 30 qt ; 60 pt   b. 3.5 gal ; 28 pt   c. 6.25 gal ; 25 qt

49. a. 19 pt   b. 66 c   c. 49 qt   d. 0.75 c

51. a. 9.5 qt   b. 19.5 pt   c. 18 tsp   d. 45 fl oz

53. 6 qt, 14 pt, 29 c , 2 gal   55. 3.75 gal

57. 9 cups

Exercises 6.3

1. a. 155.38 mi   b. 193.08 km

3. a. 19.14 yd   b. 20.12 m

5. a. 820.21 ft   b. 22.86 m

7. a. 39.37 in.   b. 8.89 cm

9. a. 8.20 ft   b. 3,657.6 cm

11. a. 6.89 in.   b. 133.35 mm

13. 4,250 cm ; 28 yd ; 82.5 ft ; 24m ; 900 in.

15. 2.45 metres   17. 159 km

19. a. 3.86 tons   b. 2,268 kg

21. a. 34.17 lb   b. 20.41 kg

23. a. 2.65 lb   b. 2,948.4 g

25. a. 7.05 oz   b. 113.4 g

27. 5.7 lb ; 2.5 kg ; 2,450 g ; 80 oz

29. 607.2 g   31. 68.66 kg

33. 3.97 kg

35. a. 13.21 gal   b. 39.74 L

37. a. 15.85 qt   b. 13.25 L

39. a. 15.85 pt   b. 6.62 L

41. a. 19.02 c   b. 3.31 L

43. a. 0.27 fl oz   b. 606.19 mL

45. a. 2.11 c   b. 828.1 mL

47. 10.5 pt , 4.8 qt , 1 gal , 3.5 L

49. 139.11 mL   51. 1.18 fl oz

Exercises 6.4

1. 69.8   3. 37

5. 284   7. −26.11

9. 6.85   11. 292.15

13. 26.85   15. 253.15

17. 283.15   19. 620.33

21. 210.93   23. 243.15

25. 300 K ; 24 °C ; 56 °F   27. 78 °C ; 345 K ; 110 °F

29. 229 K ; −49 °F ; −46 °C   31. 37.4

33. −129.15   35. Another patient

37. 194.65   39. 4 °F under

Exercises 6.5

1. a. 10   b. 2

3. a. 40   b. 58

5. a. 24   b. 470

7. a. 669   b. 956

9. a. 110.5   b. 795

11. a. 13   b. 447

13. a. 34.5   b. 117

15. a. 759   b. 251

17. a. 507   b. 100.5

19. a. 729   b. 11

21. a. XLIX   b. vi

23. a. LXVII   b. XC

25. a. ii   b. $\overline{\text{VII}}$DCCC

27. a. LXXV   b. XLIII

29. a. XXXIX   b. $\overline{\text{V}}$DCCLXIV

31. a. xxviii   b. CMss

33. a. XXXVIII   b. DVI

35. a. $\overline{\text{VII}}$DXLV   b. MCCCLXXXIX

37. a. $\overline{\text{VIII}}$DLV   b. xv

39. a. XXXI   b. CCC

Exercises 6.6

1. 1112 h
3. 2245h
5. 0319 h
7. 1429 h
9. 1010 h
11. 2047 h
13. 0735 h
15. 1250 h
17. 0015 h
19. 1825 h
21. 12:05 PM
23. 4:58 AM
25. 8:20 AM
27. 9:38 PM
29. 9:45 AM
31. 2:17 PM
33. 11:49 PM
35. 12:07 AM
37. 11:23 AM
39. 6:57 AM

Review Exercises 6

1. a. 705 cm
   b. 15,050 m
   c. 7.5 cm
   d. 9.05 m
3. a. 117.99 ft
   b. 54.96 in.
   c. 9.58 ft
   d. 3.01 mi
5. a. 10,032 g
   b. 45,052 mg
   c. 0.36 kg
   d. 42.07 g
7. a. 103.04 oz
   b. 9,821 lb
   c. 16 tons
   d. 7.5 lb
9. a. 6,049 mL
   b. 9.01 L
   c. 38 qt
   d. 37.5 qt
11. a. 0.00014 km^2
    b. 4,000,000 cm^3
    c. 0.005 dm^3
    d. 2,400 L
13. a. 40.40 miles
    b. 29.53 ft
    c. 228.6 cm
    d. 5,148.8 m
15. a. 11.02 lb
    b. 44.09 oz
    c. 113.4 g
    d. 9.07 kg
17. a. 9.25 gal
    b. 0.88 fl oz
    c. 64.35 L
    d. 1.24 L
19. a. 210
    b. 176
    c. −9.44
    d. −22
21. a. −33.15
    b. 294.15
    c. 278.71
    d. 80.33
23. a. 1400 h
    b. 0420 h
    c. 1218 h
    d. 0545 h
25. a. 0820 h
    b. 1709 h
    c. 2100 h
    d. 0715 h
27. a. 9:24 AM
    b. 11:20 AM
    c. 11:46 PM
    d. 4:12 PM
29. a. 5:38 AM
    b. 12:00 PM
    c. 10:54 PM
    d. 12:30 AM
31. 5.25 mi , 9,200 yd, 7.5 km

33. 115 oz, 7 lb, 3 kg
35. 75 qt , 70 L , 18 gal
37. a. 400
    b. 159
    c. 15
    d. 2.5
39. a. 30
    b. 14
    c. 229
    d. 950
41. a. $\overline{\text{XXIII}}$DCCXLIX
    b. LXII
    c. CDLVI
    d. ix
43. a. DLXVIIss
    b. CDLXI
    c. xv
    d. $\overline{\text{XIV}}$CMLX
45. a. 224.13 km
    b. 139.29 mi
47. a. 200.16 lb
    b. 90.79 kg
49. a. 2.73 gal
    b. 10.33 L
51. 25 minutes and 18 seconds

Self-test Exercises 6

1. a. 273 mm
   b. 1,250 cm
   c. 8.11 km
   d. 106.5 cm
2. a. 47.01 ft
   b. 62 in
   c. 35.83 ft
   d. 3.24 mi
3. a. 53,107 g
   b. 6,223 mg
   c. 5.52 g
   d. 84.18 kg
4. a. 127 oz
   b. 8,030 lb
   c. 20 ton
   d. 9.31 lb
5. a. 5,700 mL
   b. 9.06 L
   c. 50 pt
   d. 20.75 qt
6. a. 65.56 °C
   b. 14 °F
   c. 76.85 °C
   d. 267.59 K
7. a. 40
   b. 11.5
   c. 54
   d. 1,450
8. a. 24
   b. 26
   c. 159
   d. 2,924
9. a. 69
   b. 2.5
   c. 946
   d. 19
10. a. 1,620
    b. 209
    c. 21.5
    d. 1,594
11. a. xix
    b. $\overline{\text{V}}$DC
    c. CDXII
    d. iiiss
12. a. MDCCLXXXIII
    b. CXIIss
    c. CM
    d. DCLXXIX
13. a. $\overline{\text{VI}}$DCCCXCV
    b. CDLXXIV
    c. xviiiss
    d. XLIX
14. a. LXII
    b. $\overline{\text{LIX}}$
    c. $\overline{\text{XLV}}$CCCLXXXV
    d. DXCI

15. a. 0000 h   b. 1830 h
    c. 1915 h   d. 0824 h

16. a. 1638 h   b. 1215 h
    c. 1914 h   d. 1700 h

17. a. 0321 h   b. 1950 h
    c. 0100 h   d. 2345 h

18. a. 0856 h   b. 2100 h
    c. 1027 h   d. 1845 h

19. a. 5:00 PM   b. 1:25 AM
    c. 7:34 PM   d. 4:36 PM

20. a. 7:15 AM   b. 3:10 AM
    c. 8:30 PM   d. 8:45 AM

21. a. 7:25 PM   b. 3:50 PM
    c. 6:27 AM   d. 1:29 PM

22. a. 2:52 PM   b. 9:44 PM
    c. 11:00 PM   d. 6:45 AM

23. a. 155.38 mi   b. 147.64 ft
    c. 800.1 cm   d. 4,022.5 m

24. a. 5.51 lb   b. 14.11 oz
    c. 793.8   d. 6.38 kg

25. a. 15.85 gal   b. 14.37 fl oz
    c. 9.46 L   d. 0.89 L

26. a. 25,000 dm^2 b. 0.0105 hm^2
    c. 0.04 dm^2 d. 0.07 km^2

27. a. 450,000 mm^3
    b. 0.00006 m^3
    c. 0.004 dm^3
    d. 0.0007 km^3

28. a. 12,500 L   b. 6,000 cm^3
    c. 5 daL   d. 0.1 L

29. 215 ft ; 65 m ; 2,500 in   30. 2.5 lb ; 1,200 g ; 45 oz

31. 84 L ; 22 gal ; 175 pt.

32. a. 1,005.91 ft   b. 306.60 m

33. a. 18.03 oz   b. 511.28 g

34. 32 days   35. Increase by 36 °F

36. 176.85 °C   37. 1,530 tablets

38. 3:15 AM (on Tuesday)

Chapter 7

Exercises 7.1

1. a.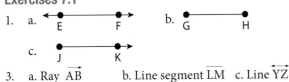
    c.

3. a. Ray $\overrightarrow{AB}$ b. Line segment $\overline{LM}$ c. Line $\overleftrightarrow{YZ}$

5. a. i) ∠DPC   ii) acute   iii) 60°   iv) 120°; 30°
    b. i) ∠AQB   ii) acute   iii) 80°   iv) 100°; 10°

7. a. i) ∠ZXY   ii) right
    iii) 90°   iv) 90° ; no complement
    b. i) ∠RPQ   ii) acute
    iii) 50°   iv) 130°; 40°

9. a. 57.5°   b. 72°

11. a. 56.6°   b. 91°

13. a. ∠AOC = ∠BOD; ∠AOB = ∠COD
    b. ∠q = ∠r = ∠s = ∠t

15. ∠a = ∠c = ∠e = ∠g; ∠b = ∠d = ∠f

17. a. ∠a = ∠c = 132°; ∠b = ∠d = 48°
    b. ∠a = 120° ; ∠b = 60°; ∠c = 70°

19. a. ∠a = ∠c = 63°; ∠b = 59°; ∠d = 58°
    b. ∠a = 50°; ∠b = 30°; ∠c = 130°

21. 32°

23. a. 48°   b. a = 70°; b = 60°; c = 50°

Exercises 7.2

1. a. acute, isosceles triangle
    b. right, scalene triangle
    c. obtuse, isosceles triangle

3. a. square
    b. parallelogram
    c. kite

5. ∠A = ∠B = ∠C = ∠D = 90°

7. ∠C = 105°, ∠B = 98°

9. rhombus   11. trapezoid

13. a. Rectangle or square   b. Rhombus or square

15. a. Square, rhombus, rectangle or parallelogram
    b. Square, rhombus, rectangle, parallelogram,
       or isosceles trapezoid

Exercises 7.3

1. a. P = 32 mm, A = 64 mm^2
    b. P = 21.8 m, A = 28.8 m^2

3. P = 65 cm, A = 207.1875 cm^2

5. P = 32 cm, A = 42 cm^2

7. P = 5.5 m, A = 1.2 m^2

9. P = 24 cm, A = 27 cm^2

11. C = 50.27 cm, A = 201.06 cm^2

13. C = 5.781 m, A = 2.659 m^2

15. P = 314 cm, A = 6,107 cm^2

17. P = 70.7 mm, A = 107.2 mm^2

19. 744 m^2 21. 5.32 cm

23. 1,296 cm^2

25. 960 cm^2

27. $58.09

29. 9 km/h

31. 258cm; 2,520 cm^2

33. 93.14 m; 485.97 m^2

35. 39.42 m; 86.14 m^2

37. 163.45 cm; 1,418.08 cm^2

39. 97.12 cm; 198.29 cm^2

Exercises 7.4

1. 3,750 mm^2; 15,625 mm^3 3. 261 m^2; 225 m^3

5. 678.58 cm^2; 1,696.46 cm^3

7. 23,524.25 mm^2; 273,444.22 mm^3

9. 318.09 cm^2; 466.53 cm^3

11. 6,082.12 cm^2; 44,602.24 cm^3

13. 5.31 m^2; 1.15 m^3

15. 1,720 cm^2; 3,200 cm^3

17. 18.9 m^3 19. 252 cm^3

21. 1.35 m^3; 7.635 m^2 off cardboard

23. 7,180.96 cm^3 25. 14.6 m^2

27. 2,748.89 cm^2 29. 0.020 mL

31. 12.42 m^2; 4.48 m^3 33. 130.69 mm^2; 93.83 mm^3

Exercises 7.5

1. a. 25 cm   b. 6 cm   c. 1.75 cm

3. a. 19.21 cm   b. 15 cm   c. 5.57 cm

5. 2.51 m   7. 2.65 cm

9. 5.73 cm   11. 98 cm; 420 cm^2

13. 30.90 m ; 40.96 m^2 15. 35.6 cm

17. 3.50 m   19. 1.80 m

21. no; yes

23. 27.5 cm; 1,583 cm^2; 4,147 cm^3

25. 69.3 m; 26,239 m^2; 221,852 m^3

27. 16.1 cm; 3,519 cm^2; 13,218 cm^3

Review Exercises 7

1. a. 20°; 160°; 70°   b. 50°; 130°; 40°

3. a. *a* is adjacent to θ.

   b is opposite to θ.

   c is co-interior to θ.

   d is alternate to θ.

   e is corresponding to θ.

   b. *b = d = e =* 113° ; *a = c =* 67°

5. a. *a* = 100°; *b* = 144°; *c* = 64°

   b. *b* = 72°; *a* = 162°; *c* = 40°

7. a. rectangle   b. kite   c. parallelogram

9. a. 58°; right, scalene triangle

   b. Both unknown angles are 48°; acute, isosceles triangle

11. a. 55.7cm ; 115.5 cm^2

    b. 75 cm ; 270.63 cm^2

13. 84 cm   15. 100 cm; 480 cm^2

17. a. 148.28 m; 1,749.74 m^2 b. 157.72 cm; 1,022.65 cm^2

19. 1,207 cm^2 21. 50.27 mm^2

23. 74.14 cm ; 252.62 cm^2 25. 54.6 cm; 128 cm^2

27. 8,846.72 mm^2; 38,603.89 mm^3

29. 47.04 m^2; 16.46 m^3

31. 2,789.73 mm^2; 8,180.71 mm^3

33. a. 15 m   b. 17.32 cm

35. 20 cm

37. 152 cm; 936 cm^2

39. no; move at least 6 cm closer to machine so he is no more than 1.24 m away.

Self-test Exercises 7

1. a. Acute; 146°; 56°   b. Obtuse; 64°; n/a

   c. Acute; 113°; 23°   d. Right; 90°; n/a

2. a. *a* = 62°; *b* = 126°; *c* = 64°

   b. *a* = 75°; *b* = 143°; *c* = 68°

3. a. right, isosceles

   b. equilateral ; acute

   c. obtuse, scalene

4. a. square

   b. rhombus

   c. kite

5. a. 49.5 cm; 117.89 cm^2 b. 56.91 in; 127.02 in^2

6. a. 3 m; 8m; 2.4 m^2

   b. 7 cm; 56 cm; 84 cm^2

7. a. 61.2 cm^2

   b. 1.47 m^2

   c. 804.25 cm^2

8. a. 7.85 m; 4.91m^2 b. 112.84 cm; 735.13 cm^2

9. 114 km/h

10. 91.89 m^2

11. a. 178,128.30 mm^3

    b. 111.37 cm^3

    c. 553.35 cm^3

12. a. 7.98 cm   b. 1,152 cm^2

13. a. 5.98 cm   b. 896 cm^3

14. 169.88 cm^2

15. a. 1,658.76 cm^2; 4,155.28 cm^3

    b. 21,840.50 cm^2; 189,018.59 cm^3

16. 69.02 cm^3 17. 424.12 in^3

18. 17,190.80 cm^2; 240,432.37 cm^3

19. 150.80 cm^2; 113.10 cm^3

20. 11,494.04 μm^3

21. 5,654.87 μm^3

22. 114.02 cm

23. x = 1.41 cm; y = 1 cm

24. a. 22.41 m; 18m^2

   b. 100 cm; 480 cm^2

25. a. 82.96 cm^2; 59.81 cm^3

   b. 1,373.89 cm^2; 5,890.49 cm^3

26. x = 14.4 cm; 72 cm; 216 cm^2

Chapter 8

Exercises 8.1

1.

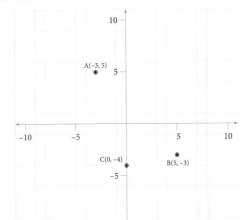

3.

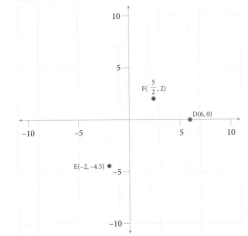

5. a. II   b. IV   c. I

7. a. x-axis   b. III   c. y-axis

9. a. 2 units   b. 9 units

11. a. 5.4 units   b. 4.3 units

13. a. 5 units   b. 7 units

15. a. $4\frac{1}{2}$ units   b. $1\frac{7}{15}$ units

17. D(–3, –1)   19. S(–3, –1)

21. (1, 12); (1, –2)   23. (–7, 3); (5, 3); (–1, 9); (–1, –3)

25. Domain : {0, 1, 4}

   Range: {–2, –1, 0, 1, 2}; Not a function

27. Domain: {–4, –2, –1, 0, 4, 6}

   Range: {3}; A function

29. Domain: {$x \in \mathbf{R}$}

   Range: {$y \in \mathbf{R}$}; A function

31. Domain: {$x \in \mathbf{R} \mid -4 \leq x \leq 4$}

   {$y \in \mathbf{R} \mid -2 \leq y \leq 2$} ; Not a function

33. Domain: {$x \in \mathbf{R}$}

   Range: {$y \in \mathbf{R} \mid y \geq 0$} ; A function

35. Domain: {–4, –3, –2, –1, 0, 1, 2, 3, 4, 5}

   Range: {–7, –6, –5, –4, –3, –2, –1, 0, 1, 2}; A function

37. Domain: {$x \in \mathbf{R} \mid -6 < x < 1$}

   Range: {$y \in \mathbf{R} \mid -1 < y < 2.5$} ; A function

Exercises 8.2

1. a. (3, 4)   b. (–6, 10)   c. (0, 6)

   d. (9, 0)   e. (15, –4)   f. (6, 2)

3. a. (6, –3)   b. (–3, 3)   c. (0, 1)

   d. ($\frac{3}{2}$, 0)   e. (6, –3)   f. (–6, 5)

5. $y = -\frac{3}{2}x - \frac{3}{4}$ 7. $y = \frac{2}{3}x + 5$

9. $y = -\frac{3}{2}x + 3$ 11. $5x - 2y = -2$

13. $3x + 4y = -12$ 15. $5x - 10y = -6$

17.   19.

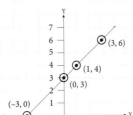

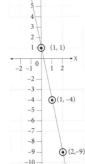

21.   23.

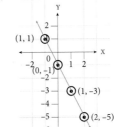

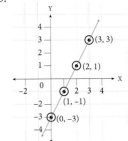

25.

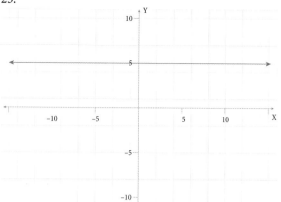

27.

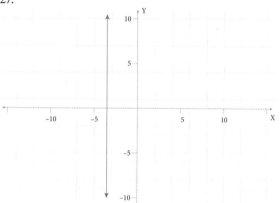

29.

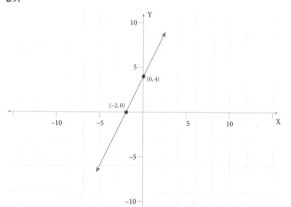

31.

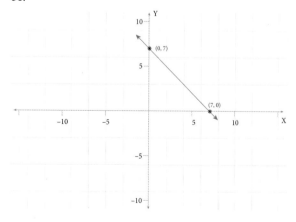

33.

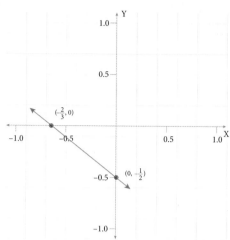

35. positive

37. Slope $= \dfrac{2}{3}$; y-intercept: $(0, -6)$

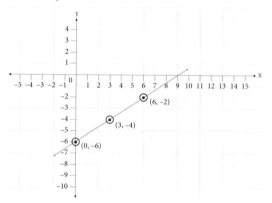

39. Slope $= \dfrac{4}{7}$; y-intercept: $(0, 3)$

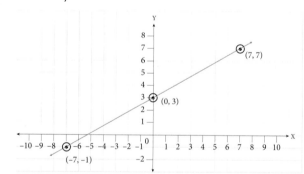

41. $y = -2$ **43.** $x = 3$

45. $y = -2x + 10$ **47.** $y = \dfrac{2}{3}x$

49. $y = -\dfrac{3}{2}x + 6$

51. $m = 0$

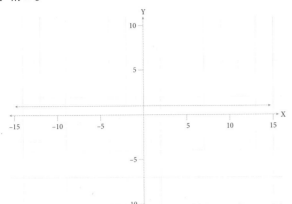

53. m is Undefined

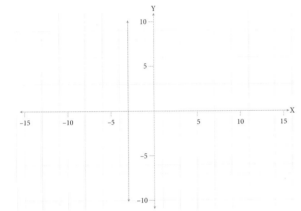

55. $y = 2$

57. $x = 2$

59. $5x + 3y = 15$

61. $15x - y = 0$

63. $y = \dfrac{3}{2}x - 6$

65. $y = \dfrac{1}{3}x - 5$

67. $y = -7$

69. $y = x + 7$

71. $y = -\dfrac{5}{2}x + 5$

73. $x = 4$

75. a. 140 mL/hour

b. $y = 500 - 140x$

c. 80 mL

77. $y = \dfrac{15}{2}x + 35$; 6:00 PM

79. $y = 5 + 15x$

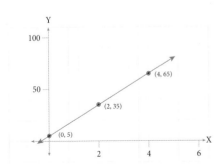

Slope = 15; represents the $15 cost-per-item to be shipped

y-intercept: (0, 5); represents the base shipping cost of $5, regardless of the number of items shipped

Exercises 8.3

1. perpendicular
3. parallel
5. perpendicular
7. intersecting
9. One solution
11. One solution
13. No solution
15. Infinitely many solutions
17. 4
19. −2
21. (1, 1); Consistent/Independent.
23. No solutions ; Inconsistent/Independent
25. Infinitely many solutions; Consistent/Dependant
27. (3, 1) ; Consistent/Independent
29. $\left(\dfrac{5}{3}, \dfrac{2}{3}\right)$; Consistent/Independent
31. (−2, 1) ; Consistent/Independent
33. Infinitely many solutions , Consistent/Dependant
35. No Solutions ; Inconsistent/Independent
37. (3, −3), Consistent/Independent
39. (0, 1) ; Consistent/Independent

Exercises 8.4

1. $x = 2$; $y = -2$
3. $x = 6$; $y = 3$
5. Infinitely many solutions
7. $x = 2$; $y = 1$
9. $x = 6$; $y = -1$
11. $x = 1$; $y = 2$
13. No solutions
15. $x = 9$; $y = 2$
17. $x = 2$; $y = 3$
19. $x = -\dfrac{11}{8}$; $y = -\dfrac{37}{24}$
21. Infinitely many solutions
23. $x = 2$; $y = 4$
25. $x = 3$; $y = -2$
27. $x = 3$; $y = -2$
29. $x = -\dfrac{3}{5}$; $y = -\dfrac{1}{5}$
31. $x = -30$; $y = 54$
33. $x = \dfrac{9}{7}$; $y = \dfrac{27}{7}$
35. $x = 1$; $y = 3$
37. Infinitely many solutions

Exercises 8.5

1. $12
3. 60; 32
5. $15,000 ; $10,000
7. Alcohol wipes: 98; gauze strips: 32
9. 51°; 129°
11. 15% sugar: 3 L; 5% sugar: 7 L

Review Exercises 8

1. a. IV   b. II   c. x-axis

d. IV   e. III   f. y-axis

3. Rectangle; Perimeter: 22 units; Area; 24 units^2

5. a. Domain: {1, 2, 4, 9}; Range: {−4, −3, 2, 4}

b. Domain: $\{x \in \mathbf{R} \mid 5 < x < 11\}$; Range : $\{y \in \mathbf{R} \mid 11 < y < 23\}$

7.
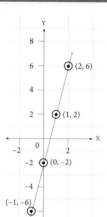

9.
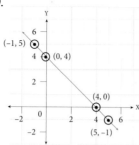

19.
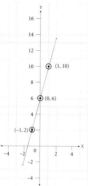

11.
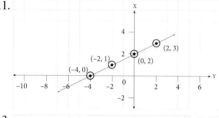

21.
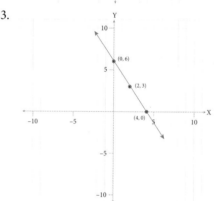

13.
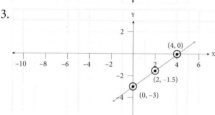

23.

15.
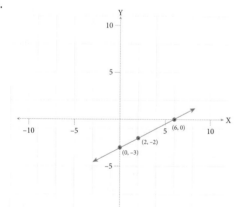

25. $y = \dfrac{3}{4}x - \dfrac{1}{4}$

27. $y = -\dfrac{4}{3}x + \dfrac{8}{3}$

29. $x = 1$

31. $3x - 4y = -18$

33. $y = -2x + 1$

35. One solution

37. No solutions

39. Infinitely many Solutions

41. $(2, -5)$

43. $(6, 2)$

45. $(2, 1)$

47. $x = 4; y = 1$

49. No solutions

51. $x = 1; y = 1$

53. $x = 2; y = 1$

55. $x = -4; y = -2$

57. Infinitely many solutions

59. $x = 3; y = 4$

61. $x = 15; y = 12$

63. $x = 4; y = -2$

65. 65; 30

67. 210 adults; 90 children

69. $6.75 for acetaminophen and $7.50 for ibuprofen tablet

71. 92 pounds of 30%; 8 pounds of 55%

73. 20% : 0.48 L ; 70% : 1.52 L.

17.
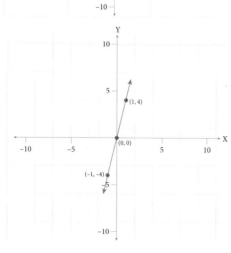

Self-test Exercises 8

1. a. $2x - 3y = 6$ b. $8x - 24y = 1$

2. $(-3, -1)$, 40 units^2

3. a. $\dfrac{2}{3}$; $(0, 2)$ b. $-\dfrac{3}{4}$; $(0, \dfrac{5}{4})$

4.
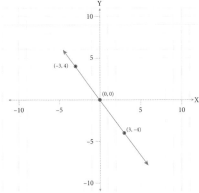

5.
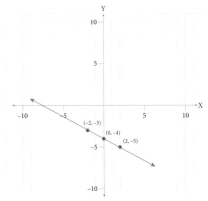

6. a. $x + 2y = -8$
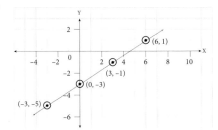

b. $2x - 3y = 6$
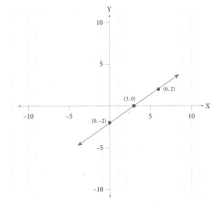

7. $y = -\dfrac{3}{4}x + \dfrac{11}{4}$

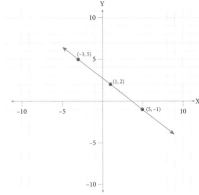

8. a. Parallel   b. Not parallel

9. $y = -\dfrac{2}{3}x - 5$ 10. $y = -\dfrac{1}{5}x + \dfrac{11}{5}$

11. $y = -\dfrac{3}{4}x + \dfrac{11}{4}$ 12. $y = \dfrac{3}{5}x - 3$

13. $y = 5x$ 14. $y = \dfrac{4}{3}x$

15. one solution   16. no solution

17. many solutions

18. No solutions

19. $(-2; 1)$

20. $x = 2; y = -3$ 21. $x = -4; y = 4$

22. $x = y = -\dfrac{3}{2}$ 23. $x = 3; y = 2$

24. a. $y = 0.1x + 500$ b. $5,500   c. $70,000

25. a. $9,500   b. 1,275

26. 35; 30

27. Small : $0.11; Large : $0.18

28. 54

29. Stock A : $6,500; Stock B: $3,500

30. 6L Solution A and 4 L Solution B

Chapter 9

Exercises 9.1

1. x^{10} 3. $8x^5$ 5. $15x^8$

7. $-6x^8$ 9. x^{14} 11. $24x^6$

13. x^3 15. $3x^4$ 17. x^3

19. x^{23} 21. $128x^{22}$ 23. $\dfrac{1}{16x^8}$

25. $\dfrac{8x^{12}}{27y^6}$ 27. $\dfrac{4x^6}{25y^4}$ 29. y

31. x 33. $\dfrac{x^6}{9y^6}$ 35. $\dfrac{125x^6}{y^{12}}$

37. $\dfrac{x}{y}$ 39. $\dfrac{x}{y}$ 41. $\dfrac{1}{x^3}$

43. $-8x^4$ 45. $\dfrac{x^8}{16y^6}$ 47. $\dfrac{-x^2}{y}$

49. $-8x^4y^7$

51. $\dfrac{3x^2}{y^4}$

53. x^3y^5

55. $\dfrac{x^6}{y^2}$

57. $x^{\frac{5}{3}}$

59. $\dfrac{1}{x^{\frac{1}{3}}}$

61. $x^{\frac{1}{2}}$

63. $\dfrac{1}{x^{\frac{3}{4}}}$

65. x^6

67. $\dfrac{1}{2^{\frac{1}{3}}x^{\frac{1}{3}}}$

69. x^4

71. x^3y^4

73. $\dfrac{x^3}{y^4}$

75. $3x^2$

77. x^3

79. $\dfrac{-1}{x^{\frac{2}{3}}}$

Exercises 9.2

1.

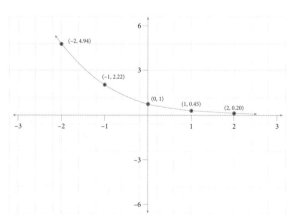

3.

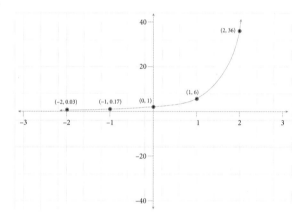

5.

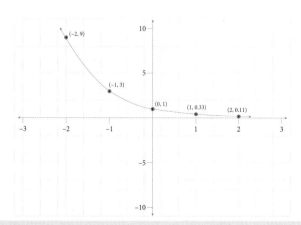

7.

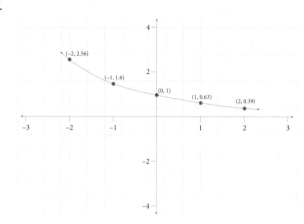

9.

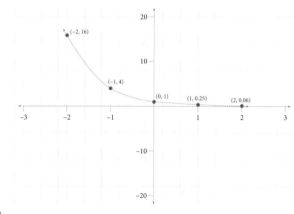

11.

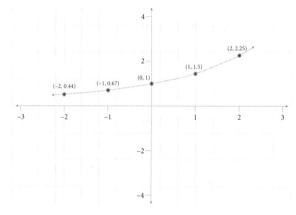

13.

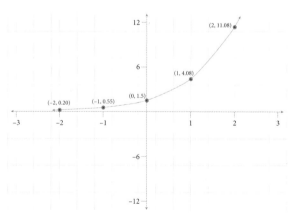

15.

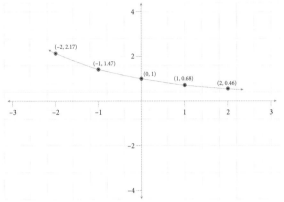

17. 19,487   19. 102,400

21. 0.39%   23. 12.78%

Exercises 9.3

1. a. $\log_{10}100{,}000 = 5$ b. $\log_4 1{,}024 = 5$

3. a. $\log_2 64 = 6$ b. $\log_6 7{,}776 = 5$

5. a. $\log_3 9 = 2$ b. $\log_9 6{,}561 = 4$

7. a. $10^2 = 100$ b. $4^3 = 64$

9. a. $2^5 = 32$ b. $5^4 = 625$

11. a. $3^6 = 729$ b. $6^3 = 216$

13. a. 2.3522   b. 0.1875

15. a. 3.2362   b. –0.8614

17. a. 2.3076   b. 0.0050

19. a. –9.8826   b. –14.8659

21. $\log 3 - \log 7$ 23. $\ln 4 + \ln 9$

25. $\log A + \log B - \log C$ 27. $\ln X - \ln Y - \ln Z$

29. $\log 3 + \log x - \log 2 - \log y - \log z$

31. $\ln x + \ln y - 0.5\ln z$ 33. $M - N$

35. $M + 2N$ 37. $2M - N$

39. $-4M - 6N$ 41. $\dfrac{4M}{5}$

43. $\dfrac{-2M - N}{3}$ 45. $\log 40 = 1.6021$

47. $\ln 5 = 1.6094$ 49. $\log \dfrac{32}{9} = 0.5509$

51. $\ln 675 = 6.5147$ 53. $\log 25 = 1.3979$

55. $\ln 216 = 5.3753$ 57. $\log \left(\dfrac{x}{y}\right)^2$

59. $\ln (ab)^4$ 61. $\log \dfrac{81}{2} = 1.6075$

63. $\ln \dfrac{a^3 b^2}{c^5}$ 65. $\dfrac{1}{2} \log_{10} 1{,}000 = \dfrac{3}{2}$

67. $\dfrac{1}{2} \log_2 64 = 3$ 69. $\dfrac{2}{3} \log_3 9 = \dfrac{4}{3}$

71. $-\dfrac{1}{4} \log_{27} 81 = -\dfrac{1}{3}$

Exercises 9.4

1.

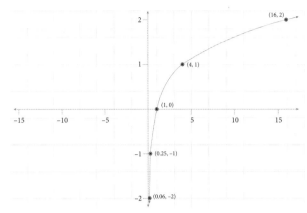

3.

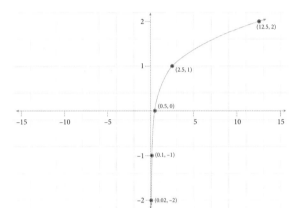

5.

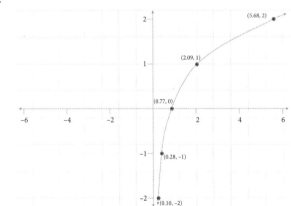

7.

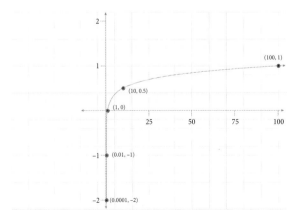

9. a. 2.4; acidic   b. 12.6; alkaline

11. 28.08 hours   13. 3.98

15. 9.10   17. 27.19 dB

19. −35.50 dB

Exercises 9.5

1. 0.06   3. 2.76

5. 35.64   7. 132.53

9. 1.62   11. 5.53

13. 2.33   15. 8.83

17. 100   19. 4 days

21. 280.06 days

23. 158,489 times Vega's intensity

25. 316.23 times more intense

27. a. 1.32×10^{-9} b. 3.09×10^{-4}

29. 22.58%   31. 2.70 mm

Review Exercises 9

1. a. $\dfrac{1}{x^2}$ b. $-x^7$

3. a. x^4 b. $\dfrac{1}{x^2}$

5. a. $\left(\dfrac{y^{\frac{1}{2}}}{x^{\frac{1}{2}}}\right)$ b. x^2

7. a. x^2 b. 1

9. a. $3x^7$ b. x^4

11. a. $\dfrac{x^8}{4y^7}$ b. $\dfrac{y^{10}}{x^8}$

13. a. $\dfrac{27x^9}{8y^6}$ b. x^{14}

15. a. $2x^2$ b. $\dfrac{4x^{10}}{y^{24}}$

17. a.

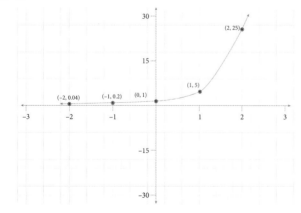

b.

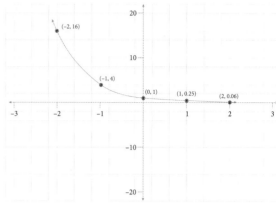

19. a.

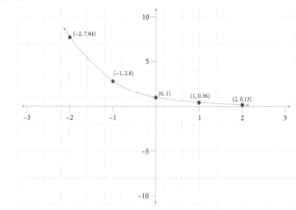

b.

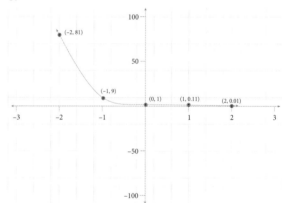

21. a. 26.25   b. 1,691.63

23. a. 7   b. 4

25. a. 3.19   b. 14.21

27. 47.5   29. 53.36

31. 1.89

33. a.

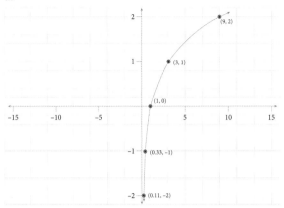

b.

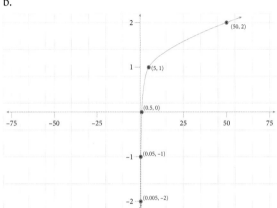

35. 64,000   37. 332.19 years

39. 162

41. a. 3.16×10^{-7} b. 0.84

43. 50.12 times   45. 28.44 dB

47. a. 3.40 cm^2 b. 6.93 days

49. Fake

Self-test Exercises 9

1. a. $-x^7$ b. y^{18}

2. a. $-x^3$ b. x^6

3. a. $\dfrac{1}{x^2}$ b. $\dfrac{1}{x^9}$

4. a. x^2 b. x^{17}

5. a. $9x^6$ b. $16x^4y^6$

6. a. $4y^2$ b. $\dfrac{-2y^4}{x^2}$

7. a. $\dfrac{1}{x^2}$ b. $\dfrac{y^2}{x^6}$

8. a. x^2 b. $\dfrac{-y^5}{2x^3}$

9. a.

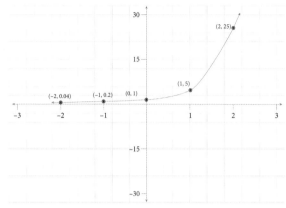

b.

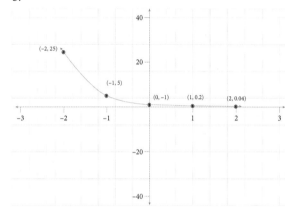

10. a.

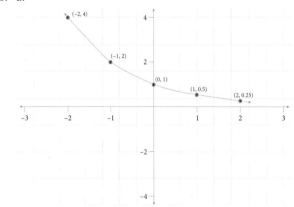

b.

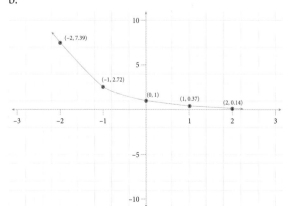

11. 5,160   12. 232.19 years

13. a. 7.75   b. 17.59

14. a. 13.34   b. 102.70

15. a.

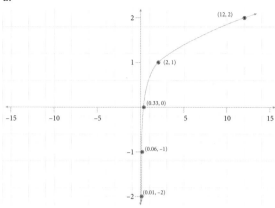

b.

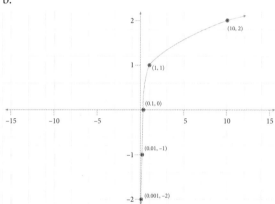

16. a.

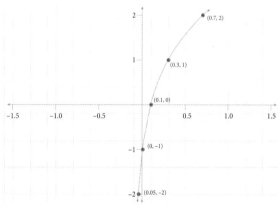

b.

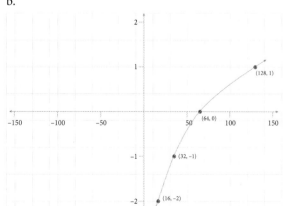

17. 400,000   18. 0.27

19. −0.33   20. 0.84

21. 2.0   22. 3.90

23. 1 : 1,000   24. 41.48%

25. 4.27 mm   26. 1.25 dB

27. 1,301.17 kW   28. 4.42 W

Chapter 10

Exercises 10.1

1. (i) Trade Name - Avandia

   (ii) Generic Name - rosiglitazone maleate

   (iii) Drug Identification Number – 02241113

   (iv) Form of Drug - tablets

   (v) Dosage Strength - 4 mg per tablet

   (vi) Standard Adult Dosage - starting dose of 4mg/day.

   (vii) Storage directions - Store between 15°C - 30°C

   (viii) Expiration Date - N/A

3. (i) Trade Name - Mepron

   (ii) Generic Name - atovaquone

   (iii) Drug Identification Number - 02217422

   (iv) Form of Drug - oral suspension

   (v) Dosage Strength - 750 mg/5 ml

   (vi) Standard Adult Dosage - 750 mg twice per day or 1,500 mg once per day (with food)

   (vii) Storage directions - Store at room temperature (15°C-25°C); Protect from light; Do not freeze

   (viii) Expiration Date - N/A

5. (i) Trade Name - Blincyto

   (ii) Generic Name - blinatumomab

   (iii) Drug Identification Number - 02450283

   (iv) Form of Drug - intravenous infusion

   (v) Dosage Strength - 38.5 mcg/vial

   (vi) Standard Adult Dosage - N/A

   (vii) Storage directions - Store at 2°C to 8°C. Protect from light.

   (viii) Expiration Date - N/A

7. (i) Trade Name - Stieva-A

   (ii) Generic Name - tretinoin

   (iii) Drug Identification Number - 00578576

   (iv) Form of Drug - cream

   (v) Dosage Strength - 0.025% w/w (weight per weight)

   (vi) Standard Adult Dosage - Once daily before bedtime.

   (vii) Storage directions - Store between 15° and 30°; do not freeze.

   (viii) Expiration Date - N/A

9. 100 mg of Demerol to be administered subcutaneously, as needed for pain, but no more frequently than every 3 hours

11. 125 mcg of Synthroid to be administered orally, daily

13. 175 mg of Gentamicin to be administered intramuscularly, twice a day

15. 15 mg of Codeine to be administered orally, as needed for pain, but no more frequently than every 4 hours

17. 300 mg of Ancef to be administered intravenously, every 8 hours

19. 1% Hydrocortisone cream, to be administered to the affected area as needed, but no more frequently than 4 times a day

Exercise 10.2

1. 2 tablets   3. 3 tablets

5. 14 mL

7. a. 2.5 caplets   b. no more than 10 caplets

9. 2 capsules per dose;

    60 capsules for a 10-day prescription

11. 400 mg of amoxicillin to be administered orally, every 8 hours;

    12.5 mL per dose

13. 3 tablets per dose ; the bottle will last for 15 days.

15. 0.75 mL per dose ; 3 mL per day

17. a. 325/30 mg   b. 2 tablets per dose

    c. 120 tablets to fill the prescription

19. 1 g of ampicillin to be administered orally, daily in 4 divided doses;

    0.5 caplets per dose;

    28 caplets to fill the prescription

21. 2.2 mL

23. a. 404-674 mg per dose   b. 2 capsules

25. a. 0.96 m^2 b. 2.16 m^2

27. 896-1,344 mg per day

29. 2.17 m^2 ; 9 mL per dose

Exercises 10.3

1. (i) 1 mL (ii) 0.01 mL (iii) 0.78 mL

3. (i) 5 mL (ii) 0.2 mL (iii) 3.4 mL

5. (i) 20 mL (ii) 1 mL (iii) 16 mL

7. (i) 3 mL (ii) 0.1 mL (iii) 2.5 mL

9. A   11. E

13. B   15. F

Exercises 10.4

1. 0.6 mL

3. 0.25 mL

5. 0.80 mL

7. a. 24.5-36.8 mg

    b. Yes

    c. 0.60 mL

    d. 1 mL syringe

9. a. 250 mg/mL

    b. 1.5 mL per dose ; 6 mL per day

    c. 2 mL syringe

11. 16 units of insulin to be administered subcutaneously, 4 times a day;

    0.40 mL per dose;

    0.5 mL syringe

13. 20 mg of morphine sulfate to be administered intramuscularly, immediately;

    2.5 mL

15. 150 mcg of morphine per kilogram of body weight, to be administered intramuscularly, as needed for pain, but no more frequently than every 4 hours;

    0.60 mL per dose ; no more than 3.60 mL per day

17. 1 mg of enoxaparin per kilogram of body weight, to be administered subcutaneously, twice a day;

    0.85 mL per dose

Exercises 10.5

1. 47 gtt/min

3. 2 hours and 30 minutes

5. 5 hours

7. 312.5 mL;

    6 hours and 40 minutes

9. 15 gtt/mL drop factor; 35 gtt/min flow rate

11. 60 gtt/mL drop factor; 4:20 PM

13. a. 1.25 mg/min   b. yes

15. 75 mcgtt/min

17. a. 33.33 mg/min   b. 20 gtt/min

19. a. 0.98 mg/min   b. 147 mL/h

Review Exercises

1. a. (i) Trade Name - Sensipar

    (ii) Generic Name - cinacalcet hydrochloride

    (iii) Drug Identification Number - 02257130

    (iv) Form of Drug - tablets

    (v) Dosage Strength - 30 mg per tablet

    (vi) Storage directions - Store at 15°C - 30°C

    b. 1 tablet per dose

3.   a. (i) Trade Name - Ceftin

   (ii) Generic Name - cefuroxime axetil

   (iii) Drug Identification Number - 02212307

   (iv) Form of Drug - oral suspension

   (v) Dosage Strength - 125 mg/5 mL

   (vi) Storage directions - store reconstituted suspension between 2 °C and 8 °C, in a refrigerator

   b. 10 mL per dose

5.   a. (i) Trade Name - Nucala

   (ii) Generic Name - mepolizumab

   (iii) Drug Identification Number - 02449781

   (iv) Form of Drug - Iyophilized powder for subcutaneous injection

   (v) Dosage Strength - 100 mg/mL after reconstitution

   (vi) Storage directions - N/A

   b. 2.5 mL per dose

7.   (i) Trade Name - Typherix

   (ii) Generic Name - Typh-1 vaccine

   (iii) Drug Identification Number - 02242727

   (iv) Form of Drug - IM

   (v) Dosage Strength - 2.5 mcg/0.5 mL

   (vi) Storage directions - Store at 2°C to 8°C.

   b. 0.5 mL per dose

9.   (i) 1 g of Cephalexin to be administered orally, three times a day

   (ii) 2 capsules

11.   (i) 0.16 g of acetaminophen to be administered orally, as needed for fever, but no more frequently then every 4 hours

   (ii) 10 mL

13.   (i) 5 mg of Nalbuphine Hydrochloride to be administered subcutaneously, as needed for pain, but no more frequently than every 6 hours

   (ii) 0.5 mL

15.   (i) 100 mg of Hydroxyzine Hydrochloride to be administered intramuscularly, immediately

   (ii) 2 mL

17.   (i) 1 mL   (ii) 0.01 mL   (iii) 0.66 mL

19.   a. 2.02 m^2 b. 1.72 m^2 c. 1.02 m^2

21.   15 mg of hydrocodone to be administered orally, as needed for pain, but no more frequently than every 12 hours, for 14 days;

   1.5 tablets per dose

   42 tablets to fill prescription

23.   15 mg of acetaminophen per kilogram of body weight, to be administered orally, as needed for pain, but no more frequently than every 4 to 6 hours;

   1.65 mL per dose

25.   3.33 mL per dose; 10 mL per day

27.   731 mg per dose

29.   a. 5 mg/mL   b. 0.80 mL   c. 1 mL syringe

31.   47 gtt/min   33.   2:20 AM

35.   15 gtt/mL drop factor ; 18 gtt/min flow rate

37.   a. 1 mg/min   b. Yes

39.   a. 96 mL   b. 72 mL/h   c. 18 gtt/min

Self Test Exercise

1.   (i) Aranesp

   (ii) darbepoetin alfa

   (iii) 02391783

   (iv) prefilled syringe for SC or IV

   (v) 130mcg/0.65 mL

   (vi) refrigerate at 2 °C to 8 °C; do not freeze or shake; protect from light

2.   2.4 cc

3.   a. 200 mg of Solu-Medrol to be administered intravenously, 4 times a day

   b. 650 mg of Acetaminophen to be administered orally, as needed for headaches, but no more frequently than every 4 hours

4.   0.5 tablets per dose, 7 tablets per week

5.   2 tsp per dose; 6 tsp per 24 hours

6.   2.40 m^2; 12 mL per dose

7.   Yes; 2.5 mL per day

8.   a. 750 mg   b. 3 mL

9.   2.4 mL   10.   25 mL

11.   2 hours and 55 minutes

12.   a. 25 gtt/min   b. 1,000 mL

   c. 28 gtt/min   d. Yes

13.   15 gtt/mL drop factor ; 20 gtt/min flow rate

14.   a. 0.06 mg/min

   b. Yes, 60mcg is within the safe dose range

15.   a. 840 mg   b. 210 mL   c. 18 gtt/min

Answer Key

Glossary

Absolute value of a number is its distance from the origin '0' on the number line. Since it is a distance, it is always positive and the direction does not matter.

Addend represents each of the numbers being added.

Addition refers to combining (finding the total or sum of) numbers.

Algebra is a branch of mathematics that deals with different relations and operations by using letters and symbols to represent numbers, values, etc.

Algebraic expression consists of one or more terms, with a combination of variables, numbers, and operation sign.

Alternate angles are formed on the opposite sides of the transversal on the interior of the parallel lines.

Angle is formed when two rays intersect at their endpoints.

Area(A) of a plane figure is the amount of 2-dimensional surface that is enclosed within the figure.

Base(B) refers to the whole quantity or value (100%). It is usually followed by the word 'of', or 'percent of '.

Billions group is the fourth group of three digits starting from the right of a whole number.

Binomial is a polynomial with two terms.

Celsius scale (°C) is part of the metric system. It has a basis in which water freezes at 0°C and boils at 100°C.

Co-interior angles are formed on the same side of the transversal and on the interior of the parallel lines.

Coefficient is the numerical factor in front of the variable in a term.

Common factor is a factor that is common to two or more numbers.

Common logarithm is a logarithm to the base 10.

Complex fraction is a fraction in which one or more fractions are found in the numerator or denominator.

Composite number is a whole number that has at least one factor other than 1 and the number itself.

Conditional equations are equations whose left side and right side are equal only for a certain value of the variable.

Consistent linear system is a linear system of two equations that has one or many solutions.

Constant is a term that has only a number, without any variables.

Contradiction is an equation that is not true for any value of the variable.

Corresponding angles are formed on the same corner of the intersection between the transversal and each of the parallel lines.

Decimal numbers represent a part or a portion of a whole number.

Denominator represents the total number of equal parts into which the whole unit is divided.

Dependent system of equations is a system of equations that has an infinite number of solutions.

Difference refers to the result of subtracting two or more numbers.

Dividend refers to the number that is being divided.

Division can be thought of as repeated subtractions.

Divisor is the number by which the dividend is divided.

Domain of a relation is defined as the set of all the 'x' values in the ordered pairs.

Elimination method is a method of solving systems of linear equations, when none of the equations in the system has a variable with a coefficient of 1 or –1.

Equivalent equations are equations that have the same solution.

Equivalent ratio is obtained when all the terms of the ratio are multiplied by the same number or divided by the same number.

Exponent represents the number of times the base of an exponential notation is multiplied.

Exponential notation is used to represent a number that is multiplied by itself repeatedly.

Expression is a combination of terms. It usually refers to a statement of relations among variables.

Factor refers to each of the combinations of variables and/or numbers multiplied together in a term.

Factor of a number is a whole number that can divide the number with no remainder.

Factor tree helps to find all the prime factors of a number.

Fahrenheit scale (°F) is primarily used in the US. It has a basis in which water freezes at 32°F and boils at 212°F.

Formula is similar to an equation. In a formula, the relationship among many variables is written as a rule for performing calculations.

Fraction is a method of representing numbers, where one non-zero integer is divided by another non-zero integer.

Fraction in lowest terms is a fraction in which the numerator and denominator have no factors in common (other than 1).

Fraction bar represents the division sign.

Fractional exponent is when the exponent of a number or variable is a fraction.

Geometry is a branch of Mathematics that deals with the study of relative positions, properties, and relations of geometric objects.

Greatest Common Factor (GCF) of two or more numbers is the largest common number that divides the numbers with no remainder.

Hypotenuse is the longest side of a right-triangle opposite the right-angle.

Identity is an equation which is true for any value of the variable.

Improper fraction is a fraction in which the numerator is greater than the denominator; i.e., the value of the entire fraction is more than 1.

Inconsistent linear system is a linear system of two equations that has no solutions.

Independent system of equations is a system of equations that has one or no solutions.

Irrational number is a number that cannot be expressed as a fraction.

Least Common Denominator (LCD) of a set of two or more fractions is the smallest whole number that is divisible by each of the denominators.

Least Common Multiple (LCM) of two or more numbers is the smallest multiple that is common to those numbers.

Like terms are terms that have the same variables and exponents.

Line is an object that has only one dimension: length.

Line segment is the portion of a line bound between two points.

Linear equation is an algebraic equation with one or two variables (each to the power of one), which produces a straight line when plotted on a graph.

Logarithm is a faster method of solving for an unknown exponent. It is the exponent to which the base is raised to get the number.

Metric system of measurement uses metre (m), gram (g), and litre (L) as the base units for the measurements of length, mass, and capacity, respectively. The Celsius (°C) scale is used for temperature.

Millions group is the third group of three digits starting from the right of a whole number.

Minuend is the number from which another number is subtracted.

Mixed number consists of both a whole number and a proper fraction, written side-by-side, which implies that the whole number and proper fraction are added.

Monomial is an algebraic expression that has only one term.

Multiple of a number is a whole number that can be divided by the number with no remainder.

Multiplication can be thought of as repeated additions.

Natural logarithm is a logarithm to the base 'e', where the constant

$e = 2.71828....$

Number line is used to represent numbers graphically as points on a horizontal line.

Numerator represents the number of equal parts in a fractional number.

Opposite angles are formed by any intersecting lines that are opposite to the same vertex.

Order of a ratio is the order in which a ratio is presented.

Order of operations is the order in which arithmetic operations are carried out in an equation. The order that is followed is: Brackets, Exponents, Division and Multiplication, Addition, and Subtraction (BEDMAS).

Ordered pair is used to locate a point in the coordinate system. The ordered pair (x, y) describes a point in the plane by its x- and y-coordinates.

Parallel lines are lines that have the same slope. All vertical lines are parallel to each other and all horizontal lines are parallel to each other.

Percent (per cent or per hundred in the literal meaning) is used to express a quantity out of 100 units and is represented by the symbol '%'.

Percent change is often used to express the amount of change to the initial (original) value; i.e., the amount of change (increase or decrease) is calculated as a percent change (%C) of its initial value.

Perfect root is a whole number whose root is also a whole number.

Perfect square is any whole number base with an exponent of 2; i.e., a whole number multiplied by itself results in a perfect square.

Perimeter (P) of a plane figure is the total length of the boundary of the plane figure.

Perpendicular lines are lines that have slopes that multiply to –1. The lines are also perpendicular if one of them is vertical and the other is horizontal.

Place value is the position of each digit in a number.

Plane Geometry is the study of the properties and relations of plane figures such as triangles, quadrilaterals, circles, etc.

Polynomial is an algebraic expression that has two or more terms.

Portion (P) refers to the portion of the whole quantity or value (portion of the base).

Prime number is a whole number that has only two factors: 1 and the number itself.

Principal root is the positive root of a number.

Pro-ration is defined as sharing or allocating the quantities, usually the amounts, on a proportionate basis.

Product refers to the result from multiplying numbers.

Proper fraction is a fraction in which the numerator is less than the denominator.

Proportion is used to describe two sets of ratios that are equal.

Pythagorean Theorem is a famous theorem in Mathematics that states that the squares of the lengths of the two shorter sides that meet at the right-angle equals the square of the longest side opposite the right-angle.

Quadrant is one of the four regions that is formed by the X- and Y-axes in the rectangular coordinate system. They are numbered counter-clockwise from one (I) to four (IV).

Quotient refers to the result of dividing numbers.

Range of a relation is defined as the set of all 'y' values in the ordered pairs

Rate is a special ratio that is used to compare two quantities or amounts having different units of measure.

Rate (R) refers to the percent relationship between the base and portion. It usually carries the percent sign (%) or the word 'percent'.

Ratio is a comparison or relationship between two or more quantities with the same unit.

Rational number is a fraction where one integer is divided by another non-zero integer.

Ray is the portion of a line bound in one direction by a point.

Real number includes rational and non-rational numbers.

Reciprocal is the fraction that is obtained by inverting the original fraction.

Remainder refers to the number left over when the dividend cannot be divided evenly by the divisor.

Repeating decimal is a decimal that does not end but shows a repeating pattern.

Root is the inverse of exponents.

Rounding numbers makes them easier to work with and easier to remember. Rounding changes some of the digits in a number but keeps its value close to the original.

Rules of Logarithms can be used to combine two or more logarithmic expressions into a single logarithmic expression.

Rules or Laws of Exponents are used to simplify expressions that involve exponents.

Scientific notation is a method of expressing numbers using decimal numbers with one non-zero digit to the left of the decimal point multiplied by the power of 10.

Sharing quantities refers to the allocation or distribution of a quantity into two or more portions (or units) based on a given ratio.

Short ton is the US customary unit for ton and is represented by 'ton'.

Significant digits are used to determine the accuracy of a number.

Simplifying fractions is when you divide both the numerator and denominator of a fraction by the same number, which results in an equivalent fraction.

Slope (m) is the steepness of the line relative to the X-axis. It is the ratio of the change in the value of y (called 'rise') to the corresponding change in the value of x (called 'run').

Substitution method is a method of solving systems of linear equations, when one of the equations in the system has a variable with a coefficient of 1 or –1.

Subtraction refers to finding the difference between numbers.

Sum refers to the result from adding two or more numbers.

System of equations refers to two or more equations analyzed together.

Term is a number, variable, or a combination of numbers and variables that are multiplied and/or divided together.

Term of a ratio is the quantity in a ratio.

Terminating decimal is a decimal that ends.

Thousands group is the second group of three digits starting from the right of a whole number.

Trillions group is the fifth group of three digits starting from the right of a whole number.

Trinomial is a polynomial with three terms.

Unit price is the unit rate when it is expressed in unit currency (dollars, cents, etc.).

Unit rate represents the number of units of the first quantity (or measurement) that corresponds to one unit of the second quantity.

Units group is the first group of three digits starting from the right of a whole number.

Unlike terms are terms that have different variables or the same variables with different exponents.

US Customary system of measurement uses the yard (yd), the pound (lb), and the gallon (gal) as the base units for the measurements of length, mass, and capacity, respectively. The Fahrenheit (°F) scale is used for temperature.

Variable is a letter that represents one or more numbers.

Vertex of an angle is the point of intersection of two rays.

Whole number is any counting number (0, 1, 2, 3, 4…), including zero (0) and any natural number or positive integer (1, 2, 3, 4…).

x-intercept is the point at which the line crosses the X-axis and where the y-coordinate is zero.

y-intercept is the point at which the line crosses the Y-axis and where the x-coordinate is zero.

Zero is the smallest whole number.

Index